THIN ELASTIC SHELLS

THIN ELASTIC SHELLS

An Introduction to the Theoretical Foundations and the Analysis of Their Static and Dynamic Behavior

HARRY KRAUS

State University of New York at Stony Brook

John Wiley & Sons, Inc., New York · London · Sydney

Library of Congress Catalog Card Number: 67–23328
Printed in the United States of America

To Elaine, Peter, and James

Preface

The thin shell appears as a load-carrying element in some part of virtually every item of modern industrial equipment. This is especially true of the aerospace, nuclear, marine, and petrochemical industries where dramatic and sophisticated uses of shells are currently being made in missiles and space vehicles, submarines, nuclear reactor vessels, refinery equipment, and the like. These applications have acted as a stimulus to which research specialists in the field of solid mechanics (both in industry and in the universities) have responded with a wide variety of solutions of technically important shell problems as well as with critical reappraisals and contributions to the foundations of the theory upon which these solutions are based.

To support this effort, technical schools have also begun to offer courses in the theory of shells and it has become evident that an introductory text that presents a unified approach to the theoretical and applied aspects of shell analysis is needed. It is my goal to fill this need with the present volume.

The text is largely an outgrowth of classroom notes used in the teaching of a course in the theory of shells at the Hartford Graduate Center of the Rensselaer Polytechnic Institute. The coverage of subjects and the point of view have been selected in order to present a combination of the foundations and the applications of the theory so that the reader may gain an understanding and an appreciation of each of these areas. The book is aimed primarily at graduate students at the intermediate level in engineering mechanics, aerospace engineering, mechanical engineering and civil engineering, whose field of specialization is solid mechanics. Stress analysts in industry will find the book a useful introduction that will equip them to read further in the literature of solutions to technically important shell problems, while research specialists will find it useful as an introduction to current theoretical work. This volume is not intended to be an exhaustive treatise on the theory of thin elastic shells but, rather, a broad introduction from which each reader can follow his own interests further.

In the pursuit of my goal of providing a text which presents the fundamentals of the theory of thin elastic shells and the application of that theory in the solution of problems of technical interest, the book is divided into four major parts. Part I is concerned with the fundamentals of the theory. It contains the development of necessary results from the theory of surfaces, the derivation of Reissner's version of Love's first approximation to the theory of thin elastic shells, and the derivation of additional theories that have been presented by Sanders, Flugge—Lur'e—Byrne, and Reissner—Naghdi. Part II is devoted to the solution of problems involving statically loaded shells by exact and approximate methods. The dynamic analysis of shells is considered in Part III, where both free and forced vibration analyses are carried out. Finally, in Part IV, numerical solutions are covered that, with the recent advent of the digital computer, have made feasible the analysis of the most general problems that can be conceived within the framework of any theory of thin elastic shells. In this discussion, the application of various numerical methods to the solution of the equations of shell theory are described and sample solutions are obtained with computer programs that are currently in industrial use.

The development of the subject matter presupposes that the reader is generally familiar with the field of solid mechanics and that he has had courses in advanced stress analysis, elasticity, and vibrations. As a mathematical preparation, the text assumes that the reader is familiar with vector algebra, variational methods, and the solution of the partial differential equations of mathematical physics. Vector algebra will facilitate the development of results on surfaces. Variational methods are utilized in the derivation of the differential equations and natural boundary conditions of the theory as well as in the approximate analytical solution of free-vibration problems, while the methods of solving partial differential equations are relied upon rather heavily in the exact analytical solutions that are covered in Parts II and III of the book.

Certain broad areas have been deliberately omitted. These are, in particular, the inelastic analysis and the stability analysis of shells, which are each generally included in separate courses and texts on inelastic behavior and structural stability. In the cases of heat conduction and numerical analysis only the application of these fields to shell theory is discussed. Thus, when the behavior of shells under thermal loadings is considered in Parts II and III, it is assumed that the temperature distribution in the shell is known. However, to connect the subject of heat conduction to the theory of thin elastic shells, the equation of heat conduction in shell coordinates is presented in Part I along with the fundamental equations of shell theory. Similarly, in the case of numerical analysis as presented in Part IV, only the application of specific numerical techniques to the solution of the equations of shell theory is discussed.

The amount of material presented here obviously exceeds the requirements for a typical one-semester course in thin elastic shells. Consequently the text gives the instructor considerable latitude in choosing topics for any particular course on shells. As an aid in his selection, I suggest that an introductory course on shells might cover Chapters 1 to 5 and Chapter 8. A detailed course, limited to static behavior, might cover Chapters 1 to 3, 5 to 7, and Chapter 10. And a detailed course on shell dynamics could involve Chapters 1 to 3, 8, 9, and Chapter 11. In a two-semester course on statics and dynamics of shells, sufficient time is available to discuss selected topics from every chapter.

Exercises to be worked out by the student are included at the end of every chapter. These are designed to amplify and supplement the matters treated in the development. In some instances, the exercises bring out additional information that is not specifically covered in the text.

Many individuals and organizations contributed to the completion of the present volume. In particular, I am indebted to Dr. Edwin N. Nilson, of the Pratt and Whitney Aircraft Division of the United Aircraft Corporation, for his encouragement and support during the writing of the book. The sponsorship of the Pressure Vessel Research Committee of the Welding Research Council, which provided the funds for my study of numerical analysis and computer programs as applied to shells, is gratefully acknowledged, as is the financial support by the Army Research Office (Durham, North Carolina) of my work on forced-vibration analysis.

Of the individuals who contributed their effort to the writing of the book, I must, particularly, thank Dominick Lombari, Dorothy Woodard, Daniel Minior, James Arnold, Abraham Brot, and Alf Alver for programming and carrying out many of the illustrative calculations, Robert Cross for his aid with the illustrations, Anthony Dennis for reviewing the manuscript, and Eleanor Deskis for her capable typing of the text.

Finally, I express my thanks to Albert R. Beckett, Editor, and to the Editorial and Production Staffs of the publisher for their contributions to the successful completion of the effort that is represented by this volume.

HARRY KRAUS

Stony Brook, New York
January 1967

Contents

THIN ELASTIC SHELLS

I

Foundations of the Theory of Thin Elastic Shells

The geometry of a thin elastic shell is described. Equations that govern the behavior of the shell are derived, using as a basis a set of postulates originally formulated by Love. Improved theories that have been suggested recently are described.

1

Introduction: Results from Differential Geometry

1.1 INTRODUCTION

A thin shell is a body that is bounded by two closely spaced curved surfaces. As such, it can be considered as the materialization of a curved surface, just as the beam and the flat plate can be considered as the materializations of a line and a flat surface.

A shell has three fundamental identifying features: its reference surface, its thickness, and its edges. Of these, the reference surface is the most significant because it defines the shape of the shell and because, within the framework of the theory that is to be adopted here, the behavior of the shell is governed by the behavior of its reference surface. Generally, if the shell is composed of a single homogeneous material, the middle surface (that is, the locus of points that are equidistant from the bounding surfaces) is selected as the reference surface. If the shell is of layered or other nonhomogeneous construction, it is usually more convenient to use, as the reference surface, one of the bounding surfaces or a so-called neutral surface that is analogous to the neutral axis of a beam.

Once the shell's reference surface has been selected, the shell can be described completely. Thus, the thickness of the shell at a given point is determined as the distance between its bounding surfaces as measured along a normal to the reference surface that passes through the point. The thickness need not be uniform although, in most practical cases, it is either a linear or a constant function of position. Furthermore, the edges of the shell are designated by appropriate values of coordinates that are established on the reference surface. The shell's edges are formed, in general, by curved surfaces whose normals are perpendicular to the normals of the reference surface along the intersections of the edge surfaces with the reference surface. It is possible that the shell might have no edges at all, in which case it is referred to as a closed (or complete) shell.

Shells can be composed of any type of material. However, our interest is restricted to shells that are made of elastic materials so that Hooke's law can be used. For generality, however, we shall not require that the materials be isotropic or homogeneous. Shells that are composed of work hardening or viscoelastic materials, for example, can be treated by extensions of the basic procedures that will be set forth here and will not, therefore, be specifically included in our treatment.

Since the reference surface has been identified as the most important characteristic of a thin shell, and since (as we shall demonstrate later) the behavior of the shell is governed by the behavior of its reference surface, it is appropriate to have an understanding of the basic principles of the theory of surfaces before embarking upon the derivation of the theory of thin elastic shells. With these fundamentals in mind, we shall be able to describe the reference surface of a thin elastic shell to develop the theory of thin elastic shells. Since the theory of surfaces relies on results from the theory of space curves and since both of these theories belong to the subject of differential geometry, it is our goal in this chapter to observe those results from differential geometry that will facilitate our later derivation of the theory of thin elastic shells.

Our coverage of differential geometry is not exhaustive; instead, it is somewhat streamlined, since only a few specific results are required in the theory of thin elastic shells. Thus, the present chapter contains sections on space curves and on surfaces followed by a section on surfaces of revolution. The purpose of the section on surfaces of revolution is to illustrate the principles developed in the first two sections and to record some results that we shall use frequently in the text.

1.2 SPACE CURVES

We begin our exposition of differential geometry by giving some basic results from the theory of space curves. These results will facilitate our later development of results from the theory of surfaces where, in particular, we shall make use of the properties of curves on surfaces.

1.2*a* Parametric Representation of a Curve

A three-dimensional curve in a rectangular coordinate system (x_1, x_2, x_3) can be represented by the locus of the end point of the position vector (Fig. 1.1):

$$\mathbf{x} = x_1(t)\mathbf{e}_1 + x_2(t)\mathbf{e}_2 + x_3(t)\mathbf{e}_3 \tag{1.1}$$

for all values of the parameter t that lie in the interval $t_1 \leqslant t \leqslant t_2$. If we require that the x_i ($i = 1, 2, 3$) be single-valued functions of the parameter t, then we shall insure that a given value of t defines only one point on the space curve.

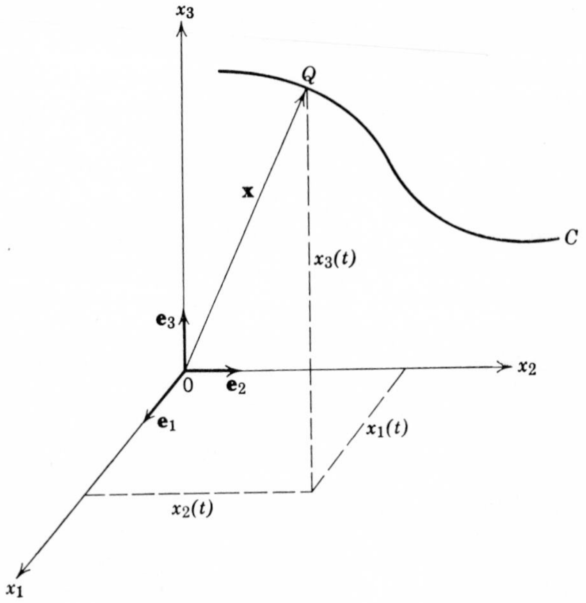

Figure 1.1

1.2*b* Unit Tangent Vector

Let us call s the variable of arc length along the space curve defined by Eq. 1.1 and take the derivative of the position vector $\mathbf{x}$ with respect to s,

$$\frac{d\mathbf{x}}{ds} = \frac{dx_1}{ds}\mathbf{e}_1 + \frac{dx_2}{ds}\mathbf{e}_2 + \frac{dx_3}{ds}\mathbf{e}_3. \tag{1.2}$$

Now if we form the scalar product of the foregoing derivative with itself, we obtain

$$\frac{d\mathbf{x}}{ds}\cdot\frac{d\mathbf{x}}{ds} = \left(\frac{dx_1}{ds}\right)^2 + \left(\frac{dx_2}{ds}\right)^2 + \left(\frac{dx_3}{ds}\right)^2 \tag{1.3}$$

From the differential calculus, we know that

$$(ds)^2 = (dx_1)^2 + (dx_2)^2 + (dx_3)^2$$

hence

$$\frac{d\mathbf{x}}{ds}\cdot\frac{d\mathbf{x}}{ds} = 1. \tag{1.4}$$

This tells us that $d\mathbf{x}/ds$ is a unit vector. Its geometrical interpretation is as follows (Fig. 1.2). The vector $\Delta\mathbf{x}$ joins two consecutive points Q and Q' on a curve C. Thus, the vector $\Delta\mathbf{x}/\Delta s$ has the same direction as $\Delta\mathbf{x}$ and, as Δs approaches zero, $\Delta\mathbf{x}/\Delta s$ becomes the vector tangent to the curve C at the point Q. We call the vector

$$\mathbf{t} = \frac{d\mathbf{x}}{ds} = \lim_{\Delta s \to 0} \frac{\Delta\mathbf{x}}{\Delta s} \tag{1.5}$$

the unit tangent vector. We note further that

$$\dot{\mathbf{x}} = \frac{d\mathbf{x}}{dt} = \frac{d\mathbf{x}}{ds}\frac{ds}{dt} \tag{1.6}$$

is also a tangent vector but it is not necessarily of unit length.

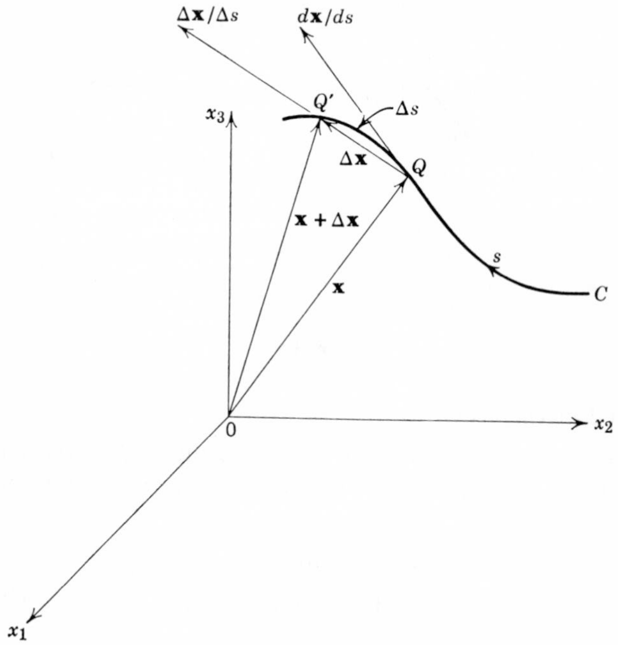

Figure 1.2

1.2*c* Osculating Plane, Principal Normal

In the preceding section, the tangent to a curve at a point Q was found to be the limiting position of the line connecting the points Q and Q' as Q' approaches Q. Thus, it could be stated that the tangent to a curve passes through two consecutive points on the curve. As a next step, it is natural to consider the limiting position of a plane passing through three consecutive points of a curve as two of the points approach the third. Such a plane is called the osculating plane. It can be found by specifying that the vector $(\mathbf{X} - \mathbf{x})$ from a general point $\mathbf{X}$ in the osculating plane to a general point $\mathbf{x}$ on the curve must lie in the same plane as the tangent vector $\dot{\mathbf{x}}$ joining two points on the curve and the vector of the rate of change in the tangent vector $(\ddot{\mathbf{x}})$ which occurs in passing to the third point. Since the triple scalar product of three coplanar vectors is zero, an expression for the osculating plane is found from

$$(\mathbf{X} - \mathbf{x}) \cdot (\dot{\mathbf{x}} \times \ddot{\mathbf{x}}) = 0. \tag{1.7}$$

It is now appropriate to define the principal normal to a curve at a point Q as that vector in the osculating plane at Q which is perpendicular to the tangent $\mathbf{t}$ to the curve at Q.

1.2*d* Curvature

By Eq. 1.4, $\mathbf{t}\cdot\mathbf{t} = 1$. If we differentiate this scalar product with respect to arc length, we obtain

$$\frac{d}{ds}(\mathbf{t}\cdot\mathbf{t}) = 2\mathbf{t}\cdot\mathbf{t}' = 0, \tag{1.8}$$

where the prime denotes differentiation with respect to s. This result indicates that the vector $\mathbf{t}'$ is perpendicular to $\mathbf{t}$. From the definition of $\mathbf{t}$, we can write

$$\mathbf{t} = \frac{d\mathbf{x}}{ds} = \frac{d\mathbf{x}}{dt}\frac{dt}{ds} = \dot{\mathbf{x}}t', \tag{1.9}$$

and upon differentiation with respect to the arc length s the result is

$$\mathbf{t}' = \dot{\mathbf{x}}t'' + \ddot{\mathbf{x}}(t')^2. \tag{1.10}$$

This indicates that the vector $\mathbf{t}'$ lies in the plane of the vectors $\dot{\mathbf{x}}$ and $\ddot{\mathbf{x}}$ (that is, in the osculating plane). Since $\mathbf{t}'$ has also been shown to be perpendicular to the tangent $\mathbf{t}$, we conclude that $\mathbf{t}'$ is parallel to the principal normal and is, therefore, proportional to it as follows:

$$\mathbf{t}' = \mathbf{k} = k\mathbf{N}, \tag{1.11}$$

where $\mathbf{N}$ is a unit normal vector in the direction of the principal normal to the curve at a point. The vector $\mathbf{k}$ is called the curvature vector and expresses the rate of change of the tangent vector as a point moves along the curve. The proportionality factor k is called the curvature, and its reciprocal $(R = k^{-1})$ is the radius of curvature. It is the radius of the osculating circle that passes through three consecutive points of the curve. Although the sense of $\mathbf{t}'$ is determined solely by the curve, the sense of the principal normal $\mathbf{N}$ is arbitrary. The sign of the factor k, therefore, depends on the sense of $\mathbf{N}$. To maintain consistency in our development, we shall assume that the normal vector $\mathbf{N}$ points away from the center of curvature. Thus, Eq. 1.11 tells us that when the sense of $\mathbf{N}$ and $\mathbf{k}$ are the same, $k > 0$, and when the sense of $\mathbf{N}$ is opposite to that of $\mathbf{k}$, we have $k < 0$.

1.3 SURFACES

With the preliminary results of the previous section, we are now able to consider the development of those results on surfaces that form our primary interest in this chapter.

1.3*a* Parametric Curves of a Surface; First Fundamental Form

Every surface S in the rectangular coordinate system (which we have previously defined) may be written as a function of two parameters α_1 and α_2 as follows:

$$x_1 = f_1(\alpha_1, \alpha_2), \qquad x_2 = f_2(\alpha_1, \alpha_2), \qquad x_3 = f_3(\alpha_1, \alpha_2), \tag{1.12}$$

where f_1, f_2, and f_3 are single-valued and continuous functions of α_1 and α_2. The parameters α_1 and α_2 are called the curvilinear coordinates of the surface. By fixing, in turn, one of the parameters and varying the other, we obtain a family of curves called the parametric curves of the surface as shown in Fig. 1.3. Equation 1.12 can also be written as a vector equation

$$\mathbf{r}(\alpha_1, \alpha_2) = f_1(\alpha_1, \alpha_2)\mathbf{e}_1 + f_2(\alpha_1, \alpha_2)\mathbf{e}_2 + f_3(\alpha_1, \alpha_2)\mathbf{e}_3. \tag{1.13}$$

A differential change $d\mathbf{r}$ in the vector $\mathbf{r}$ as we move from a point P to an infinitesimally close point P' on the surface S can be written as

$$d\mathbf{r} = \mathbf{r}_{,1}\, d\alpha_1 + \mathbf{r}_{,2}\, d\alpha_2, \tag{1.14}$$

where we have introduced the notation

$$\mathbf{r}_{,i} = \frac{\partial \mathbf{r}}{\partial \alpha_i}, \qquad i = 1, 2 \tag{1.15}$$

for partial derivatives of vectors. The square of the magnitude of the differential change vector $d\mathbf{r}$ is obtained by taking the scalar product of $d\mathbf{r}$ with itself. Thus

$$(ds)^2 = d\mathbf{r}\cdot d\mathbf{r} = E(d\alpha_1)^2 + 2F\, d\alpha_1\, d\alpha_2 + G(d\alpha_2)^2 \tag{1.16}$$

where

$$E = \mathbf{r}_{,1}\cdot\mathbf{r}_{,1}, \qquad F = \mathbf{r}_{,1}\cdot\mathbf{r}_{,2}, \qquad G = \mathbf{r}_{,2}\cdot\mathbf{r}_{,2}. \tag{1.17}$$

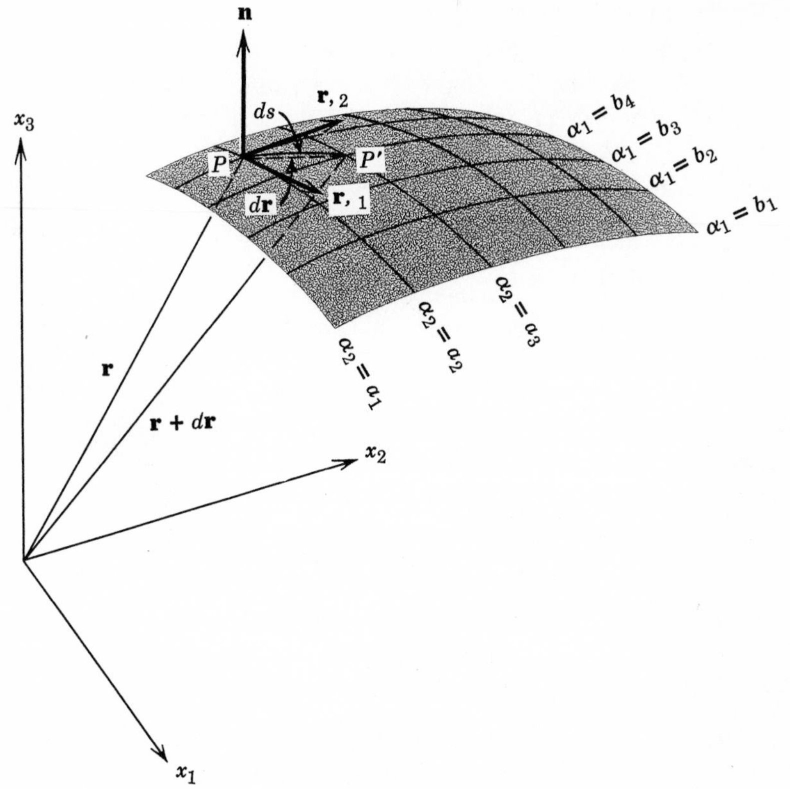

Figure 1.3

Equation 1.16 is known as the first fundamental form of the surface S defined by the vector $\mathbf{r}(\alpha_1, \alpha_2)$; E, F, and G are called the first fundamental magnitudes. Along the parametric curves themselves, the differential length of arc takes the simplified forms

$$\begin{aligned} ds_1 &= \sqrt{E}\, d\alpha_1 \text{ along a curve of constant } \alpha_2, \\ ds_2 &= \sqrt{G}\, d\alpha_2 \text{ along a curve of constant } \alpha_1. \end{aligned} \tag{1.18}$$

We notice here that since $\mathbf{r}_{,1}$ and $\mathbf{r}_{,2}$ are tangent to curves of constant α_2 and α_1, respectively, the quantity F will be zero if the parametric curves form an orthogonal net. In such cases, it is customary to write the first fundamental form as

$$(ds)^2 = A_1{}^2(d\alpha_1)^2 + A_2{}^2(d\alpha_2)^2, \tag{1.19}$$

where $A_1 = \sqrt{E}$, $A_2 = \sqrt{G}$, and $F = 0$.

1.3*b* Normal to a Surface

At every point P of a surface there exists a unit normal vector $\mathbf{n}(\alpha_1, \alpha_2)$ which is perpendicular to $\mathbf{r}_{,1}$ and $\mathbf{r}_{,2}$ and hence to the plane at P that contains these vectors (the tangent plane at P). The unit normal vector is thus parallel to the cross product of $\mathbf{r}_{,1}$ and $\mathbf{r}_{,2}$. Since a unit vector is a vector divided by its magnitude, an expression for $\mathbf{n}(\alpha_1, \alpha_2)$ is given as

$$\mathbf{n}(\alpha_1, \alpha_2) = (\mathbf{r}_{,1} \times \mathbf{r}_{,2})/|\mathbf{r}_{,1} \times \mathbf{r}_{,2}|. \tag{1.20}$$

From vector algebra, we have

$$|\mathbf{r}_{,1} \times \mathbf{r}_{,2}| = |\mathbf{r}_{,1}|\,|\mathbf{r}_{,2}| \sin\theta \tag{1.21}$$

and

$$\mathbf{r}_{,1}\cdot\mathbf{r}_{,2} = |\mathbf{r}_{,1}|\,|\mathbf{r}_{,2}| \cos\theta, \tag{1.22}$$

where θ is the angle between the vectors $\mathbf{r}_{,1}$ and $\mathbf{r}_{,2}$. Thus, from Eq. 1.17, we obtain

$$\cos\theta = F/\sqrt{EG} \tag{1.23}$$

and, therefore,

$$\sin\theta = \sqrt{(EG - F^2)/EG}. \tag{1.24}$$

The final expression for the unit normal vector is

$$\mathbf{n}(\alpha_1, \alpha_2) = \left(\frac{\mathbf{r}_{,1} \times \mathbf{r}_{,2}}{H}\right), \qquad H = \sqrt{EG - F^2} \tag{1.25}$$

provided that H does not vanish (see the Exercises). We should point out here that the principal normal $\mathbf{N}$ of a curve on a surface need not be normal to the surface (that is, generally $\mathbf{N}\cdot\mathbf{n} \neq 1$).

Like the principal normal of a curve, the sense of the normal to a surface is arbitrary. Therefore, we shall adopt the convention that the parametric curves should always be arranged in such a manner that the normal $\mathbf{n}$ points from the concave side to the convex side of the surface.

1.3*c* Second Fundamental Form

In our previous discussion, we have described the curvature vector $\mathbf{k}$ of a space curve. We shall now consider a curve on a surface and use the properties of the curvature vector to derive an important feature of surfaces called the second fundamental form. To do this, we recall that the curvature vector $\mathbf{k}$ is given by $d\mathbf{t}/ds$ where $\mathbf{t}$ is the unit vector tangent to a curve. Since a vector can be resolved into its components, let us resolve the curvature vector $\mathbf{k}$ of the curve into its components normal and tangential to the surface. Thus

$$\mathbf{k} = \frac{d\mathbf{t}}{ds} = \mathbf{k}_n + \mathbf{k}_t. \tag{1.26}$$

Here $\mathbf{k}_n$ and $\mathbf{k}_t$ are referred to as the normal curvature vector and tangential curvature vector, respectively. In the present context, we are interested only in the former. Since $\mathbf{k}_n$ is in the direction of the normal to the surface, it is proportional to $\mathbf{n}$ and can be expressed in terms of it as follows:

$$\mathbf{k}_n = -K_n\mathbf{n} \tag{1.27}$$

where K_n is called the normal curvature. The minus sign takes into account the fact that the sense of the curvature vector $\mathbf{k}$ is opposite to that of the normal vector $\mathbf{n}$ (see Sections 1.2*d* and 1.3*b*).

Since $\mathbf{n}$ is perpendicular to $\mathbf{t}$, differentiation of the scalar product $\mathbf{n}\cdot\mathbf{t} = 0$ with respect to s along the curve on the surface gives

$$\frac{d\mathbf{n}}{ds}\cdot\mathbf{t} = -\mathbf{n}\cdot\frac{d\mathbf{t}}{ds}. \tag{1.28}$$

If we form the scalar product of Eq. 1.27 with $\mathbf{n}$, we find that

$$-(\mathbf{k}_n\cdot\mathbf{n}) = K_n \tag{1.29}$$

and the scalar product of Eq. 1.26 with $\mathbf{n}$ gives (since $\mathbf{n}$ is perpendicular to $\mathbf{k}_t$):

$$\mathbf{n}\cdot\frac{d\mathbf{t}}{ds} = \mathbf{n}\cdot\mathbf{k}_n. \tag{1.30}$$

Finally, if we combine Eqs. 1.30, 1.29, and 1.28, we obtain

$$K_n = \frac{d\mathbf{r}\cdot d\mathbf{n}}{d\mathbf{r}\cdot d\mathbf{r}} \tag{1.31}$$

where we have used $(ds)^2 = d\mathbf{r}\cdot d\mathbf{r}$. Now, if we notice that

$$d\mathbf{n} = \mathbf{n}_{,1}\,d\alpha_1 + \mathbf{n}_{,2}\,d\alpha_2, \qquad d\mathbf{r} = \mathbf{r}_{,1}\,d\alpha_1 + \mathbf{r}_{,2}\,d\alpha_2 \tag{1.32}$$

and if we substitute the foregoing expressions into Eq. 1.31, we obtain

$$K_n = \frac{\mathrm{II}}{\mathrm{I}} = \frac{L(d\alpha_1)^2 + 2M\,d\alpha_1\,d\alpha_2 + N(d\alpha_2)^2}{E(d\alpha_1)^2 + 2F\,d\alpha_1\,d\alpha_2 + G(d\alpha_2)^2} \tag{1.33}$$

where the following new quantities (called the second fundamental magnitudes) have been defined:

$$L = \mathbf{r}_{,1}\cdot\mathbf{n}_{,1}, \qquad 2M = (\mathbf{r}_{,1}\cdot\mathbf{n}_{,2} + \mathbf{r}_{,2}\cdot\mathbf{n}_{,1}), \qquad N = \mathbf{r}_{,2}\cdot\mathbf{n}_{,2}. \tag{1.34}$$

By differentiation of the expressions $\mathbf{r}_{,1}\cdot\mathbf{n} = 0$, and $\mathbf{r}_{,2}\cdot\mathbf{n} = 0$, we obtain the alternative expressions:

$$L = -\mathbf{r}_{,11}\cdot\mathbf{n}, \qquad M = -\mathbf{r}_{,12}\cdot\mathbf{n}, \qquad N = -\mathbf{r}_{,22}\cdot\mathbf{n}, \tag{1.35}$$

where, by extension of Eq. 1.15, we have used the notation

$$\mathbf{r}_{,ij} = \frac{\partial^2\mathbf{r}}{\partial\alpha_i\partial\alpha_j}, \qquad i, j = 1, 2. \tag{1.36}$$

We have also assumed, in the derivation of the alternate expression for M, that $\mathbf{r}$ has continuous second derivatives. This will insure that $\mathbf{r}_{,12} = \mathbf{r}_{,21}$.

In the expression (1.33) for the normal curvature, we notice that the denominator (I) is the first fundamental form that we have derived previously. The numerator (II) is referred to as the second fundamental form. Since E, F, G, L, M, and N can all be expressed as functions of α_1 and α_2 and are constants at a given point, it is seen upon consideration of Eq. 1.33 that the normal curvature depends only on the direction $d\alpha_1/d\alpha_2$. It can thus be stated that all curves through a point on a surface which are tangent to the same direction have the same normal curvature.

1.3*d* Principal Curvatures

It is interesting at this point to seek those directions $(d\alpha_2/d\alpha_1)$ for which the normal curvature K_n has a maximum or a minimum. If, from now on, we drop the subscript n, and if we define the direction to be $\lambda = d\alpha_2/d\alpha_1$, the expression for the normal curvature becomes

$$K(\lambda) = \frac{L + 2M\lambda + N\lambda^2}{E + 2F\lambda + G\lambda^2} \tag{1.37}$$

The normal curvature attains an extremum in a particular direction λ if $dK/d\lambda = 0$, or

$$(E + 2F\lambda + G\lambda^2)(M + N\lambda) - (L + 2M\lambda + N\lambda^2)(F + G\lambda) = 0. \tag{1.38}$$

By noting also that

$$\begin{aligned} E + 2F\lambda + G\lambda^2 &= (E + F\lambda) + \lambda(F + G\lambda), \\ L + 2M\lambda + N\lambda^2 &= (L + M\lambda) + \lambda(M + N\lambda), \end{aligned} \tag{1.39a}$$

we find that

$$(E + F\lambda)(M + N\lambda) = (F + G\lambda)(L + M\lambda) \tag{1.39b}$$

The extremum curvature is now found by substituting Eq. 1.38 into Eq. 1.37 and then making use of Eq. 1.39b. This procedure gives

$$K = \frac{M + N\lambda}{F + G\lambda} = \frac{L + M\lambda}{E + F\lambda}. \tag{1.40}$$

An equation for determining the direction λ corresponding to the extremum curvatures is found by expanding Eq. 1.39b, with the result that

$$(MG - NF)\lambda^2 + (LG - NE)\lambda + (LF - ME) = 0. \tag{1.41}$$

This quadratic equation yields two roots, λ_1 and λ_2, corresponding to two directions, $(d\alpha_2/d\alpha_1)_1$ and $(d\alpha_2/d\alpha_1)_2$, of extremum curvature. One of these solutions is the maximum curvature while the other is the minimum curvature. K_1 and K_2, corresponding to λ_1 and λ_2, are called the principal curvatures, and $R_1 = K_1^{-1}$, $R_2 = K_2^{-1}$ are the principal radii of curvature.

At this point, our intuition might lead us to suppose that the directions of principal curvature are orthogonal. To show that this is indeed the case, we consider the angle θ between two directions tangent to a surface given by, for example, $d\alpha_2/d\alpha_1$ and $\delta\alpha_2/\delta\alpha_1$. Along these two directions a differential change in the position vector $\mathbf{r}$ is given by

$$\begin{aligned} d\mathbf{r} &= \mathbf{r}_{,1}\, d\alpha_1 + \mathbf{r}_{,2}\, d\alpha_2, \\ \delta\mathbf{r} &= \mathbf{r}_{,1}\, \delta\alpha_1 + \mathbf{r}_{,2}\, \delta\alpha_2. \end{aligned} \tag{1.42}$$

By use of the definition of the scalar product, the cosine of the angle between $d\mathbf{r}$ and $\delta\mathbf{r}$ can be found from

$$\cos\theta = \frac{d\mathbf{r}\cdot\delta\mathbf{r}}{|d\mathbf{r}|\,|\delta\mathbf{r}|} = E\frac{d\alpha_1}{ds}\frac{\delta\alpha_1}{\delta s} + F\left(\frac{d\alpha_1}{ds}\frac{\delta\alpha_2}{\delta s} + \frac{d\alpha_2}{ds}\frac{\delta\alpha_1}{\delta s}\right) + G\frac{d\alpha_2}{ds}\frac{\delta\alpha_2}{\delta s}, \tag{1.43}$$

where ds and δs are obtained from the first fundamental form along each tangent direction. When $\theta = \pi/2$, we obtain the orthogonality condition for two directions on a surface:

$$E\, d\alpha_1\, \delta\alpha_1 + F(d\alpha_1\, \delta\alpha_2 + \delta\alpha_1\, d\alpha_2) + G\, d\alpha_2\, \delta\alpha_2 = 0. \tag{1.44}$$

If we divide Eq. 1.44 by $d\alpha_1\, \delta\alpha_1$, and identify λ_1 with $d\alpha_2/d\alpha_1$, and λ_2 with $\delta\alpha_2/\delta\alpha_1$, we obtain

$$E + F(\lambda_1 + \lambda_2) + G\lambda_1\lambda_2 = 0. \tag{1.45}$$

We now observe that the two roots of Eq. 1.41 are, by the quadratic formula,

$$\begin{Bmatrix}\lambda_1\\ \lambda_2\end{Bmatrix} = \frac{-(LG - NE) \pm \sqrt{(LG - NE)^2 - 4(MG - NF)(LF - ME)}}{2(MG - NF)} \tag{1.46}$$

and, therefore, for the purpose of substitution into Eq. 1.45, we find that

$$\begin{aligned} \lambda_1 + \lambda_2 &= -(LG - NE)/(MG - NF), \\ \lambda_1\lambda_2 &= (LF - ME)/(MG - NF). \end{aligned} \tag{1.47}$$

Upon substitution of $\lambda_1\lambda_2$ and $(\lambda_1 + \lambda_2)$ into Eq. 1.45, we find that the orthogonality condition is identically satisfied. Therefore, the directions of principal curvature are orthogonal. Integration of Eq. 1.41 gives us the lines of curvature on the surface. These form an orthogonal family of curves on the surface.

Now let us examine the situation in which the lines of curvature are taken as the parametric lines (curves) of the surface. In this case, Eq. 1.41 must be satisfied by both $d\alpha_1/d\alpha_2 = 0$ and $d\alpha_2/d\alpha_1 = 0$. For this to be possible, we must have

$$LF - ME = 0 \qquad \text{and} \qquad MG - NF = 0. \tag{1.48}$$

Since we have postulated that the parametric lines are to be the lines of curvature and since the latter have been shown to be orthogonal, $F = 0$. It can be shown (see the Exercises) that $EG - F^2 > 0$, so that for $F = 0$, neither E nor G can be zero. Thus, we are led to the conclusion, from Eq. 1.48, that $M = 0$ and, therefore, the conditions under which the parametric lines are also lines of curvature are

$$F = M = 0. \tag{1.49}$$

When the parametric curves are the lines of curvature, we can find their curvatures by setting $F = M = 0$ in Eq. 1.33, and then letting $d\alpha_1 = 0$ and $d\alpha_2 = 0$, in turn, to give

$$K_1 = \frac{1}{R_1} = \frac{L}{E}, \qquad K_2 = \frac{1}{R_2} = \frac{N}{G}. \tag{1.50}$$

The development of the theory of thin elastic shells is considerably clarified if the lines of curvature of the reference surface are used as the parametric lines. Thus, we shall assume that Eq. 1.49 is satisfied in our subsequent work.

1.3*e* Derivatives of Unit Vectors along Parametric Lines

In our development of the fundamental theorem of the theory of surfaces, it will be necessary to have on hand some expressions for the derivatives of unit vectors along the parametric lines. With this in mind, let us, therefore, consider a triplet of mutually orthogonal unit vectors ($\mathbf{t}_1$, $\mathbf{t}_2$, and $\mathbf{n}$) that are oriented at a given point on a surface so as to be tangent to the α_1 and α_2 directions and normal to the surface, respectively. As the triplet of unit vectors is moved over the surface, the magnitudes of the vectors will remain constant at unity and their directions will remain mutually orthogonal. However, the orientation of the triplet will vary and, as a result, special attention must be given to the derivatives of the unit vectors. To begin, we notice that a unit vector can be defined to be any vector divided by its magnitude. Thus

$$\begin{aligned} \mathbf{t}_1 &= \mathbf{r}_{,1}/|\mathbf{r}_{,1}| = \mathbf{r}_{,1}/A_1, \\ \mathbf{t}_2 &= \mathbf{r}_{,2}/|\mathbf{r}_{,2}| = \mathbf{r}_{,2}/A_2, \\ \mathbf{n} &= (\mathbf{t}_1 \times \mathbf{t}_2) = (\mathbf{r}_{,1} \times \mathbf{r}_{,2})/A_1A_2, \end{aligned} \tag{1.51}$$

where we have adopted the notation introduced by Eq. 1.19 for orthogonal systems of parametric lines. Since the derivatives $\mathbf{n}_{,1}$ and $\mathbf{n}_{,2}$ are perpendicular to $\mathbf{n}$, they lie in the plane formed by $\mathbf{t}_1$ and $\mathbf{t}_2$ and each can be decomposed into its components along $\mathbf{t}_1$ and $\mathbf{t}_2$. For example,

$$\mathbf{n}_{,1} = a\mathbf{t}_1 + b\mathbf{t}_2 \tag{1.52}$$

where a and b are unknowns which represent the projections of $\mathbf{n}_{,1}$ on $\mathbf{t}_1$ and $\mathbf{t}_2$, respectively. To determine a and b, we form the following scalar products:

$$\mathbf{t}_1 \cdot \mathbf{n}_{,1} = \frac{\mathbf{r}_{,1} \cdot \mathbf{n}_{,1}}{A_1} = \frac{L}{A_1} = a(\mathbf{t}_1 \cdot \mathbf{t}_1) + b(\mathbf{t}_1 \cdot \mathbf{t}_2),$$

$$\mathbf{t}_2 \cdot \mathbf{n}_{,1} = \frac{\mathbf{r}_{,2} \cdot \mathbf{n}_{,1}}{A_2} = \frac{M}{A_2} = a(\mathbf{t}_2 \cdot \mathbf{t}_1). + b(\mathbf{t}_2 \cdot \mathbf{t}_2).$$

On account of our restriction to orthogonal systems, $M = 0 = \mathbf{t}_1 \cdot \mathbf{t}_2$ and, therefore,

$$a = \frac{L}{A_1}, \qquad b = 0. \tag{1.53}$$

An expression for $\mathbf{n}_{,1}$ is then,

$$\mathbf{n}_{,1} = \frac{L}{A_1}\mathbf{t}_1 \tag{1.54}$$

and since, by Eq. 1.50

$$K_1 = \frac{1}{R_1} = \frac{L}{A_1{}^2}$$

we obtain as the final result

$$\mathbf{n}_{,1} = \frac{A_1}{R_1}\mathbf{t}_1. \tag{1.55}$$

In a similar fashion, it follows that (see the Exercises):

$$\mathbf{n}_{,2} = \frac{A_2}{R_2}\mathbf{t}_2. \tag{1.56}$$

To find the derivatives of $\mathbf{t}_1$ and $\mathbf{t}_2$ along the parametric lines we proceed as we did for the case of the derivatives of $\mathbf{n}$. The manipulations are slightly more involved in this case and are facilitated by noting, first, that for functions with continuous second derivatives, $\mathbf{r}_{,12} = \mathbf{r}_{,21}$. This permits us to write, taking into account Eqs. 1.51,

$$(A_1\mathbf{t}_1)_{,2} = (A_2\mathbf{t}_2)_{,1} \tag{1.57}$$

or

$$\mathbf{t}_{2,1} = \frac{1}{A_2}[A_1\mathbf{t}_{1,2} + \mathbf{t}_1 A_{1,2} - \mathbf{t}_2 A_{2,1}].$$

To find $\mathbf{t}_{1,1}$, for example, we observe that this derivative will be perpendicular to $\mathbf{t}_1$ and will thus lie in the plane formed by $\mathbf{t}_2$ and $\mathbf{n}$. We may, therefore, express $\mathbf{t}_{1,1}$ in terms of $\mathbf{t}_2$ and $\mathbf{n}$ as

$$\mathbf{t}_{1,1} = c\mathbf{n} + d\mathbf{t}_2, \tag{1.58}$$

where c and d are the unknown projections of $\mathbf{t}_{1,1}$ on $\mathbf{t}_2$ and $\mathbf{n}$. To determine c and d we form the scalar products

$$\begin{aligned}\mathbf{n}\cdot\mathbf{t}_{1,1} &= c(\mathbf{n}\cdot\mathbf{n}) + d(\mathbf{n}\cdot\mathbf{t}_2) = c,\\ \mathbf{t}_2\cdot\mathbf{t}_{1,1} &= c(\mathbf{t}_2\cdot\mathbf{n}) + d(\mathbf{t}_2\cdot\mathbf{t}_2) = d.\end{aligned}$$

We now proceed by noting that, since $(\mathbf{t}_1\cdot\mathbf{n}) = 0$,

$$(\mathbf{t}_1\cdot\mathbf{n})_{,1} = \mathbf{t}_1\cdot\mathbf{n}_{,1} + \mathbf{n}\cdot\mathbf{t}_{1,1} = 0 \tag{1.59}$$

and, therefore,

$$c = \mathbf{n}\cdot\mathbf{t}_{1,1} = -\mathbf{t}_1\cdot\mathbf{n}_{,1} = -\frac{A_1}{R_1}, \tag{1.60}$$

where we have employed Eq. 1.55. In the same way,

$$d = \mathbf{t}_2\cdot\mathbf{t}_{1,1} = -\mathbf{t}_1\cdot\mathbf{t}_{2,1}$$

and becomes, upon use of Eq. 1.57,

$$d = -\frac{\mathbf{t}_1}{A_2}\cdot[A_1\mathbf{t}_{1,2} + \mathbf{t}_1 A_{1,2} - \mathbf{t}_2 A_{2,1}].$$

Since $\mathbf{t}_{1,2}$ is perpendicular to $\mathbf{t}_1$, the above expression simplifies to

$$d = -\frac{1}{A_2}A_{1,2}. \tag{1.61}$$

The final result for $\mathbf{t}_{1,1}$ is

$$\mathbf{t}_{1,1} = -\frac{A_1}{R_1}\mathbf{n} - \frac{1}{A_2}\frac{\partial A_1}{\partial \alpha_2}\mathbf{t}_2. \tag{1.62}$$

By proceeding in an analogous manner, we can show (see the Exercises) that the remaining derivatives are given by

$$\begin{aligned}\mathbf{t}_{1,2} &= \frac{1}{A_1}\frac{\partial A_2}{\partial \alpha_1}\mathbf{t}_2,\\ \mathbf{t}_{2,1} &= \frac{1}{A_2}\frac{\partial A_1}{\partial \alpha_2}\mathbf{t}_1,\\ \mathbf{t}_{2,2} &= -\frac{A_2}{R_2}\mathbf{n} - \frac{1}{A_1}\frac{\partial A_2}{\partial \alpha_1}\mathbf{t}_1.\end{aligned} \tag{1.63}$$

1.3*f* Fundamental Theorem of the Theory of Surfaces

We shall now derive three differential equations (known as the Gauss–Codazzi conditions) that relate the quantities A_1, A_2, R_1, and R_2 of a given surface. These equations, as part of the fundamental theorem of the theory of surfaces, are used to ascertain whether an arbitrary choice of these four parameters will define a valid surface. The relationships are found from the equality of the mixed second derivatives of the unit vectors, a result which presumes that these vectors have continuous second derivatives. For example, if we start with

$$\mathbf{n}_{,12} = \mathbf{n}_{,21} \tag{1.64}$$

we notice, upon use of the expressions for the derivatives of $\mathbf{n}$ along the parametric lines derived in the previous section, that

$$\left(\frac{A_1}{R_1}\mathbf{t}_1\right)_{,2} - \left(\frac{A_2}{R_2}\mathbf{t}_2\right)_{,1} = 0. \tag{1.65}$$

If we carry out the differentiations indicated in the foregoing and make use of the expressions for the derivatives of $\mathbf{t}_1$ and $\mathbf{t}_2$, we obtain

$$\mathbf{t}_1\left[\frac{-1}{R_2}A_{1,2} + \left(\frac{A_1}{R_1}\right)_{,2}\right] + \mathbf{t}_2\left[\frac{1}{R_1}A_{2,1} - \left(\frac{A_2}{R_2}\right)_{,1}\right] = 0. \tag{1.66}$$

This vector equation will be true only if the square brackets vanish; hence we obtain

$$\frac{1}{R_2}A_{1,2} = \left(\frac{A_1}{R_1}\right)_{,2}, \qquad \frac{1}{R_1}A_{2,1} = \left(\frac{A_2}{R_2}\right)_{,1}. \tag{1.67}$$

These are known as the Codazzi conditions. If we proceed in a similar fashion from the equation

$$\mathbf{t}_{1,12} = \mathbf{t}_{1,21} \tag{1.68}$$

we obtain two more relations of which only the following is new:

$$\left(\frac{1}{A_1}A_{2,1}\right)_{,1} + \left(\frac{1}{A_2}A_{1,2}\right)_{,2} = -\frac{A_1A_2}{R_1R_2}. \tag{1.69}$$

This is known as the Gauss condition. The fact that four quantities can be related by no more than three homogeneous equations, if they are to possess nontrivial solutions, leads us to the conclusion that no new information will be obtained from a consideration of the remaining equality

$$\mathbf{t}_{2,12} = \mathbf{t}_{2,21}. \tag{1.70}$$

We now indicate, in a formal manner, the role of the Gauss–Codazzi conditions by stating the fundamental theorem of the theory of surfaces:

> If E, G, L, and N are given as functions of the real curvilinear coordinates α_1 and α_2, and are sufficiently differentiable and satisfy the Gauss–Codazzi conditions while $E > 0$ and $G > 0$, then there exists a real surface which has as its first and second fundamental forms
>
> $$\mathrm{I} = E(d\alpha_1)^2 + G(d\alpha_2)^2, \qquad \mathrm{II} = L(d\alpha_1)^2 + N(d\alpha_2)^2.$$
>
> This surface is uniquely determined except for its position in space.

As a consequence of the fundamental theorem, we might refer to the Gauss–Codazzi conditions as the compatibility conditions of the theory of surfaces. It should be noticed that, as stated above, the theorem is already restricted to surfaces whose lines of principal curvature are also its parametric lines (since $F = M = 0$). The extension to more general parametric lines can be made but requires more general forms of the Gauss–Codazzi conditions than we have derived here.

1.4 APPLICATION TO SURFACES OF REVOLUTION

In our subsequent applications of the theory of thin elastic shells to problems of technical interest, we shall be concerned mainly with shell structures whose reference surfaces are surfaces of revolution. Let us, therefore, use this category of surfaces to illustrate some of the results which have been developed here.

A surface of revolution is formed by rotating a plane curve about an axis which lies in its plane. The plane curve is called a meridian of the surface and, when the curve is rotated about the axis, a given point on the curve sweeps out a latitude circle (also called a parallel). Here we may cite the familiar example of the globe with its meridians and parallels that is formed by rotating a circle about a diameter. If we let the position of the parallels of the surface of revolution be defined by the coordinate x_3 (Fig. 1.4), the equation of the meridian curve is given by $R_0 = R_0(x_3)$ where R_0 is the radius of the latitude circle at position x_3. With this definition we note, upon inspection of Fig. 1.4, that the position vector of a point on a surface of revolution is given by (see Eq. 1.13):

$$\mathbf{r}(x_3, \theta) = R_0(x_3)\cos\theta\mathbf{e}_1 + R_0(x_3)\sin\theta\mathbf{e}_2 + x_3\mathbf{e}_3. \tag{1.71}$$

Now let us determine the quantities which make up the first and second fundamental forms of the surface given by $\mathbf{r}(x_3, \theta)$. In doing this, let us associate α_1 with x_3 and α_2 with θ. With this notation, we calculate:

$$\begin{aligned} \mathbf{r}_{,1} &= R_0'\cos\theta\mathbf{e}_1 + R_0'\sin\theta\mathbf{e}_2 + \mathbf{e}_3, \\ \mathbf{r}_{,2} &= -R_0\sin\theta\mathbf{e}_1 + R_0\cos\theta\mathbf{e}_2, \end{aligned} \tag{1.72}$$

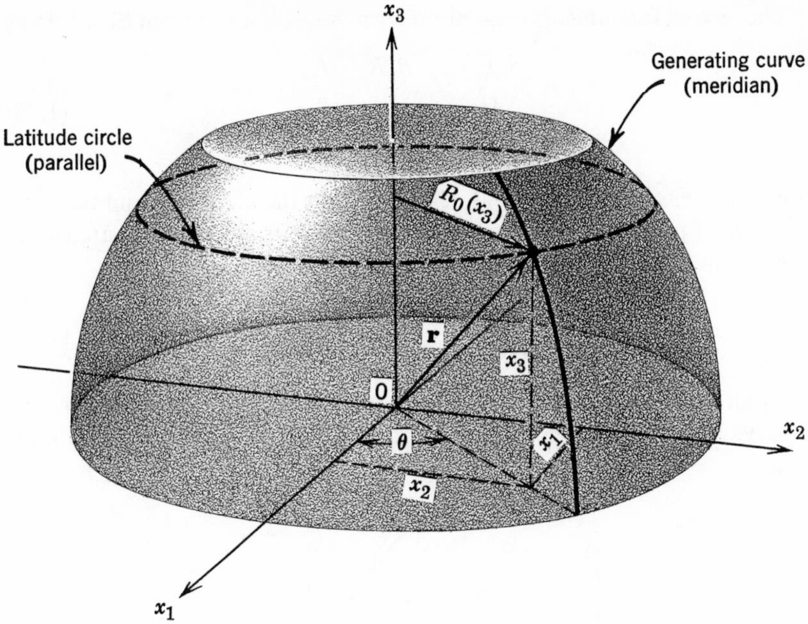

Figure 1.4 Geometry of a surface of revolution.

where a prime denotes differentiation with respect to x_3. For the first fundamental magnitudes, we obtain by use of Eq. 1.17:

$$\begin{aligned} E &= 1 + (R_0')^2, \\ F &= 0, \\ G &= R_0^2, \\ H &= \sqrt{EG - F^2} = R_0\sqrt{1 + (R_0')^2}. \end{aligned} \tag{1.73}$$

We see, therefore, that the meridians and parallels form an orthogonal family of parametric lines, and

$$A_1 = \sqrt{E} = \sqrt{1 + (R_0')^2}, \qquad A_2 = \sqrt{G} = R_0.$$

The first fundamental form of the surface of revolution is thus

$$(ds)^2 = [1 + (R_0')^2](dx_3)^2 + R_0^2(d\theta)^2. \tag{1.74}$$

The normal to a surface of revolution is, by Eq. 1.25,

$$\mathbf{n} = \left(\frac{\mathbf{r}_{,1} \times \mathbf{r}_{,2}}{H}\right) = -\frac{R_0}{H}[\cos\theta\mathbf{e}_1 + \sin\theta\mathbf{e}_2 - R_0'\mathbf{e}_3] \tag{1.75}$$

and acts, as we have previously assumed, from the concave side to the convex side of the surface.

The second fundamental magnitudes are now obtained from Eqs. 1.35 as

$$\begin{aligned} L &= -R_0 R_0''/H, \\ M &= 0, \\ N &= R_0^2/H. \end{aligned} \tag{1.76}$$

It is thus seen, since both F and M vanish, that the meridians and parallels are lines of principal curvature. The principal radii of curvature are calculated from Eqs. 1.50 with the result that

$$\begin{aligned} R_1 &= E/L = -[1 + (R_0')^2]^{3/2}/R_0'', \\ R_2 &= G/N = R_0\sqrt{1 + (R_0')^2}. \end{aligned} \tag{1.77}$$

Upon consideration of the expressions for the radii of curvature we observe first, from the calculus, that R_1 represents the radius of curvature

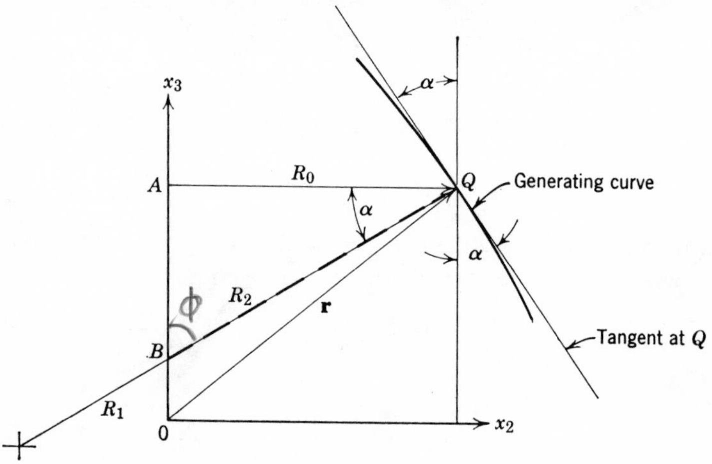

Figure 1.5

of the meridian curve $R_0(x_3)$. The negative sign of R_1 signifies only that R_1 is opposite in direction to **n**. The interpretation of R_2 is made with the aid of Fig. 1.5 where it may be seen that

$$\begin{aligned} \tan\alpha &= R_0', \\ AB = AQ\tan\alpha &= R_0 R_0', \\ BQ = \sqrt{\overline{AQ}^2 + \overline{AB}^2} &= R_0\sqrt{1 + (R_0')^2} = R_2. \end{aligned} \tag{1.78}$$

Thus we see that R_2 is the distance along a normal to the curve $R_0(x_3)$ drawn from a point Q to the axis of revolution of the surface.

To check if the above combination of A_1, A_2, R_1, and R_2 defines a valid surface, we apply the test furnished by the fundamental theorem of the theory of surfaces. By substituting the expressions for A_1, A_2, R_1, and R_2 into the Gauss–Codazzi conditions, it is found (see the Exercises) that they are identically satisfied. Therefore, our choice of A_1, A_2, R_1, and R_2 defines a valid surface.

An alternate, and equally useful description of a surface of revolution is based on the independent variables φ and θ where φ is the angle between the axis of revolution of the surface and a normal to the surface at the point. For such coordinate systems, the first fundamental form is

$$(ds)^2 = R_1{}^2(d\varphi)^2 + R_0{}^2(d\theta)^2 \tag{1.79}$$

where the first term on the right-hand side represents the square of the differential length of arc along a meridian, and the second term represents (as in Eq. 1.74) the square of the differential length of arc along a parallel. Now we associate α_1 with φ and α_2 with θ, and obtain from Eq. 1.79, $A_1 = R_1$ and $A_2 = R_0$. If the foregoing are substituted into the Gauss–Codazzi conditions expressed in the (φ, θ) coordinate system, it is found that the Codazzi conditions are identically satisfied and that the Gauss condition reduces to

$$\frac{dR_0}{d\varphi} = R_1 \cos \varphi. \tag{1.80}$$

If we consider Fig. 1.6, we find that

$$\begin{aligned} BQ &= R_2, \\ AQ &= R_0 = R_2 \sin \varphi, \\ A'Q' - AQ &= dR_0, \\ dR_0 &= QQ' \cos \varphi = R_1\, d\varphi \cos \varphi, \\ \therefore \frac{dR_0}{d\varphi} &= R_1 \cos \varphi. \end{aligned} \tag{1.81}$$

Thus the Gauss condition 1.80 is indeed satisfied, and the alternate formulation in terms of the coordinates φ and θ is also valid.

1.5 CLOSURE

In the preceding sections, we have set down for later use all of the necessary concepts and results from differential geometry. In particular, in the derivation of the theory of thin elastic shells, we shall make extensive use of the concept of the first fundamental form of a surface and the associated first fundamental magnitudes, the orthogonality of the lines of principal

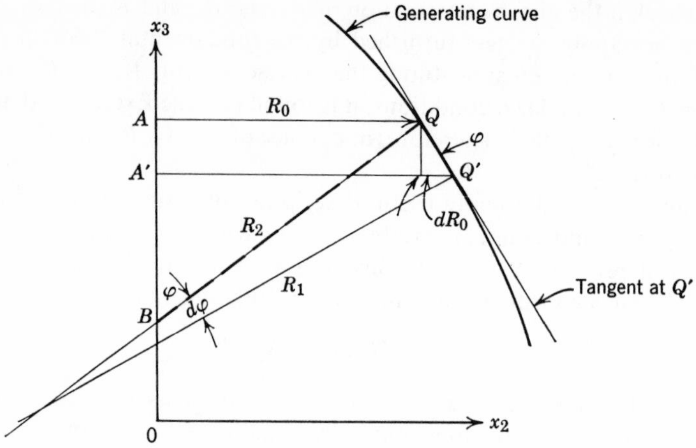

Figure 1.6

curvature, the Gauss–Codazzi conditions, and the properties of surfaces of revolution.

To fix the ideas set forth herein, the Exercises listed at the end should be worked out. Since the treatment of the subject of differential geometry has been limited to those results which are relied upon in the derivation of the theory of thin elastic shells, the reader is invited to broaden his understanding of differential geometry by consulting the references.

SUPPLEMENTARY REFERENCES

Struik, D. J., *Differential Geometry*, Reading, Pa.: Addison-Wesley, 1950.
Graustein, W. C., *Differential Geometry*, New York: Macmillan, 1935.
Lass, H., *Vector and Tensor Analysis*, New York: McGraw-Hill, 1950.

EXERCISES

1.1 Show that $H = EG - F^2 > 0$.

1.2 Determine $\mathbf{N} \cdot \mathbf{n}$ for the parametric lines of a shell of revolution.

1.3 Verify Eqs. 1.56 and 1.63.

1.4 Verify that no new information is obtained from a consideration of Eq. 1.70 in the derivation of relationships between A_1, A_2, R_1, and R_2 for a shell of revolution.

1.5 Show that Eq. 1.71 defines a valid surface.

1.6 Derive the first fundamental forms of the following surfaces of revolution:
(a) Flat circular sheet.
(b) Right circular cylinder.

(c) Sphere.
(d) Cone.
(e) Toroid.
(f) Paraboloid.
(g) Ellipsoid.

1.7 Suppose that a surface of revolution is defined by $r(\xi)$ and $z(\xi)$ where ξ is a parameter on the surface and r and z are the radial and axial coordinates of a point on the surface. The first fundamental form of such a surface is

$$(ds)^2 = \alpha^2(d\xi)^2 + r^2(d\theta)^2.$$

Show that

$$\alpha^2 = (r')^2 + (z')^2,$$

$$\cos\varphi = r'/\alpha, \qquad \sin\varphi = z'/\alpha, \qquad R_\xi = \alpha/\varphi', \qquad R_\theta = r/\sin\varphi,$$

where φ is the angle formed by the normal to the generating curve and the vertical axis of the shell and a prime denotes a derivative with respect to ξ.

2

Fundamental Equations of the Theory of Thin Elastic Shells

2.1 INTRODUCTION

The basic equations which describe the behavior of a thin elastic shell were originally derived by Love [1,2] in 1888. These equations, together with the assumptions upon which they are based, form a theory of thin elastic shells which is commonly referred to as Love's first approximation. In this chapter, we shall derive the basic differential equations of the first approximation using, as a basis, E. Reissner's[3] version of the Love theory.

The present chapter proceeds as follows: first, the underlying assumptions of the theory are described. This is followed by derivations of the elastic law that relates the stresses and displacements in a thin shell, the equations of motion of a shell element, and the natural boundary conditions that are to be used with the theory. To allow as much generality as possible, and to make the development more meaningful for application to modern materials of construction, the derivation of the theory is carried out for an elastic orthotropic material. The effect of a known temperature distribution is incorporated wherever it is appropriate, and a brief discus-

[1] Love, A. E. H., "On the Small Free Vibrations and Deformations of Thin Elastic Shells," *Phil. Trans. Roy. Soc.* (*London*), **17A**, 491–546 (1888).

[2] Love, A. E. H., *A Treatise on the Mathematical Theory of Elasticity*, 4th ed., New York: Dover Publications, 1944, Chapter 24.

[3] Reissner, E., "A New Derivation of the Equations for the Deformation of Elastic Shells," *Amer. J. Math.*, **63**, 177–184 (1941). There is a difference in the Love theory as derived by Love and by Reissner. Hence, our use of the word version.

sion of the theory of heat conduction as applied to the thermal analysis of a thin shell is given in an appendix to the chapter.

2.2 BASIC ASSUMPTIONS

In the three dimensional theory of elasticity, the fundamental equations occur in three broad categories. Thus, it will be recalled that in elasticity we have equations of motion which are obtained from a balance of the forces acting on some fundamental element of the medium considered, that we have strain-displacement relations which are obtained from a strictly geometrical consideration of the process of deformation, and that we have the constitutive law of elasticity (Hooke's law) which is introduced in order to provide a relationship between the stresses and the strains in the elastic medium. It will also be remembered that the solution of problems in the three-dimensional theory of elasticity involves vast complications which have been overcome in only a few special cases. Thus, a group of simplifying assumptions that provide a reasonable description of the behavior of thin elastic shells was proposed by Love and has led to the development of a sub-class of the theory of elasticity known as the theory of thin elastic shells. We find, therefore, that each of the three categories of equations referred to previously has a reduced counterpart in the theory of thin elastic shells. It is to the basis of these reductions that we now turn our attention.

Love's first approximation to the theory of thin elastic shells is based upon the following postulates:

1. The shell is thin.
2. The deflections of the shell are small.
3. The transverse normal stress is negligible.
4. Normals to the reference surface of the shell remain normal to it and undergo no change in length during deformation.

Let us now discuss these assumptions and their implications individually.

The assumption of thinness sets the stage for the entire theory. Indeed, as will be noted presently, the rest of Love's postulates seem to be appropriate only to thin shells and are, therefore, consequences of this first postulate. Although no precise definition of thinness is available, it will be sufficient in our subsequent derivations of the theory to neglect the ratio of the thickness to the radius of curvature of the reference surface in comparison to unity. As a rule of thumb, however, it is suggested that the resulting theory be applied only to shells whose thickness is everywhere less than one tenth of the radius of curvature of the reference surface.

The assumption that the deflections of the shell are small permits us to refer all derivations and calculations to the original configuration of the shell and, together with Hooke's law, assures us that the resulting theory will be a linear, elastic one.

The two remaining hypotheses of the Love theory deal with the constitutive equations of thin elastic shells and represent the most significant features of the first approximation. In preparing for our discussion of these assumptions, it is well to set down Hooke's law for an homogeneous, orthotropic elastic medium. In such a material, there are three mutually perpendicular planes of elastic symmetry that, in anticipation of our later choice of the lines of principal curvature as coordinates, we associate with the mutually perpendicular α_1, α_2 and normal directions of Section 1.3*e*. For such a material, Hooke's law with temperature effects included is[4]

$$\begin{aligned} \epsilon_1 &= \frac{\sigma_1}{E_1} - \frac{\nu_{12}}{E_2}\sigma_2 - \frac{\nu_{1n}}{E_n}\sigma_n + \alpha_{t1}T, \\ \epsilon_2 &= \frac{\sigma_2}{E_2} - \frac{\nu_{21}}{E_1}\sigma_1 - \frac{\nu_{2n}}{E_n}\sigma_n + \alpha_{t2}T, \\ \epsilon_n &= \frac{\sigma_n}{E_n} - \frac{\nu_{n1}}{E_1}\sigma_1 - \frac{\nu_{n2}}{E_2}\sigma_2 + \alpha_{tn}T, \end{aligned} \tag{2.1a}$$

$$\gamma_{12} = \frac{\tau_{12}}{G_{12}}, \qquad \gamma_{1n} = \frac{\tau_{1n}}{G_{1n}}, \qquad \gamma_{2n} = \frac{\tau_{2n}}{G_{2n}}, \tag{2.1b}$$

where σ_1, σ_2, σ_n are the normal stresses along three mutually perpendicular directions, ϵ_1, ϵ_2, ϵ_n are the corresponding normal strains, and γ_{12}, γ_{1n}, γ_{2n} and τ_{1n}, τ_{2n}, τ_{12} are, respectively, the shearing strains and stresses. T is a known temperature distribution[5] while α_{t1}, α_{t2}, α_{tn} are the coefficients of linear thermal expansion in the three coordinate directions. Finally, E_1, E_2, E_n, G_{12}, G_{1n}, G_{2n} and ν_{12}, ν_{21}, ν_{1n}, ν_{2n}, ν_{n1}, ν_{n2} are the elastic constants (Young's modulus, shear modulus and Poisson's ratio) along the three coordinate directions. It should be noted that the Young's moduli and Poisson's ratios are not independent and are related by the expressions

$$\frac{\nu_{1n}}{E_n} = \frac{\nu_{n1}}{E_1}, \qquad \frac{\nu_{2n}}{E_n} = \frac{\nu_{n2}}{E_2}, \qquad \frac{\nu_{12}}{E_2} = \frac{\nu_{21}}{E_1}. \tag{2.1c}$$

If these are substituted into the last of Eqs. 2.1a, a form which will be more useful in our later discussions is obtained:

$$\epsilon_n = \frac{1}{E_n}\left[\sigma_n - \nu_{2n}\sigma_2 - \nu_{1n}\sigma_1\right] + \alpha_{tn}T. \tag{2.1d}$$

---

[4] See, for example, Hearmon, R. F. S., *Introduction to Applied Anisotropic Elasticity*, London: Oxford University Press, 1961, pp. 65–67.

[5] A discussion of the thermal analysis of thin shells is given in the appendix to this chapter.

We point out also the fact that, in accordance with the usual practice in thermoelasticity, a total normal strain made up of a mechanical component and a thermal component has been defined. Such a definition is not appropriate to the shearing strains since in isotropic and orthotropic media heating is accompanied by normal strains only.

We now return to the discussion of Love's postulates by noting that the fourth hypothesis that concerns the preservation of the normal element represents an extension to the case of a thin elastic shell of the familiar Bernoulli–Euler hypothesis of beam theory which states that "plane sections remain plane." The assumption of the preservation of the normal implies that all of the strain components in the direction of the normal to the reference surface vanish, or that

$$\epsilon_n = \gamma_{1n} = \gamma_{2n} = 0, \tag{2.2}$$

and in view of Eqs. 2.1b, the shearing stress components τ_{1n} and τ_{2n} also vanish.

Our restriction to the consideration of thin shells makes reasonable the third assumption of the Love theory that is expressed as

$$\sigma_n = 0. \tag{2.3}$$

It is expected that this assumption will be generally valid except in the vicinity of highly concentrated loads.

As a consequence of the third and fourth postulates of the Love theory (as expressed by Eqs. 2.2 and 2.3), the system of stress–strain relations given by Eqs. 2.1 is reduced to the following two-dimensional constitutive law of thin elastic shells:

$$\begin{aligned} \epsilon_1 &= \frac{\sigma_1}{E_1} - \frac{\nu_{12}}{E_2}\sigma_2 + \alpha_{t1}T, \\ \epsilon_2 &= \frac{\sigma_2}{E_2} - \frac{\nu_{21}}{E_1}\sigma_1 + \alpha_{t2}T, \\ \gamma_{12} &= \frac{\tau_{12}}{G_{12}}, \qquad \epsilon_n = \gamma_{1n} = \gamma_{2n} = \sigma_n = 0. \end{aligned} \tag{2.4}$$

This completes the presentation of Love's hypotheses. In the remainder of the chapter, we shall be concerned with the derivation of a set of differential equations which embody the assumptions set forth here and thus describe to a first approximation the behavior of a thin elastic shell.

2.3 SHELL COORDINATES

Love's assumption regarding the preservation of the normal element in a thin shell implies that the displacements are linearly distributed across the thickness and that, therefore, the behavior of a generic point in the shell can be determined from the behavior of a corresponding point on some reference surface. Generally, the middle surface is selected as the reference surface; however, this is most convenient only for shells composed of but one material. In the case of layered shells, it may be more convenient to use as a reference surface the inner or the outer surface of the shell or even some neutral surface which is analogous to the neutral axis of a beam of irregular cross section. Regardless of the choice that is made for the reference surface, the reasons for presenting results on surfaces in Chapter 1 are now clear.

In Chapter 1, we emphasized the use of a curvilinear coordinate system which coincides with the orthogonal lines of principal curvature of the surface under consideration; we now adopt, formally, such a coordinate system. The choice of an orthogonal curvilinear coordinate system allows a convenient derivation by standard procedures of the fundamental equations of the theory of thin elastic shells. Derivations of the theory in which nonorthogonal coordinate systems are employed have also appeared in the literature; however, these will not be considered here.

To describe the location of an arbitrary point in the space occupied by a thin shell, we define the following position vector (see Section 1.3a):

$$\mathbf{R}(\alpha_1, \alpha_2, \zeta) = \mathbf{r}(\alpha_1, \alpha_2) + \zeta\mathbf{n}(\alpha_1, \alpha_2), \qquad {\alpha_1}^0 \leqslant \alpha_1 \leqslant {\alpha_1}^1, \quad {\alpha_2}^0 \leqslant \alpha_2 \leqslant {\alpha_2}^1, \tag{2.5}$$

where $\mathbf{r}$ is the position vector of a corresponding point on the reference surface, $\mathbf{n}$ is the unit normal vector from the reference surface to the point, and ζ denotes the distance of the point from the corresponding point on the reference surface along $\mathbf{n}$ and ranges over the local thickness $h(\alpha_1, \alpha_2)$. Here, as in Chapter 1, α_1 and α_2 are the parametric lines of the reference surface and coincide, according to our choice, with the orthogonal lines of principal curvature. The quantities ${\alpha_1}^0$, ${\alpha_1}^1$, ${\alpha_2}^0$, and ${\alpha_2}^1$ are bounding parametric lines which define, on the reference surface, the extent of the shell.

The magnitude of an arbitrary differential element of length in the space defined by the vector $\mathbf{R}(\alpha_1, \alpha_2, \zeta)$ is now obtained by the use of Eq. 1.16. This gives

$$(ds)^2 = d\mathbf{R}\cdot d\mathbf{R} = (d\mathbf{r} + \zeta\, d\mathbf{n} + \mathbf{n}\, d\zeta)\cdot(d\mathbf{r} + \zeta\, d\mathbf{n} + \mathbf{n}\, d\zeta). \tag{2.6}$$

If the indicated operations are carried out, keeping in mind the orthogonality of the coordinate system which is being employed, the result is (see the Exercises):

$$(ds)^2 = {A_1}^2(1 + \zeta/R_1)^2(d\alpha_1)^2 + {A_2}^2(1 + \zeta/R_2)^2(d\alpha_2)^2 + (d\zeta)^2. \tag{2.7}$$

This expression contains all of the information which will be necessary in later manipulations involving the shell coordinate system. For example, the first two terms on the right-hand side of Eq. 2.7 can be thought of as the first fundamental form (see Eq. 1.19) of a surface located a distance ζ from the reference surface. For such a surface, the Codazzi conditions (see Eqs. 1.67) become

$$\begin{aligned}[A_1(1 + \zeta/R_1)]_{,2} &= (1 + \zeta/R_2)A_{1,2} \\ [A_2(1 + \zeta/R_2)]_{,1} &= (1 + \zeta/R_1)A_{2,1}.\end{aligned} \tag{2.8}$$

We shall make extensive use of this form of the Codazzi conditions in the derivation of the equations of the theory.

Having thus established the coordinate system of the shell space, it is natural to define the fundamental element of a thin shell as that element which is bounded by two surfaces $d\zeta$ apart at a distance ζ from the reference surface and four cuts made perpendicular to the reference surface, each pair of cuts coinciding with a pair of adjacent parametric lines of the reference surface. The lengths of the edges of this fundamental element are, according to Eq. 2.7 (see Fig. 2.1),

$$\begin{aligned}ds_1(\zeta) &= A_1(1 + \zeta/R_1)\,d\alpha_1, \\ ds_2(\zeta) &= A_2(1 + \zeta/R_2)\,d\alpha_2,\end{aligned} \tag{2.9}$$

and the differential areas of the edge faces of the fundamental element defined above are

$$\begin{aligned}d\Sigma_1(\zeta) &= A_1(1 + \zeta/R_1)\,d\alpha_1\,d\zeta, \\ d\Sigma_2(\zeta) &= A_2(1 + \zeta/R_2)\,d\alpha_2\,d\zeta.\end{aligned} \tag{2.10}$$

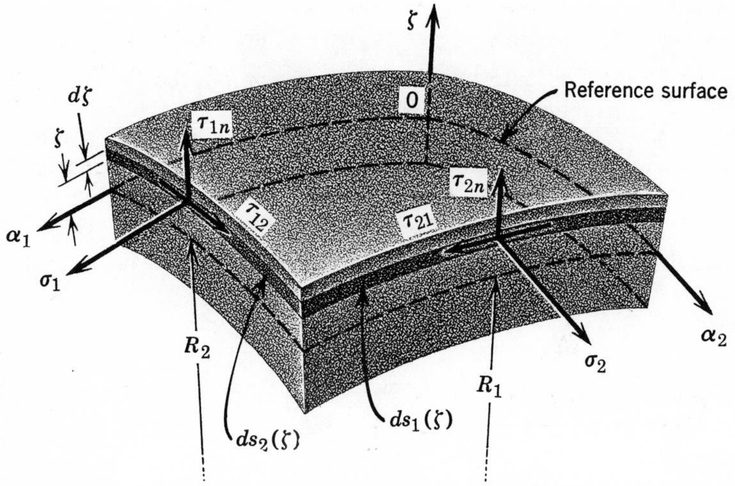

Figure 2.1 Differential element of a shell.

The definitions of the coordinate system and the fundamental element of the shell space complete our preparations for the derivation of the equations of the theory.

2.4 STRAIN DISPLACEMENT RELATIONS

We now define, in the shell space that has been adopted in the preceding section, the following displacement vector:

$$\mathbf{U}(\alpha_1, \alpha_2, \zeta) = U_1(\alpha_1, \alpha_2, \zeta)\mathbf{t}_1 + U_2(\alpha_1, \alpha_2, \zeta)\mathbf{t}_2 + W(\alpha_1, \alpha_2, \zeta)\mathbf{n}, \quad (2.11)$$

where (as in Section 1.3*e*) $\mathbf{t}_1$, $\mathbf{t}_2$, $\mathbf{n}$ are unit vectors along α_1, α_2 and the normal to the reference surface, respectively, and U_1, U_2, W are the components of the displacement vector in the corresponding orthogonal coordinate directions. In texts on the theory of elasticity,[6] it is shown that in an orthogonal curvilinear coordinate system wherein the square of the magnitude of a differential element of length is given by an expression such as Eq. 2.7, the normal and shearing strain components are related to the components of the displacement vector by

$$\begin{aligned} \epsilon_i &= \frac{\partial}{\partial \alpha_i}\left(\frac{u_i}{\sqrt{g_i}}\right) + \frac{1}{2g_i}\sum_{k=1}^{3}\frac{\partial g_i}{\partial \alpha_k}\frac{u_k}{\sqrt{g_k}}, \qquad i = 1, 2, 3 \\ \gamma_{ij} &= \frac{1}{\sqrt{g_i g_j}}\left[g_i \frac{\partial}{\partial \alpha_j}\left(\frac{u_i}{\sqrt{g_i}}\right) + g_j \frac{\partial}{\partial \alpha_i}\left(\frac{u_j}{\sqrt{g_j}}\right)\right], \qquad i = 1, 2, 3, \quad i \neq j \end{aligned} \quad (2.12)$$

where, for the application to shells (see Eq. 2.7):

$$\begin{aligned} &\alpha_1 = \alpha_1, && \alpha_2 = \alpha_2, && \alpha_3 = \zeta, \\ &u_1 = U_1, && u_2 = U_2, && u_3 = W, \\ &g_1 = A_1^2(1 + \zeta/R_1)^2, && g_2 = A_2^2(1 + \zeta/R_2)^2, && g_3 = 1. \end{aligned} \quad (2.13)$$

If we substitute Eqs. 2.13 into Eqs. 2.12, we obtain the following strain-displacement equations in the shell space:

$$\begin{aligned} \epsilon_1 &= \frac{1}{A_1(1 + \zeta/R_1)}\left(\frac{\partial U_1}{\partial \alpha_1} + \frac{U_2}{A_2}\frac{\partial A_1}{\partial \alpha_2} + \frac{A_1 W}{R_1}\right), \\ \epsilon_2 &= \frac{1}{A_2(1 + \zeta/R_2)}\left(\frac{\partial U_2}{\partial \alpha_2} + \frac{U_1}{A_1}\frac{\partial A_2}{\partial \alpha_1} + \frac{A_2 W}{R_2}\right), \\ \epsilon_n &= \frac{\partial W}{\partial \zeta}, \\ \gamma_{1n} &= \frac{1}{A_1(1 + \zeta/R_1)}\frac{\partial W}{\partial \alpha_1} + A_1(1 + \zeta/R_1)\frac{\partial}{\partial \zeta}\left[\frac{U_1}{A_1(1 + \zeta/R_1)}\right], \end{aligned}$$

---

[6] It is assumed that the reader is familiar with the derivation of the strain-displacement equations of linear elasticity, as given by, for example, Sokolnikoff, I. S., *Mathematical Theory of Elasticity*, 2nd ed., New York: McGraw-Hill, 1956, pp. 177–184.

p53 Love 54 cf (36)

$$\gamma_{2n} = \frac{1}{A_1(1 + \zeta/R_2)} \frac{\partial W}{\partial \alpha_2} + A_2(1 + \zeta/R_2) \frac{\partial}{\partial \zeta} \left[\frac{U_2}{A_2(1 + \zeta/R_2)} \right],$$

$$\gamma_{12} = \frac{A_2(1 + \zeta/R_2)}{A_1(1 + \zeta/R_1)} \frac{\partial}{\partial \alpha_1} \left[\frac{U_2}{A_2(1 + \zeta/R_2)} \right] + \frac{A_1(1 + \zeta/R_1)}{A_2(1 + \zeta/R_2)} \frac{\partial}{\partial \alpha_2} \left[\frac{U_1}{A_1(1 + \zeta/R_1)} \right]. \quad (2.14)$$

For later purposes, the above strain-displacement relations do not as yet reflect any of Love's postulates. To introduce these, we first recall that it has been previously indicated that the assumption on the preservation of the normal element implies that the displacements are linearly distributed through the thickness of the shell. Thus, we may assume that the displacement components are represented by the following relationships:

$$\begin{aligned} U_1(\alpha_1, \alpha_2, \zeta) &= u_1(\alpha_1, \alpha_2) + \zeta u_1'(\alpha_1, \alpha_2, 0), \\ U_2(\alpha_1, \alpha_2, \zeta) &= u_2(\alpha_1, \alpha_2) + \zeta u_2'(\alpha_1, \alpha_2, 0), \\ W(\alpha_1, \alpha_2, \zeta) &= w(\alpha_1, \alpha_2), \end{aligned} \quad (2.15)$$

where a prime denotes a derivative with respect to ζ. The quantities u_1, u_2, and w represent the components of the displacement vector of a point on the reference surface, and the quantities u_1' and u_2' represent the rotations of tangents to the reference surface oriented along the parametric lines α_1 and α_2, respectively. Notice that the assumed representation of the normal displacement component leads, through the fourth of Eqs. 2.12, to the result that $\epsilon_n = 0$, as postulated. The rotations u_1' and u_2' which will henceforth be denoted by β_1 and β_2, respectively, can be determined from the hypothesis that $\gamma_{1n} = \gamma_{2n} = 0$. Thus, if we substitute U_1, U_2, and W from Eqs. 2.15 into the fourth and fifth of Eqs. 2.14 and set the results equal to zero, we find that

$$\begin{aligned} \beta_1 &= \frac{u_1}{R_1} - \frac{1}{A_1} \frac{\partial w}{\partial \alpha_1}, \\ \beta_2 &= \frac{u_2}{R_2} - \frac{1}{A_2} \frac{\partial w}{\partial \alpha_2}. \end{aligned} \quad (2.16)$$

Now, if we invoke the additional assumption that the shell is thin, that is, $\zeta/R \ll 1$, we find upon substitution of Eqs. 2.15 into the remainder of Eqs. 2.14 that the nonvanishing strains in a thin elastic shell are given by

$$\begin{aligned} \epsilon_1 &= \frac{1}{A_1} \frac{\partial}{\partial \alpha_1} (u_1 + \zeta\beta_1) + \frac{u_2 + \zeta\beta_2}{A_1 A_2} \frac{\partial A_1}{\partial \alpha_2} + \frac{w}{R_1}, \\ \epsilon_2 &= \frac{1}{A_2} \frac{\partial}{\partial \alpha_2} (u_2 + \zeta\beta_2) + \frac{u_1 + \zeta\beta_1}{A_1 A_2} \frac{\partial A_2}{\partial \alpha_1} + \frac{w}{R_2}, \\ \gamma_{12} &= \frac{A_2}{A_1} \frac{\partial}{\partial \alpha_1} \left(\frac{u_2 + \zeta\beta_2}{A_2} \right) + \frac{A_1}{A_2} \frac{\partial}{\partial \alpha_2} \left(\frac{u_1 + \zeta\beta_1}{A_1} \right). \end{aligned} \quad (2.17)$$

The strains can also be expressed in the form:

$$\begin{aligned}\epsilon_1 &= \epsilon_1{}^0 + \zeta\kappa_1,\\ \epsilon_2 &= \epsilon_2{}^0 + \zeta\kappa_2,\\ \gamma_{12} &= \gamma_{12}{}^0 + \zeta\tau,\end{aligned} \tag{2.18}$$

where

$$\begin{aligned}\epsilon_1{}^0 &= \frac{1}{A_1}\frac{\partial u_1}{\partial \alpha_1} + \frac{u_2}{A_1 A_2}\frac{\partial A_1}{\partial \alpha_2} + \frac{w}{R_1},\\ \epsilon_2{}^0 &= \frac{1}{A_2}\frac{\partial u_2}{\partial \alpha_2} + \frac{u_1}{A_1 A_2}\frac{\partial A_2}{\partial \alpha_1} + \frac{w}{R_2},\\ \gamma_{12}{}^0 &= \frac{A_2}{A_1}\frac{\partial}{\partial \alpha_1}\left(\frac{u_2}{A_2}\right) + \frac{A_1}{A_2}\frac{\partial}{\partial \alpha_2}\left(\frac{u_1}{A_1}\right),\\ \kappa_1 &= \frac{1}{A_1}\frac{\partial \beta_1}{\partial \alpha_1} + \frac{\beta_2}{A_1 A_2}\frac{\partial A_1}{\partial \alpha_2},\\ \kappa_2 &= \frac{1}{A_2}\frac{\partial \beta_2}{\partial \alpha_2} + \frac{\beta_1}{A_1 A_2}\frac{\partial A_2}{\partial \alpha_1},\\ \tau &= \frac{A_2}{A_1}\frac{\partial}{\partial \alpha_1}\left(\frac{\beta_2}{A_2}\right) + \frac{A_1}{A_2}\frac{\partial}{\partial \alpha_2}\left(\frac{\beta_1}{A_1}\right).\end{aligned} \tag{2.19}$$

The quantities $\epsilon_1{}^0$, $\epsilon_2{}^0$, and $\gamma_{12}{}^0$ represent the normal and shearing strains of the reference surface as can be confirmed upon substitution of $\zeta = 0$ into Eqs. 2.17. The quantities κ_1 and κ_2 represent a linearly distributed bending component of strain and, in analogy to the theory of beams, it is readily seen that κ_1 and κ_2 represent the changes in the curvature of the reference surface during deformation. The quantity τ represents the torsion of the reference surface during deformation. Torsion is defined as the limit of the ratio of the relative angle of twist between opposite sides of an element of the reference surface and the distance separating them as the element shrinks to zero. Torsion has the dimensions of the reciprocal of length and is thereby analogous to curvature.

2.5 STRESS RESULTANTS AND STRESS COUPLES

Since the strains, and thereby the stresses, have been shown to be linearly distributed across the thickness of a thin elastic shell, it is convenient to integrate the stress distributions through the thickness of the shell and to replace the usual consideration of stresses by a consideration of statically equivalent stress resultants and stress couples. By performing such integrations, the variations with respect to ζ are completely eliminated to give a two-dimensional theory.

To integrate the stresses across the thickness, we first solve Eqs. 2.4 for the stresses. This leads to the result

$$\begin{aligned}\sigma_1 &= E_1{}^*\epsilon_1 + \nu_{21}E_2{}^*\epsilon_2 - (E_1{}^*\alpha_{t1} + \nu_{21}E_2{}^*\alpha_{t2})T,\\ \sigma_2 &= E_2{}^*\epsilon_2 + \nu_{12}E_1{}^*\epsilon_1 - (E_2{}^*\alpha_{t2} + \nu_{12}E_1{}^*\alpha_{t1})T,\\ \tau_{12} &= G_{12}\gamma_{12}\end{aligned} \tag{2.20}$$

where

$$E_i^* = E_i/(1 - \nu_{12}\nu_{21}), \qquad i = 1, 2.$$

When Eqs. 2.18 are substituted into the above, the final expressions for the stresses in terms of the reference surface strains and changes in curvature are

$$\begin{aligned}\sigma_1 &= E_1{}^*\epsilon_1{}^0 + E_2{}^*\nu_{21}\epsilon_2{}^0 + \zeta(E_1{}^*\kappa_1 + E_2{}^*\nu_{21}\kappa_2)\\ &\qquad - (E_1{}^*\alpha_{t1} + \nu_{21}E_2{}^*\alpha_{t2})T,\\ \sigma_2 &= E_2{}^*\epsilon_2{}^0 + E_1{}^*\nu_{12}\epsilon_1{}^0 + \zeta(E_2{}^*\kappa_2 + E_1{}^*\nu_{12}\kappa_1)\\ &\qquad - (E_2{}^*\alpha_{t2} + \nu_{12}E_1{}^*\alpha_{t1})T,\\ \tau_{12} &= G_{12}(\gamma_{12}{}^0 + \zeta\tau).\end{aligned} \tag{2.21}$$

We are now in a position to integrate the stress distributions across the thickness of the shell. For convenience, the stress resultants and couples that are obtained in this way are defined per unit of arc length on the reference surface. For example, the resultants and couples of the stresses σ_1 distributed over an α_1 = constant face of the fundamental element of the shell are given by

$$N_1 = \int_\zeta \frac{\sigma_1\, d\Sigma_2(\zeta)}{ds_2(0)} = \int_\zeta \sigma_1(1 + \zeta/R_2)\, d\zeta, \tag{2.22a}$$

and

$$M_1 = \int_\zeta \frac{\zeta\sigma_1\, d\Sigma_2(\zeta)}{ds_2(0)} = \int_\zeta \sigma_1(1 + \zeta/R_2)\zeta\, d\zeta, \tag{2.22b}$$

where we have employed the definitions of differential area and arc length given by Eqs. 2.9 and 2.10. By extension of the foregoing, we find that the stress resultants and stress couples that correspond to the remaining stresses are given by:

$$\begin{aligned}\begin{Bmatrix} N_1 \\ N_{12} \\ Q_1 \end{Bmatrix} &= \int_\zeta \begin{Bmatrix} \sigma_1 \\ \tau_{12} \\ \tau_{1n} \end{Bmatrix} (1 + \zeta/R_2)\, d\zeta,\\ \begin{Bmatrix} N_2 \\ N_{21} \\ Q_2 \end{Bmatrix} &= \int_\zeta \begin{Bmatrix} \sigma_2 \\ \tau_{21} \\ \tau_{2n} \end{Bmatrix} (1 + \zeta/R_1)\, d\zeta,\\ \begin{Bmatrix} M_1 \\ M_{12} \end{Bmatrix} &= \int_\zeta \begin{Bmatrix} \sigma_1 \\ \tau_{12} \end{Bmatrix} (1 + \zeta/R_2)\zeta\, d\zeta,\\ \begin{Bmatrix} M_2 \\ M_{21} \end{Bmatrix} &= \int_\zeta \begin{Bmatrix} \sigma_2 \\ \tau_{21} \end{Bmatrix} (1 + \zeta/R_1)\zeta\, d\zeta.\end{aligned} \tag{2.23}$$

We notice, in the above definitions, that the symmetry of the stress tensor (that is, $\tau_{12} = \tau_{21}$) does not necessarily imply that N_{12} and N_{21} are equal or that M_{12} and M_{21} are equal except for a spherical shell, a flat plate, or a thin shell of any shape. Although our interest is in thin shells, we have, for later purposes, not as yet neglected ζ/R with respect to unity. No couples from the stresses τ_{1n} and τ_{2n} appear in Eqs. 2.23. They are neglected because the stresses τ_{1n} and τ_{2n} have $d\alpha_1/2$ and $d\alpha_2/2$ as their respective moment arms instead of the moment arm ζ that is associated with the other stresses. Thus, the couples M_{1n} and M_{2n} are smaller, by an order of magnitude, than the other couples and are, therefore, negligible.

The force-displacement relations of a thin shell are now obtained by substituting the stress distributions given by Eqs. 2.21 into the definitions of the stress resultants and couples and by assuming that ζ/R_i is small compared to unity. Since $\epsilon_1{}^0$, $\epsilon_2{}^0$, $\gamma_{12}{}^0$, κ_1, κ_2, and τ are independent of ζ, this results in the following:

$$\begin{aligned}
N_1 &= \epsilon_1{}^0 \int_\zeta E_1{}^* \, d\zeta + \epsilon_2{}^0 \int_\zeta E_2{}^* \nu_{21} \, d\zeta \\
&\qquad + \kappa_1 \int_\zeta \zeta E_1{}^* \, d\zeta + \kappa_2 \int_\zeta E_2{}^* \nu_{21} \zeta \, d\zeta - N_{T1}{}^*, \\
N_2 &= \epsilon_2{}^0 \int_\zeta E_2{}^* \, d\zeta + \epsilon_1{}^0 \int_\zeta E_1{}^* \nu_{12} \, d\zeta \\
&\qquad + \kappa_2 \int_\zeta \zeta E_2{}^* \, d\zeta + \kappa_1 \int_\zeta E_1{}^* \nu_{12} \zeta \, d\zeta - N_{T2}{}^*, \\
N_{12} &= N_{21} = \gamma_{12}{}^0 \int_\zeta G_{12} \, d\zeta + \tau \int_\zeta G_{12} \zeta \, d\zeta, \\
M_1 &= \epsilon_1{}^0 \int_\zeta \zeta E_1{}^* \, d\zeta + \epsilon_2{}^0 \int_\zeta E_2{}^* \nu_{21} \zeta \, d\zeta \\
&\qquad + \kappa_1 \int_\zeta E_1{}^* \zeta^2 \, d\zeta + \kappa_2 \int_\zeta E_2{}^* \nu_{21} \zeta^2 \, d\zeta - M_{T1}{}^*, \\
M_2 &= \epsilon_2{}^0 \int_\zeta E_2{}^* \zeta \, d\zeta + \epsilon_1{}^0 \int_\zeta E_1{}^* \nu_{12} \zeta \, d\zeta \\
&\qquad + \kappa_2 \int_\zeta E_2{}^* \zeta^2 \, d\zeta + \kappa_1 \int_\zeta E_1{}^* \nu_{12} \zeta^2 \, d\zeta - M_{T2}{}^*, \\
M_{12} &= M_{21} = \gamma_{12}{}^0 \int_\zeta G_{12} \zeta \, d\zeta + \tau \int_\zeta G_{12} \zeta^2 \, d\zeta,
\end{aligned} \tag{2.24}$$

where resultant thermal "forces" and "moments" have been defined, respectively, as

$$\begin{aligned}
\begin{Bmatrix} N_{T1}{}^* \\ M_{T1}{}^* \end{Bmatrix} &= \int_\zeta (E_1{}^* \alpha_{t1} + \nu_{21} E_2{}^* \alpha_{t2}) \begin{Bmatrix} 1 \\ \zeta \end{Bmatrix} T \, d\zeta, \\
\begin{Bmatrix} N_{T2}{}^* \\ M_{T2}{}^* \end{Bmatrix} &= \int_\zeta (E_2{}^* \alpha_{t2} + \nu_{12} E_1{}^* \alpha_{t1}) \begin{Bmatrix} 1 \\ \zeta \end{Bmatrix} T \, d\zeta.
\end{aligned} \tag{2.25}$$

The integrals in the above relationships between the stress resultants and the strains of the reference surface cannot be carried out until the variations of the material properties across the thickness of the shell are known. It is most likely, in modern practice, that any such variations will be associated with the fact that the shell will be of layered construction. In such a case, the material properties are generally assumed to be constant through the thickness of any layer although they are allowed to vary from layer to layer. In consideration of such materials, we notice that the above formulation implies that there is no initial interference between the layers. In spite of the fact that the variation of material properties across a layered shell is discontinuous, we do not suspend the assumption that the displacements are linearly distributed across the thickness of the shell. Hence, although the displacements will be continuous across the interfaces between the layers, the stresses may be discontinuous at such interfaces, that is, the layers are not free to slide over each other. A continuous variation of material properties across the thickness of the shell can, of course, be postulated and will result in continuous displacements and stresses.

Beyond this point our considerations will always involve the stress resultants and couples. However, since Eqs. 2.24 are rather unwieldy, it is more convenient to restrict our attention to shells composed of a single isotropic layer for which

$$\begin{aligned} &E_1 = E_2 = E, \qquad \nu_{12} = \nu_{21} = \nu, \qquad G_{12} = G_{21} = G, \\ &\alpha_{t1} = \alpha_{t2} = \alpha_t, \qquad E_1{}^* = E_2{}^* = E/(1 - \nu^2). \end{aligned} \tag{2.26}$$

If, for such shells, the reference surface is taken as the middle surface (that is, $-h/2 \leqslant \zeta \leqslant h/2$), Eqs. 2.24 reduce to

$$\begin{aligned} N_1 &= K(\epsilon_1{}^0 + \nu\epsilon_2{}^0) - N_T/(1 - \nu), \\ N_2 &= K(\epsilon_2{}^0 + \nu\epsilon_1{}^0) - N_T/(1 - \nu), \\ N_{12} &= N_{21} = K(1 - \nu)\gamma_{12}{}^0/2 = Gh\gamma_{12}{}^0, \\ M_1 &= D(\kappa_1 + \nu\kappa_2) - M_T/(1 - \nu), \\ M_2 &= D(\kappa_2 + \nu\kappa_1) - M_T/(1 - \nu), \\ M_{12} &= M_{21} = D(1 - \nu)\tau/2 = Gh^3\tau/12 \end{aligned} \tag{2.27}$$

where

$$\begin{aligned} N_T &= E\alpha_t \int_{-h/2}^{h/2} T\,d\zeta, \\ M_T &= E\alpha_t \int_{-h/2}^{h/2} T\zeta\,d\zeta. \end{aligned} \tag{2.28}$$

Here,

$$\begin{aligned} K &= Eh/(1 - \nu^2), \\ D &= Eh^3/12(1 - \nu^2), \end{aligned} \tag{2.29}$$

are, respectively, the extensional rigidity and the bending rigidity of a thin shell composed of a single isotropic elastic layer (whose properties may still vary with α_1 and α_2 but not with ζ). Such a material and the above definitions of the stress resultants and couples will be assumed henceforth for clarity and ease in the manipulations. However, when we discuss the solution of problems later in the text we shall consider orthotropic and layered materials.

Although, in the theory of shells, the consideration of stress resultants and couples replaces the consideration of individual stress components, in technical problems, we are primarily interested in the eventual determination of the stresses acting in the shell. Thus, after the stress resultants and stress couples have been determined in a given problem, it is still necessary to convert these back to stresses. To accomplish this conversion, we recall the stress–strain relations (Eqs. 2.21) which, for an isotropic material, become

$$\begin{aligned}
\sigma_1 &= \frac{E}{1-\nu^2}\left[(\epsilon_1{}^0 + \nu\epsilon_2{}^0) + \zeta(\kappa_1 + \nu\kappa_2) - (1+\nu)\alpha_t T\right], \\
\sigma_2 &= \frac{E}{1-\nu^2}\left[(\epsilon_2{}^0 + \nu\epsilon_1{}^0) + \zeta(\kappa_2 + \nu\kappa_1) - (1+\nu)\alpha_t T\right], \\
\tau_{12} &= G(\gamma_{12}{}^0 + \zeta\tau).
\end{aligned} \tag{2.30}$$

Now we rearrange Eqs. 2.27 as follows:

$$\begin{aligned}
\epsilon_1{}^0 + \nu\epsilon_2{}^0 &= [N_1 + N_T/(1-\nu)]/K, \\
\epsilon_2{}^0 + \nu\epsilon_1{}^0 &= [N_2 + N_T/(1-\nu)]/K, \\
\gamma_{12}{}^0 &= 2N_{12}/K(1-\nu), \\
\kappa_1 + \nu\kappa_2 &= [M_1 + M_T/(1-\nu)]/D, \\
\kappa_2 + \nu\kappa_1 &= [M_2 + M_T/(1-\nu)]/D, \\
\tau &= 2M_{12}/D(1-\nu),
\end{aligned} \tag{2.31}$$

and substitute these quantities into Eqs. 2.30 with the result that

$$\begin{aligned}
\sigma_1 &= \frac{N_1}{h} + \frac{12M_1}{h^3}\zeta - \frac{1}{1-\nu}\left[E\alpha_t T - \frac{N_T}{h} - \frac{12M_T}{h^3}\zeta\right], \\
\sigma_2 &= \frac{N_2}{h} + \frac{12M_2}{h^3}\zeta - \frac{1}{1-\nu}\left[E\alpha_t T - \frac{N_T}{h} - \frac{12M_T}{h^3}\zeta\right], \\
\tau_{12} &= \frac{N_{12}}{h} + \frac{12M_{12}}{h^3}\zeta.
\end{aligned} \tag{2.32}$$

The determination of the transverse shearing stresses τ_{1n} and τ_{2n} from their resultants Q_1 and Q_2 is not as precise, even within the framework of the present theory, as is the determination of σ_1, σ_2, and τ_{12}. In this case, it is reasoned, as in the theory of beams, that the transverse shearing stresses are parabolically distributed across the thickness of the shell, and that they reach prescribed values of the surfaces of the shell. Thus, we obtain the following expressions for the transverse shearing stresses:

$$\tau_{in} = \frac{6}{5}\frac{Q_i}{h}\left[1 - \left(\frac{\zeta}{h/2}\right)^2\right] - \frac{1}{4}\left\{q_i^+\left[1 - 2\left(\frac{\zeta}{h/2}\right) - 3\left(\frac{\zeta}{h/2}\right)^2\right] + q_i^-\left[1 + 2\left(\frac{\zeta}{h/2}\right) - 3\left(\frac{\zeta}{h/2}\right)^2\right]\right\}, \quad i = 1, 2 \qquad (2.33)$$

where, for the sake of convenience, we have introduced a "form factor"[7] of $\frac{6}{5}$, which represents the ratio of peak shear stress to average shear stress across the thickness of the shell. q_i^+ and q_i^- are, respectively, the distributed shearing loads that are applied to the outer and inner surfaces of the shell in the i direction.

At this point, it is well to make some remarks on the consequences of Love's postulates and their relationship to the preceding derivations of the stress resultants and stress couples.

First, we have found that as a result of Love's fourth postulate $\gamma_{1n} = \gamma_{2n} = 0$ and, therefore, $\tau_{1n} = \tau_{2n} = 0$ from Hooke's law. Nevertheless, we have defined nonvanishing shearing stress resultants Q_1 and Q_2 as integrals of τ_{1n} and τ_{2n} over the thickness. A similar situation arises in the elementary theory of beams. Here, as in the case of beams, the Q_1 and Q_2 resultants must be retained for purposes of equilibrium.

Second, we have found that as a result of Love's third and fourth postulates $\epsilon_n = \sigma_n = 0$. If only σ_n were assumed to vanish, then the following expression for the normal strain ϵ_n could be obtained by solving Eqs. 2.1a for σ_n and setting the result to zero:

$$\epsilon_n - \alpha_{tn}T = -\frac{E_1(\epsilon_1 - \alpha_{t1}T)(\nu_{12}\nu_{2n} + \nu_{1n}) + E_2(\epsilon_2 - \alpha_{t2}T)(\nu_{21}\nu_{1n} + \nu_{2n})}{E_n(1 - \nu_{21}\nu_{12})}. \qquad (2.34)$$

From this expression it would appear that the simultaneous vanishing of both the transverse normal stress and normal strain is inconsistent.

The preceding difficulties can be avoided entirely if the physical reasoning represented by Love's third and fourth postulates is replaced by the assumption that a thin elastic shell is approximated by a material with a special type of orthotropy[8] wherein $1/E_n = 1/G_{1n} = 1/G_{2n} = \nu_{1n} = \nu_{2n} = \alpha_{tn} = 0$. Upon introduction of these special values into Eqs. 2.1a,

[7] See, for example, Timoshenko, S., *Strength of Materials, Part I*, 3rd ed., Princeton, N.J.: D. Van Nostrand, 1955, pp. 113–125.

[8] Hildebrand, F. B., Reissner, E., and Thomas, G. B., "Notes on the Foundations of the Theory of Small Displacements of Orthotropic Shells," NACA-TN-1833, March 1949.

2.1b, and 2.1c, they reduce immediately to Eqs. 2.4 without any statement about σ_n, τ_{1n}, and τ_{2n}. It is possible, therefore, to speak of transverse shearing stress resultants which depend on τ_{1n} and τ_{2n} without any additional comment and to ignore the effect of σ_n which, according to our previous arguments, is expected to be negligible for a thin shell anyway. Indeed, as a consequence of Eq. 2.34, the simultaneous vanishing of σ_n and ϵ_n is valid for the special material that has been postulated.

The foregoing choice of the elastic constants represents the assumption that the shell material is rigid in the direction of the normal to the reference surface. It is intuitively plausible that the postulation of such a material should lead to the same results and be just as reasonable as the assumption that normals to the reference surface remain normal to it and undergo no change in length during deformation. Depending on his preference the reader may, therefore, adopt either point of view.

2.6 EQUATIONS OF MOTION

It is now appropriate to establish the relationships which express the equilibrium of the fundamental element of a thin shell. Since we have replaced, by means of integrations through the thickness, the consideration of stresses with the consideration of stress resultants and couples, it is appropriate to alter our definition of the fundamental element of a thin shell. Accordingly, it will be assumed, henceforth, that the element which was formerly defined to be $d\zeta$ thick is replaced, on account of our integrations with respect to ζ, with an element of thickness h. Such an element is acted upon by the internal stress resultants and couples which were defined in the preceding section and by external forces which include both body forces and surface forces. The internal forces act upon the edges of the modified fundamental element while the surface forces act upon its inner and outer surfaces and the body forces act over its volume. Since the internal stress resultants have been defined per unit of arc length on the reference surface it is appropriate, for consistency, to also replace the body and surface forces by statically equivalent forces which act upon the reference surface. Since we are dealing with thin shells, we may make, in this first approximation, the further assumption that the body and surface forces induce negligibly small moments with respect to the reference surface.

2.6*a* Internal and External Force Vectors

The external force vector has the definition

$$\mathbf{q}(\alpha_1, \alpha_2, t) = q_1(\alpha_1, \alpha_2, t)\mathbf{t}_1 + q_2(\alpha_1, \alpha_2, t)\mathbf{t}_2 - q_n(\alpha_1, \alpha_2, t)\mathbf{n}, \quad (2.35)$$

where q_1, q_2, and q_n are the components along α_1, α_2, and the normal and

t is time. This vector includes all possible types of body and surface loadings acting on a unit of area of the reference surface. For example, if we wish to consider the transient response of a shell resting on a viscoelastic foundation made up of distributed springs and dashpots to some time-dependent load, the components q_i of the external force vector would be defined by

$$\begin{aligned} q_1 &= p_1 - k_1 u_1 - \lambda_1 \dot{u}_1, \\ q_2 &= p_2 - k_2 u_2 - \lambda_2 \dot{u}_2, \\ q_n &= p + kw - \lambda \dot{w}. \end{aligned} \tag{2.35a}$$

Here the q_i are the static equivalents, on the reference surface, of the loads applied to the inner and outer surfaces of the shell in the i direction. Assuming, in this first approximation, that the inner and outer surface areas of the fundamental element are equal, these equivalent loads are given by $q_i^+ - q_i^-$. The term $k_i u_i$ represents the resisting force of a foundation to the displacement u_i where k_i is the spring rate of the foundation in the i direction. Similarly, the term $\lambda_i \dot{u}_i$ represents the reaction of the foundation to a velocity $\dot{u}_i$ where λ_i is the damping coefficient of the foundation in the i direction. Additional terms representing reactions to the rotation and angular velocity could also be conceived.

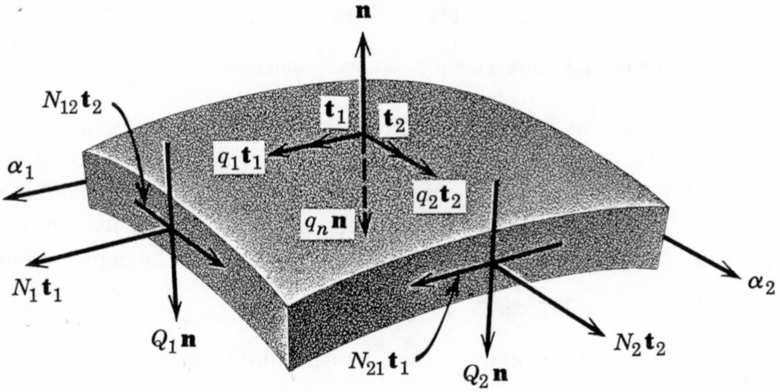

Figure 2.2 Stress resultants and surface loads acting on differential element.

We now turn to a consideration of the internal stress resultants and couples and note that these can be expressed as components of internal force and moment vectors, as shown in Figs. 2.2 and 2.3. Thus, we notice that the stress resultants on an edge of constant α_1 can be thought of as the components of the vector

$$\mathbf{F}_1 = (N_1\mathbf{t}_1 + N_{12}\mathbf{t}_2 - Q_1\mathbf{n})A_2\, d\alpha_2, \tag{2.36}$$

while the stress resultants on an edge of constant α_2 comprise the vector

$$\mathbf{F}_2 = (N_{21}\mathbf{t}_1 + N_2\mathbf{t}_2 - Q_2\mathbf{n})A_1\, d\alpha_1. \tag{2.37}$$

The action of the force vectors is shown in Fig. 2.2 where, in addition, the positive directions of the force components are defined. Notice that the force vectors as given above are total forces.

To express the stress couples in vector form, we denote a moment vector by a double-headed arrow pointing in the direction in which a right-handed screw would advance if it were turned in the sense of the associated moment. These vectors are shown in Fig. 2.3 where, in addition, a positive

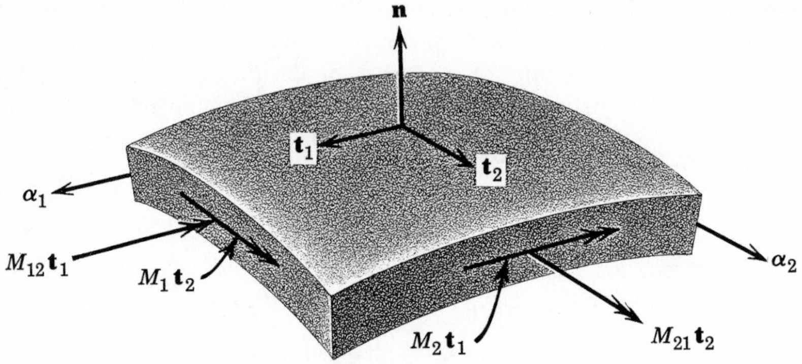

Figure 2.3 Stress couples acting on differential element.

moment is defined as one which produces tension on the outer surface of a shell. The total stress couple vectors can be expressed in terms of components along α_1 and α_2 only, since, as we have previously pointed out, the stresses τ_{1n} and τ_{2n} produce higher order negligible moments. Thus, the total stress couple vector on an edge of constant α_1 can be expressed as

$$\mathbf{M}_1 = (-M_{12}\mathbf{t}_1 + M_1\mathbf{t}_2)A_2\, d\alpha_2, \tag{2.38}$$

while on an edge of constant α_2 the corresponding vector is given by

$$\mathbf{M}_2 = (-M_2\mathbf{t}_1 + M_{21}\mathbf{t}_2)A_1\, d\alpha_1. \tag{2.39}$$

2.6*b* Derivation of Equations of Motion from Hamilton's Principle

Of the many procedures that are available to us for the derivation of the equations of motion of a thin elastic shell, we choose Hamilton's principle on account of its simplicity and elegance and because it gives us, at the same time, the natural boundary conditions that are to be used with the theory.

Let us, therefore, consider an elastic body (shell) that is continuously changing its state between two instants of time (t_0 and t_1) and that is in equilibrium under a specified body force vector **F** and a surface force vector **T**. Generally, we assume that the surface forces are known over a portion of the surface (which we shall denote as S_t) while the displacements are known over the remainder of the surface (denoted by S_u) where the total surface S of the body is $S = S_u + S_t$. We let **U** be the displacement vector at equilibrium and consider an arbitrary displacement vector $\mathbf{U} + \delta\mathbf{U}$. Over the portion S_u of the surface, $\delta\mathbf{U}$ must vanish since **U** is prescribed there. However, over the portion S_t, $\delta\mathbf{U}$ is arbitrary. The components of the vector $\delta\mathbf{U}$ are known as the virtual displacements. Hamilton's principle states that the actual path followed by a dynamical process is such as to make

$$\delta \int_{t_0}^{t_1} (\Pi - K)\, dt = 0. \tag{2.40}$$

That is, the integral of $(\Pi - K)$ takes an extremum value which can be shown to be a minimum. If the process is steady, the above principle reduces to the principle of minimum potential energy, or

$$\delta\Pi = 0, \qquad \Pi = \text{minimum}. \tag{2.40a}$$

The quantity Π is known as the potential energy and is given by

$$\Pi = U - \int_S \mathbf{T}\cdot\mathbf{U}\, dS - \int_V \mathbf{F}\cdot\mathbf{U}\, dV. \tag{2.41}$$

Here U is the strain energy which is defined in terms of a strain energy density function P as

$$U = \int_V P\, dV, \tag{2.42}$$

where

$$P = \tfrac{1}{2}\sigma_{ij}\epsilon_{ij} - E\alpha_t T\epsilon_{kk}/(1 - 2\nu), \qquad i, j, k = 1, 2, 3 \tag{2.42a}$$

and the integrals in the definition of Π represent the work of the surface forces and of the body forces. The quantity K is the kinetic energy of the body and is given by

$$K = \tfrac{1}{2} \int_V \rho\dot{\mathbf{U}}\cdot\dot{\mathbf{U}}\, dV. \tag{2.43}$$

Substitution of Eqs. 2.41 to 2.43 into the mathematical statement of Hamilton's principle then gives

$$\delta \int_{t_0}^{t_1} \left\{\int_V P\, dV - \int_S \mathbf{T}\cdot\mathbf{U}\, dS - \int_V \mathbf{F}\cdot\mathbf{U}\, dV - \tfrac{1}{2}\int_V \rho\dot{\mathbf{U}}\cdot\dot{\mathbf{U}}\, dV\right\} dt = 0. \tag{2.44}$$

We now apply the foregoing to the derivation of the equations of motion and the natural boundary conditions of the theory of thin elastic shells. In consideration of this, we notice first that since we have previously assumed that all of the body and surface forces acting on the shell may be replaced by statically equivalent forces acting on the reference surface, the work done by these forces is

$$W_s = \int_{\alpha_1}\int_{\alpha_2} \mathbf{q}\cdot\mathbf{U}(\alpha_1, \alpha_2, 0)A_1A_2\, d\alpha_1\, d\alpha_2. \tag{2.45}$$

If the scalar product is carried out and the definitions (2.15) of the displacement components are introduced into the above, keeping in mind that we are dealing with the reference surface, the final expression for the work of the body and surface forces is

$$W_s = \int_{\alpha_1}\int_{\alpha_2} (q_1u_1 + q_2u_2 - q_nw)A_1A_2\, d\alpha_1\, d\alpha_2. \tag{2.46}$$

In the determination of the work of the external forces, we must also account for the fact that the edge stresses do work and, thus, we add the contribution

$$W_{e_1} = \int_{\alpha_2}\int_{\zeta} (\bar{\sigma}_1U_1 + \bar{\tau}_{12}U_2 + \bar{\tau}_{1n}W)A_2(1 + \zeta/R_2)\, d\alpha_2\, d\zeta \tag{2.47}$$

on a typical edge of constant α_1, and

$$W_{e_2} = \int_{\alpha_1}\int_{\zeta} (\bar{\tau}_{21}U_1 + \bar{\sigma}_2U_2 + \bar{\tau}_{2n}W)A_1(1 + \zeta/R_1)\, d\alpha_1\, d\zeta \tag{2.48}$$

on an edge of constant α_2 where the bars refer to edge values. In terms of the displacements given by Eqs. 2.15, the contributions from the edge stresses take the form

$$\begin{aligned} W_{e_1} &= \int_{\alpha_2}\int_{\zeta} [\bar{\sigma}_1(u_1 + \zeta\beta_1) \\ &\qquad + \bar{\tau}_{12}(u_2 + \zeta\beta_2) + \bar{\tau}_{1n}w]A_2(1 + \zeta/R_2)\, d\alpha_2\, d\zeta, \\ W_{e_2} &= \int_{\alpha_2}\int_{\xi} [\bar{\sigma}_2(u_2 + \zeta\beta_2) \\ &\qquad + \bar{\tau}_{21}(u_1 + \zeta\beta_1) + \tau_{2n}w]A_1(1 + \zeta/R_1)\, d\alpha_1\, d\zeta. \end{aligned} \tag{2.49}$$

Since we have previously found that u_1, u_2, w, β_1, and β_2 are independent of ζ, the integrations with respect to ζ can be conveniently carried out, making use of the definitions (2.23) of the stress resultants and couples. This gives

$$\begin{aligned} W_{e_1} &= \int_{\alpha_2} (\overline{N}_1u_1 + \overline{N}_{12}u_2 + \overline{Q}_1w + \overline{M}_1\beta_1 + \overline{M}_{12}\beta_2)A_2\, d\alpha_2, \\ W_{e_2} &= \int_{\alpha_1} (\overline{N}_{21}u_1 + \overline{N}_2u_2 + \overline{Q}_2w + \overline{M}_{21}\beta_1 + \overline{M}_2\beta_2)A_1\, d\alpha_1. \end{aligned} \tag{2.50}$$

If we proceed in a similar fashion, the kinetic energy expression (Eq. 2.43) can be expressed in terms of the shell variables as

$$K = \frac{h\rho}{2}\int_{\alpha_1}\int_{\alpha_2}\left[\dot{u}_1^{\,2} + \dot{u}_2^{\,2} + \dot{w}^2 + \frac{h^2}{12}(\dot{\beta}_1^{\,2} + \dot{\beta}_2^{\,2})\right] A_1A_2\,d\alpha_1\,d\alpha_2, \quad (2.51)$$

where ζ/R_i has been neglected in comparison to unity. Finally, in shell coordinates the expression for the strain energy becomes

$$U = \int_{\alpha_1}\int_{\alpha_2}\int_{\zeta} PA_1A_2(1 + \zeta/R_1)(1 + \zeta/R_2)\,d\alpha_1\,d\alpha_2\,d\zeta. \quad (2.52)$$

To apply Hamilton's principle, we note that in terms of Eqs. 2.46, 2.50, 2.51, and 2.52, the principle may be rewritten for a thin elastic shell as

$$\delta\int_{t_0}^{t_1}(U - W_s - W_{e1} - W_{e2} - K)\,dt = 0. \quad (2.53)$$

We perform the variations indicated in Eq. 2.53 one by one, beginning with the variation of the strain energy, and assume that the operations of integration over time and variation are commutative. Thus,

$$\delta U = \int_{\alpha_1}\int_{\alpha_2}\int_{\zeta} \delta PA_1A_2(1 + \zeta/R_1)(1 + \zeta/R_2)\,d\alpha_1\,d\alpha_2\,d\zeta. \quad (2.54)$$

The variation of the strain energy function is given by

$$\delta P = \frac{\partial P}{\partial \epsilon_1}\,\delta\epsilon_1 + \frac{\partial P}{\partial \epsilon_2}\,\delta\epsilon_2 + \frac{\partial P}{\partial \epsilon_n}\,\delta\epsilon_n + \frac{\partial P}{\partial \gamma_{12}}\,\delta\gamma_{12} + \frac{\partial P}{\partial \gamma_{1n}}\,\delta\gamma_{1n} + \frac{\partial P}{\partial \gamma_{2n}}\,\delta\gamma_{2n}. \quad (2.55)$$

It can be shown from the definition of the strain energy function P that (see the Exercises):

$$\sigma_{ij} = \frac{\partial P}{\partial \epsilon_{ij}}. \quad (2.56)$$

As a result,

$$\delta P = \sigma_1\,\delta\epsilon_1 + \sigma_2\,\delta\epsilon_2 + \sigma_n\,\delta\epsilon_n + \tau_{12}\,\delta\gamma_{12} + \tau_{1n}\,\delta\gamma_{1n} + \tau_{2n}\,\delta\gamma_{2n}. \quad (2.57)$$

In view of the assumption $W = w(\alpha_1, \alpha_2)$ and the definition of the transverse normal strain ϵ_n, it follows that $\delta\epsilon_n \equiv 0$. Thus, the expression for the variation of the strain energy takes the form

$$\delta U = \int_{\alpha_1}\int_{\alpha_2}\int_{\zeta}(\sigma_1\,\delta\epsilon_1 + \sigma_2\,\delta\epsilon_2 + \tau_{12}\,\delta\gamma_{12} + \tau_{1n}\,\delta\gamma_{1n} + \tau_{2n}\,\delta\gamma_{2n})A_1A_2(1 + \zeta/R_1)(1 + \zeta/R_2)\,d\alpha_1\,d\alpha_2\,d\zeta. \quad (2.58)$$

Let us, as an example, consider the leading term of the variation of the strain energy. To carry out the necessary manipulations, we first recall from Eqs. 2.14 and 2.15 that

$$\epsilon_1 = \frac{1}{A_1(1 + \zeta/R_1)} \left[\frac{1}{A_1} \frac{\partial u_1}{\partial \alpha_1} + \frac{U_2}{A_1 A_2} \frac{\partial A_1}{\partial \alpha_2} + \frac{w}{R_1} + \zeta \left(\frac{1}{A_1} \frac{\partial \beta_1}{\partial \alpha_1} + \frac{\beta_2}{A_1 A_2} \frac{\partial A_1}{\partial \alpha_2} \right) \right], \tag{2.59}$$

where we have not yet neglected ζ/R in comparison to unity. If we take the variation of ϵ_1 and note that the variation and partial derivative operations are commutative, we find that

$$\delta\epsilon_1 = \frac{1}{A_1(1 + \zeta/R_1)} \left[\frac{1}{A_1} \frac{\partial \delta u_1}{\partial \alpha_1} + \frac{\delta u_2}{A_1 A_2} \frac{\partial A_1}{\partial \alpha_2} + \frac{\delta w}{R_1} + \zeta \left(\frac{1}{A_1} \frac{\partial \delta\beta_1}{\partial \alpha_1} + \frac{\delta\beta_2}{A_1 A_2} \frac{\partial A_1}{\partial \alpha_2} \right) \right], \tag{2.60}$$

and the contribution of $\delta\epsilon_1$ to the variation of the strain energy is

$$\int_{\alpha_1} \int_{\alpha_2} \int_{\zeta} \left[\sigma_1 \left(A_2 \frac{\partial \delta u_1}{\partial \alpha_1} + \delta u_2 \frac{\partial A_1}{\partial \alpha_2} + \frac{A_1 A_2}{R_1} \delta w \right) + \zeta\sigma_1 \left(A_2 \frac{\partial \delta\beta_1}{\partial \alpha_1} + \delta\beta_2 \frac{\partial A_1}{\partial \alpha_2} \right) \right] \left(1 + \frac{\zeta}{R_2} \right) d\alpha_1\, d\alpha_2\, d\zeta. \tag{2.61}$$

Upon integration of the above over the thickness of the shell and use of definitions 2.23, the result is

$$\int_{\alpha_1} \int_{\alpha_2} \left[N_1 \left(A_2 \frac{\partial \delta u_1}{\partial \alpha_1} + \delta u_2 \frac{\partial A_1}{\partial \alpha_2} + \frac{A_1 A_2}{R_1} \delta w \right) + M_1 \left(A_2 \frac{\partial \delta\beta_1}{\partial \alpha_1} + \delta\beta_2 \frac{\partial A_1}{\partial \alpha_2} \right) \right] d\alpha_1\, d\alpha_2. \tag{2.62}$$

By proceeding in the same fashion with the remaining terms of the integral in Eq. 2.58, the total expression for the variation of the strain energy can be shown to be

$$\begin{aligned} \delta U = \int_{\alpha_1} \int_{\alpha_2} \Bigg\{ & N_1 \left(A_2 \frac{\partial \delta u_1}{\partial \alpha_1} + \delta u_2 \frac{\partial A_1}{\partial \alpha_2} + \frac{A_1 A_2}{R_1} \delta w \right) \\ & + M_1 \left(A_2 \frac{\partial \delta\beta_1}{\partial \alpha_1} + \delta\beta_2 \frac{\partial A_1}{\partial \alpha_2} \right) \\ & + N_2 \left(A_1 \frac{\partial \delta u_1}{\partial \alpha_2} + \delta u_1 \frac{\partial A_2}{\partial \alpha_1} + \frac{A_1 A_2}{R_2} \delta w \right) \\ & + M_2 \left(A_1 \frac{\partial \delta\beta_2}{\partial \alpha_2} + \delta\beta_1 \frac{\partial A_2}{\partial \alpha_1} \right) + N_{12} \left(A_2 \frac{\partial \delta u_2}{\partial \alpha_1} - \delta u_1 \frac{\partial A_1}{\partial \alpha_2} \right) \\ & + M_{12} \left(A_2 \frac{\partial \delta\beta_2}{\partial \alpha_1} - \delta\beta_1 \frac{\partial A_1}{\partial \alpha_2} \right) + N_{21} \left(A_1 \frac{\partial \delta u_1}{\partial \alpha_2} - \delta u_2 \frac{\partial A_2}{\partial \alpha_1} \right) \end{aligned}$$

$$+ M_{21}\left(A_1 \frac{\partial \delta\beta_1}{\partial \alpha_2} - \delta\beta_2 \frac{\partial A_2}{\partial \alpha_1}\right)$$

$$+ Q_1\left[A_2 \frac{\partial \delta w}{\partial \alpha_1} + A_1 A_2\left(\delta\beta_1 - \frac{\delta u_1}{R_1}\right)\right]$$

$$+ Q_2\left[A_1 \frac{\partial \delta w}{\partial \alpha_2} + A_1 A_2\left(\delta\beta_2 - \frac{\delta u_2}{R_2}\right)\right]\Bigg\} \, d\alpha_1 \, d\alpha_2. \qquad (2.63)$$

The variations of the kinetic energy and of the work of the edge forces and surface forces as a result of the virtual displacements ($\delta\mathbf{U}$) follow directly from Eqs. 2.46, 2.50, and 2.51 and take the form:

$$\delta W_s = \int_{\alpha_1}\int_{\alpha_2} (q_1\,\delta u_1 + q_2\,\delta u_2 - q_n\,\delta w) A_1 A_2 \, d\alpha_1 \, d\alpha_2, \qquad (2.64)$$

$$\delta W_{e_1} = \oint_{\alpha_2} (\bar{N}_1\,\delta u_1 + \bar{N}_{12}\,\delta u_2 + \bar{Q}_1\,\delta w + \bar{M}_1\,\delta\beta_1 + \bar{M}_{12}\,\delta\beta_2) A_2 \, d\alpha_2, \qquad (2.65)$$

$$\delta W_{e_2} = \oint_{\alpha_1} (\bar{N}_{21}\,\delta u_1 + \bar{N}_2\,\delta u_2 + \bar{Q}_2\,\delta w + \bar{M}_{21}\,\delta\beta_1 + \bar{M}_2\,\delta\beta_2) A_1 \, d\alpha_1, \qquad (2.66)$$

$$\delta K = \rho h \int_{\alpha_1}\int_{\alpha_2} \Bigg[\dot{u}_1\,\delta\dot{u}_1 + \dot{u}_2\,\delta\dot{u}_2 + \dot{w}\,\delta\dot{w} + \frac{h^2}{12}(\dot{\beta}_1\,\delta\dot{\beta}_1 + \dot{\beta}_2\,\delta\dot{\beta}_2)\Bigg] A_1 A_2 \, d\alpha_1 \, d\alpha_2. \qquad (2.67)$$

To eliminate the time derivatives of the variations in the kinetic energy expression, we note that upon integration by parts with respect to time we obtain

$$\int_{t_0}^{t_1} \delta K \, dt = \rho h \int_{\alpha_1}\int_{\alpha_2} (\dot{u}_1\,\delta u_1 + \dot{u}_2\,\delta u_2 + \dot{w}\,\delta w)\Big|_{t=t_0}^{t=t_1} A_1 A_2 \, d\alpha_1 \, d\alpha_2$$
$$- \rho h \int_{t_0}^{t_1}\int_{\alpha_1}\int_{\alpha_2} (\ddot{u}_1\,\delta u_1 + \ddot{u}_2\,\delta u_2 + \ddot{w}\,\delta w) A_1 A_2 \, d\alpha_1 \, d\alpha_2 \, dt. \qquad (2.67a)$$

As a first approximation we have, as in the case of beams, neglected the contribution from the rotatory inertia terms $\rho h^3 \ddot{\beta}_1/12$ and $\rho h^3 \ddot{\beta}_2/12$. If we prescribe, further, that the virtual displacements vanish at the end points of the arbitrary interval $t_0 \leqslant t \leqslant t_1$, the first term on the right-hand side also vanishes and we are left with

$$\int_{t_0}^{t_1} \delta K \, dt = -\rho h \int_{t_0}^{t_1}\int_{\alpha_1}\int_{\alpha_2} (\ddot{u}_1\,\delta u_1 + \ddot{u}_2\,\delta u_2 + \ddot{w}\,\delta w) A_1 A_2 \, d\alpha_1 \, d\alpha_2 \, dt. \qquad (2.67b)$$

In a similar fashion, we remove the derivatives of the virtual displacements from the expression for δU. For example, if we take the leading term

$$\int_{\alpha_1}\int_{\alpha_2} N_1 A_2 \frac{\partial \delta u_1}{\partial \alpha_1}\, d\alpha_1\, d\alpha_2 \tag{2.68}$$

from Eq. 2.63, we obtain, upon integration by parts,

$$\oint_{\alpha_2} N_1 A_2\, \delta u_1\, d\alpha_2 - \int_{\alpha_1}\int_{\alpha_2} \frac{\partial (N_1 A_2)}{\partial \alpha_1}\, \delta u_1\, d\alpha_1\, d\alpha_2. \tag{2.69}$$

If we proceed in the same way for the remaining terms of Eq. 2.63 and set the sum of all of the variations equal to zero according to Eq. 2.53 the result can be shown to be (see the Exercises):

$$\begin{aligned}
\int_{t_0}^{t_1}\int_{\alpha_1}\int_{\alpha_2} \Bigg\{ & \Bigg[\frac{\partial N_1 A_2}{\partial \alpha_1} + \frac{\partial N_{21} A_1}{\partial \alpha_2} + N_{12}\frac{\partial A_1}{\partial \alpha_2} - N_2 \frac{\partial A_2}{\partial \alpha_1} \\
& \qquad + Q_1 \frac{A_1 A_2}{R_1} + (q_1 - \rho h \ddot{u}_1) A_1 A_2\Bigg]\delta u_1 \\
& + \Bigg[\frac{\partial N_{12} A_2}{\partial \alpha_1} + \frac{\partial N_2 A_1}{\partial \alpha_2} + N_{21}\frac{\partial A_2}{\partial \alpha_1} - N_1 \frac{\partial A_1}{\partial \alpha_2} \\
& \qquad + Q_2 \frac{A_1 A_2}{R_1} + (q_2 - \rho h \ddot{u}_2) A_1 A_2\Bigg]\delta u_2 \\
& + \Bigg[\frac{\partial Q_1 A_2}{\partial \alpha_1} + \frac{\partial Q_2 A_1}{\partial \alpha_2} - \left(\frac{N_1}{R_1} + \frac{N_2}{R_2}\right) A_1 A_2 \\
& \qquad - (q_n + \rho h \ddot{w}) A_1 A_2\Bigg]\delta w \\
& + \Bigg[\frac{\partial M_1 A_2}{\partial \alpha_1} + \frac{\partial M_{21} A_1}{\partial \alpha_2} + M_{12}\frac{\partial A_1}{\partial \alpha_2} - M_2 \frac{\partial A_2}{\partial \alpha_1} - Q_1 A_1 A_2\Bigg]\delta\beta_1 \\
& + \Bigg[\frac{\partial M_{12} A_2}{\partial \alpha_1} + \frac{\partial M_2 A_1}{\partial \alpha_2} + M_{21}\frac{\partial A_2}{\partial \alpha_1} - M_1 \frac{\partial A_1}{\partial \alpha_2} \\
& \qquad - Q_2 A_1 A_2\Bigg]\delta\beta_2\Bigg\}\, d\alpha_1\, d\alpha_2\, dt \\
+ \int_{t_0}^{t_1}\oint_{\alpha_1} & [(\overline{N}_2 - N_2)\,\delta u_2 + (\overline{N}_{21} - N_{21})\,\delta u_1 + (\overline{Q}_2 - Q_2)\,\delta w \\
& + (\overline{M}_2 - M_2)\,\delta\beta_2 + (\overline{M}_{21} - M_{21})\,\delta\beta_1] A_1\, d\alpha_1\, dt \\
+ \int_{t_0}^{t_1}\oint_{\alpha_2} & [(\overline{N}_1 - N_1)\,\delta u_1 + (\overline{N}_{12} - N_{12})\,\delta u_2 + (\overline{Q}_1 - Q_1)\,\delta w \\
& + (\overline{M}_1 - M_2)\,\delta\beta_1 + (\overline{M}_{12} - M_{12})\,\delta\beta_2] A_2\, d\alpha_2\, dt = 0.
\end{aligned} \tag{2.70}$$

Now let us examine the foregoing expression. We have previously stated that the variations δu_1, δu_2, δw, $\delta\beta_1$, and $\delta\beta_2$ are completely arbitrary. Thus, Eq. 2.70 can vanish as required only if the coefficients of the variations each vanish individually. Using this reasoning we obtain, from the vanishing of the coefficients of the variations in the double integral, five equations of motion:

$$\frac{\partial N_1 A_2}{\partial \alpha_1} + \frac{\partial N_{21} A_1}{\partial \alpha_2} + N_{12} \frac{\partial A_1}{\partial \alpha_2} - N_2 \frac{\partial A_2}{\partial \alpha_1} + A_1 A_2 \left(\frac{Q_1}{R_1} + q_1 \right) = A_1 A_2 \rho h \ddot{u}_1,$$

$$\frac{\partial N_{12} A_2}{\partial \alpha_1} + \frac{\partial N_2 A_1}{\partial \alpha_2} + N_{21} \frac{\partial A_2}{\partial \alpha_1} - N_1 \frac{\partial A_1}{\partial \alpha_2} + A_1 A_2 \left(\frac{Q_2}{R_2} + q_2 \right) = A_1 A_2 \rho h \ddot{u}_2, \quad (2.71)$$

$$\frac{\partial Q_1 A_2}{\partial \alpha_1} + \frac{\partial Q_2 A_1}{\partial \alpha_2} - \left(\frac{N_1}{R_1} + \frac{N_2}{R_2} \right) A_1 A_2 - q_n A_1 A_2 = A_1 A_2 \rho h \ddot{w},$$

$$\frac{\partial M_1 A_2}{\partial \alpha_1} + \frac{\partial M_{21} A_1}{\partial \alpha_2} + M_{12} \frac{\partial A_1}{\partial \alpha_2} - M_2 \frac{\partial A_2}{\partial \alpha_1} - Q_1 A_1 A_2 = 0,$$

$$\frac{\partial M_{12} A_2}{\partial \alpha_1} + \frac{\partial M_2 A_1}{\partial \alpha_2} + M_{21} \frac{\partial A_2}{\partial \alpha_1} - M_1 \frac{\partial A_1}{\partial \alpha_2} - Q_2 A_1 A_2 = 0,$$

which (in anticipation of some later discussions in Chapter 3) do not as yet reflect the results $N_{12} = N_{21}$ and $M_{12} = M_{21}$ (see Eqs. 2.24). A sixth equilibrium equation also exists and can be found, from the vanishing of the moments about the normal to the fundamental element (see the Exercises), to have the form

$$\frac{M_{21}}{R_2} - \frac{M_{12}}{R_1} + N_{21} - N_{12} = 0. \quad (2.72)$$

This equation was not obtained from Hamilton's principle because it is an identity. Indeed, if we employ the integral definitions of M_{12}, M_{21}, N_{12}, and N_{21} from Eqs. 2.23, the above equation is replaced by

$$\int_\zeta (1 + \zeta/R_1)(1 + \zeta/R_2)(\tau_{12} - \tau_{21})\, d\zeta = 0 \quad (2.73)$$

and is identically satisfied on account of the symmetry of the stress tensor.

It will also be noticed that Q_1 and Q_2 can be eliminated from consideration by solving the fourth and fifth equations of equilibrium for these quantities and substituting the resulting expressions into the remaining equations wherever they appear. Thus, the precise definition of Q_1 and Q_2 as integrals of τ_{1n} and τ_{2n} has no influence on the resulting analysis.

This completes the derivation of the differential equations of the theory of thin elastic shells. By way of recapitulation, we may note that we have derived five equations of equilibrium (Eqs. 2.71), six force-strain relations (Eqs. 2.27), and six strain-displacement relations (Eqs. 2.19) for a total of seventeen fundamental equations in terms of seventeen dependent variables: N_1, N_2, Q_1, Q_2, $N_{12} = N_{21}$, M_1, M_2, $M_{12} = M_{21}$, $\epsilon_1{}^0$, $\epsilon_2{}^0$, $\gamma_{12}{}^0$, κ_1, κ_2, τ, u_1, u_2, and w. The problem is, therefore, well set and can be solved once the boundary conditions and initial conditions are specified.

2.7 BOUNDARY CONDITIONS

If we consider the line integrals in Eq. 2.70, we find, for the case of the integral over an edge of constant α_2, for example, that this can be rewritten as

$$\int_{t_0}^{t_1}\int_{\alpha_1} A_1\, d\alpha_1 \Big[(\overline{N}_2 - N_2)\,\delta u_2 + (\overline{N}_{21} - N_{21})\,\delta u_1 + (\overline{Q}_2 - Q_2)\,\delta w + (\overline{M}_2 - M_2)\,\delta\beta_2 + (\overline{M}_{21} - M_{21})\left(\frac{\delta u_1}{R_1} - \frac{1}{A_1}\frac{\partial \delta w}{\partial \alpha_1}\right)\Big]\, dt. \quad (2.74)$$

The term involving the derivative with respect to α_1 can be integrated by parts to give

$$\begin{aligned} -\int_{t_0}^{t_1}\int_{\alpha_1} (\overline{M}_{21} - M_{21})\frac{\partial \delta w}{\partial \alpha_1}\, d\alpha_1\, dt &= -\int_{t_0}^{t_1} (\overline{M}_{21} - \overline{M}_{21})\,\delta w\, dt + \int_{t_0}^{t_1}\int_{\alpha_1}\frac{\partial}{\partial \alpha_1}(\overline{M}_{21} - M_{21})\, d\alpha_1\,\delta w\, dt \\ &= \int_{t_0}^{t_1}\int_{\alpha_1}\frac{\partial}{\partial \alpha_1}(\overline{M}_{21} - M_{21})\, d\alpha_1\,\delta w\, dt. \end{aligned} \quad (2.75)$$

With this result, the line integral takes the form

$$\int_{t_0}^{t_1}\int_{\alpha_1} [(\overline{T}_{21} - T_{21})\,\delta u_1 + (\overline{N}_2 - N_2)\,\delta u_2 + (\overline{V}_2 - V_2)\,\delta w + (\overline{M}_2 - M_2)\,\delta\beta_2] A_1\, d\alpha_1\, dt. \quad (2.76)$$

Similarly, the integral over an edge of constant α_1 becomes

$$\int_{t_0}^{t_1}\int_{\alpha_2} [(\overline{N}_1 - N_1)\,\delta u_1 + (\overline{T}_{12} - T_{12})\,\delta u_2 + (\overline{V}_1 - V_1)\,\delta w + (\overline{M}_1 - M_1)\,\delta\beta_1] A_2\, d\alpha_2\, dt \quad (2.77)$$

where we have introduced what are known as Kirchoff's effective shearing-stress resultants:

$$\begin{aligned} T_{nt} &= N_{nt} + \frac{M_{nt}}{R_t}, \\ V_n &= Q_n + \frac{1}{A_t}\frac{\partial M_{nt}}{\partial \alpha_t}, \end{aligned} \qquad n, t = 1, 2. \quad (2.78)$$

Here n, t denote the normal and tangential directions on a given edge. As a consequence of Eq. 2.70, the terms involving the arbitrary displacement variations in the above line integrals must each vanish. Thus, we require that

$$\begin{aligned} (\overline{N}_1 - N_1)\,\delta u_1 &= 0, & (\overline{T}_{21} - T_{21})\,\delta u_1 &= 0, \\ (\overline{T}_{12} - T_{12})\,\delta u_2 &= 0, & (\overline{N}_2 - N_2)\,\delta u_2 &= 0, \\ (\overline{V}_1 - V_1)\,\delta w &= 0, & (\overline{V}_2 - V_2)\,\delta w &= 0, \\ (\overline{M}_1 - M_1)\,\delta\beta_1 &= 0, & (\overline{M}_2 - M_2)\,\delta\beta_2 &= 0. \end{aligned} \quad (2.79)$$

Each of the above will be satisfied if the appropriate displacement or force are prescribed. We are, therefore, led to the following four "natural" boundary conditions on an edge of constant α_1:

$$\begin{aligned} N_1 &= \bar{N}_1 \quad &\text{or} \quad u_1 &= \bar{u}_1, \\ T_{12} &= \bar{T}_{12} \quad &\text{or} \quad u_2 &= \bar{u}_2, \\ V_1 &= \bar{V}_1 \quad &\text{or} \quad w &= \bar{w}, \\ M_1 &= \bar{M}_1 \quad &\text{or} \quad \beta_1 &= \bar{\beta}_1, \end{aligned} \tag{2.80a}$$

whereas on an edge of constant α_2 the boundary conditions are:

$$\begin{aligned} N_2 &= \bar{N}_2 \quad &\text{or} \quad u_2 &= \bar{u}_2, \\ T_{21} &= \bar{T}_{21} \quad &\text{or} \quad u_1 &= \bar{u}_1, \\ V_2 &= \bar{V}_2 \quad &\text{or} \quad w &= \bar{w}, \\ M_2 &= \bar{M}_2 \quad &\text{or} \quad \beta_2 &= \bar{\beta}_2. \end{aligned} \tag{2.80b}$$

From a consideration of the original form of the line integrals in Eq. 2.70 we might be led to believe that five and not four separate quantities constitute the natural boundary conditions that are to be applied at a given edge. However, it was shown by Kirchoff, for the flat plate, and by Basset and Lamb, for cylindrical and spherical shells[10], that N_{nt}, M_{nt}, and Q_{nt} cannot in general be individually prescribed on an edge α_n = constant, and that these three shearing stress resultants must be replaced by the two statically equivalent effective shearing forces defined by Eqs. 2.78.

It will now be shown for the case of an edge α_n = constant that V_n and T_{nt} are statically equivalent to M_{nt}, N_{nt}, and Q_n. For this purpose, we consider the boundary curve of the reference surface and approximate it by a polygon having very many infinitesimal sides of equal length (see Fig. 2.4), such that the length of each segment is, in approximation, equal to the length of the arc of which it is the chord. Thus, $ab = bc = ds_t$. The forces acting on the element ds_t are shown in Fig. 2.4a.

We replace the couple M_{nt} acting at a' midway between a and b by two forces M_{nt} and the couple $M_{nt} + (\partial M_{nt}/\partial s_t)ds_t$ acting at b' midway between b and c by two forces $M_{nt} + (\partial M_{nt}/\partial s_t)ds_t$. The action of these forces is shown in Fig. 2.4b. If we project these forces upon the normal to the curve, we find that they represent an additional normal force:

$$\left(M_{nt} + \frac{\partial M_{nt}}{\partial s_t} ds_t\right) \cos\varphi - M_{nt}\cos\varphi. \tag{2.81}$$

For a small angle φ for which $\cos\varphi \approx 1$, this becomes

$$\frac{\partial M_{nt}}{\partial s_t} ds_t. \tag{2.82}$$

[10] See, for example, Love's treatise (footnote 2), pp. 536–537.

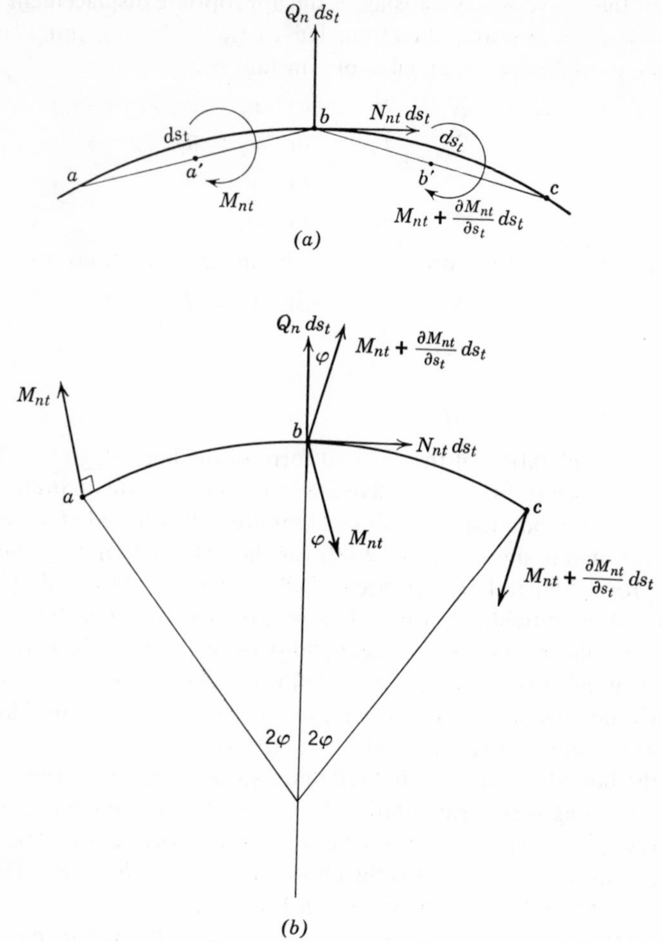

Figure 2.4

In a similar way, if we project the added forces on the tangent to the element, we find that they represent an additional tangential force:

$$\left(2M_{nt} + \frac{\partial M_{nt}}{\partial s_t}\, ds_t\right) \varphi, \tag{2.83}$$

where, since the angle φ is small, we have made the substitution $\sin \varphi \approx \varphi$. For small angles φ, we note further that $2\varphi \approx ds_t/R_t$ and, therefore, the above expression is replaced by

$$M_{nt}\, ds_t/R_t, \tag{2.84}$$

where we have neglected infinitesimals of higher order. Thus, we have shown that the twisting moment M_{nt} is statically equivalent to a tangential shearing force M_{nt}/R_t and a normal shearing force $\partial M_{nt}/\partial s_t$. Therefore, the effect of M_{nt} can be included by defining the effective shearing forces

$$V_n = Q_n + \frac{1}{A_t}\frac{\partial M_{nt}}{\partial \alpha_t},$$
$$T_{nt} = N_{nt} + \frac{M_{nt}}{R_t}. \tag{2.85}$$

as we have already done with Eqs. 2.78. Of course, the above approximation implies a redistribution of the stresses on and near the edges of the shell. Using St. Venant's principle as a basis, we may argue that the effect of the replacement is only felt within a distance from the boundary which is of the order of the shell thickness.

Before ending this discussion, it is well to present some specific combinations of the boundary conditions which often arise in the analysis of shell structures. If the shell under consideration is closed with respect to one or both of its coordinates, we can only specify that upon going around the shell and returning to a given point the same result must be obtained. That is, for shells closed with respect to a certain coordinate, we require that the solution be periodic with respect to that coordinate. If the shell has edges, we may specify certain common support conditions. For example, taking an edge having α_n = constant, we may specify that any of the following support conditions are to be applied:

(*a*) Free edge:

$$\bar{N}_n = \bar{V}_n = \bar{T}_{nt} = \bar{M}_n = 0; \tag{2.86}$$

(*b*) Clamped edge:

$$\bar{u}_n = \bar{u}_t = \bar{w} = \bar{\beta}_n = 0; \tag{2.87}$$

(*c*) Simply supported edge, not free to move:

$$\bar{M}_n = \bar{u}_n = \bar{u}_t = \bar{w} = 0; \tag{2.88}$$

(*d*) Simply supported edge, free to move in normal direction:

$$\bar{M}_n = \bar{V}_n = \bar{u}_n = \bar{u}_t = 0. \tag{2.89}$$

Other combinations can of course be conceived but, in any event, one must be certain to select only one condition from each of the pairs given by Eqs. 2.80a and 2.80b or else the variational equation (Eq. 2.70) will be violated. That is, we cannot specify both the force and the displacement in a given direction at the edge of the shell.

By way of summary, we may express the boundary conditions in the following general form:

$$B_k\{u_1, u_2, w\} = \bar{B}_k, \qquad k = 1, 2, \ldots, N. \tag{2.90}$$

Here B_k is an operator that has been shown, generally, to act upon all three displacement components, and that can be obtained by expressing any of the conditions of Eqs. 2.86 to 2.89, for example, in terms of displacements only by using Eqs. 2.27 and 2.19. The index k ranges from 1 to N where N is the total number of boundary conditions that are to be applied. For example, if a shell segment with four edges is to be considered, there will, by Eqs. 2.80, be four conditions to be prescribed at each edge and, therefore, $N = 16$. If a shell of revolution with two edges is under consideration, then for unsymmetrical loads four boundary conditions will have to be prescribed at each edge and $N = 8$. For axisymmetric loads only three boundary conditions will be required at each edge and $N = 6$. If the shell of revolution has only one edge, then $N = 4$ and 3 for the unsymmetric and axisymmetric load cases, respectively.

2.8 CLOSURE

We have derived, in this chapter, a set of differential equations which describes the behavior of a thin elastic shell within the framework of Love's postulates. There is, however, one other class of equations in the theory of elasticity which has a counterpart in the theory of thin elastic shells—the equations of compatibility. The reader will no doubt recall from the theory of elasticity that the compatibility equations insure that, when a problem is solved in terms of the stresses, the displacements which are obtained by integration of the strains will be single valued. That is, the compatibility equations insure that no gaps will occur in the body during deformation. Since, in the theory that has been derived here, the distribution of the displacements across the thickness of the shell is specified by the assumption on the preservation of the normal (and in particular by Eqs. 2.15), the role of the compatibility equations is to insure that no gaps occur in the reference surface during deformation. The derivation of the compatibility equations which will not be given here,[11] is based, as the perceptive reader might presume, on the Gauss–Codazzi conditions of the deformed middle surface which we have discussed in Section 1.3*f*. We are thus provided with an additional indication of the importance of the Gauss–Codazzi equations. Not only do they tell us if a given set of parameters defines a valid surface, but they insure that as a result of deformation the surface will remain, so to speak, valid.

From the engineer's point of view, the equations which have been derived here have provided an extremely successful model for the analysis of thin elastic shells. Since they form the basis of most of the shell analyses which

[11] See, for example, Goldenveiser, A. L., *Theory of Thin Elastic Shells*, New York: Pergamon Press, 1961, pp. 55–59.

have been carried out in the past, these equations will be used, with a few illustrative exceptions, in all applications that are to be presented in this text. However, before embarking upon the solution of these equations we shall, in the next chapter, present a discussion of some additional theories which have been proposed to describe the behavior of thin elastic shells.

APPENDIX: CONDUCTION OF HEAT IN A THIN SHELL

In the development of the theory of thin elastic shells, we included as part of Hooke's law a contribution to the normal strains caused by a known temperature distribution T which is obtained from a solution of the equation of heat conduction. It seems appropriate, therefore, to present also the equation of heat conduction in terms of the shell coordinates which we have adopted in Section 2.3. The discussion which follows will, of necessity, be brief, since a detailed development of the theory is beyond the scope of this text; thus, a prior familiarity with the subject of heat conduction will be assumed here.

To begin this review, we recall that the equation of heat conduction in an orthotropic medium described by an orthogonal coordinate system is, in the absence of thermomechanical coupling effects, given by[12]

$$\begin{aligned}(g_1g_2g_3)^{1/2}c\rho\frac{\partial T}{\partial t} &= k_{t1}\frac{\partial}{\partial\alpha_1}\left[\left(\frac{g_2g_3}{g_1}\right)^{1/2}\frac{\partial T}{\partial\alpha_1}\right]\\ &\quad + k_{t2}\frac{\partial}{\partial\alpha_2}\left[\left(\frac{g_1g_3}{g_2}\right)^{1/2}\frac{\partial T}{\partial\alpha_2}\right]\\ &\quad + k_{t3}\frac{\partial}{\partial\alpha_3}\left[\left(\frac{g_1g_2}{g_3}\right)^{1/2}\frac{\partial T}{\partial\alpha_3}\right] + Q''', \qquad (2.91)\end{aligned}$$

where c is the specific heat of the material, the k_{ti} are the constant thermal conductivities in the three mutually orthogonal coordinate directions, and $Q'''(\alpha_1, \alpha_2, \alpha_3, t)$ is the rate at which heat is generated by sources distributed in the body under consideration. To apply the above equation to a shell, we adopt the notation of Eqs. 2.13, whereupon it takes the form

$$\begin{aligned}A_1A_2(1+\zeta/R_1)(1+\zeta/R_2)\rho c\frac{\partial T}{\partial t} &= k_{t1}\frac{\partial}{\partial\alpha_1}\left[\frac{A_2(1+\zeta/R_2)}{A_1(1+\zeta/R_1)}\frac{\partial T}{\partial\alpha_1}\right]\\ &\quad + k_{t2}\frac{\partial}{\partial\alpha_2}\left[\frac{A_1(1+\zeta/R_1)}{A_2(1+\zeta/R_2)}\frac{\partial T}{\partial\alpha_2}\right]\\ &\quad + k_{tn}\frac{\partial}{\partial\zeta}\left[A_1A_2\left(1+\frac{\zeta}{R_1}\right)\right.\\ &\quad \left.\times\left(1+\frac{\zeta}{R_2}\right)\frac{\partial T}{\partial\zeta}\right] + Q'''. \qquad (2.92)\end{aligned}$$

---

[12] See, for example, Carslaw, H. S., and Jaeger, J. C., *Conduction of Heat in Solids*, 2nd ed., London: Oxford University Press, 1959, Chapter 1.

If the indicated differentiations are carried out and the ratio ζ/R is neglected with respect to unity, in accordance with our interest in thin shells the result is

$$\rho c \frac{\partial T}{\partial t} = k_{t1}\left[\frac{1}{A_1{}^2}\frac{\partial^2 T}{\partial \alpha_1{}^2} + \frac{1}{A_1 A_2}\frac{\partial T}{\partial \alpha_1}\frac{\partial}{\partial \alpha_1}\left(\frac{A_2}{A_1}\right)\right] + k_{t2}\left[\frac{1}{A_2{}^2}\frac{\partial^2 T}{\partial \alpha_2{}^2} + \frac{1}{A_1 A_2}\frac{\partial T}{\partial \alpha_2}\frac{\partial}{\partial \alpha_2}\left(\frac{A_1}{A_2}\right)\right] + k_{tn}\left[\frac{\partial^2 T}{\partial \zeta^2} + \left(\frac{1}{R_1} + \frac{1}{R_2}\right)\frac{\partial T}{\partial \zeta}\right] + \frac{Q'''}{A_1 A_2}. \tag{2.93}$$

For the special case of an isotropic material ($k = k_{t1} = k_{t2} = k_{tn}$), the above equation is replaced by

$$\frac{1}{\kappa}\frac{\partial T}{\partial t} = \frac{1}{A_1{}^2}\frac{\partial^2 T}{\partial \alpha_1{}^2} + \frac{1}{A_2{}^2}\frac{\partial^2 T}{\partial \alpha_2{}^2} + \frac{\partial^2 T}{\partial \zeta^2} + \frac{1}{A_1 A_2}\left[\frac{\partial T}{\partial \alpha_1}\frac{\partial}{\partial \alpha_1}\left(\frac{A_2}{A_1}\right) + \frac{\partial T}{\partial \alpha_2}\frac{\partial}{\partial \alpha_2}\left(\frac{A_1}{A_2}\right)\right] + \left(\frac{1}{R_1} + \frac{1}{R_2}\right)\frac{\partial T}{\partial \zeta} + \frac{Q'''}{k A_1 A_2}, \tag{2.94}$$

where $\kappa = k/\rho c$ is called the thermal diffusivity.

The above equation may be reduced further upon consideration of the term $(1/R_1 + 1/R_2)\,\partial T/\partial \zeta$ which represents the tangential flow of heat across the sloping sides of the fundamental element of a thin shell in a situation where the thermal conditions do not vary with α_1 and α_2. To examine such a situation, we may define the dimensionless variables $\eta = \zeta/h$ and $\tau = \kappa t/h^2$ whereupon Eq. 2.94 (for the case of thermal conditions that are independent of α_1 and α_2) becomes, in the absence of heat sources,

$$\frac{\partial^2 T}{\partial \eta^2} + \left(\frac{h}{R_1} + \frac{h}{R_2}\right)\frac{\partial T}{\partial \eta} = \frac{\partial T}{\partial \tau}. \tag{2.95}$$

If we presume that all of the derivatives in Eq. 2.95 are of the same order of magnitude, it is reasonable, as a result of our restriction to thin shells, to conclude that the second term on the left hand side is negligible in comparison to the others. Thus, we may replace Eq. 2.95 by

$$\frac{\partial^2 T}{\partial \eta^2} = \frac{\partial T}{\partial \tau} \tag{2.96}$$

and as a result of these arguments Eq. 2.94 can be reduced to

$$\frac{1}{\kappa}\frac{\partial T}{\partial t} = \frac{1}{A_1{}^2}\frac{\partial^2 T}{\partial \alpha_1{}^2} + \frac{1}{A_2{}^2}\frac{\partial^2 T}{\partial \alpha_2{}^2} + \frac{\partial^2 T}{\partial \zeta^2} + \frac{Q'''}{k A_1 A_2} + \frac{1}{A_1 A_2}\left[\frac{\partial T}{\partial \alpha_1}\frac{\partial}{\partial \alpha_1}\left(\frac{A_2}{A_1}\right) + \frac{\partial T}{\partial \alpha_2}\frac{\partial}{\partial \alpha_2}\left(\frac{A_1}{A_2}\right)\right]. \tag{2.97}$$

Equation 2.97 is accepted as the governing equation for the conduction of heat in a thin shell.[13] It can be shown that Eq. 2.97, unlike its forerunner Eq. 2.94, can always be solved by the method of separation of variables for a shell of any geometrical shape. Also, it represents what is known as a "slab approximation" since, for the case where the thermal conditions vary with ζ but not with α_1 and α_2, it reduces to the equation which is appropriate to the one-dimensional flow of heat in a slab.

The solution of the equation of heat conduction in a thin shell subject to suitable initial and boundary conditions can be obtained by any of the standard methods of solving partial differential equations, such as integral transforms and separation of variables. Solutions of the heat conduction equation will not be pursued here since so many excellent references on the subject are available both in the mathematical and the engineering literature. It will thus be assumed, from now on, that in those cases where it is relevant the temperature distribution in the shell is available.

SUPPLEMENTARY REFERENCES

Flügge, W., *Stresses in Shells*, Berlin: Springer-Verlag, 1962.

Novozhilov, V. V., *The Theory of Thin Elastic Shells*, Groningen: P. Noordhoff, 1959.

Nowacki, W., *Thermoelasticity*, Reading, Pa.: Addison-Wesley, 1962.

Parkus, H., "Warmespannungen in Rotationsschalen bei drehsymmetrischer Temperaturverteilung," *Sitzungsber. Osterr. Akad. Wiss.* Abt. II*a*, **160**, 1 (1951).

Radkowski, P. P., "Stress Analysis of Orthotropic Thin Multilayer Shells of Revolution," AIAA Launch and Space Vehicle Structures Conference, Palm Springs, Calif., April 1963, Preprint 2889–63.

Reissner, E., "A Note on Deflections of Plates on a Visco-elastic Foundation," *J. Appl. Mech.*, **25**, 144–145 (1958).

Schneider, P. J., *Conduction Heat Transfer*, Cambridge: Addison-Wesley, 1955.

Timoshenko, S., and Woinowsky-Krieger, S., *Theory of Plates and Shells*, 2nd ed., New York: McGraw-Hill, 1959.

Timoshenko, S., and Young, D. H., *Advanced Dynamics*, New York: McGraw-Hill, 1948.

Vlasov, V. Z., *General Theory of Shells and its Application to Engineering*, Moscow–Leningrad (1949), NASA Technical Translation NASA-TT-F-99 (1964).

EXERCISES

2.1 Verify Eqs. 2.7 and 2.8.

2.2 The reference surface could be defined as that surface which experiences no bending stress. By using this definition, show that the location of the

---

[13] Brull, M. A., and Vinson, J. R., "Approximate Three Dimensional Solutions for Transient Temperature Distribution in Thin Shells of Revolution", *J. Aero Space Sci.*, **25**, 742–750 (1958).

reference surface of an isotropic shell (whose Young's modulus may vary and whose Poisson's ratio is constant over its thickness) is obtained from

$$\int_{\xi} E(\zeta)\zeta \, d\zeta = 0.$$

Use this formula to locate the reference surface, as defined above, of a shell made up of N isotropic layers. Assume that the properties are constant over the thickness of each layer but that they vary from layer to layer. Find the extensional rigidity K and the bending rigidity D of such a shell.

2.3 Show that the conditions of equilibrium in terms of the stress resultant and stress couple vectors defined by Eqs. 2.34 and 2.36 to 2.39 are:

$$\frac{\partial \mathbf{F}_1}{\partial \alpha_1} d\alpha_1 + \frac{\partial \mathbf{F}_2}{\partial \alpha_2} d\alpha_2 + A_1 A_2 \, \mathbf{q} \, d\alpha_1 \, d\alpha_2 = 0,$$

$$\frac{\partial \mathbf{M}_1}{\partial \alpha_1} d\alpha_1 + \frac{\partial \mathbf{M}_2}{\partial \alpha_2} d\alpha_2 + \left(\mathbf{F}_1 \times \frac{\partial \mathbf{r}}{\partial \alpha_1}\right) d\alpha_1 + \left(\mathbf{F}_2 \times \frac{\partial \mathbf{r}}{\partial \alpha_2}\right) d\alpha_2 = 0.$$

Use the above to derive six scalar equations which describe the equilibrium of the components of the stress resultant and stress couple vectors.

2.4 The equations of stress equilibrium in an elastic medium which is described by an orthogonal curvilinear coordinate system are given by[14]

$$\frac{\partial (g\sigma_i)}{\partial \alpha_i} - \frac{1}{2} \sum_{j=1}^{3} \frac{g\sigma_j}{g_j} \frac{\partial g_j}{\partial \alpha_j} + \sum_{\substack{j=1 \\ (j \neq i)}}^{3} \frac{\partial}{\partial \alpha_j} \left(\frac{g g_i \tau_{ij}}{\sqrt{g_i g_j}} \right) = 0, \qquad i, j = 1, 2, 3.$$

where body forces have been neglected and $g = \sqrt{g_1 g_2 g_3}$. By using the notation of Eqs. 2.13, derive the three equations of stress equilibrium in the shell space defined in Section 2.3 and then derive, by suitable integrations of these three equations, the equations which express the equilibrium of the stress resultants and couples.

2.5 Show that the stresses can be obtained from the following derivative of the strain energy density:

$$\sigma_{ij} = \frac{\partial P}{\partial \epsilon_{ij}}.$$

2.6 Verify Eq. 2.70.

2.7 Let small, constant, rigid body motions be defined by the vectors (see Fig. 2.5)

$$\mathbf{\Delta} = \delta_1 \mathbf{t}_1 + \delta_2 \mathbf{t}_2 + \delta_n \mathbf{n},$$

$$\mathbf{\Omega} = -\omega_2 \mathbf{t}_1 + \omega_1 \mathbf{t}_2 + \omega_n \mathbf{n}.$$

For such motions, the displacement vector of a point on the reference surface is given by

$$\mathbf{U} = \mathbf{\Delta} + (\mathbf{\Omega} \times \mathbf{r}).$$

[14] See Sokolnikoff, I. S. (cited in footnote 6).

where δ_1, δ_2, δ_3 are small rigid body translations, ω_1, ω_2, ω_n are small rigid body rotations in the three orthogonal coordinate directions, and $\mathbf{r}$ is the position vector of the point on the reference surface. Establish the following relationships among the components of the rigid body motion vectors:

$$\frac{\partial \delta_1}{\partial \alpha_1} = -\frac{\delta_2}{A_2}\frac{\partial A_1}{\partial \alpha_2} - \frac{A_1\delta_n}{R_1}, \qquad \frac{\partial \delta_1}{\partial \alpha_2} = \frac{\delta_2}{A_1}\frac{\partial A_2}{\partial \alpha_1},$$

$$\frac{\partial \delta_2}{\partial \alpha_1} = \frac{\delta_1}{A_2}\frac{\partial A_1}{\partial \alpha_2}, \qquad \frac{\partial \delta_2}{\partial \alpha_2} = -\frac{\delta_1}{A_1}\frac{\partial A_2}{\partial \alpha_1} - \frac{A_2\delta_n}{R_2},$$

$$\frac{\partial \delta_n}{\partial \alpha_1} = \frac{A_1\delta_1}{R_1}, \qquad \frac{\partial \delta_n}{\partial \alpha_2} = \frac{A_2\delta_2}{R_2},$$

$$\frac{\partial \omega_1}{\partial \alpha_1} = -\frac{\omega_2}{A_2}\frac{\partial A_1}{\partial \alpha_2}, \qquad \frac{\partial \omega_1}{\partial \alpha_2} = \frac{\omega_2}{A_1}\frac{\partial A_2}{\partial \alpha_1} - \frac{A_2\omega_n}{R_2},$$

$$\frac{\partial \omega_2}{\partial \alpha_1} = \frac{\omega_1}{A_2}\frac{\partial A_1}{\partial \alpha_2} + \frac{A_1\omega_n}{R_1}, \qquad \frac{\partial \omega_2}{\partial \alpha_2} = -\frac{\omega_1}{A_1}\frac{\partial A_2}{\partial \alpha_1},$$

$$\frac{\partial \omega_n}{\partial \alpha_1} = -\frac{A_1\omega_2}{R_1}, \qquad \frac{\partial \omega_n}{\partial \alpha_2} = \frac{A_2\omega_1}{R_2}.$$

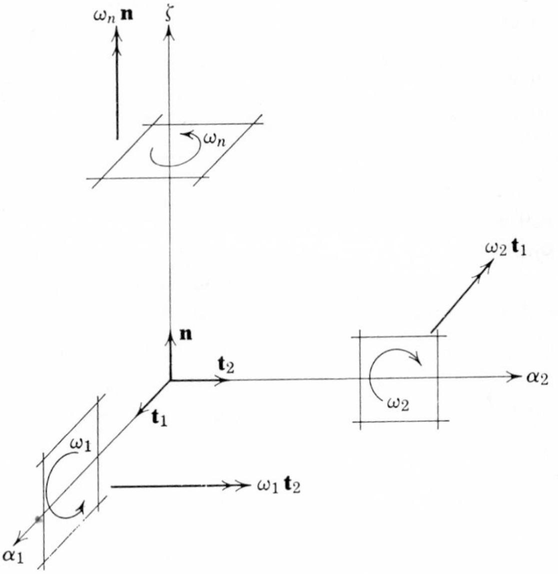

Figure 2.5

2.8 Derive an expression for the strain energy of a shell in terms of κ_1, κ_2, τ, $\epsilon_1{}^0$, $\epsilon_2{}^0$, and $\gamma_{12}{}^0$.

2.9 Show that for steady state thermal problems the temperature distribution obtained by solving Eq. 2.97 will be linear in ζ and that under these conditions the thermal terms in Eqs. 2.32 will vanish.

3

Some Additional Theories of Thin Elastic Shells

3.1 INTRODUCTION

While the derivation of the theory of thin elastic shells is fresh in our minds, it seems appropriate, before beginning a discussion of the solution of various classes of problems of shell analysis, to outline the derivations of several additional shell theories.

Many additional theories of thin elastic shells have been proposed. Rather than attempt to provide a chronicle of these efforts, which has been done elsewhere,[1-4] we shall concentrate our efforts on four representative theories which we shall present in three sections. In the first of these sections, we shall discuss one of a class of alternate theories in which all of Love's original assumptions are preserved. In the second section, we shall outline the derivation of two so-called "higher order" linear theories in which one or another of Love's assumptions, with the exception of the small deflection assumption, are suspended. In the last category, we shall consider a nonlinear theory of thin elastic shells.

---

[1] Naghdi, P. M., "A Survey of Recent Progress in the Theory of Thin Elastic Shells," *Appl. Mech. Revs.*, **9**, 365–368 (1956).

[2] Koiter, W. T., "A Consistent First Approximation in the General Theory of Thin Elastic Shells," *Proc. Symp. on Theory of Thin Elastic Shells* (Delft, August 1959), Amsterdam: North-Holland, 12–33 (1960).

[3] Naghdi, P. M., "Foundations of Elastic Shell Theory" in *Progress in Solid Mechanics*, I. N. Sneddon and R. Hill, eds., Amsterdam: North-Holland, **IV**, Chapter 1 (1963).

[4] Hildebrand, F. B., Reissner, E., and Thomas, G. B., "Notes on the Foundations of the Theory of Small Displacements of Orthotropic Shells," NACA-TN-1833, March 1949.

3.2 SANDERS' FIRST APPROXIMATION TO THE THEORY OF THIN ELASTIC SHELLS

Let us now examine the theory derived in Chapter 2 more carefully. We have shown, in the preceding chapter, that one of the results of that derivation is the equality of the shearing forces and moments in the plane of the reference surface, that is,

$$N_{12} = N_{21}, \qquad M_{12} = M_{21}. \tag{3.1}$$

We have also shown that a sixth equation of equilibrium, namely,

$$N_{12} - N_{21} + \frac{M_{12}}{R_1} - \frac{M_{21}}{R_2} \equiv 0, \tag{3.2}$$

which is obtained from the equilibrium of moments about a normal to the reference surface, is identically satisfied by the integral definitions of the shearing-stress resultants in terms of the shearing-stress components. Now, if we substitute the result 3.1 into Eq. 3.2, we find that the identity is violated except for spherical shells for which $R_1 = R_2$, flat plates for which $1/R_1 = 1/R_2 = 0$, and symmetrically loaded shells of revolution for which $M_{12} = M_{21} = N_{12} = N_{21} = 0$. In the past, it has been argued that $N_{12} - N_{21}$ vanishes in every case, the difference $M_{12}/R_1 - M_{21}/R_2$ is likely to be small, especially if the shell is nearly spherical, and therefore the inconsistency can be overlooked for engineering purposes.

Let us also consider the application of the theory of Chapter 2 to small rigid body motions of a thin elastic shell. For this purpose, we have (in Exercise 2.7) derived a set of relationships among the derivatives of the components of the rigid body motion vectors. With the latter relationships we may consider the torsion τ given by the sixth of Eqs. 2.19 as

$$\tau = \frac{1}{A_2}\frac{\partial \beta_1}{\partial \alpha_2} + \frac{1}{A_1}\frac{\partial \beta_2}{\partial \alpha_1} - \frac{1}{A_1 A_2}\left(\beta_1 \frac{\partial A_1}{\partial \alpha_2} + \beta_2 \frac{\partial A_2}{\partial \alpha_1}\right). \tag{3.3}$$

For the case of rigid rotation components ω_1, ω_2, and ω_n, we let $\beta_1 = \omega_1$, $\beta_2 = \omega_2$, and $\beta_n = \omega_n$. If we substitute the appropriate derivatives of these quantities (as obtained in Exercise 2.7) into the foregoing expression, we find that

$$\tau = \left(\frac{1}{R_1} - \frac{1}{R_2}\right)\omega_n. \tag{3.4}$$

This indicates that for a rigid body rotation the theory of Chapter 2 gives a nonvanishing torsion except, again, in the case of a spherical shell, a flat plate, or a symmetrically loaded shell of revolution. If the rotation ω_n is of the same order of magnitude as the strain components then, as noted by

Koiter,[2] the torsion given by Eq. 3.4 is negligible. However, if the rotation is large, then the torsion will not be negligible and the theory could lead to substantial errors as found by Cohen[5] for a helicoidal shell and by Reissner[6] for pure torsion of a cylindrical shell.

Although, for engineering purposes, the foregoing inconsistencies can generally be overlooked, they have, nevertheless, presented a challenge to applied mathematicians who have sought to formulate a theory in which such loose ends do not occur. Of the many theories which have been proposed in the pursuit of this goal, we choose to outline here the treatment of Sanders.[7] The derivation will be carried out for the simplest case of a free shell since our primary interest is in the development of the relevant strain-displacement equations and equilibrium equations. As a result, the variational equation (Eq. 2.70) reduces to

$$\begin{aligned}\int_{\alpha_1}\int_{\alpha_2}\Bigg\{&\left[\frac{\partial N_1A_2}{\partial\alpha_1}+\frac{\partial N_{21}A_1}{\partial\alpha_2}+N_{12}\frac{\partial A_1}{\partial\alpha_2}-N_2\frac{\partial A_2}{\partial\alpha_1}+Q_1\frac{A_1A_2}{R_1}\right]\delta u_1\\
&+\left[\frac{\partial N_{12}A_2}{\partial\alpha_1}+\frac{\partial N_2A_1}{\partial\alpha_2}+N_{21}\frac{\partial A_2}{\partial\alpha_1}-N_1\frac{\partial A_1}{\partial\alpha_2}+Q_2\frac{A_1A_2}{R_2}\right]\delta u_2\\
&+\left[\frac{\partial Q_1A_2}{\partial\alpha_1}+\frac{\partial Q_2A_1}{\partial\alpha_2}-\left(\frac{N_1}{R_1}+\frac{N_2}{R_2}\right)A_1A_2\right]\delta w\\
&+\left[\frac{\partial M_1A_2}{\partial\alpha_1}+\frac{\partial M_{21}A_1}{\partial\alpha_2}+M_{12}\frac{\partial A_1}{\partial\alpha_2}-M_2\frac{\partial A_2}{\partial\alpha_1}-Q_1A_1A_2\right]\delta\beta_1\\
&+\left[\frac{\partial M_{12}A_2}{\partial\alpha_1}+\frac{\partial M_2A_1}{\partial\alpha_2}+M_{21}\frac{\partial A_2}{\partial\alpha_1}-M_1\frac{\partial A_1}{\partial\alpha_2}-Q_2A_1A_2\right]\delta\beta_2\\
&+A_1A_2\left[N_{12}-N_{21}+\frac{M_{12}}{R_1}-\frac{M_{21}}{R_2}\right]\delta\beta_n\Bigg\}\,d\alpha_1\,d\alpha_2=0. \qquad (3.5)\end{aligned}$$

Here we have added a "contribution" from the sixth equation of equilibrium, which we previously showed to be an identity, multiplied by an arbitrary variation of β_n. The absence of such a contribution in the theory

[5] Cohen, J. W., "The Inadequacy of the Classical Stress–Strain Relations for the Right Helicoidal Shell," *Proc. Symp. on Theory of Thin Elastic Shells* (Delft, August 1959), Amsterdam: North-Holland, 415–433 (1960).

[6] See, for example, Reissner, E., "On the Form of Variationally Derived Shell Equations," *J. Appl. Mech.*, **31**, 233–238 (1964).

[7] Sanders, J. L., "An Improved First Approximation Theory for Thin Shells," NASA-TR-R24 (1959). The derivation was repeated in tensor form by Budiansky, B., and Sanders, J. L., "On the 'Best' First Order Linear Shell Theory," *Progress in Applied Mechanics, The Prager Anniversary Volume*, New York: Macmillan, pp. 129–140 (1963). The equations are identical to those derived by Koiter, loc. cit.

of Chapter 2 led to the inconsistency associated with rigid body rotations. If we now integrate by parts, we obtain the equivalent equation:

$$\begin{aligned}
\int_{\alpha_1}\int_{\alpha_2} \Big\{ & N_1\,\delta\left(A_2\frac{\partial u_1}{\partial\alpha_1} + \frac{\partial A_1}{\partial\alpha_2}u_2 + \frac{A_1A_2}{R_1}w\right) \\
& + N_{12}\,\delta\left(A_2\frac{\partial u_2}{\partial\alpha_1} - \frac{\partial A_1}{\partial\alpha_2}u_1 - A_1A_2\beta_n\right) \\
& + N_{21}\,\delta\left(A_1\frac{\partial u_1}{\partial\alpha_2} - \frac{\partial A_2}{\partial\alpha_1}u_2 + A_1A_2\beta_n\right) \\
& + N_2\,\delta\left(A_1\frac{\partial u_2}{\partial\alpha_2} + \frac{\partial A_2}{\partial\alpha_1}u_1 + \frac{A_1A_2}{R_2}w\right) \\
& + Q_1\,\delta\left(A_2\frac{\partial w}{\partial\alpha_1} - \frac{A_1A_2}{R_1}u_1 + A_1A_2\beta_1\right) \\
& + Q_2\,\delta\left(A_1\frac{\partial w}{\partial\alpha_2} - \frac{A_1A_2}{R_2}u_2 + A_1A_2\beta_2\right) \\
& + M_1\,\delta\left(A_2\frac{\partial\beta_1}{\partial\alpha_1} + \frac{\partial A_1}{\partial\alpha_2}\beta_2\right) + M_{12}\,\delta\left(A_2\frac{\partial\beta_2}{\partial\alpha_1} - \frac{\partial A_1}{\partial\alpha_2}\beta_1 - \frac{A_1A_2}{R_1}\beta_n\right) \\
& + M_{21}\,\delta\left(A_1\frac{\partial\beta_1}{\partial\alpha_2} - \frac{\partial A_2}{\partial\alpha_1}\beta_2 + \frac{A_1A_2}{R_2}\beta_n\right) \\
& + M_{22}\,\delta\left(A_1\frac{\partial\beta_2}{\partial\alpha_2} + \frac{\partial A_2}{\partial\alpha_1}\beta_1\right)\Big\}\,d\alpha_1\,d\alpha_2 \\
- \oint_{\alpha_2} & [N_1\,\delta u_1 + N_{12}\,\delta u_2 + Q_1\,\delta w + M_1\,\delta\beta_1 + M_{12}\,\delta\beta_2]A_2\,d\alpha_2 \\
- \oint_{\alpha_1} & [N_{21}\,\delta u_1 + N_2\,\delta u_2 + Q_2\,\delta w + M_{21}\,\delta\beta_1 + M_2\,\delta\beta_2]A_1\,d\alpha_1 = 0.
\end{aligned} \tag{3.6}$$

Upon comparison of this equation to its counterpart, Eq. 2.63, where the effect of β_n is not included, we may rewrite it as

$$\begin{aligned}
\int_{\alpha_1}\int_{\alpha_2} & [N_1\,\delta\epsilon_1{}^0 + N_{12}\,\delta\epsilon_{12}{}^0 + N_{21}\,\delta\epsilon_{21}{}^0 + N_2\,\delta\epsilon_2{}^0 + Q_1\,\delta\gamma_{1n} + Q_2\,\delta\gamma_{2n} \\
& \quad + M_1\,\delta\kappa_1 + M_{12}\,\delta\kappa_{12} + M_{21}\,\delta\kappa_{21} + M_2\,\delta\kappa_2]A_1A_2\,d\alpha_1\,d\alpha_2 \\
- \oint_{\alpha_2} & [N_1\,\delta u_1 + N_{12}\,\delta u_2 + Q_1\,\delta w + M_1\,\delta\beta_1 + M_{12}\,\delta\beta_2]A_2\,d\alpha_2 \\
- \oint_{\alpha_1} & [N_{21}\,\delta u_1 + N_2\,\delta u_2 + Q_2\,\delta w \\
& \quad + M_{21}\,\delta\beta_1 + M_2\,\delta\beta_2]A_1\,d\alpha_1 = 0,
\end{aligned} \tag{3.7}$$

where the following new strain quantities have been defined:

$$\begin{aligned}
\epsilon_{12}{}^0 &= \frac{1}{A_1}\frac{\partial u_2}{\partial \alpha_1} - \frac{1}{A_1A_2}\frac{\partial A_1}{\partial \alpha_2}u_1 - \beta_n,\\
\epsilon_{21}{}^0 &= \frac{1}{A_2}\frac{\partial u_1}{\partial \alpha_2} - \frac{1}{A_1A_2}\frac{\partial A_2}{\partial \alpha_1}u_2 + \beta_n,\\
\kappa_{12} &= \frac{1}{A_1}\frac{\partial \beta_2}{\partial \alpha_1} - \frac{1}{A_1A_2}\frac{\partial A_1}{\partial \alpha_2}\beta_1 - \frac{\beta_n}{R_1},\\
\kappa_{21} &= \frac{1}{A_2}\frac{\partial \beta_1}{\partial \alpha_2} - \frac{1}{A_1A_2}\frac{\partial A_2}{\partial \alpha_1}\beta_2 + \frac{\beta_n}{R_2},
\end{aligned} \tag{3.8}$$

and the remaining quantities are still given by Eqs. 2.19. Since Love's postulates are retained here, the transverse normal shearing strains vanish and Eqs. 2.16 for the rotations β_1 and β_2 remain valid. The quantity β_n that appears in the new strain quantities can be determined as a function of u_1 and u_2 by taking the curl of the displacement vector **U** and retaining that component which expresses the rotation about the normal to the reference surface; thus, we obtain

$$\beta_n = \frac{1}{2A_1A_2}\left(\frac{\partial A_2 u_2}{\partial \alpha_1} - \frac{\partial A_1 u_1}{\partial \alpha_2}\right), \tag{3.9}$$

If we now compare the expressions for $\epsilon_{12}{}^0$, $\epsilon_{21}{}^0$, and β_n, we may show from these that

$$\epsilon_{12}{}^0 = \epsilon_{21}{}^0 \tag{3.10}$$

and from a consideration of the expressions for β_1, β_2, β_n, κ_{12}, and κ_{21}

$$\kappa_{12} - \kappa_{21} = \left(\frac{1}{R_2} - \frac{1}{R_1}\right)\epsilon_{12}{}^0. \tag{3.11}$$

Finally it is important to observe that, in view of Eqs. 2.19,

$$\begin{aligned}
\epsilon_{12}{}^0 + \epsilon_{21}{}^0 &= 2\epsilon_{12}{}^0 = \gamma_{12}{}^0,\\
\kappa_{12} + \kappa_{21} &= \tau - \beta_n\left(\frac{1}{R_1} - \frac{1}{R_2}\right).
\end{aligned} \tag{3.12}$$

The effect of the proposed strain displacement equations upon the remainder of the theory can now be determined from the area integral of Eq. 3.7 which becomes, upon using Eqs. 3.10 and 3.11,

$$\begin{aligned}
\int_{\alpha_1}\int_{\alpha_2} \Bigg\{ & N_1\,\delta\epsilon_1{}^0 + 2\left[\frac{1}{2}(N_{12} + N_{21}) + \frac{1}{4}\left(\frac{1}{R_2} - \frac{1}{R_1}\right)(M_{12} - M_{21})\right]\delta\epsilon_{12}{}^0\\
& + N_2\,\delta\epsilon_2{}^0 + M_1\,\delta\kappa_1 + \frac{1}{2}(M_{12} + M_{21})\\
& \times \delta(\kappa_{12} + \kappa_{21}) + M_2\,\delta\kappa_2\Bigg\} A_1A_2\,d\alpha_1\,d\alpha_2.
\end{aligned} \tag{3.13}$$

If we let

$$\tilde{N}_{12} = \frac{1}{2}(N_{12} + N_{21}) = \frac{Eh}{1+\nu}\epsilon_{12}{}^0,$$
$$\tilde{M}_{12} = \frac{1}{2}(M_{12} + M_{21}) = \frac{Eh^3}{12(1+\nu)}\tilde{\kappa}_{12}, \tag{3.14}$$
$$\tilde{\kappa}_{12} = \frac{1}{2}(\kappa_{12} + \kappa_{21}),$$

and if we neglect the second term in the square bracket of Eq. 3.13 in comparison to the first, we may rewrite the foregoing integral as

$$\int_{\alpha_1}\int_{\alpha_2} [N_1\,\delta\epsilon_1{}^0 + \tilde{N}_{12}\,2\delta\epsilon_{12}{}^0 + N_2\,\delta\epsilon_2{}^0 + M_1\,\delta\kappa_1 + \tilde{M}_{12}\,2\delta\,\tilde{\kappa}_{12} + M_2\,\delta\kappa_2]A_1A_2\,d\alpha_1\,d\alpha_2 \tag{3.15}$$

It is appropriate to recall here that, in the theory of Chapter 2, the number of stress resultants and couples was reduced from eight to six by means of the results $N_{12} = N_{21}$ and $M_{12} = M_{21}$. In the present theory, the number of stress quantities is reduced from eight to six by means of the consideration of the rotation β_n and the definitions 3.14. To find the relevant equilibrium equations that are to be satisfied by the new set of stress resultants and couples, we note that the variation of the strain energy can now be written as (see Eqs. 3.5 and 3.15):

$$\int_{\alpha_1}\int_{\alpha_2}\Big\{N_1\,\delta\left(A_2\frac{\partial u_1}{\partial\alpha_1} + \frac{\partial A_1}{\partial\alpha_2}u_2 + \frac{A_1A_2}{R_1}w\right)$$
$$+ N_2\,\delta\left(A_1\frac{\partial u_2}{\partial\alpha_2} + \frac{\partial A_2}{\partial\alpha_1}u_1 + \frac{A_1A_2}{R_2}w\right)$$
$$+ \tilde{N}_{12}\,\delta\left(A_2\frac{\partial u_2}{\partial\alpha_1} + A_1\frac{\partial u_1}{\partial\alpha_2} - \frac{\partial A_1}{\partial\alpha_2}u_1 - \frac{\partial A_2}{\partial\alpha_1}u_2\right)$$
$$+ M_1\,\delta\left(A_2\frac{\partial\beta_1}{\partial\alpha_1} + \frac{\partial A_1}{\partial\alpha_2}\beta_2\right) + M_2\,\delta\left(A_1\frac{\partial\beta_2}{\partial\alpha_2} + \frac{\partial A_2}{\partial\alpha_1}\beta_1\right)$$
$$+ \tilde{M}_{12}\,\delta\left[A_2\frac{\partial\beta_2}{\partial\alpha_1} + A_1\frac{\partial\beta_1}{\partial\alpha_2} - \beta_1\frac{\partial A_1}{\partial\alpha_2} - \beta_2\frac{\partial A_2}{\partial\alpha_1} + \frac{1}{2}\left(\frac{1}{R_2} - \frac{1}{R_1}\right)\right.$$
$$\left.\times\left(A_2\frac{\partial u_2}{\partial\alpha_1} - A_1\frac{\partial u_1}{\partial\alpha_2} + u_2\frac{\partial A_2}{\partial\alpha_1} - u_1\frac{\partial A_1}{\partial\alpha_2}\right)\right]$$
$$+ Q_1\,\delta\left(A_2\frac{\partial w}{\partial\alpha_1} - \frac{A_1A_2}{R_1}u_1 + A_1A_2\beta_1\right)$$
$$+ Q_2\,\delta\left(A_1\frac{\partial w}{\partial\alpha_2} - \frac{A_1A_2}{R_2}u_2 + A_1A_2\beta_2\right)\Big\}\,d\alpha_1\,d\alpha_2 = 0. \tag{3.16}$$

Integration by parts then gives

$$\oint_{\alpha_2} \left\{N_1 \, \delta u_1 + \tilde{N}_{12} \, \delta u_2 + Q_1 \, \delta w + M_1 \, \delta\beta_1 + \tilde{M}_{12} \, \delta \left[\beta_2 + \frac{1}{2}\left(\frac{1}{R_2} - \frac{1}{R_1}\right) u_2\right]\right\} A_2 \, d\alpha_2$$
$$+ \oint_{\alpha_1} \left\{\tilde{N}_{12} \, \delta u_1 + N_2 \, \delta u_2 + Q_2 \, \delta w + \tilde{M}_{12} \, \delta \left[\beta_1 - \frac{1}{2}\left(\frac{1}{R_2} - \frac{1}{R_1}\right) u_1\right] + M_2 \, \delta\beta_2\right\} A_1 \, d\alpha_1$$
$$- \int_{\alpha_1} \int_{\alpha_2} \left\{[\ldots] \, \delta u_1 + [\ldots] \, \delta u_2 + [\ldots] \, \delta w + [\ldots] \, \delta\beta_1 + [\ldots] \, \delta\beta_2\right\} d\alpha_1 \, d\alpha_2 = 0. \quad (3.17)$$

Since the variations are arbitrary, their coefficients must vanish independently in order to make the entire expression 3.17 vanish. The, as yet, unspecified quantities in the square brackets contained in the area integral thus become the following equations of equilibrium:

$$\frac{\partial A_2 N_1}{\partial \alpha_1} + \frac{\partial A_1 \tilde{N}_{12}}{\partial \alpha_2} + \tilde{N}_{12} \frac{\partial A_1}{\partial \alpha_2} - N_2 \frac{\partial A_2}{\partial \alpha_1} + \frac{A_1 A_2 Q_1}{R_1} + \frac{A_1}{2} \frac{\partial}{\partial \alpha_2} \left[\left(\frac{1}{R_1} - \frac{1}{R_2}\right) \tilde{M}_{12}\right] = 0,$$

$$\frac{\partial A_2 \tilde{N}_{12}}{\partial \alpha_1} + \frac{\partial A_1 N_2}{\partial \alpha_2} + \tilde{N}_{12} \frac{\partial A_2}{\partial \alpha_1} - N_1 \frac{\partial A_1}{\partial \alpha_2} + \frac{A_1 A_2 Q_2}{R_2} + \frac{A_2}{2} \frac{\partial}{\partial \alpha_1} \left[\left(\frac{1}{R_2} - \frac{1}{R_1}\right) \tilde{M}_{12}\right] = 0, \quad (3.18)$$

$$\frac{\partial A_2 Q_1}{\partial \alpha_1} + \frac{\partial A_1 Q_2}{\partial \alpha_2} - \left(\frac{N_1}{R_1} + \frac{N_2}{R_2}\right) A_1 A_2 = 0,$$

$$\frac{\partial A_2 M_1}{\partial \alpha_1} + \frac{\partial A_1 \tilde{M}_{12}}{\partial \alpha_2} + \tilde{M}_{12} \frac{\partial A_1}{\partial \alpha_2} - M_2 \frac{\partial A_2}{\partial \alpha_1} - A_1 A_2 Q_1 = 0$$

$$\frac{\partial A_2 \tilde{M}_{12}}{\partial \alpha_1} + \frac{\partial A_1 M_2}{\partial \alpha_2} + \tilde{M}_{12} \frac{\partial A_2}{\partial \alpha_1} - M_1 \frac{\partial A_1}{\partial \alpha_2} - A_1 A_2 Q_2 = 0.$$

Thus, there are only five equations of equilibrium in Sanders' theory. As could be expected, Eqs. 3.18 reduce to Eqs. 2.71 of Chapter 2 for a flat plate, a spherical shell, or a symmetrically loaded shell of revolution.

Equation 3.17 also provides us with the natural boundary conditions that are to be used with Sanders' theory. Indeed, if we carry out the same type of partial integration as we did in Section 2.7 we find that, for the case of free edges, the boundary conditions are:

$$\begin{aligned} \frac{M_n}{R_n} + N_n &= 0 \qquad \text{or} \quad u_n = \bar{u}_n \\ \tilde{N}_{nt} + \left(\frac{3}{R_t} - \frac{1}{R_n}\right)\frac{\tilde{M}_{nt}}{2} &= 0 \qquad \text{or} \quad u_t = \bar{u}_t \\ Q_n + \frac{1}{A_t}\frac{\partial \tilde{M}_{nt}}{\partial \alpha_t} &= 0 \qquad \text{or} \quad w = \bar{w} \\ M_n &= 0 \qquad \text{or} \quad \beta_n = \bar{\beta}_n \end{aligned} \tag{3.19}$$

on an edge of constant α_n. Again we may note that, for the flat plate, spherical shell, and symmetrically loaded shell of revolution, the foregoing boundary conditions reduce to their counterparts in the theory of Chapter 2. Since free shells have been considered here, the conditions listed in Eqs. 3.19 all involve vanishing forces. In the event that the shells are not free, we should (as shown in Section 2.7) have to specify nonzero edge values of the appropriate forces. As in the previous theory, we have derived four boundary conditions per edge for the general case.

This completes the derivation of Sanders' theory. As shown in the development, the sixth equation of equilibrium has been removed from consideration. To investigate the theory for rigid body motions of a shell, we may examine the quantity $\tilde{\kappa}_{12}$ which is the counterpart in Sanders' theory of the quantity τ in Chapter 2. We recall here that

$$2\tilde{\kappa}_{12} = \frac{1}{A_1}\frac{\partial \beta_2}{\partial \alpha_1} - \frac{1}{A_1 A_2}\left(\beta_1 \frac{\partial A_1}{\partial \alpha_1} + \beta_2 \frac{\partial A_2}{\partial \alpha_1}\right) + \frac{1}{A_2}\frac{\partial \beta_1}{\partial \alpha_2} + \beta_n\left(\frac{1}{R_2} - \frac{1}{R_1}\right). \tag{3.20}$$

If, as before, we have constant rigid body rotation components ω_1, ω_2, and ω_n, and we let $\beta_1 = \omega_1$, $\beta_2 = \omega_2$, and $\beta_n = \omega_n$, then, upon substitution of the relevant relationships from Exercise 2.7 into the foregoing, we find that

$$\begin{aligned} 2\tilde{\kappa}_{12} = {} & \frac{1}{A_1}\left(\frac{1}{A_2}\frac{\partial A_1}{\partial \alpha_2}\omega_1 + \frac{A_1\omega_n}{R_1}\right) - \frac{1}{A_1A_2}\frac{\partial A_1}{\partial \alpha_2}\omega_1 - \frac{\omega_n}{R_1} \\ & + \frac{1}{A_2}\left(\frac{1}{A_1}\frac{\partial A_2}{\partial \alpha_1}\omega_2 - \frac{A_2\omega_n}{R_2}\right) - \frac{1}{A_1A_2}\frac{\partial A_2}{\partial \alpha_1}\omega_2 + \frac{\omega_n}{R_2} \equiv 0. \end{aligned} \tag{3.21}$$

Thus, it is seen that the Sanders' theory has successfully removed the inconsistencies which arose in the theory of Chapter 2.

3.3 HIGHER-ORDER APPROXIMATIONS

A second class of theories of thin elastic shells, which we shall denote as higher-order approximations, has also developed. To this grouping, we arbitrarily assign all *linear* shell theories in which one or another of Love's original postulates (except the one on small deflections) are suspended. In particular, we shall be concerned here with two representative theories which involve, in the first case, the relaxation of the thinness assumption and, in the second case, the inclusion of transverse shear and normal stress effects.

3.3*a* Theory of Flügge—Lur'e—Byrne

A theory of elastic shells in which the thinness assumption is delayed in the derivations while the rest of Love's postulates are retained was independently derived by Flügge[8], Lur'e,[9] and Byrne[10] and will now be developed.

In deriving the Flügge–Lur'e–Byrne theory, the first point of departure from the derivation in Chapter 2 occurs in the reduction of the strain-displacement relations which are given for the general case by Eqs. 2.14. If the assumption on the preservation of the normal element is retained but ζ/R_i is not neglected with respect to unity, Eqs. 2.14 reduce upon introduction of Eqs. 2.15 to

$$\begin{aligned}
\epsilon_n &= \gamma_{1n} = \gamma_{2n} = 0,\\
\epsilon_1 &= \frac{1}{1+\zeta/R_1}(\epsilon_1{}^0 + \zeta\kappa_1),\\
\epsilon_2 &= \frac{1}{1+\zeta/R_2}(\epsilon_2{}^0 + \zeta\kappa_2),\\
\gamma_{12} &= \frac{1}{(1+\zeta/R_1)(1+\zeta/R_2)}\\
&\quad\times\left\{\gamma_{12}{}^0\left(1-\frac{\zeta^2}{R_1R_2}\right) + 2\zeta\kappa_{12}{}^0\left[1+\frac{\zeta}{2}\left(\frac{1}{R_1}+\frac{1}{R_2}\right)\right]\right\},
\end{aligned} \tag{3.22}$$

where $\epsilon_1{}^0$, $\epsilon_2{}^0$ κ_1, κ_2, $\gamma_{12}{}^0$, and τ are as defined by Eqs. 2.19 and

$$\begin{aligned}
2\kappa_{12}{}^0 &= \tau + \frac{\beta_2{}^0}{R_1} + \frac{\beta_1{}^0}{R_2},\\
\beta_1{}^0 &= \frac{1}{A_1}\frac{\partial u_2}{\partial \alpha_1} - \frac{u_1}{A_1A_2}\frac{\partial A_1}{\partial \alpha_2},\\
\beta_2{}^0 &= \frac{1}{A_2}\frac{\partial u_1}{\partial \alpha_2} - \frac{u_2}{A_1A_2}\frac{\partial A_2}{\partial \alpha_1},\\
\gamma_{12}{}^0 &= \beta_1{}^0 + \beta_2{}^0.
\end{aligned} \tag{3.23}$$

[8] Flügge, W., *Statik und Dynamik der Schalen*, Berlin: Julius Springer Verlag (1934).
[9] Lur'e, A. I., "The General Theory of Thin Elastic Shells," *Prikl. Mat. Mekh.*, **4**, 7 (1940).
[10] Byrne, R., "Theory of Small Deformations of a Thin Elastic Shell," University of California (Los Angeles) Publications in Mathematics, N. S., **2**, 103–152 (1944).

As could be expected, when ζ/R_i is neglected with respect to unity, Eqs. 3.22 reduce to Eqs. 2.18.

To derive new expressions for the stress resultants and stress couples, we first substitute the strain relations (Eqs. 3.22) into the stress–strain relations (Eqs. 2.20). Assuming, for simplicity, that thermal effects are neglected and that the shell material is isotropic, the resulting stress–strain relations are:

$$\sigma_1 = \frac{E}{1-\nu^2}\left\{\frac{\epsilon_1{}^0 + \zeta\kappa_1}{1+\zeta/R_1} + \nu\frac{\epsilon_2{}^0 + \zeta\kappa_2}{1+\zeta/R_2}\right\},$$

$$\sigma_2 = \frac{E}{1-\nu^2}\left\{\frac{\epsilon_2{}^0 + \zeta\kappa_2}{1+\zeta/R_2} + \nu\frac{\epsilon_1{}^0 + \zeta\kappa_1}{1+\zeta/R_1}\right\},$$

$$\tau_{12} = G\left\{\frac{\gamma_{12}{}^0(1-\zeta^2/R_1R_2) + 2\kappa_{12}{}^0\zeta[1+(1/R_1+1/R_2)\zeta/2]}{(1+\zeta/R_1)(1+\zeta/R_2)}\right\}. \qquad (3.24)$$

These stress expressions are now substituted into the definitions of the stress resultants and couples given by Eqs. 2.23 (in which, incidentally, the thinness assumption had not been made in anticipation of the present discussion). This yields the expressions

$$N_1 = \int_{-h/2}^{h/2} \frac{E}{1-\nu^2}\left\{\frac{(1+\zeta/R_2)}{(1+\zeta/R_1)}(\epsilon_1{}^0 + \zeta\kappa_1) + \nu(\epsilon_2{}^0 + \zeta\kappa_2)\right\} d\zeta,$$

$$N_{12} = \int_{-h/2}^{h/2} G\left\{\frac{\gamma_{12}{}^0(1-\zeta^2/R_1R_2) + 2\kappa_{12}{}^0\zeta[1+\zeta(1/R_1+1/R_2)/2]}{1+\zeta/R_1}\right\} d\zeta,$$

$$M_1 = \int_{-h/2}^{h/2} \frac{E}{1-\nu^2}\left\{\frac{1+\zeta/R_2}{1+\zeta/R_1}(\epsilon_1{}^0 + \zeta\kappa_1) + \nu(\epsilon_2{}^0 + \nu\kappa_2)\right\} \zeta\, d\zeta, \qquad (3.25)$$

$$M_{12} = \int_{-h/2}^{h/2} G\left\{\frac{\gamma_{12}{}^0(1-\zeta^2/R_1R_2) + 2\kappa_{12}{}^0\zeta[1+\zeta(1/R_1+1/R_2)/2]}{1+\zeta/R_1}\right\} \zeta\, d\zeta,$$

and four more expressions with the subscripts interchanged. The integrations indicated in the foregoing expressions are extremely cumbersome to perform, thus, it is appropriate at this point to make the assumption that ζ/R_i is less than unity so that expansions of the type

$$\left(1 + \frac{\zeta}{R_i}\right)^{-1} \cong 1 - \frac{\zeta}{R_i} + \left(\frac{\zeta}{R_i}\right)^2 - \cdots \qquad (3.26)$$

may be carried out. Notice that this expansion requires only that $(\zeta/R_i)^2 < 1$, and that, therefore, this is not as tight a restriction on the ratio ζ/R_i as was Love's thinness assumption. If the foregoing expansion is substituted into expressions of the type 3.25, and if, throughout the ensuing analysis, terms of higher order than the third in the thickness are discarded, the following expressions for the stress resultants and couples are obtained:

$$
\begin{aligned}
N_1 &= K\left[\epsilon_1{}^0 + \nu\epsilon_2{}^0 - \frac{h^2}{12}\left(\frac{1}{R_1} - \frac{1}{R_2}\right)\left(\kappa_1 - \frac{\epsilon_1{}^0}{R_1}\right)\right],\\
N_{12} &= Gh\left[\gamma_{12}{}^0 - \frac{h^2}{12}\left(\frac{1}{R_1} - \frac{1}{R_2}\right)\left(\kappa_{12}{}^0 - \frac{\gamma_{12}{}^0}{R_1}\right)\right],\\
M_1 &= D\left[\kappa_1 + \nu\kappa_2 - \left(\frac{1}{R_1} - \frac{1}{R_2}\right)\epsilon_1{}^0\right],\\
M_{12} &= \frac{Gh^3}{12}\left[\tau - \left(\frac{1}{R_1} - \frac{1}{R_2}\right)\beta_1{}^0\right],
\end{aligned}
\tag{3.27}
$$

along with four additional expressions in which the subscripts are interchanged.

A comparison of Eqs. 3.27 with Eqs. 2.27 indicates that the result of the modified thinness assumption is the appearance of several additional terms beyond those of the theory of Chapter 2. These terms, however, disappear when the system of equations is applied to the consideration of spherical shells and flat plates. It is also to be noted that, in the present theory, $N_{12} \neq N_{21}$ and $M_{12} \neq M_{21}$ in contrast to the theory in Chapter 2, where these expressions were equalities.

The derivation of the equations of motion and of the natural boundary conditions is unaffected by the thinness assumption and, therefore, the equations derived in Sections 2.6*b* and 2.7 carry over to the present case. It is interesting to point out, however, that although the Flügge–Lur'e–Byrne theory involves all six of the equilibrium equations of Chapter 2, no problems are encountered in connection with the sixth equation since N_{12}, N_{21}, M_{12}, and M_{21} from Eqs. 3.27 satisfy that equation identically. Furthermore, it can be shown (see the Exercises) that the strains resulting from rigid body motions vanish for this theory.

3.3*b* Incorporation of Transverse Shear and Normal Stress Effects

Another class of shell theories has arisen in which the assumptions on the vanishing of the transverse normal stresses and on the preservation of the normal element are abandoned. Such theories were proposed, for example, by Hildebrand, Reissner and Thomas[4], by Reissner,[11] and by Naghdi[3,12]. In this section, we shall outline the derivation proposed by Hildebrand, Reissner, and Thomas[4] and will include certain refinements which were added by Naghdi.[12]

[11] Reissner, E., "Stress Strain Relations in the Theory of Thin Elastic Shells," *J. Math. Phys.*, **31**, 109–119 (1952).

[12] Naghdi, P. M., "On the Theory of Thin Elastic Shells," *Q. Appl. Math.*, **14**, 369–380 (1957).

The derivation proceeds in the same fashion as did the derivation of the theory in Chapter 2 with several basic changes, of which the most important involves the replacement of Eqs. 2.15 by the following:

$$\begin{aligned} U_1(\alpha_1, \alpha_2, \zeta) &= u_1(\alpha_1, \alpha_2) + \zeta\beta_1(\alpha_1, \alpha_2), \\ U_2(\alpha_1, \alpha_2, \zeta) &= u_2(\alpha_1, \alpha_2) + \zeta\beta_2(\alpha_1, \alpha_2), \\ W(\alpha_1, \alpha_2, \zeta) &= w(\alpha_1, \alpha_2) + \zeta w'(\alpha_1, \alpha_2) + \tfrac{1}{2}\zeta^2 w''(\alpha_1, \alpha_2). \end{aligned} \tag{3.28}$$

Here the additional terms w' and w'' represent contributions to a nonvanishing transverse normal strain. Quadratic terms could also be added to the U_i; however, these have been found[4] to lead to a negligible improvement over the theory resulting from Eqs. 3.28. With the assumed forms (Eqs. 3.28), the six strain-displacement equations of the present theory become

$$\begin{aligned} \epsilon_1 &= \frac{1}{1 + \zeta/R_1}(\epsilon_1^0 + \zeta\epsilon_1' + \tfrac{1}{2}\zeta^2\epsilon_1''), \\ \epsilon_2 &= \frac{1}{1 + \zeta/R_2}(\epsilon_2^0 + \zeta\epsilon_2' + \tfrac{1}{2}\zeta^2\epsilon_2''), \\ \epsilon_n &= w' + \zeta w'', \\ \gamma_{12} &= \frac{1}{1 + \zeta/R_1}(\beta_1^0 + \zeta\beta_1') + \frac{1}{1 + \zeta/R_2}(\beta_2^0 + \zeta\beta_2'), \\ \gamma_{1n} &= \frac{1}{1 + \zeta/R_1}(\mu_1^0 + \zeta\mu_1' + \tfrac{1}{2}\zeta^2\mu_1''), \\ \gamma_{2n} &= \frac{1}{1 + \zeta/R_2}(\mu_2^0 + \zeta\mu_2' + \tfrac{1}{2}\zeta^2\mu_2''), \end{aligned} \tag{3.29}$$

where

$$\begin{aligned} \epsilon_1' &= \kappa_1 + \frac{w'}{R_1}, \qquad \epsilon_2' = \kappa_2 + \frac{w'}{R_2}, \\ \epsilon_1'' &= \frac{w''}{R_1}, \qquad \epsilon_2'' = \frac{w''}{R_2}, \\ \beta_1' &= \frac{1}{A_1}\frac{\partial \beta_2}{\partial \alpha_1} - \frac{\beta_1}{A_1 A_2}\frac{\partial A_1}{\partial \alpha_2}, \qquad \beta_2' = \frac{1}{A_2}\frac{\partial \beta_1}{\partial \alpha_2} - \frac{\beta_2}{A_1 A_2}\frac{\partial A_2}{\partial \alpha_1}, \\ \mu_1^0 &= \frac{1}{A_1}\frac{\partial w}{\partial \alpha_1} - \frac{u_1}{R_1} + \beta_1, \\ \mu_2^0 &= \frac{1}{A_2}\frac{\partial w}{\partial \alpha_2} - \frac{u_2}{R_2} + \beta_2, \\ \mu_1' &= \frac{1}{A_1}\frac{\partial w'}{\partial \alpha_1}, \qquad \mu_2' = \frac{1}{A_2}\frac{\partial w'}{\partial \alpha_2}, \\ \mu_1'' &= \frac{1}{A_1}\frac{\partial w''}{\partial \alpha_1}, \qquad \mu_2'' = \frac{1}{A_2}\frac{\partial w''}{\partial \alpha_2}, \end{aligned} \tag{3.29a}$$

and $\epsilon_1{}^0$, ϵ_2, κ_1, κ_2 are given by Eqs. 2.19 while $\beta_1{}^0$ and $\beta_2{}^0$ are given by Eqs. 3.23. Notice also that $\beta_1' + \beta_2' = \tau$. A second basic change represented by the present theory is that all six strain components are non-vanishing. Thus, the rotations β_1 and β_2 can no longer be expressed in the simple forms represented by Eqs. 2.16 which are appropriate only when the transverse shearing strains vanish.

The stress resultants and couples are now found, as before, by suitable integrations of the stress distributions over the thickness of the shell. However, to clarify the role of the transverse stress effects, it is well to define a material with a special type of orthotropy for which the elastic properties in the α_1 and α_2 directions are the same but different from those in the direction of the normal to the reference surface. Thus, in Eqs. 2.1, we choose

$$
\begin{aligned}
&E_1 = E_2 = E, \qquad \nu_{12} = \nu_{21} = \nu, \\
&\nu_{1n} = \nu_{2n} = \nu_n, \qquad G_{1n} = G_{2n} = G_n, \qquad G_{12} = G,
\end{aligned}
\tag{3.30}
$$

and, therefore, Eqs. 2.1 become, in the absence of thermal effects,

$$
\begin{aligned}
\epsilon_1 &= \frac{\sigma_1 - \nu\sigma_2}{E} - \frac{\nu_n}{E_n}\sigma_n, \\
\epsilon_2 &= \frac{\sigma_2 - \nu\sigma_1}{E} - \frac{\nu_n}{E_n}\sigma_n, \\
\epsilon_n &= \frac{\sigma_n}{E_n} - \frac{\nu_n}{E_n}(\sigma_2 + \sigma_1), \\
\gamma_{12} &= \frac{\tau_{12}}{G}, \qquad \gamma_{1n} = \frac{\tau_{1n}}{G_n}, \qquad \gamma_{2n} = \frac{\tau_{2n}}{G_n}.
\end{aligned}
\tag{3.31}
$$

The first three of the above may be solved for the normal stresses with the result

$$
\begin{aligned}
\sigma_1 &= \frac{\bar{E}}{1 - \nu^2}[(1 - \bar{\nu}^2)\epsilon_1 + (\nu + \bar{\nu}^2)\epsilon_2 + \nu_n(1 + \nu)\epsilon_n], \\
\sigma_2 &= \frac{\bar{E}}{1 - \nu^2}[(1 - \bar{\nu}^2)\epsilon_2 + (\nu + \bar{\nu}^2)\epsilon_1 + \nu_n(1 + \nu)\epsilon_n], \\
\sigma_n &= \bar{E}\left[\frac{\nu_n}{1 - \nu}(\epsilon_1 + \epsilon_2) + \frac{E_n}{E}\epsilon_n\right],
\end{aligned}
\tag{3.32}
$$

where

$$
\bar{\nu} = \sqrt{\frac{E}{E_n}}\,\nu_n, \qquad \bar{E} = \frac{1 - \nu}{1 - \nu - 2\bar{\nu}^2}E.
$$

Notice that if we select a material which is rigid in the direction of the normal, that is, $1/E_n = 1/G_n = \nu_n = 0$, we have $\bar{\nu} = 0$, $\bar{E} = E$ and the stress–strain relations reduce to those of Chapter 2 (see our remarks at the end of Section 2.5). Since there are now six nonvanishing stress components, since linear and quadratic terms have been added to the normal deflection function, and since transverse normal stresses are not being neglected, we shall have later need of the following additional stress resultants:

$$\begin{Bmatrix} S_i \\ P_i \\ T_i \\ A \\ B \end{Bmatrix} = \int_{-h/2}^{h/2} \begin{Bmatrix} \tau_{in}\zeta(1 + \zeta/R_j) \\ \sigma_i(\zeta^2/2)(1 + \zeta/R_j) \\ \tau_{in}(\zeta^2/2)(1 + \zeta/R_j) \\ \sigma_n(1 + \zeta/R_1)(1 + \zeta/R_2) \\ \sigma_n(1 + \zeta/R_1)(1 + \zeta/R_2)\zeta \end{Bmatrix} d\zeta, \qquad \begin{matrix} i, j = 1, 2 \\ i \neq j \end{matrix} \tag{3.33}$$

If the stress–strain relations (Eqs. 3.32) are substituted into Eqs. 2.23 and 3.33, the following relationships between the stress resultants and couples and the reference surface strains are obtained:

$$\begin{aligned}
N_1 &= \frac{\bar{E}h}{1 - \nu^2}\Big\{[(1 - \bar{\nu}^2)\epsilon_1{}^0 + (\nu + \bar{\nu}^2)\epsilon_2{}^0 + \nu_n(1 + \nu)w'] \\
&\quad + \frac{h^2}{24}\left[(1 - \bar{\nu}^2)\epsilon_1{}'' + (\nu + \bar{\nu}^2)\epsilon_2{}'' + 2\nu_n(1 + \nu)\frac{w''}{R_2}\right] \\
&\quad + \left(\frac{1}{R_1} - \frac{1}{R_2}\right)\frac{h^2}{12}(1 - \bar{\nu}^2)\left[\frac{\epsilon_1{}^0}{R_1} - \epsilon_1{}' + \frac{3h^2}{40R_1}\epsilon_1{}''\right]\Big\}, \\
N_{12} &= Gh\left\{\gamma_{12}{}^0 + \left(\frac{1}{R_1} - \frac{1}{R_2}\right)\frac{h^2}{12}\left[\frac{\beta_1{}^0}{R_1} - \beta_1{}'\right]\right\}, \\
M_1 &= \frac{\bar{E}h^3}{12(1 - \nu^2)}\Big\{\Big[(1 - \bar{\nu}^2)\epsilon_1{}' + (\nu + \bar{\nu}^2)\epsilon_2{}' \\
&\quad + \nu_n(1 + \nu)\left(w'' + \frac{w'}{R_2}\right)\Big] \\
&\quad - \left(\frac{1}{R_1} - \frac{1}{R_2}\right)(1 - \bar{\nu}^2)\left[\epsilon_1{}^0 - \frac{3h^2}{20}\left(\frac{\epsilon_1{}'}{R_1} - \frac{\epsilon_1{}''}{2}\right)\right]\Big\}, \\
M_{12} &= \frac{Gh^3}{12}\left\{\tau - \left(\frac{1}{R_1} - \frac{1}{R_2}\right)\left[\beta_1{}^0 - \frac{3h^2}{20}\frac{\beta_1{}'}{R_1}\right]\right\}, \\
Q_1 &= G_n h\Big\{\mu_1{}^0 + \frac{h^2}{24}\mu_1{}'' \\
&\quad + \left(\frac{1}{R_1} - \frac{1}{R_2}\right)\frac{h^2}{12}\left[\frac{\mu_1{}^0}{R_1} - \mu_1{}' + \frac{3h^2}{40R_1}\mu_1{}''\right]\Big\}, \\
S_1 &= \frac{G_n h^3}{12}\left\{\mu_1{}' - \left(\frac{1}{R_1} - \frac{1}{R_2}\right)\left[\mu_1{}^0 - \frac{3h^2}{20}\left(\frac{\mu_1{}'}{R_1} - \frac{\mu_1{}''}{2}\right)\right]\right\}, \qquad (3.34) \\
T_1 &= \frac{G_n h^3}{24}\Big\{\mu_1{}^0 + \frac{3h^2}{40}\mu_1{}'' \\
&\quad + \left(\frac{1}{R_1} - \frac{1}{R_2}\right)\frac{3h^2}{20}\left[\frac{\mu_1{}^0}{R_1} - \mu_1{}' + \frac{5h^2}{56R_1}\mu_1{}''\right]\Big\},
\end{aligned}$$

$$P_1 = \frac{\bar{E}h^3}{12(1-\nu^2)}\left\{[(1-\bar{\nu}^2)\epsilon_1{}^0 + (\nu+\bar{\nu}^2)\epsilon_2{}^0 + \nu_n(1+\nu)w'] + \frac{3h^2}{40}\left[(1-\bar{\nu}^2)\epsilon_1{}'' + (\bar{\nu}^2+\nu)\epsilon_2{}'' + 2\nu_n(1+\nu)\frac{w''}{R_2}\right] + \left(\frac{1}{R_1}-\frac{1}{R_2}\right)\frac{3h^2}{20}(1-\bar{\nu}^2) \times \left[\frac{\epsilon_1{}^0}{R_1} - \epsilon_1{}' + \frac{5h^2}{56R_1}\epsilon_1{}''\right]\right\},$$

An additional eight expressions are obtained by interchanging the subscripts 1 and 2. In deriving the above, we have made use of the following approximate expressions which are valid for $(\zeta/R_i)^2 < 1$:

$$\int_{-h/2}^{h/2} \frac{1+\zeta/R_2}{1+\zeta/R_1}\,d\zeta = h\left[1 + \left(\frac{1}{R_1}-\frac{1}{R_2}\right)\frac{h^2}{12R_1}\right],$$
$$\int_{-h/2}^{h/2} \frac{1+\zeta/R_2}{1+\zeta/R_1}\,\zeta\,d\zeta = -\left(\frac{1}{R_1}-\frac{1}{R_2}\right)\frac{h^3}{12},$$
$$\int_{-h/2}^{h/2} \frac{1+\zeta/R_2}{1+\zeta/R_1}\,\zeta^2\,d\zeta = \frac{h^3}{12}\left[1 + \left(\frac{1}{R_1}-\frac{1}{R_2}\right)\frac{3h^2}{20R_1}\right], \tag{3.35}$$
$$\int_{-h/2}^{h/2} \frac{1+\zeta/R_2}{1+\zeta/R_1}\,\zeta^3\,d\zeta = -\left(\frac{1}{R_1}-\frac{1}{R_2}\right)\frac{h^5}{80},$$
$$\int_{-h/2}^{h/2} \frac{1+\zeta/R_2}{1+\zeta/R_1}\,\zeta^4\,d\zeta = \frac{h^5}{80}\left[1 + \left(\frac{1}{R_1}-\frac{1}{R_2}\right)\frac{5h^2}{28R_1}\right],$$

and similar expressions with the subscripts interchanged. The foregoing were obtained by using expansions of the type 3.26 which were used by Flügge–Lur'e–Byrne.

We now turn to the derivation of the equations of motion which, with the exception of some new quantities, proceeds in the same fashion as the derivation contained in Section 2.6*b*. To begin, we consider the work done by the surface forces which, since we are interested in a higher order theory, we shall no longer replace by their static equivalents on the reference surface. Thus, we now write

$$W_s = \int_{\alpha_1}\int_{\alpha_2}\left[(q_1{}^+U_1{}^+ + q_2{}^+U_2{}^+ - q_n{}^+W^+)\left(1+\frac{h}{2R_1}\right)\left(1+\frac{h}{2R_2}\right) + (q_1{}^-U_1{}^- + q_2{}^-U_2{}^- - q_n{}^-W^-) \times \left(1-\frac{h}{2R_1}\right)\left(1-\frac{h}{2R_2}\right)\right] A_1A_2\,d\alpha_1\,d\alpha_2, \tag{3.36}$$

where the superscripts + and − identify the appropriate quantities at the outer and inner surfaces of the shell, respectively. If Eqs. 3.28 are substituted into the above, the expression becomes

$$W_s = \int_{\alpha_1}\int_{\alpha_2} (q_1u_1 + q_2u_2 - q_nw + m_1\beta_1 + m_2\beta_2 - m_nw' - \tfrac{1}{8}h^2q_nw'')A_1A_2\, d\alpha_1\, d\alpha_2 \quad (3.37)$$

where

$$q_i = q_i^+\left(1 + \frac{h}{2R_1}\right)\left(1 + \frac{h}{2R_2}\right) + q_i^-\left(1 - \frac{h}{2R_1}\right)\left(1 - \frac{h}{2R_2}\right),$$

$$m_i = \frac{h}{2}\left[q_i^+\left(1 + \frac{h}{2R_1}\right)\left(1 + \frac{h}{2R_2}\right) - q_i^-\left(1 - \frac{h}{2R_1}\right)\left(1 - \frac{h}{2R_2}\right)\right], \quad i = 1, 2, n. \quad (3.37a)$$

and the m_i are the moments of the surface forces about the reference surface. Recall that in Chapter 2 these were neglected. The work of the edge forces is determined by using the definitions 2.47 and 2.48 with the assumed deflections (Eqs.3.28). This gives, upon taking into account the definitions (3.33) of the new stress resultants,

$$W_{e1} = \int_{\alpha_2}\int_{\zeta} (\bar{N}_1u_1 + \bar{N}_{12}u_2 + \bar{Q}_1w + \bar{M}_1\beta_1 + \bar{M}_{12}\beta_2 + \bar{S}_1w' + \bar{T}_1w'')A_2\, d\alpha_2,$$

$$W_{e2} = \int_{\alpha_1}\int_{\zeta} (\bar{N}_{21}u_1 + \bar{N}_2u_2 + \bar{Q}_2w + \bar{M}_{21}\beta_1 + \bar{M}_2\beta_2 + S_2w' + T_2w'')A_1\, d\alpha_1. \quad (3.38)$$

The kinetic energy associated with the motion of the shell is obtained by substituting the assumed deflection functions (Eqs. 3.28) into the kinetic energy expression (Eq. 2.43) with the result that

$$K = \frac{\rho}{2}\int_{\alpha_1}\int_{\alpha_2}\int_{\zeta} [(\dot{u}_1 + \zeta\dot{\beta}_1)^2 + (\dot{u}_2 + \zeta\dot{\beta}_2)^2 + (\dot{w} + \zeta\dot{w}' + \tfrac{1}{2}\zeta^2\dot{w}'')^2] \times (1 + \zeta/R_1)(1 + \zeta/R_2)A_1A_2\, d\alpha_1\, d\alpha_2. \quad (3.39)$$

Finally, the strain energy is determined from Eq. 2.52 with contributions from all of the stresses and strains, or

$$U = \int_{\alpha_1}\int_{\alpha_2}\int_{\zeta} (\sigma_1\epsilon_1 + \sigma_2\epsilon_2 + \sigma_n\epsilon_n + \gamma_{12}\tau_{12} + \gamma_{1n}\tau_{1n} + \gamma_{2n}\tau_{2n})A_1A_2(1 + \zeta/R_1)(1 + \zeta/R_2)\, d\alpha_1\, d\alpha_2. \quad (3.40)$$

Hamilton's principle is now applied to the problem at hand by substituting the contributions from Eqs. 3.37, 3.38, 3.39, and 3.40 into Eq. 2.53. By proceeding in exactly the same manner as we did in Section 2.6*b*, we arrive, without giving the details, at the following variational equation which replaces Eq. 2.70 of the former theory:

$$\int_{t_0}^{t_1}\int_{\alpha_1}\int_{\alpha_2}\left\{\left(\frac{\partial A_2N_1}{\partial\alpha_1}+\frac{\partial A_1N_{21}}{\partial\alpha_2}+N_{12}\frac{\partial A_1}{\partial\alpha_2}-N_2\frac{\partial A_2}{\partial\alpha_1}+\frac{Q_1A_1A_2}{R_1}\right.\right.$$
$$+A_1A_2\left(q_1-\rho h\left[\left(1+\frac{h^2}{12R_1R_2}\right)\ddot{u}_1\right.\right.$$
$$\left.\left.\left.+\frac{h^2}{12}\left(\frac{1}{R_1}+\frac{1}{R_2}\right)\ddot{\beta}_1\right]\right)\right]\delta u_1$$
$$+\left[\frac{\partial A_2N_{12}}{\partial\alpha_1}+\frac{\partial A_1N_2}{\partial\alpha_2}+N_{21}\frac{\partial A_2}{\partial\alpha_1}-N_1\frac{\partial A_1}{\partial\alpha_2}+\frac{Q_2A_1A_2}{R_2}\right.$$
$$+A_1A_2\left(q_2-\rho h\left[\left(1+\frac{h^2}{12R_1R_2}\right)\ddot{u}_2\right.\right.$$
$$\left.\left.\left.+\frac{h^2}{12}\left(\frac{1}{R_1}+\frac{1}{R_2}\right)\ddot{\beta}_2\right]\right)\right]\delta u_2$$
$$+\left[\frac{\partial A_2Q_1}{\partial\alpha_1}+\frac{\partial A_1Q_2}{\partial\alpha_2}-A_1A_2\left(\frac{N_1}{R_1}+\frac{N_2}{R_2}\right)\right.$$
$$-A_1A_2\left(q_n+\rho h\left[\left(1+\frac{h^2}{12R_1R_2}\right)\ddot{w}\right.\right.$$
$$\left.\left.\left.+\frac{h^2}{12}\left(\frac{1}{R_1}+\frac{1}{R_2}\right)\ddot{w}'+\frac{h^2}{24}\left(1+\frac{3h^2}{20R_1R_2}\right)\ddot{w}''\right]\right)\right]\delta w$$
$$+\left[\frac{\partial A_2M_1}{\partial\alpha_1}+\frac{\partial A_1M_{21}}{\partial\alpha_2}+M_{12}\frac{\partial A_1}{\partial\alpha_2}-M_2\frac{\partial A_2}{\partial\alpha_1}-Q_1A_1A_2\right.$$
$$+A_1A_2\left(m_1-\frac{\rho h^3}{12}\left[\left(\frac{1}{R_1}+\frac{1}{R_2}\right)\ddot{u}_1\right.\right.$$
$$\left.\left.\left.+\left(1+\frac{3h^2}{20R_1R_2}\right)\ddot{\beta}_1\right]\right)\right]\delta\beta_1$$
$$+\left[\frac{\partial A_2M_{12}}{\partial\alpha_1}+\frac{\partial A_1M_2}{\partial\alpha_2}+M_{21}\frac{\partial A_2}{\partial\alpha_1}-M_1\frac{\partial A_1}{\partial\alpha_2}-Q_2A_1A_2\right.$$
$$+A_1A_2\left(m_2-\frac{\rho h^3}{12}\left[\left(\frac{1}{R_1}+\frac{1}{R_2}\right)\ddot{u}_2\right.\right.$$
$$\left.\left.\left.+\left(1+\frac{3h^2}{20R_1R_2}\right)\ddot{\beta}_2\right]\right)\right]\delta\beta_2$$
$$+\left[\frac{\partial A_2\,S_1}{\partial\alpha_1}+\frac{\partial A_1\,S_2}{\partial\alpha_2}-\left(\frac{M_1}{R_1}+\frac{M_2}{R_2}\right)A_1A_2-AA_1A_2\right.$$
$$+A_1A_2\left(-m_n+\frac{\rho h^3}{12}\left[\left(\frac{1}{R_1}+\frac{1}{R_2}\right)\ddot{w}+\left(1+\frac{3h^2}{20R_1R_2}\right)\ddot{w}'\right.\right.$$
$$\left.\left.\left.+\frac{3h^2}{40}\left(\frac{1}{R_1}+\frac{1}{R_2}\right)\ddot{w}''\right]\right)\right]\delta w'$$
$$+\left[\frac{\partial A_2T_1}{\partial\alpha_1}+\frac{\partial A_1T_2}{\partial\alpha_2}-A_1A_2\left(\frac{P_1}{R_1}+\frac{P_2}{R_2}\right)-BA_1A_2\right.$$

$$+ A_1A_2\left(-\frac{h^2q_n}{8} + \frac{\rho h^3}{24}\left[\left(1 + \frac{3h^2}{20R_1R_2}\right)\ddot{w} + \frac{3}{20}\left(\frac{1}{R_1} + \frac{1}{R_2}\right)\ddot{w}' + \frac{3h^2}{40}\left(1 + \frac{5h^2}{28R_1R_2}\right)\ddot{w}''\right]\right)\right] \delta w''\bigg\} \, d\alpha_1 \, d\alpha_2 \, dt$$

$$+ \int_{t_0}^{t_1}\oint_{\alpha_1} [(\overline{N}_{21} - N_{21})\,\delta u_1 + (\overline{N}_2 - N_2)\,\delta u_2 + (\overline{Q}_2 - Q_2)\,\delta w + (\overline{M}_{21} - M_{21})\,\delta\beta_1 + (\overline{M}_2 - M_2)\,\delta\beta_2 + (\overline{S}_2 - S_2)\,\delta w' + (\overline{T}_2 - T_2)\,\delta w'']A_1\,d\alpha_1\,dt$$

$$+ \int_{t_0}^{t_1}\oint_{\alpha_2} [(\overline{N}_1 - N_1)\,\delta u_1 + (\overline{N}_{12} - N_{12})\,\delta u_2 + (\overline{Q}_1 - Q_1)\,\delta w + (\overline{M}_1 - M_1)\,\delta\beta_1 + (\overline{M}_{12} - M_{12})\,\delta\beta_2 + (\overline{S}_1 - S_1)\,\delta w' + (\overline{T}_1 - T_1)\,\delta w'']A_2\,d\alpha_2\,dt = 0. \quad (3.41)$$

The foregoing equation will be an identity only if each of the coefficients of the arbitrary variations vanishes. Thus we are led, from the coefficients in the surface integral, to the following equations of motion:

$$\frac{\partial A_2N_1}{\partial\alpha_1} + \frac{\partial A_1N_{21}}{\partial\alpha_2} + N_{12}\frac{\partial A_1}{\partial\alpha_2} - N_2\frac{\partial A_2}{\partial\alpha_1} + \frac{Q_1A_1A_2}{R_1} + A_1A_2\left[q_1 - \rho h\left\{\left(1 + \frac{h^2}{12R_1R_2}\right)\ddot{u}_1 + \frac{h^2}{12}\left(\frac{1}{R_1} + \frac{1}{R_2}\right)\ddot{\beta}_1\right\}\right] = 0,$$

$$\frac{\partial A_2N_{12}}{\partial\alpha_1} + \frac{\partial A_1N_2}{\partial\alpha_2} + N_{21}\frac{\partial A_2}{\partial\alpha_1} - N_1\frac{\partial A_1}{\partial\alpha_2} + \frac{Q_2A_1A_2}{R_2} + A_1A_2\left[q_2 - \rho h\left\{\left(1 + \frac{h^2}{12R_1R_2}\right)\ddot{u}_2 + \frac{h^2}{12}\left(\frac{1}{R_1} + \frac{1}{R_2}\right)\ddot{\beta}_2\right\}\right] = 0,$$

$$\frac{\partial A_2Q_1}{\partial\alpha_1} + \frac{\partial A_1Q_2}{\partial\alpha_2} - A_1A_2\left(\frac{N_1}{R_1} + \frac{N_2}{R_2}\right) - A_1A_2\left[q_n + \rho h\left\{\left(1 + \frac{h^2}{12R_1R_2}\right)\ddot{w} + \frac{h^2}{12}\left(\frac{1}{R_1} + \frac{1}{R_2}\right)\ddot{w}' + \frac{h^2}{24}\left(1 + \frac{3h^2}{20R_1R_2}\right)\ddot{w}''\right\}\right] = 0,$$

$$\frac{\partial A_2M_1}{\partial\alpha_1} + \frac{\partial A_1M_{21}}{\partial\alpha_2} + M_{12}\frac{\partial A_1}{\partial\alpha_2} - M_2\frac{\partial A_2}{\partial\alpha_1} - Q_1A_1A_2 + A_1A_2\left[m_1 - \frac{\rho h^3}{12}\left\{\left(\frac{1}{R_1} + \frac{1}{R_2}\right)\ddot{u}_1 + \left(1 + \frac{3h^2}{20R_1R_2}\right)\ddot{\beta}_1\right\}\right] = 0, \quad (3.42)$$

$$\frac{\partial A_2M_{12}}{\partial\alpha_1} + \frac{\partial A_1M_2}{\partial\alpha_2} + M_{21}\frac{\partial A_2}{\partial\alpha_1} - M_1\frac{\partial A_1}{\partial\alpha_2} - Q_2A_1A_2 + A_1A_2\left[m_2 - \frac{\rho h^3}{12}\left\{\left(\frac{1}{R_1} + \frac{1}{R_2}\right)\ddot{u}_2 + \left(1 + \frac{3h^2}{20R_1R_2}\right)\ddot{\beta}_2\right\}\right] = 0,$$

$$\frac{\partial A_2 S_1}{\partial \alpha_1} + \frac{\partial A_1 S_2}{\partial \alpha_2} - \left(\frac{M_1}{R_1} + \frac{M_2}{R_2}\right) A_1 A_2 - A A_1 A_2$$
$$+ A_1 A_2 \left[-m_n + \frac{\rho h^3}{12} \left\{ \left(\frac{1}{R_1} + \frac{1}{R_2}\right) \ddot{w} + \left(1 + \frac{3h^2}{20 R_1 R_2}\right) \ddot{w}' \right.\right.$$
$$\left.\left. + \frac{3h^2}{40} \left(\frac{1}{R_1} + \frac{1}{R_2}\right) \ddot{w}'' \right\} \right] = 0,$$

$$\frac{\partial A_2 T_1}{\partial \alpha_1} + \frac{\partial A_1 T_2}{\partial \alpha_2} - \left(\frac{P_1}{R_1} + \frac{P_2}{R_2}\right) A_1 A_2 - B A_1 A_2$$
$$+ A_1 A_2 \left[-\frac{h^2 q_n}{8} + \frac{\rho h^3}{24} \left\{ \left(1 + \frac{3h^2}{20 R_1 R_2}\right) \ddot{w} + \frac{3}{20} \left(\frac{1}{R_1} + \frac{1}{R_2}\right) \ddot{w}' \right.\right.$$
$$\left.\left. + \frac{3h^2}{40} \left(1 + \frac{5}{28} \frac{h^2}{R_1 R_2}\right) \ddot{w}'' \right\} \right] = 0.$$

Upon comparing Eqs. 3.42 with their counterparts, Eqs. 2.71 from the theory of Chapter 2, it is seen that there are now two additional equations involving the new stress resultants which have been defined for the present theory. Furthermore, rotational inertia and translational inertia terms now appear in all of the equations, the applied surface forces are no longer replaced by their static equivalents on the reference surface, and the moments of the surface forces about the reference surface are now considered.

The two resultants A and B, which appear only in the equations of motion, may be separately determined by use of the definitions 3.33 and the third of Eqs. 3.31. (See Exercise 3.2.)

The vanishing of the coefficients of the arbitrary variations in the line integrals of Eq. 3.41 gives us the natural boundary conditions that are to be used with the present theory. Thus, on an edge of constant α_n we must prescribe

$$\begin{aligned}
N_n &= \bar{N}_n &\quad \text{or} \quad u_n &= \bar{u}_n \\
N_{nt} &= \bar{N}_{nt} &\quad \text{or} \quad u_t &= \bar{u}_t \\
Q_n &= \bar{Q}_n &\quad \text{or} \quad w &= \bar{w} \\
M_n &= \bar{M}_n &\quad \text{or} \quad \beta_n &= \bar{\beta}_n \\
M_{nt} &= \bar{M}_{nt} &\quad \text{or} \quad \beta_t &= \bar{\beta}_t \\
S_n &= \bar{S}_n &\quad \text{or} \quad w' &= \bar{w}' \\
T_n &= \bar{T}_n &\quad \text{or} \quad w'' &= \bar{w}''.
\end{aligned} \tag{3.43}$$

Now we see that there are seven independent boundary conditions to be applied at a given edge and Kirchoff's effective shearing-stress resultants play no role here. This is because transverse shearing strains do not vanish in the present theory and, therefore, the β_i cannot be expressed in terms of u_i and w alone (as was the case in Chapter 2).

It may be seen, in the foregoing development, that the inclusion of transverse normal stress effects is associated solely with the presence of the terms w' and w'' in the assumed deflections (Eqs. 3.28). It is possible to neglect the effect of transverse normal stress and yet to retain the effect of transverse shear by setting $\bar{v}$, w' and w'' to zero throughout the foregoing development. In this manner, the additional resultants defined in Eqs. 3.33 are no longer required, and the remaining stress resultants and couples, upon neglecting terms of order higher than the third in the thickness, are given by

$$\begin{aligned}
N_1 &= K\left[\epsilon_1{}^0 + \nu\epsilon_2{}^0 - \frac{h^2}{12}\left(\frac{1}{R_1} - \frac{1}{R_2}\right)\left(\kappa_1 - \frac{\epsilon_1{}^0}{R_1}\right)\right],\\
N_{12} &= Gh\left[\gamma_{12}{}^0 - \frac{h^2}{12}\left(\frac{1}{R_1} - \frac{1}{R_2}\right)\left(\beta_1' - \frac{\beta_1{}^0}{R_1}\right)\right],\\
M_1 &= D\left[\kappa_1 + \nu\kappa_2 - \left(\frac{1}{R_1} - \frac{1}{R_2}\right)\epsilon_1{}^0\right],\\
M_{12} &= \frac{Gh^3}{12}\left[\tau - \left(\frac{1}{R_1} - \frac{1}{R_2}\right)\beta_1{}^0\right],\\
Q_1 &= Gh\left[1 + \left(\frac{1}{R_1} - \frac{1}{R_2}\right)\frac{h^2}{12R_1}\right]\gamma_{1n},
\end{aligned} \tag{3.44}$$

along with five additional relationships wherein the subscripts are interchanged. Furthermore, the equations of motion reduce to the first five of Eqs. 3.42 with w' and w'' set to zero, and the boundary conditions reduce to the first five of Eqs. 3.43. In this case, it is also interesting to note that the first four of Eqs. 3.44 agree with the results of a transverse shear theory obtained later by Naghdi,[3] who also found, instead of the fifth of Eqs. 3.44, that

$$Q_1 = \tfrac{5}{6}Gh\left[1 - \frac{h^2}{28R_1}\left(\frac{1}{R_1} - \frac{1}{R_2}\right)\right]\gamma_{1n}. \tag{3.45}$$

With $\epsilon_1{}^0/R_1$ neglected in the first of Eqs. 3.44 and the square bracket of Eqs. 3.45 replaced by unity, the resulting formulation agrees with the transverse shear theories of Reissner[11] and Naghdi.[12] It was found, however, by Naghdi,[3] that his earlier theory [12] and that of Reissner[11] are not invariant under a transformation of coordinates, while Eqs. 3.44, with the last replaced by Eq. 3.45, are. Thus, it is felt that the best description of a shell with transverse shear effects included is given by the first four of Eqs. 3.44 and Eq. 3.45. We leave it to the Exercises to show that the sixth equation of equilibrium is satisfied by the appropriate equations of the set 3.44 and that the transverse shear theory recommended here leads to no strains during rigid body motions.

If we also neglect the effect of transverse shear, then β_1 and β_2 can, as before, be found from Eqs. 2.16; the fifth of Eqs. 3.44 (or Eq. 3.45) is deleted, and the rest of the theory reduces to the Flügge–Lur'e–Byrne theory of Section 3.3*a*.

3.4 A NONLINEAR THEORY OF THIN ELASTIC SHELLS

All of the theoretical treatments of the behavior of thin elastic shells which we have described thus far retain the small deflection assumption while suspending one or more of Love's other assumptions. Theories in which the small deflection assumption is abandoned and the remaining assumptions are retained have also appeared although the level of attention given to this aspect of shell theory has remained fairly low until recently. As an illustration of such treatments, we shall now outline Reissner's[13] theory of thin elastic shells with finite deformations.

The development which follows is restricted to symmetrically loaded shells of revolution for which the first fundamental form is (see Eq. 2.7, Exercise 1.7, and Fig. 3.1):

$$(ds_0)^2 = \alpha_0{}^2(1 + \xi\varphi_0{}'/\alpha_0)^2(d\xi)^2 + r_0{}^2(1 + \xi \sin \varphi_0/r_0)^2(d\theta)^2 + (d\zeta)^2 \quad (3.46)$$

before deformation, and

$$(ds)^2 = \alpha^2(1 + \xi\varphi'/\alpha)^2(d\xi)^2 + r^2(1 + \xi \sin \varphi/r)^2(d\theta)^2 + (d\zeta)^2 \quad (3.47)$$

after a finite deformation. Here the zero subscripted variables refer to the original configuration of the shell, the unsubscripted variables refer to the final configuration of the shell, and we have assumed that the normal element is preserved during deformation.

The original and final configurations of the shell are related by

$$r = r_0 + u_r, \qquad z = z_0 + u_z, \qquad \varphi = \varphi_0 - \beta, \quad (3.48)$$

where u_r and u_z are respectively the radial and axial displacement and β is the rotation of a tangent to a meridian at a given material point. The strain components can be obtained by comparison of Eqs. 3.46 and 3.47, thus:

$$\epsilon_\xi = \frac{\alpha - \alpha_0 + \zeta(\varphi' - \varphi_0{}')}{\alpha_0(1 + \zeta\varphi_0{}'/\alpha_0)},$$
$$\epsilon_\theta = \frac{r - r_0 + \zeta(\sin \varphi - \sin \varphi_0)}{r_0(1 + \zeta \sin \varphi_0/r_0)}. \quad (3.49)$$

We now introduce the assumption of thinness by neglecting the terms with

[13] Reissner, E., "On the Theory of Thin Elastic Shells," *H. Reissner Anniversary Volume*, Ann Arbor: J. W. Edwards, pp. 231–247 (1949).

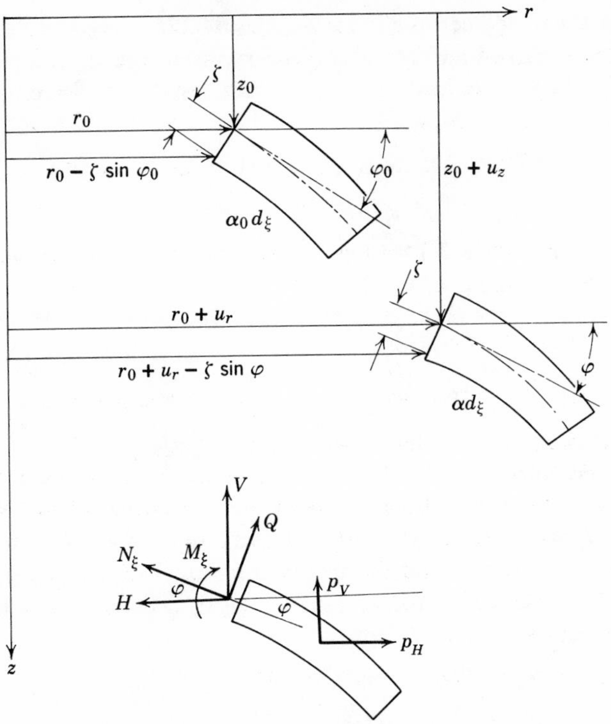

Figure 3.1

ζ in the denominators of the strain expressions, and this gives, in view of Eqs. 3.48,

$$\epsilon_\xi = \epsilon_\xi{}^0 + \zeta\kappa_\xi, \qquad \epsilon_\theta = \epsilon_\theta{}^0 + \zeta\kappa_\theta, \tag{3.50}$$

where

$$\begin{aligned}
\epsilon_\xi{}^0 &= \frac{\alpha - \alpha_0}{\alpha_0} = \left(\frac{\cos\varphi_0}{\cos\varphi}\right)\left(\frac{1 + u_r'}{r'}\right) - 1, \\
\epsilon_\theta{}^0 &= \frac{r - r_0}{r_0} = \frac{u_r}{r_0}, \\
\kappa_\xi &= \frac{\varphi' - \varphi_0'}{\alpha_0} = -\frac{\beta'}{\alpha_0}, \\
\kappa_\theta &= \frac{\sin\varphi - \sin\varphi_0}{r_0}.
\end{aligned} \tag{3.51}$$

Here, as in the rest of our discussions, the stress resultants and couples are defined as in Eqs. 2.23 with ζ/R_i neglected in comparison to unity. Thus, in the present coordinate system, we are concerned only with the stress resultants N_ξ, N_θ, Q, and the stress couples M_ξ, M_θ. Since we have chosen to consider the axial and radial displacements u_r and u_z, it is well to replace N_ξ and Q by statically equivalent radial and axial forces (H and V) by use of the relationships

$$\begin{aligned} N_\xi &= H\cos\varphi + V\sin\varphi, \\ Q &= -H\sin\varphi + V\cos\varphi, \end{aligned} \tag{3.52}$$

which follow from Fig. 3.1. In terms of these forces, the equilibrium equations can be shown to be

$$\begin{aligned} (rV)' + r\alpha p_V &= 0, \\ (rH)' - \alpha N_\theta + r\alpha p_H &= 0, \\ (rM_\xi)' - M_\theta\alpha\cos\varphi + r\alpha(H\sin\varphi - V\cos\varphi) &= 0. \end{aligned} \tag{3.53}$$

These equations were obtained by substituting $\xi = \alpha_1$, $\theta = \alpha_2$, $A_1 = \alpha$, $A_2 = r$, $1/R_1 = \varphi'/\alpha$, and $1/R_2 = \sin\varphi/r$ into Eqs. 2.71 along with Eqs. 3.52. They are nonlinear because they involve products of the dependent variables. Finally, the stress resultants and couples for an isotropic shell are related to the strains and changes in curvature by the following expressions in the absence of the transverse shear and normal stresses and thermal effects (see Eqs. 2.27):

$$\begin{aligned} N_\xi &= K(\epsilon_\xi{}^0 + \nu\epsilon_\theta{}^0), & M_\xi &= D(\kappa_\xi + \nu\kappa_\theta), \\ N_\theta &= K(\epsilon_\theta{}^0 + \nu\epsilon_\xi{}^0), & M_\theta &= D(\kappa_\theta + \nu\kappa_\xi). \end{aligned} \tag{3.54}$$

As a result of Eqs. 3.51, it follows that

$$\begin{aligned} \alpha &= \alpha_0(1 + \epsilon_\xi{}^0), \\ r &= r_0(1 + \epsilon_\theta{}^0). \end{aligned} \tag{3.55}$$

Thus, in view of the fact that we are still using Hooke's law in the present formulation, it seems reasonable to neglect the strains with respect to unity in Eqs. 3.55 and, therefore, to use $\alpha = \alpha_0$ and $r = r_0$ throughout. Indeed, it was argued by Naghdi and Nordgren,[14] in the discussion of their own more general finite deformation theory of shells, that this is consistent with the assumption on the preservation of the normal because the change in length of the normal to the reference surface is expected to be negligible only for small strains anyway. With this assumption, the equilibrium equations 3.53 are replaced by

$$\begin{aligned} (r_0V)' + r_0\alpha_0 p_V &= 0, \\ (r_0H)' - \alpha_0 N_\theta + \alpha_0 r_0 p_H &= 0, \\ (r_0M_\xi)' - M_\theta\alpha_0\cos\varphi + r_0\alpha_0(H\sin\varphi - V\cos\varphi) &= 0. \end{aligned} \tag{3.56}$$

---

[14] Naghdi, P. M., and Nordgren, R. P., "On the Nonlinear Theory of Shells Under the Kirchoff Hypothesis," *Q. Appl. Math.*, **21**, 49–60 (1963).

Although the neglect of the strains has simplified the equilibrium equations somewhat, they are still nonlinear.

The preceding analysis is restricted to finite deflections of symmetrically loaded shells of revolution under the assumption of small strains. Derivations of more general nonlinear shell theories have been carried out by Naghdi and Nordgren[14] and by Sanders.[15]

3.5 CLOSURE

In the foregoing, we have described three groups of theories which represent attempts to improve and to extend the theory of Chapter 2. As a conclusion, it is well to take up these categories one at a time and to discuss their usefulness in problems of shell analysis.

The improved first approximations, such as the Sanders theory which we have described, have been limited to the derivation of systems of differential equations and, to this date, no numerical comparisons to the results obtained for a given problem by the theory of Chapter 2 have been undertaken. However, in view of our remarks in Section 3.2, it is expected that, except in cases that involve large torsion τ, the differences in numerical results which would be obtained for a given problem by use of the various first approximation theories will be negligible. As a result, there is no trend under way to abandon the use of theories of the type derived in Chapter 2 for design purposes.

In cases where exact results using a solution based upon the theory of elasticity happen to be available, numerical results obtained with the higher order theories which were described in Section 3.3 do not necessarily agree more closely with the exact results than do the results obtained by the theory of Chapter 2. Thus, it is not necessarily worth the extra complications associated with the higher order theories to abandon the theory of Chapter 2 in their favor. This point will be discussed further in Chapters 5 and 8. For finite deflections, however, only the nonlinear theories are applicable. These have only recently been applied to problems of technical interest and a sufficient body of results has not yet been accumulated with these theories to comment on the extent of their success.

As a result of these considerations, the theory of Chapter 2 is adopted as the fundamental theory of thin elastic shells in this text.

This concludes the theoretical treatment of our subject. In the chapters that follow, we shall deal with the application of the theory derived in Chapter 2 to problems of shell analysis. This will involve analytical

[15] Sanders, J. L., "Nonlinear Theories for Thin Shells," *Q. Appl. Math.*, **21**, 21–36 (1963).

solutions to both static and dynamic problems.[16] In some cases it will be expedient to make additional assumptions, based on physical grounds, which will simplify the theory further. In other cases, mathematical approximations that permit a more convenient solution will be employed. As part of the latter approach, we shall also consider the application of modern electronic computers to the problems of shell analysis. In those instances where experimental data are available, they will be included to give an indication of the accuracy of the theory which has been adopted.

EXERCISES

3.1 Show that Eqs. 3.27 follow from Eqs. 3.25.

3.2 Show that, in connection with Section 3.3*b*,

$$A = \nu_n\left(N_1 + N_2 + \frac{M_1}{R_1} + \frac{M_2}{R_2}\right) + E_n h\left[\left(1 + \frac{h^2}{12R_1R_2}\right)w' + \left(\frac{1}{R_1} + \frac{1}{R_2}\right)\frac{h^2}{12}w''\right],$$

$$B = \nu_n\left(M_1 + M_2 + \frac{2P_1}{R_1} + \frac{2P_2}{R_2}\right) + \frac{E_n h^3}{12}\left[\left(\frac{1}{R_1} + \frac{1}{R_2}\right)w' + \left(1 + \frac{3h^2}{20R_1R_2}\right)w''\right].$$

3.3 Modify the development of Section 3.3*b* by assuming deflections in the form

$$U_1 = u_1(\alpha_1, \alpha_2) + \zeta u_1'(\alpha_1, \alpha_2) + \tfrac{1}{2}\zeta^2 u_1''(\alpha_1, \alpha_2),$$
$$U_2 = u_2(\alpha_1, \alpha_2) + \zeta u_2'(\alpha_1, \alpha_2) + \tfrac{1}{2}\zeta^2 u_2''(\alpha_1, \alpha_2),$$
$$W = w(\alpha_1, \alpha_2) + \zeta w'(\alpha_1, \alpha_2) + \tfrac{1}{2}\zeta^2 w''(\alpha_1, \alpha_2).$$

3.4 Investigate the theories of Sections 3.3*a* and 3.3*b* for rigid body motions and satisfaction of the sixth equation of equilibrium.

[16] The stability of thin elastic shells will not be considered. Discussions of this important aspect of the behavior of thin elastic shells are given in the following texts: Gerard, G., *Introduction to Structural Stability Theory*, New York: McGraw-Hill, (1962); Timoshenko, S., and Gere, J. M., *Theory of Elastic Stability*, New York: McGraw-Hill, 2nd ed. (1961).

II

Static Analysis of Shells

Analyses of shells subjected to static loadings are carried out by exact methods. Approximate analytical methods are also developed and illustrated.

4

Membrane Shells

4.1 INTRODUCTION

In Part I it was shown that a thin elastic shell supports arbitrary external loadings by means of internal stress resultants and stress couples (bending moments). Under appropriate loading conditions, however, the resulting bending moments are either zero or so small that they may be neglected. Such a state of stress is referred to as the membrane state of stress because of the analogy to membranes which cannot support bending moments. As a first exposure to the analysis of thin elastic shells, we shall now consider a class of shells, to which we shall refer as membrane shells, in which the state of stress is *approximately* the membrane state of stress.

To begin the discussion, it is appropriate to set down the fundamental equations which describe the membrane state of stress. These equations can be obtained from the system that we developed in Chapter 2 by making the basic assumption

$$M_1 = M_2 = M_{12} = M_{21} = 0. \tag{4.1}$$

As a result, the equations of equilibrium are reduced from Eqs. 2.71 to the following set:

$$\begin{gathered}\frac{\partial N_1 A_2}{\partial \alpha_1} + \frac{\partial N_{21} A_1}{\partial \alpha_2} + N_{12}\frac{\partial A_1}{\partial \alpha_2} - N_2\frac{\partial A_2}{\partial \alpha_1} + q_1 A_1 A_2 = 0,\\ \frac{\partial N_{12} A_2}{\partial \alpha_1} + \frac{\partial N_2 A_1}{\partial \alpha_2} + N_{21}\frac{\partial A_2}{\partial \alpha_1} - N_1\frac{\partial A_1}{\partial \alpha_2} + q_2 A_1 A_2 = 0,\\ \frac{N_1}{R_1} + \frac{N_2}{R_2} + q = 0,\end{gathered} \tag{4.2}$$

where dynamic effects have been neglected. We also notice, on account of assumption 4.1, that the fourth and fifth of Eqs. 2.71 lead to the additional result

$$Q_1 = Q_2 = 0. \tag{4.3}$$

Thus, we see that in the membrane state of stress, external loads are supported by internal loads which act only in the plane of the shell. These stress resultants are given by Eqs. 2.24 as

$$\begin{aligned} N_1 &= K_1[\epsilon_1{}^0 + \nu_{12}\epsilon_2{}^0 - (\alpha_{t1} + \nu_{12}\alpha_{t2})T_0], \\ N_2 &= K_2[\epsilon_2{}^0 + \nu_{21}\epsilon_1{}^0 - (\alpha_{t2} + \nu_{21}\alpha_{t1})T_0], \\ N_{12} &= N_{21} = G_{12}h\gamma_{12}{}^0, \end{aligned} \tag{4.4}$$

for a single orthotropic layer of material. In the foregoing, we have defined (see Eqs. 2.28 and 2.29):

$$\{K_1, K_2\} = \{E_1, E_2\}h/(1 - \nu_{12}\nu_{21}), \tag{4.5a}$$

$$T_0 = \frac{1}{h}\int_\zeta T\,d\zeta, \tag{4.5b}$$

and these are based on the assumption that the properties of the shell material are constant across the thickness of the shell. In keeping with assumption 4.1, it is further implied in Eq. 4.5b that the temperature distribution across the thickness of the shell may induce a thermal force but not a thermal moment in the shell.

The stress resultants in the membrane shell are related to the displacements of its reference surface by means of the following strain-displacement relationships (which follow from Eqs. 2.19):

$$\begin{aligned} \epsilon_1{}^0 &= \frac{1}{A_1}\frac{\partial u_1}{\partial \alpha_1} + \frac{u_2}{A_1A_2}\frac{\partial A_1}{\partial \alpha_2} + \frac{w}{R_1}, \\ \epsilon_2{}^0 &= \frac{1}{A_2}\frac{\partial u_2}{\partial \alpha_2} + \frac{u_1}{A_1A_2}\frac{\partial A_2}{\partial \alpha_1} + \frac{w}{R_2}, \\ \gamma_{12}{}^0 &= \frac{A_2}{A_1}\frac{\partial}{\partial \alpha_1}\left(\frac{u_2}{A_2}\right) + \frac{A_1}{A_2}\frac{\partial}{\partial \alpha_2}\left(\frac{u_1}{A_1}\right). \end{aligned} \tag{4.6}$$

The mathematical formulation of the theory of membrane shells is completed by adding the boundary conditions which, in view of Eqs. 2.80 and assumptions 4.1, take the form

$$\begin{aligned} N_n &= \bar{N}_n \quad \text{or} \quad u_n = \bar{u}_n \\ N_{nt} &= \bar{N}_{nt} \quad \text{or} \quad u_t = \bar{u}_t \end{aligned} \tag{4.7}$$

on an edge of constant α_n where n, t each take the values 1 and 2.

Assumptions 4.1 are equivalent to two alternate approaches to the description of a membrane shell. These both arise from the definition of the stress couples which act in a shell as given, for example, by the last three of Eqs. 2.27. In the first of these alternatives, we may make the physical argument that assumptions 4.1 are equivalent to the statement that the bending rigidity D of a membrane shell is negligible in comparison to its extensional rigidity K. Since the bending rigidity of any shell is (see Eqs. 2.29) proportional to the third power of its thickness, while the extensional rigidity is proportional to the first power of its thickness, this is also equivalent to the assumption that the shell is exceedingly thin. Hence, our use of the term membrane shell. In the second alternative to assumptions 4.1, we may argue that a membrane shell is one in which the changes in curvature and twist are negligible during deformation.

Let us now examine the form of the system of Eqs. 4.2, 4.4, and 4.6, that describes the behavior of a membrane shell. The salient feature of that system is the fact that the three equations of equilibrium Eqs. 4.2 contain exactly three unknown dependent variables, namely, the stress resultants. Unlike the equations of equilibrium of the general theory of shells, these can, therefore, be solved directly for the stress resultants without calling upon the displacements. Once the stress resultants are known, the strains can be obtained from equations of the type

$$\begin{aligned} \epsilon_1{}^0 &= \frac{1}{E_1 h}(N_1 - \nu_{21} N_2) + \alpha_{t1} T_0, \\ \epsilon_2{}^0 &= \frac{1}{E_2 h}(N_2 - \nu_{12} N_1) + \alpha_{t2} T_0, \qquad (4.8) \\ \gamma_{12}{}^0 &= \frac{N_{12}}{G_{12} h}, \end{aligned}$$

which are obtained by rearrangement of Eqs. 4.4 or, equivalently, by integration of Eqs. 2.4 over the thickness of the shell.

Substitution of these strain expressions into the strain-displacement relations Eqs. 4.6 followed by suitable integration of the results then leads to the displacements in the membrane shell.

Now let us cast the system of equations which has been given here into a form which is appropriate to membrane shells of revolution. This is accomplished by noting (see Eqs. 1.79) that the first fundamental forms of the reference surfaces of such shells are given by expressions of the type

$$(ds)^2 = r_\varphi{}^2(d\varphi)^2 + r^2(d\theta)^2, \qquad (4.9)$$

where we have replaced R_1 and R_0 with r_φ and r respectively. (We shall presently replace R_2 with r_θ where $r = r_\theta \sin\varphi$.) For such surfaces, we showed previously, in connection with Eq. 1.79, that $A_1 = R_1 = r_\varphi$,

$A_2 = R_0 = r$, $\alpha_1 = \varphi$, and $\alpha_2 = \theta$. We also showed that for a surface of revolution, the Gauss condition takes the form

$$\frac{dr}{d\varphi} = r_\varphi \cos\varphi. \qquad (4.10)$$

RGF P21

We shall make frequent use of this expression in our algebraic manipulations. With the parameters that we have identified above and with the observation that in a shell of revolution r, r_φ, and r_θ are independent of θ, the equilibrium equations (Eqs. 4.2) reduce to

$$\begin{aligned}
\frac{\partial(N_\varphi r)}{\partial\varphi} + r_\varphi \frac{\partial N_{\varphi\theta}}{\partial\theta} - N_\theta r_\varphi \cos\varphi + q_\varphi r r_\varphi &= 0,\\
\frac{\partial(N_{\varphi\theta} r)}{\partial\varphi} + r_\varphi \frac{\partial N_\theta}{\partial\theta} + N_{\varphi\theta} r_\varphi \cos\varphi + q_\theta r r_\varphi &= 0,\\
\frac{N_\varphi}{r_\varphi} + \frac{N_\theta}{r_\theta} + q &= 0.
\end{aligned} \qquad (4.11)$$

The stress resultants of a membrane shell of revolution are given by

$$\begin{aligned}
N_\varphi &= K_\varphi[\epsilon_\varphi{}^0 + \nu_{\varphi\theta}\epsilon_\theta{}^0 - (\alpha_{t\varphi} + \nu_{\varphi\theta}\alpha_{t\theta})T_0],\\
N_\theta &= K_\theta[\epsilon_\theta{}^0 + \nu_{\theta\varphi}\epsilon_\varphi{}^0 - (\alpha_{t\theta} + \nu_{\theta\varphi}\alpha_{t\varphi})T_0],\\
N_{\varphi\theta} &= N_{\theta\varphi} = G_{\varphi\theta} h \gamma_{\varphi\theta}{}^0,
\end{aligned} \qquad (4.12)$$

where K_φ and K_θ follow from Eqs. 4.5a with a change of subscripts. The strain displacement relations reduce to

$$\begin{aligned}
\epsilon_\varphi{}^0 &= \frac{1}{r_\varphi}\left(\frac{\partial u_\varphi}{\partial\varphi} + w\right), \qquad \epsilon_\theta{}^0 = \frac{1}{r}\left(\frac{\partial u_\theta}{\partial\theta} + u_\varphi \cos\varphi + w \sin\varphi\right),\\
\gamma_{\varphi\theta}{}^0 &= \frac{1}{r_\varphi}\frac{\partial u_\theta}{\partial\varphi} - \frac{1}{r}\left(u_\theta \cos\varphi - \frac{\partial u_\varphi}{\partial\theta}\right).
\end{aligned} \qquad (4.13)$$

These equations, together with boundary conditions of the type of Eq. 4.7, complete the mathematical formulation of problems in the analysis of membrane shells of revolution. In the remainder of the chapter, we shall concern ourselves with the solution of these equations for membrane shells having various specific shapes.

4.2 ANALYSIS OF MEMBRANE SHELLS OF REVOLUTION WITH STRAIGHT GENERATORS

As a first category of solutions in the theory of membrane shells of revolution, let us consider the analysis of shells whose reference surfaces have straight generators. There are two types of shells in this particular category; that is, cylindrical and conical shells. In analysing each of these, it is convenient to make the following change of variable, based upon the fact that when the generators are straight the curvature is zero:

$$\lim_{r_\varphi \to \infty} (r_\varphi \, d\varphi) = dx. \tag{4.14}$$

We shall see presently, in the analysis of cylindrical and conical membrane shells, that the vanishing of the curvature $1/r_\varphi$ leads to great simplifications in the analysis. For this reason, we treat these shells as a separate category of membrane shells of revolution.

4.2*a* Cylindrical Membrane Shells

We begin the discussion by taking up the case of the cylindrical membrane shell shown in Fig. 4.1. In such a shell, the generators of the reference surface are, in addition to being straight, parallel to its axis. Thus, the angle φ between the axis of the shell and a line drawn perpendicular to a

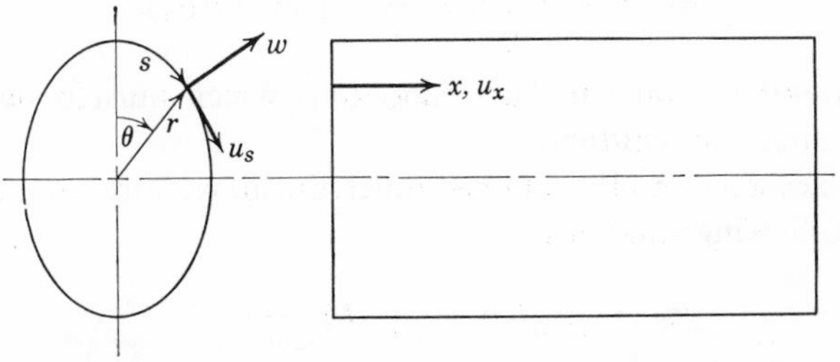

Figure 4.1 Geometry of an arbitrary cylindrical shell.

generator is $\pi/2$. It is, therefore, appropriate to make the change of variable $ds = r\, d\theta$ in addition to the change $dx = r_\varphi \, d\varphi$ defined by Eq. 4.14. Here x and s are the coordinates measured along a generator and around the circumference, respectively. The radius r is, in general, a function of s except when we are dealing with a circular cylindrical shell. In the latter case, the radius r is a constant, a.

With the new variables defined above, the equilibrium equations (Eqs. 4.11) are transformed into

$$\begin{aligned} \frac{\partial N_x}{\partial x} + \frac{\partial N_{xs}}{\partial s} + q_x &= 0, \\ \frac{\partial N_{xs}}{\partial x} + \frac{\partial N_s}{\partial s} + q_s &= 0, \\ N_s + qr &= 0, \end{aligned} \tag{4.15}$$

where we have replaced the subscripts φ and θ with x and s, respectively. The strains are related to the displacements of the reference surface by

$$\epsilon_x{}^0 = \frac{\partial u_x}{\partial x}, \qquad \epsilon_s{}^0 = \frac{\partial u_s}{\partial s} + \frac{w}{r}, \qquad \gamma_{xs}{}^0 = \frac{\partial u_x}{\partial s} + \frac{\partial u_s}{\partial x}. \tag{4.16}$$

Expressions for the stress resultants and for the boundary conditions of the cylindrical membrane shells are now obtained by merely changing the subscripts in Eqs. 4.12 and 4.7, respectively.

Since Eqs. 4.15 involve exactly three unknowns, they may, as we have already pointed out, be solved as they stand. Indeed, the last of Eqs. 4.15 gives us N_s immediately. Substitution of N_s into the second of Eqs. 4.15 followed by integration of the result gives us N_{xs} and substitution of the latter into the first of Eqs. 4.15 followed by integration gives us N_x. Thus, the general solution of Eqs. 4.15 can be written formally as

$$N_s = -qr,$$

$$N_{xs} = -\int \left(q_s + \frac{\partial N_s}{\partial_s} \right) dx + f_1(s),$$

$$N_x = -\int \left(q_x + \frac{\partial N_{xs}}{\partial s} \right) dx + f_2(s), \qquad (4.17a)$$

where $f_1(s)$ and $f_2(s)$ are arbitrary functions which must be determined from the boundary conditions.

The displacements can be obtained once the above forces are known by use of the following equations:

$$\epsilon_x{}^0 = \frac{1}{E_x h} (N_x - \nu_{sx} N_s) + \alpha_{tx} T_0,$$

$$\epsilon_s{}^0 = \frac{1}{E_s h} (N_s - \nu_{xs} N_x) + \alpha_{ts} T_0, \qquad (4.17b)$$

$$\gamma_{xs}{}^0 = \frac{N_{xs}}{G_{xs} h},$$

which follow from Eqs. 4.8 by means of a change of subscripts. General equations can now be derived for the displacements which are associated with the stress resultants (Eqs. 4.12) by substituting the latter into Eqs. 4.8, and substituting the resulting expressions into the strain-displacement relations (Eqs. 4.16), keeping in mind the current definitions of the variables and subscripts. When these are each integrated in turn, the displacements are given in the form

$$\varepsilon_x^0 = \frac{\partial u_x}{\partial x} \quad\longrightarrow\quad u_x = \int \left[\frac{1}{E_x h} (N_x - \nu_{sx} N_s) + \alpha_{tx} T_0 \right] dx + f_3(s),$$

$$\gamma_{xs} = \frac{\partial u_x}{\partial s} + \frac{\partial u_s}{\partial x} \quad\longrightarrow\quad u_s = \int \frac{1}{G_{xs} h} N_{xs}\, dx - \int \frac{\partial u_x}{\partial s}\, dx + f_4(s), \qquad (4.17c)$$

$$w = r \left[\frac{1}{E_s h} (N_s - \nu_{xs} N_x) + \alpha_{ts} T_0 - \frac{\partial u_s}{\partial s} \right],$$

where $f_3(s)$ and $f_4(s)$ are two additional arbitrary functions. Equations

$$\varepsilon_s^0 = \frac{\partial u_s}{\partial s} + \frac{w}{r}$$

4.17a and 4.17c represent the complete general solution of the problem of the cylindrical membrane shell. The four arbitrary functions (f_1, f_2, f_3, and f_4) which appear in the solution are sufficient for the satisfaction of four boundary conditions of the type 4.7. However, since the arbitrary functions depend only upon s, boundary conditions can only be applied on edges of constant x. As a result, we cannot meet conditions at edges of constant s when, for example, a segment of a cylindrical membrane shell is under consideration. These must, therefore, be abandoned. This represents a severe limitation of the theory of membrane shells as applied to segments of cylindrical shells. It can only be remedied by including the bending resistance of the shell. However, if the shell is closed with respect to the coordinate s, such difficulties do not arise.

It is well, at this point, to consider some specific examples which may be solved by means of the foregoing general solution. For this purpose, let us take up the class of problems in which $q_x = 0$ while q_s, q, and T_0 are independent of x. Thus, from Eqs. 4.17a, we find that

$$\begin{aligned} N_s &= -qr, \\ N_{xs} &= -\left(q_s + \frac{dN_s}{ds}\right)x + f_1(s), \\ N_x &= -\left(\frac{dN_{xs}}{ds}\right)x + f_2(s). \end{aligned} \tag{4.18a}$$

If we let

$$F(s) = \left(q_s + \frac{dN_s}{ds}\right) \tag{4.18b}$$

we can rewrite Eqs. 4.18a in the form

$$\begin{aligned} N_s &= -qr, \\ N_{xs} &= -xF(s) + f_1(s), \\ N_x &= \frac{x^2}{2}\frac{dF}{ds} - x\frac{df_1}{ds} + f_2(s), \end{aligned} \tag{4.18c}$$

and the displacements can be written as

$$\begin{aligned} u_x &= \frac{1}{E_x h}\left[\frac{x^3}{6}\frac{dF}{ds} - \nu_{sx} x N_s - \frac{x^2}{2}\frac{df_1}{ds} + x f_2\right] + \alpha_{tx} T_0 x + f_3, \\ u_s &= -\frac{x^2}{2}\left(\alpha_{tx}\frac{dT_0}{ds} + \frac{F}{G_{xs}h}\right) + x\left(\frac{f_1}{G_{xs}h} - \frac{df_3}{ds}\right) + f_4, \\ &\quad - \frac{1}{E_x h}\left[\frac{x^4}{24}\frac{d^2F}{ds^2} - \frac{x^3}{6}\frac{d^2 f_1}{ds^2} + \frac{x^2}{2}\left(\frac{df_2}{ds} - \nu_{sx}\frac{dN_s}{ds}\right)\right], \\ w &= \frac{r}{E_s h}\left(N_s - \frac{\nu_{xs} x^2}{2}\frac{dF}{ds} + \nu_{xs} x \frac{df_1}{ds} - \nu_{xs} f_2\right) + \alpha_{ts} r T_0 - r\frac{du_s}{ds}. \end{aligned} \tag{4.18d}$$

As an example of this class of problems, let us consider a cylindrical membrane shell of length l supported at each end by a diaphragm which can accept loads in its plane only. At such ends, one of the boundary conditions that are to be applied is $N_x = 0$. For a second condition, we have a choice of specifying either N_{xs} or u_s. Of these, we arbitrarily choose to prescribe the displacement and, therefore, we subject the solution to the conditions

$$u_s = N_x = 0 \quad \text{at} \quad x = \pm l/2, \tag{4.18e}$$

where we have taken the origin to lie at the middle of the span of the cylinder. From the force condition, we find that

$$f_1 = 0, \qquad f_2 = -\frac{l^2}{8}\frac{dF}{ds}, \tag{4.18f}$$

and from the displacement condition we find that

$$\begin{gathered} f_3 = 0, \\ f_4 = \frac{1}{E_x h}\left[\frac{l^4}{384}\frac{d^2F}{ds^2} + \frac{l^2}{8}\left(\frac{df_2}{ds} - \nu_{sx}\frac{dN_s}{ds}\right)\right] + \frac{l^2F}{8G_{xs}h} + \frac{l^2}{8}\alpha_{tx}\frac{dT_0}{ds}. \end{gathered} \tag{4.18g}$$

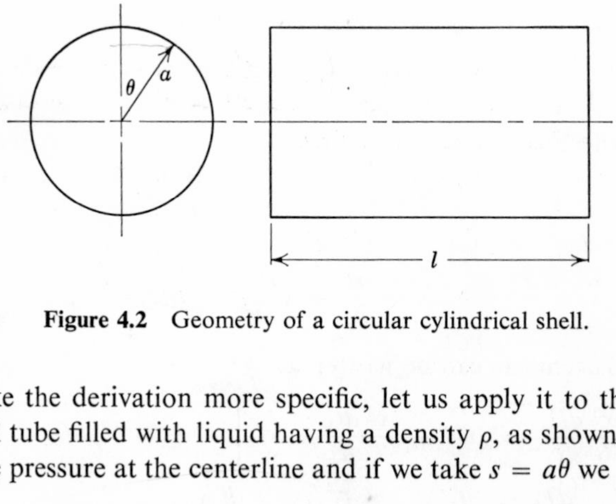

Figure 4.2 Geometry of a circular cylindrical shell.

To make the derivation more specific, let us apply it to the case of a cylindrical tube filled with liquid having a density ρ, as shown in Fig. 4.2. If p_0 is the pressure at the centerline and if we take $s = a\theta$ we have

$$q = -(p_0 - \rho a \cos\theta), \qquad T_0 = q_x = q_s = 0. \tag{4.19a}$$

Therefore,

$$\begin{aligned} N_s &= p_0 a - \rho a^2 \cos\theta, \\ F(\theta) &= \rho a \sin\theta, \end{aligned} \tag{4.19b}$$

and it follows that

$$
\begin{aligned}
N_x &= -\frac{\rho}{8}(l^2 - 4x^2)\cos\theta, \\
N_{xs} &= -x\rho a \sin\theta, \\
E_x h u_x &= -\nu_{sx} p_0 a x + \rho x \cos\theta \left[\frac{4x^2 - 3l^2}{24} + \nu_{sx} a^2\right], \\
E_x h u_s &= \frac{\rho}{8}(l^2 - 4x^2)\sin\theta \left[\left(\frac{E_x}{G_{xs}} - \nu_{sx}\right) a + \frac{5l^2 - 4x^2}{48a}\right], \\
E_s h w &= p_0 a^2 - \rho a^3 \cos\theta - \frac{a}{8}(l^2 - 4x^2)\rho\cos\theta \left(\frac{E_s}{G_{xs}} - \nu_{xs}\right) \\
&\quad - \frac{\rho}{8}\cos\theta \left[\frac{5l^2 - 4x^2}{48a} - \nu_{sx} a\right] \frac{E_s}{E_x}(l^2 - 4x^2).
\end{aligned}
\tag{4.19c}
$$

From these expressions, we note that N_s is constant along the length of the tube while N_x and N_{xs} are quadratic and linear functions of axial position, respectively. In this respect, the force distributions are similar to the shear and moment distributions in a beam subjected to a uniform transverse load. It is interesting to observe also that, if the cylindrical tube is loaded only by the pressure p_0, then the preceding relationships reduce to the set

$$
\begin{aligned}
N_s = p_0 a, \qquad N_x = N_{xs} = 0, \\
E_s h w = p_0 a^2, \qquad E_x h u_x = -\nu_{sx} p_0 a x, \qquad u_s = 0.
\end{aligned}
\tag{4.19d}
$$

Thus we see that the effect of the internal pressure is a circumferential stress accompanied by a uniform increase in the radius and a linear change in the length of the tube.

The foregoing solution is valid for the case where there is no force N_x applied at the end of the tube. If there were some type of bulkhead attached to each end of the tube, then we would find that as a result of the pressure q each end would be subjected to the total force

$$
\begin{aligned}
P &= p_0 \pi a^2 - \rho a \cos\theta \int_{-a}^{a} \sqrt{a^2 - r^2}\, dr, \\
&= p_0 \pi a^2 - \rho a^3 \pi \cos\theta,
\end{aligned}
\tag{4.19e}
$$

and the force boundary conditions at the ends would be

$$
N_x = \frac{P}{2\pi a} = \frac{p_0 a}{2} - \frac{\rho a^2}{4}\cos\theta \qquad \text{at} \quad x = \pm l/2. \tag{4.19f}
$$

Such forces would not affect N_s or N_{xs}. However, N_x would be affected through f_2 which now becomes

$$
f_2 = \frac{p_0 a}{2} - \frac{\rho}{8}\cos\theta\,(2a^2 + l^2), \tag{4.19g}
$$

and, finally,

$$N_x = \frac{p_0 a}{2} + \frac{\rho}{8}\cos\theta(4x^2 - l^2 - 2a^2). \tag{4.19h}$$

The displacements are affected only through the new definitions of f_2 and, consequently, f_4. From these, it follows that the displacments in the capped tube are

$$E_x h u_x = p_0 a x(\tfrac{1}{2} - \nu_{sx}) + \rho x \cos\theta\left[\frac{4x^2 - 3l^2}{24} + a^2(\nu_{sx} - \tfrac{1}{4})\right],$$

$$E_x h u_s = \frac{\rho}{8}\sin\theta\left\{(l^2 - 4x^2)\left[\left(\frac{E_x}{G_{sx}} - \nu_{sx}\right)a + \frac{2a^2 + l^2}{8a}\right] - \frac{l^4 - 16x^4}{48a}\right\}, \tag{4.19i}$$

$$E_s h w = p_0 a^2\left(1 - \frac{\nu_{xs}}{2}\right) - \rho a^3\cos\theta - \frac{a\rho}{8}\nu_{xs}\cos\theta(4x^2 - 2a^2 - l^2)$$
$$- \frac{E_s}{E_x}\frac{\rho\cos\theta}{8}\left\{(l^2 - 4x^2)\left[\left(\frac{E_x}{G_{sx}} - \nu_{sx}\right)a + \frac{2a^2 + l^2}{8a}\right] - \frac{l^4 - 16x^4}{48a}\right\}.$$

If the cylindrical tube is loaded only by the pressure p_0, then the preceding equations reduce to the following set:

$$N_s = p_0 a, \qquad N_x = \frac{p_0 a}{2}, \qquad N_{xs} = 0,$$
$$E_s h w = p_0 a^2\left(1 - \frac{\nu_{xs}}{2}\right), \qquad E_x h u_x = p_0 a x\,(\tfrac{1}{2} - \nu_{sx}), \qquad u_s = 0. \tag{4.19j}$$

The expressions given above for the stress resultants are the familiar pressure vessel formulas which apply to thin, capped, pressurized cylinders. However, it should be emphasized that local bending effects will be induced at the joints between the cylindrical shell and the end caps. As will be shown later, when shells are analysed with bending effects included, the results obtained here are only valid at sections that are far from the bulkheads.

4.2*b* Conical Membrane Shells

In a conical shell, the generators of the reference surface are straight and make an angle α with the axis of the shell as shown in Fig. 4.3. Now the angle φ between the axis of the shell and a line drawn perpendicular to a generator is $\pi/2 - \alpha$. In the case of the conical shell, it is convenient to

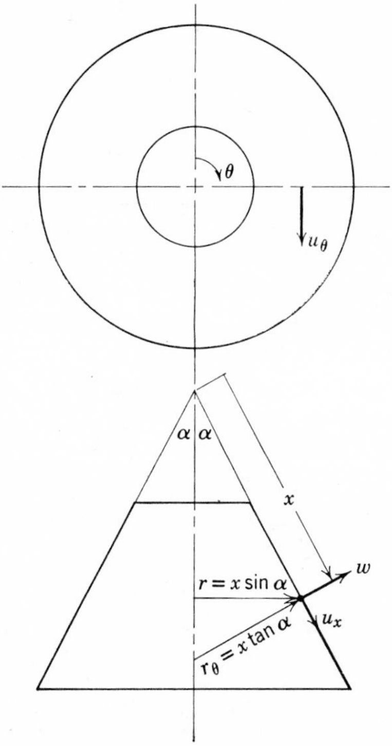

Figure 4.3 Geometry of a conical shell.

retain the variable θ of the general formulation as the coordinate of circumferential position and to again use $dx = r_\varphi \, d\varphi$ as defined by Eq. 4.14. It then follows that

$$r = x \sin \alpha, \qquad r_\theta = x \tan \alpha. \tag{4.20}$$

With these definitions of the relevant parameters, the equilibrium equations (Eqs. 4.11) become

$$\begin{aligned} \frac{\partial(xN_x)}{\partial x} + \frac{1}{\sin \alpha} \frac{\partial N_{x\theta}}{\partial \theta} - N_\theta + q_x x &= 0, \\ \frac{\partial(xN_{x\theta})}{\partial x} + \frac{1}{\sin \alpha} \frac{\partial N_\theta}{\partial \theta} + N_{x\theta} + q_\theta x &= 0, \\ N_\theta + qx \tan \alpha &= 0, \end{aligned} \tag{4.21}$$

where we have replaced the subscripts φ and θ of the general formulation with x and θ, respectively. The strains are related to the displacements by the expressions

$$\epsilon_x{}^0 = \frac{\partial u_x}{\partial x}, \qquad \epsilon_\theta{}^0 = \frac{1}{x \sin \alpha}\left(\frac{\partial u_\theta}{\partial \theta} + u_x \sin \alpha + w \cos \alpha\right),$$
$$\gamma_{x\theta}{}^0 = \frac{\partial u_\theta}{\partial x} - \frac{1}{x \sin \alpha}\left(u_\theta \sin \alpha - \frac{\partial u_x}{\partial \theta}\right). \tag{4.22}$$

The expressions for the stress resultants and the boundary conditions of the conical membrane shell are obtained from Eqs. 4.12 and 4.7 of the general formulation by a simple redefinition of the subscripts. Since our concern will be only with conical membrane shells that are closed with respect to the coordinate θ, we shall require the boundary conditions on edges of constant x only. As could be expected, Eqs. 4.21 and 4.22 reduce to the corresponding equations of the cylindrical shell by taking $\alpha = 0$.

To solve the equations of equilibrium for the unknown stress resultants, we can proceed as we did in the case of the cylindrical membrane shell. Thus, we find N_θ immediately from the third equilibrium equation. As a result

$$N_\theta = -qx \tan \alpha. \tag{4.23a}$$

Now we substitute this expression into the second equilibrium equation and obtain the following differential equation for $N_{x\theta}$

$$\frac{\partial N_{x\theta}}{\partial x} + \frac{2}{x} N_{x\theta} + \left(q_\theta - \frac{1}{\cos \alpha}\frac{\partial q}{\partial \theta}\right) = 0. \tag{4.23b}$$

To solve the foregoing equation, we can make use of the fact that equations of the type

$$\frac{dU}{d\varphi} + p(\varphi)U + q(\varphi) = 0 \tag{4.23c}$$

have the solution[1]

$$U = \left[c - \int q \exp\left(\int p\, d\varphi\right) d\varphi\right] \exp\left(-\int p\, d\varphi\right). \tag{4.23d}$$

Thus, Eq. 4.23b has the solution

$$N_{x\theta} = \frac{1}{x^2}\left[g_1(\theta) - \int\left(q_\theta - \frac{1}{\cos \alpha}\frac{\partial q}{\partial \theta}\right) x^2\, dx\right], \tag{4.23e}$$

where $g_1(\theta)$ is an arbitrary function. Equations 4.23a and 4.23c are now substituted into the first equilibrium equation with the result that

$$\frac{\partial N_x}{\partial x} + \frac{1}{x} N_x + \frac{1}{x \sin \alpha}\frac{\partial N_{x\theta}}{\partial \theta} + q \tan \alpha + q_x = 0. \tag{4.23f}$$

[1] See, for example, Sokolnikoff, I. S., and Redheffer, R. M., *Mathematics of Physics and Modern Engineering*, New York: McGraw-Hill, pp. 23–24 (1958).

This equation is another case of the standard form 4.23*c* and has, therefore, the solution

$$N_x = \frac{1}{x}\left[g_2(\theta) - \int\left(\frac{1}{x \sin\alpha}\frac{\partial N_{x\theta}}{\partial\theta} + q \tan\alpha + q_x\right) x\, dx\right], \tag{4.23g}$$

where $g_2(\theta)$ is an arbitrary function of θ. Equations 4.23a, 4.23e, and 4.23g constitute the general solution for the stress resultants in a conical membrane shell of revolution under arbitrary surface loads q, q_θ, and q_x. The displacements can be obtained from the expressions for the stress resultants by first calculating the strains from expressions which are obtained from Eqs. 4.8 by a simple redefinition of subscripts. The resulting equations are then substituted into Eqs. 4.22 from which the following expressions can be obtained by integration:

$$\begin{aligned}
u_x &= \int\left[\frac{1}{E_x h}(N_x - \nu_{\theta x}N_\theta) + \alpha_{tx}T_0\right] dx + g_3(\theta), \\
u_\theta &= x\left[g_4(\theta) + \int\left(\frac{N_{x\theta}}{G_{x\theta}h} - \frac{1}{x \sin\alpha}\frac{\partial u_x}{\partial\theta}\right)\frac{dx}{x}\right], \\
w &= \frac{x \tan\alpha}{E_\theta h}(N_\theta - \nu_{x\theta}N_x) + x\alpha_{t\theta}T_0 \tan\alpha - \frac{1}{\cos\alpha}\frac{\partial u_\theta}{\partial\theta} - u_x \tan\alpha,
\end{aligned} \tag{4.23h}$$

where we have used formula 4.23*d* for the solution of the differential equation in u_θ; $g_3(\theta)$ and $g_4(\theta)$ are two additional arbitrary functions. Here, as in the case of the cylindrical membrane shell, the nature of g_1, g_2, g_3, and g_4 requires that boundary conditions be applied only at edges of constant x. Thus, if we were to consider a segment of a conical shell having edges of constant θ, it would be impossible to specify boundary conditions on such edges. The difficulty can only be overcome by the inclusion of bending effects in the solution.

As an illustration of the preceding analysis, let us consider a conical membrane shell under the influence of an internal pressure and a uniform temperature rise T_0. Thus, we have $q = -p$, $q_\theta = q_x = 0$. If we assume that T_0 and p are independent of θ and x, and if we assume further that the boundary conditions will be independent of θ, then we may conclude that g_1, g_2, g_3, and g_4 are constants. Consequently, the stress resultants are

$$\begin{aligned}
N_\theta &= px \tan\alpha, \\
N_x &= \frac{g_2}{x} + \frac{px}{2}\tan\alpha, \\
N_{x\theta} &= 0,
\end{aligned} \tag{4.24a}$$

where, on account of the symmetry of the problem, we have set $g_1 = 0$.

The displacements that are associated with these forces then take the form

$$u_\theta = xg_4,$$

$$u_x = \frac{1}{E_x h}\left[g_2 \log x + \frac{px^2}{2} \tan \alpha(\tfrac{1}{2} - \nu_{\theta x})\right] + \alpha_{tx} x T_0 + g_3,$$

$$w = \frac{x \tan \alpha}{E_\theta h}\left[px \tan \alpha - \nu_{x\theta}\left(\frac{g_2}{x} + \frac{px}{2} \tan \alpha\right)\right] - g_3 \tan \alpha \tag{4.24b}$$

$$+ xT_0(\alpha_{t\theta} - \alpha_{tx}) \tan \alpha - \frac{\tan \alpha}{E_x h} \times \left[g_2 \log x + \frac{px^2}{2} \tan \alpha(\tfrac{1}{2} - \nu_{\theta x})\right].$$

Now let us assume that the shell is closed at $x = 0$. This makes it necessary to set $g_2 = 0$ in order to suppress the quantities $\log x$ and x^{-1} in the above expressions. Otherwise the solutions would be unbounded at the apex of the shell. The two remaining arbitrary functions are obtained from two boundary conditions at the edge $x = l$, for example, of the shell. Let us, therefore, require that the edge of the shell be restrained in such a manner that

$$u_x = u_\theta = 0 \quad \text{at} \quad x = l. \tag{4.24c}$$

These conditions give the values

$$g_4 = 0,$$

$$g_3 = -\alpha_{tx} l T_0 - \frac{pl^2}{2E_x h} \tan \alpha(\tfrac{1}{2} - \nu_{\theta x}), \tag{4.24d}$$

and the final expressions for the stress resultants and displacements take the form

$$N_\theta = px \tan \alpha,$$

$$N_x = \frac{px}{2} \tan \alpha,$$

$$N_{x\theta} = 0,$$

$$u_\theta = 0, \tag{4.24e}$$

$$u_x = \frac{p \tan \alpha}{2E_x h}(\tfrac{1}{2} - \nu_{\theta x})(x^2 - l^2) + \alpha_{tx} T_0 (x - l),$$

$$w = \frac{px^2 \tan^2 \alpha}{E_\theta h}\left(1 - \frac{\nu_{x\theta}}{2}\right) + \frac{p(l^2 - x^2) \tan^2 \alpha}{2E_x h}(\tfrac{1}{2} - \nu_{\theta x}) + T_0 \tan \alpha[l\, \alpha_{tx} + x(\alpha_{t\theta} - \alpha_{tx})].$$

As a second example, let us consider a frustum of a conical membrane

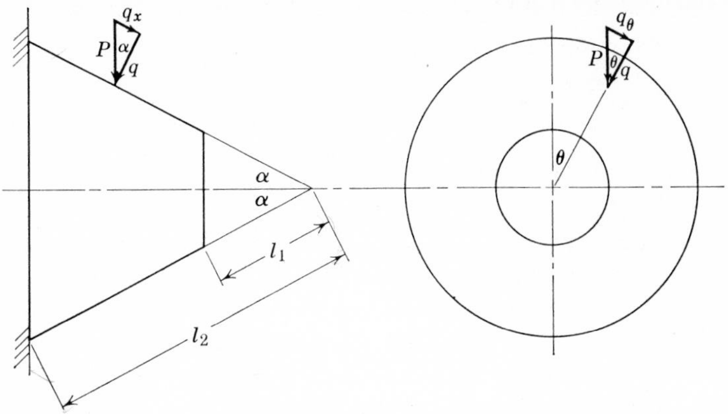

Figure 4.4 Conical shell loaded by its own weight.

shell mounted as shown in Fig. 4.4 and loaded by the action of its own weight. In this case, the surface forces can be expressed in terms of the weight P per unit area of the reference surface as

$$\begin{aligned} q &= P \cos \alpha \cos \theta, \\ q_x &= P \sin \alpha \cos \theta, \\ q_\theta &= P \sin \theta, \end{aligned} \tag{4.25a}$$

and $T_0 = 0$. The stress resultants are, in view of Eqs. 4.23a, 4.23e, and 4.23g,

$$\begin{aligned} N_\theta &= -Px \sin \alpha \cos \theta, \\ N_{x\theta} &= \frac{1}{x^2}\left[g_1(\theta) - \frac{2x^3}{3} P \sin \theta\right], \\ N_x &= \frac{1}{x}\left[g_2(\theta) + \frac{1}{x \sin \alpha}\frac{dg_1}{d\theta} + \frac{Px^2 \cos \theta}{\sin \alpha}\left(\tfrac{1}{3} - \sin^2 \alpha\right)\right]. \end{aligned} \tag{4.25b}$$

Since the narrow end of the shell is free, the boundary conditions at that end are expressed as

$$N_x = N_{x\theta} = 0 \quad \text{at} \quad x = l_1. \tag{4.25c}$$

As a result of these conditions, we find that

$$\begin{aligned} g_1(\theta) &= \frac{2l_1^{\,3}}{3} P \sin \theta, \\ g_2(\theta) &= -\frac{Pl_1^{\,2}}{\sin \alpha} \cos \theta (1 - \sin^2 \alpha), \end{aligned} \tag{4.25d}$$

and the final solutions for the stress resultants are

$$
\begin{aligned}
N_\theta &= -Px \sin\alpha \cos\theta, \\
N_{x\theta} &= \frac{2P}{3x^2}(l_1^{\,3} - x^3)\sin\theta, \\
N_x &= \frac{Pl_1^{\,2}}{x \sin\alpha}\left[\frac{2l_1}{3x} + \left(\frac{x}{l_1}\right)^2(\tfrac{1}{3} - \sin^2\alpha) - (1 - \sin^2\alpha)\right].
\end{aligned}
\tag{4.25e}
$$

We leave the determination of the displacements of the shells to the Exercises. The solution obtained above is likely to be accurate only at points that are far from the support because of the localized bending effects which are induced in the shell at the point of attachment. A more accurate solution that is valid over the entire length of the shell can only be obtained if bending effects are included in the analysis.

4.3 ANALYSIS OF MEMBRANE SHELLS OF REVOLUTION WITH CURVED GENERATORS

When the generators of the reference surface of a membrane shell of revolution are curved, the equilibrium equations, the stress–strain laws, and the strain–displacement relations that were given in the Introduction to this chapter must be solved as they stand.

In the solution of the equilibrium equations of such shells, we first find, from the third of Eqs. 4.11, that

$$
N_\theta = -qr_\theta - \frac{N_\varphi r_\theta}{r_\varphi}. \tag{4.26}
$$

This expression is used to eliminate N_θ from the first two of Eqs. 4.11 with the result that

$$
\begin{aligned}
&\frac{\partial(rN_\varphi)}{\partial\varphi} + r_\varphi\frac{\partial N_{\varphi\theta}}{\partial\theta} + N_\varphi r_\theta\cos\varphi + r_\theta r_\varphi(q_\varphi\sin\varphi + q\cos\varphi) = 0, \\
&\frac{\partial(rN_{\varphi\theta})}{\partial\varphi} + r_\varphi N_{\varphi\theta}\cos\varphi - r_\theta\frac{\partial N_\varphi}{\partial\theta} + r_\theta r_\varphi\left(q_\theta\sin\varphi - \frac{\partial q}{\partial\theta}\right) = 0.
\end{aligned}
\tag{4.27}
$$

These equations cannot be solved in as straightforward a manner as were the corresponding equations of the cylindrical and conical membrane shells (that is, Eqs. 4.15 and 4.21, respectively). As we may recall, the simplifications which were associated with the latter were a direct result of the fact that the generators of the reference surfaces of those shells were straight. In the present class of membrane shells of revolution with curved generators, it is well to consider the solution of Eqs. 4.27 for two categories of problems: those in which the applied loads are independent of, and arbitrary functions of, the polar angle θ.

4.3*a* Membrane Shells of Revolution under Loads that are Independent of the Polar Angle

When the external loads are independent of the angle θ, the second of Eqs. 4.27 reduces to

$$\frac{d}{d\varphi}(rN_{\varphi\theta}) + r_{\varphi}N_{\varphi\theta}\cos\varphi + r_{\varphi}r_{\theta}q_{\theta}\sin\varphi = 0. \tag{4.28a}$$

This equation can be solved for $N_{\varphi\theta}$ once the load q_θ has been specified. The solution will be at most a function of φ and, consequently, the first of Eqs. 4.27 becomes

$$\frac{d}{d\varphi}(rN_{\varphi}) + N_{\varphi}r_{\theta}\cos\varphi + r_{\theta}r_{\varphi}(q_{\varphi}\sin\varphi + q\cos\varphi) = 0. \tag{4.28b}$$

For convenience, therefore, we may set $N_{\varphi\theta} = q_\theta = 0$ in the present discussion. If we multiply Eq. 4.28b by $\sin\varphi$ and then integrate the result with respect to φ, we find that

$$N_{\varphi} = \frac{-1}{r\sin\varphi}\left[C_1 + \int_{\varphi_0}^{\varphi} rr_{\varphi}(q\cos\varphi + q_{\varphi}\sin\varphi)\,d\varphi\right], \tag{4.28c}$$

where C_1 is an arbitrary constant which is related to the axial component of any forces that are applied at $\varphi = \varphi_0$. Indeed, if Eq. 4.28c is evaluated at $\varphi = \varphi_0$, the integral vanishes and

$$N_{\varphi}(\varphi_0) = -C_1/r\sin\varphi_0. \tag{4.28d}$$

When we multiply both sides of this equation by the circumference, $2\pi r$, of the latitude circle at $\varphi = \varphi_0$ and rearrange the result, we find that

$$2\pi r(\varphi_0)N_{\varphi}(\varphi_0)\sin\varphi_0 = -2\pi C_1. \tag{4.28e}$$

Thus, $2\pi C_1$ is the total external axial load applied at $\varphi = \varphi_0$.

Once N_φ has been obtained from Eq. 4.28c, N_θ can be determined from Eq. 4.26. The displacements associated with the stress resultants are now obtained in the same way as were the displacements of the conical and cylindrical membrane shells. The strains are first determined from the equations

$$\begin{aligned}
\epsilon_{\varphi}{}^{0} &= \frac{1}{E_{\varphi}h}(N_{\varphi} - \nu_{\theta\varphi}N_{\theta}) + \alpha_{t\varphi}T_0,\\
\epsilon_{\theta}{}^{0} &= \frac{1}{E_{\theta}h}(N_{\theta} - \nu_{\varphi\theta}N_{\varphi}) + \alpha_{t\theta}T_0,\\
\gamma_{\varphi\theta}{}^{0} &= N_{\varphi\theta}/G_{\varphi\theta}h,
\end{aligned} \tag{4.28f}$$

which follow from Eqs. 4.8.

The strain displacement equations for shells under the influence of loads which are independent of θ are

$$\gamma_{\varphi\theta}{}^0 = 0, \qquad \epsilon_\varphi{}^0 = \frac{1}{r_\varphi}\left(\frac{du_\varphi}{d\varphi} + w\right), \qquad \epsilon_\theta{}^0 = \frac{1}{r}(u_\varphi \cos\varphi + w \sin\varphi), \quad (4.28g)$$

and, upon rearrangement, these take the form

$$\begin{aligned} \frac{du_\varphi}{d\varphi} - u_\varphi \cot\varphi &= r_\varphi \epsilon_\varphi{}^0 - r_\theta \epsilon_\theta{}^0, \\ w &= r_\theta \epsilon_\theta{}^0 - u_\varphi \cot\varphi. \end{aligned} \quad (4.28h)$$

Eqs. 4.28f are now substituted into the foregoing with the result that

$$\begin{aligned} \frac{du_\varphi}{d\varphi} - u_\varphi \cot\varphi &= \frac{N_\varphi}{E_\varphi h}(r_\varphi + \nu_{\theta\varphi} r_\theta) - \frac{N_\theta}{E_\theta h}(r_\theta + \nu_{\varphi\theta} r_\varphi) \\ &\quad + T_0(r_\varphi \alpha_{t\varphi} - r_\theta \alpha_{t\theta}), \quad (4.28i) \\ w &= \frac{r_\theta}{E_\theta h}(N_\theta - \nu_{\varphi\theta} N_\varphi) + r_\theta \alpha_{t\theta} T_0 - u_\varphi \cot\varphi. \end{aligned}$$

The solution of the first of Eqs. 4.28i can be shown, by means of formula 4.23d, to be

$$u_\varphi = \sin\varphi \left[C_2 + \int_{\varphi_0}^{\varphi} \frac{F(\varphi)\, d\varphi}{\sin\varphi}\right], \quad (4.28j)$$

where

$$F(\varphi) = \frac{N_\varphi}{E_\varphi h}(r_\varphi + \nu_{\theta\varphi} r_\theta) - \frac{N_\theta}{E_\theta h}(r_\theta + \nu_{\varphi\theta} r_\varphi) + T_0(\alpha_{t\varphi} r_\varphi - \alpha_{t\theta} r_\theta). \quad (4.28k)$$

Upon substitution of Eq. 4.28j into the second of Eqs. 4.28i, we obtain

$$w = \frac{r_\theta}{E_\theta h}(N_\theta - \nu_{\varphi\theta} N_\varphi) + r_\theta \alpha_{t\theta} T_0 - \cos\varphi \left[C_2 + \int_{\varphi_0}^{\varphi} \frac{F(\varphi)\, d\varphi}{\sin\varphi}\right]. \quad (4.28l)$$

Here C_2 is an arbitrary constant of integration which represents the axial displacement of a reference point on the shell.

To illustrate the use of the foregoing solutions, let us consider the following sample problems.

First, let us determine the forces and displacements in a spherical dome which is loaded by its own weight P per unit of area of its reference surface, as shown in Fig. 4.5. The load P has the components

$$q = P\cos\varphi, \qquad q_\varphi = P\sin\varphi, \qquad q_\theta = 0. \quad (4.29a)$$

If we take R to be the radius of the middle surface of the dome, we have $r_\varphi = r_\theta = R$, and Eq. 4.28c gives, after integration,

$$N_\varphi = \frac{-PR}{1 + \cos\varphi}, \quad (4.29b)$$

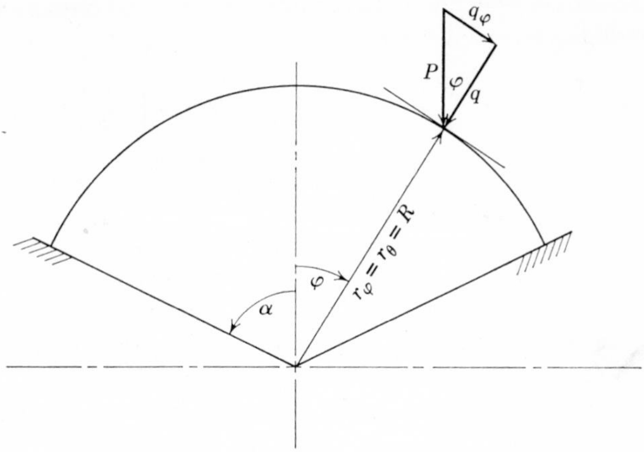

Figure 4.5 Spherical shell loaded by its own weight.

while Eq. 4.26 gives

$$N_\theta = PR\left(\frac{1}{1 + \cos\varphi} - \cos\varphi\right), \tag{4.29c}$$

where we have assumed that no other external loads act on the dome (that is, $C_1 = 0$). The displacements of the dome are determined by first noting that, in the absence of thermal effects, Eq. 4.28k reduces to

$$F(\varphi) = -\frac{PR^2}{h}\left\{\frac{1+\nu_{\theta\varphi}}{E_\varphi(1 + \cos\varphi)} + \frac{1 + \nu_{\varphi\theta}}{E_\theta}\left[\frac{1}{1 + \cos\varphi} - \cos\varphi\right]\right\}. \tag{4.29d}$$

As a result, Eq. 4.28j gives, after integration,

$$u_\varphi = -\frac{PR^2}{2h}\sin\varphi\left\{\left[\frac{1 + \nu_{\theta\varphi}}{E_\varphi} + \frac{1 + \nu_{\varphi\theta}}{E_\theta}\right]\left[\frac{1}{1 + \cos\varphi} + \log\left(\frac{\sin\varphi}{1 + \cos\varphi}\right)\right] - \frac{2(1 + \nu_{\varphi\theta})}{E_\theta}\log(\sin\varphi)\right\} + C_2\sin\varphi, \tag{4.29e}$$

and, therefore, Eq. 4.28*l* gives

$$w = \frac{PR^2}{2h}\cos\varphi\left\{\left[\frac{1 + \nu_{\theta\varphi}}{E_\varphi} + \frac{1 + \nu_{\varphi\theta}}{E_\theta}\right]\left[\frac{1}{1 + \cos\varphi} + \log\left(\frac{\sin\varphi}{1 + \cos\varphi}\right)\right] - \frac{2(1 + \nu_{\varphi\theta})}{E_\theta}\log(\sin\varphi)\right\} - C_2\cos\varphi + \frac{PR^2}{E_\theta h}\left[\frac{1 + \nu_{\varphi\theta}}{1 + \cos\varphi} - \cos\varphi\right]. \tag{4.29f}$$

The integration constant C_2 is determined from the deflection at the support. If, for example, we specify that the longitudinal displacement u_φ at the support $\varphi = \alpha$ is zero, we find that

$$C_2 = \frac{PR^2}{2h}\left\{\left[\frac{1+\nu_{\theta\varphi}}{E_\varphi} + \frac{1+\nu_{\varphi\theta}}{E_\theta}\right]\left[\frac{1}{1+\cos\alpha} + \log\left(\frac{\sin\alpha}{1+\cos\alpha}\right)\right] - \frac{2(1+\nu_{\varphi\theta})}{E_\theta}\log(\sin\alpha)\right\}. \quad (4.29g)$$

If we had wished to specify that the transverse displacement w vanishes at $\varphi = \alpha$, we should have obtained a different expression for C_2 from Eq. 4.29f. We should, however, recall from the Introduction to this chapter that it is not appropriate, within the theory of membrane shells, to specify w at a boundary. The physical reasoning associated with this statement can now be understood by referring to Fig. 4.6. In Fig. 4.6a, the dome is

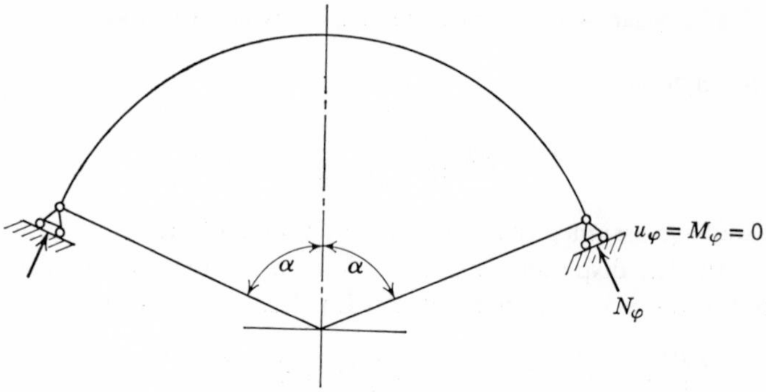

(a)

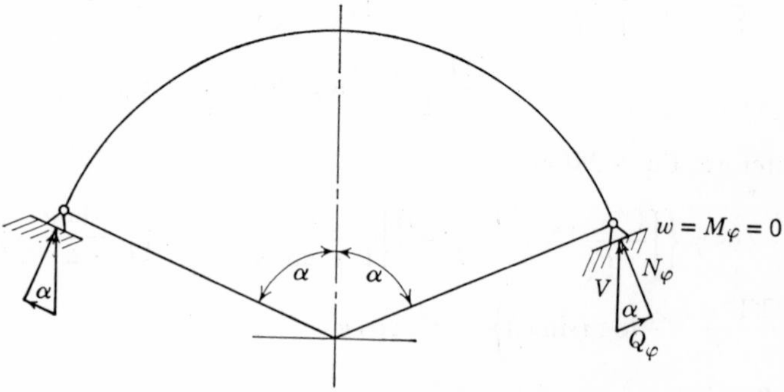

(b)

Figure 4.6

supported so as to prevent longitudinal displacement u_φ at the edge. No bending is introduced at the edge because the reactive force is tangent to the dome. Consequently, the state of stress in the dome is that of a membrane. In Fig. 4.6b, where transverse displacement w is prevented at the edge, bending is introduced because the reactive force has a transverse shearing component Q_φ. Such forces are incompatible with the membrane state of stress and, therefore, the shell cannot be treated as a membrane shell.

The preceding results bring out the connection between the boundary conditions and the state of stress. Later, when we analyze shells of revolution with bending resistance, we shall see that solutions that are based upon the membrane theory of shells will be fairly accurate away from sources of bending such as the edge in Fig. 4.6b.

As a second example, let us consider the analysis of membrane shells of revolution loaded by a uniform internal pressure, p. In this case, we have

$$q = -p, \qquad q_\varphi = 0, \tag{4.30a}$$

where the negative sign signifies that the pressure acts outward. Without specifying the shape of the shell, we can calculate the stress resultants with Eqs. 4.28c and 4.26. Thus, we find that

$$\begin{aligned} N_\varphi &= \frac{p}{r \sin \varphi} \int r r_\varphi \cos \varphi \, d\varphi \\ &= \frac{p}{r_\theta \sin^2 \varphi} \int r \, dr \\ &= \frac{p r_\theta}{2}, \end{aligned} \tag{4.30b}$$

where we have assumed that no additional external loads act on the shell, and we have used the Gauss condition (Eq. 4.10) to redefine the variable of integration.

In view of Eq. 4.26, we also find that

$$N_\theta = p r_\theta \left(1 - \frac{r_\theta}{2 r_\varphi}\right). \tag{4.30c}$$

Thus, once the radii of curvature have been defined, the forces acting in a particular pressurized membrane shell of revolution can be determined. The displacements of the shell can then be found by using Eqs. 4.28j and 4.28*l*. It is best, however, to delay the use of the latter equations until a specific shell is considered on account of the nature of the integrals that are involved. It is sufficient, in preparation for this, to indicate that

$$F(\varphi) = \frac{pr_\theta}{h}\left\{\frac{r_\varphi + \nu_{\theta\varphi}r_\theta}{2E_\varphi} - \left(1 - \frac{r_\theta}{2r_\varphi}\right)\frac{r_\theta + \nu_{\varphi\theta}r_\varphi}{E_\theta}\right\} + T_0(r_\varphi\alpha_{t\varphi} - r_\theta\alpha_{t\theta}), \quad (4.30\text{d})$$

where the effect of a uniform temperature rise (T_0) has been retained.

Let us now apply the foregoing development to several pressurized membrane shells. To begin with the familiar, we consider a pressurized cylindrical membrane shell for which $r_\theta = a$, $r_\varphi \to \infty$, and $\varphi = \pi/2$. In this case, Eqs. 4.30b and 4.30c yield the results

$$N_x = \frac{pa}{2}, \qquad N_s = pa, \quad (4.31\text{a})$$

where we have replaced the subscripts φ and θ with their counterparts x and s for the cylindrical shell. To determine the displacements, we note that $r_\varphi\, d\varphi \to dx$ and change the integrands of Eqs. 4.28j and 4.28l accordingly. It then follows that

$$\begin{aligned} u_x &= \left[\frac{pa}{E_x h}\left(\tfrac{1}{2} - \nu_{sx}\right) + \alpha_{tx}T_0\right]x, \\ w &= \frac{pa^2}{E_s h}\left(1 - \frac{\nu_{xs}}{2}\right) + a\alpha_{ts}T_0. \end{aligned} \quad (4.31\text{b})$$

With the exception of the added effect of the temperature rise T_0, Eqs. 4.31a and 4.31b agree with Eqs. 4.19j which we derived earlier for a pressurized membrane shell with closed ends.

Now let us consider a pressurized spherical shell. In this case, we have $r_\varphi = r_\theta = R$ and Eqs. 4.30b and 4.30c give the familiar formulas

$$N_\varphi = N_\theta = \frac{pR}{2}. \quad (4.32\text{a})$$

The deflections which are associated with these forces are obtained by using Eqs. 4.28j and 4.28l from which it follows that

$$\begin{aligned} u_\varphi &= \left[\frac{pR^2}{2h}\left(\frac{1}{E_\varphi} - \frac{1}{E_\theta}\right) + RT_0(\alpha_{t\varphi} - \alpha_{t\theta})\right]\sin\varphi \log\left(\frac{\sin\varphi}{1+\cos\varphi}\right) + C_2 \sin\varphi, \\ w &= -\left[\frac{pR^2}{2h}\left(\frac{1}{E_\varphi} - \frac{1}{E_\theta}\right) + RT_0(\alpha_{t\varphi} - \alpha_{t\theta})\right]\cos\varphi \log\left(\frac{\sin\varphi}{1+\cos\varphi}\right) \\ &\quad - C_2\cos\varphi + \frac{pR^2}{2E_\theta h}(1 - \nu_{\varphi\theta}) + RT_0\alpha_{t\theta}. \end{aligned} \quad (4.32\text{b})$$

For the condition of vanishing u_φ at $\varphi = \alpha$, for example, it follows from the first of Eqs. 4.32b that

$$C_2 = -\left[\frac{pR^2}{2h}\left(\frac{1}{E_\varphi} - \frac{1}{E_\theta}\right) + RT_0(\alpha_{t\varphi} - \alpha_{t\theta})\right] \log\left(\frac{\sin\alpha}{1 + \cos\alpha}\right), \tag{4.32c}$$

and, therefore,

$$\begin{aligned} u_\varphi &= \sin\varphi\left[\frac{pR^2}{2h}\left(\frac{1}{E_\varphi} - \frac{1}{E_\theta}\right)\right. \\ &\qquad \left. + RT_0(\alpha_{t\varphi} - \alpha_{t\theta})\right] \log\left(\frac{\sin\varphi}{\sin\alpha}\frac{1 + \cos\alpha}{1 + \cos\varphi}\right), \\ w &= -\cos\varphi\left[\frac{pR^2}{2h}\left(\frac{1}{E_\varphi} - \frac{1}{E_\theta}\right)\right. \\ &\qquad \left. + RT_0(\alpha_{t\varphi} - \alpha_{t\theta})\right] \log\left(\frac{\sin\varphi}{\sin\alpha}\frac{1 + \cos\alpha}{1 + \cos\varphi}\right) \\ &\qquad + \frac{pR^2}{2E_\theta h}(1 - \nu_{\varphi\theta}) + RT_0\alpha_{t\theta}. \end{aligned} \tag{4.32d}$$

It is interesting to notice that, if the shell is isotropic, then $E_\theta = E_\varphi = E$, $\nu_{\varphi\theta} = \nu_{\theta\varphi} = \nu$, $\alpha_{t\varphi} = \alpha_{t\theta} = \alpha_t$, and

$$u_\varphi = 0, \qquad w = \frac{pR^2}{2Eh}(1 - \nu) + RT_0\alpha_t. \tag{4.32e}$$

As a final example, we consider the case of the ellipsoidal membrane shell of revolution whose cross section is an ellipse having a major axis $2a$ and a minor axis $2b$, as shown in Fig. 4.7. We recall from analytic geometry that the radii of curvature of such a surface are

$$r_\varphi = \frac{a^2b^2}{(a^2\sin^2\varphi + b^2\cos^2\varphi)^{3/2}}, \qquad r_\theta = \frac{a^2}{(a^2\sin^2\varphi + b^2\cos^2\varphi)^{1/2}}, \tag{4.33a}$$

and, therefore, the stress resultants are, from Eqs. 4.30b and 4.30c,

$$\begin{aligned} N_\varphi &= \frac{pa^2}{2(a^2\sin^2\varphi + b^2\cos^2\varphi)^{1/2}}, \\ N_\theta &= \frac{pa^2}{(a^2\sin^2\varphi + b^2\cos^2\varphi)^{1/2}}\left(1 - \frac{a^2\sin^2\varphi + b^2\cos^2\varphi}{2b^2}\right). \end{aligned} \tag{4.33b}$$

Owing to the fact that the integrals in the equations for the displacements become extremely cumbersome when Eqs. 4.28j and 4.28*l* are used, we shall not derive the expressions for the displacements of the pressurized ellipsoidal membrane shell of revolution. It is, however, interesting to calculate

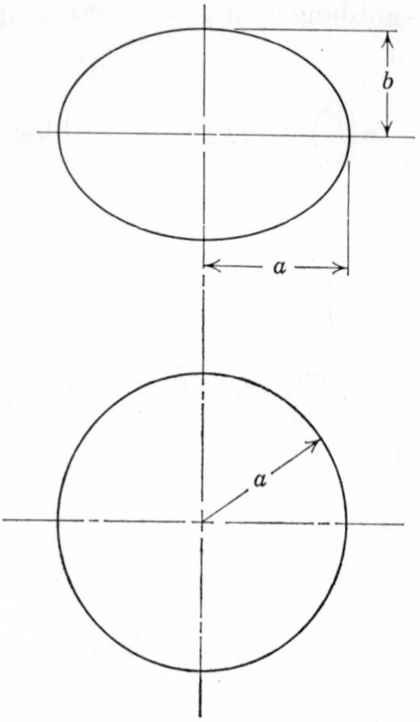

Figure 4.7 Geometry of an ellipsoidal shell.

the transverse deflection w at the equator of the shell. Thus, we find from Eq. 4.28l that

$$w\left(\frac{\pi}{2}\right) = \frac{pa^2}{E_\theta h}\left(1 - \frac{a^2}{2b^2} - \frac{\nu_{\varphi\theta}}{2}\right) + a\alpha_{t\theta}T \tag{4.33c}$$

which reduces to the corresponding result for the spherical membrane shell if $a = b = R$. At the top of the ellipsoidal membrane shell, the stress resultants attain the values

$$N_\varphi = N_\theta = \frac{pa^2}{2b}, \tag{4.33d}$$

which again reduce to the result obtained for the spherical membrane shell if $a = b = R$.

It should come as no surprise that at the apexes ($\varphi = 0$) of the two membrane shells of revolution that have been considered here, we have found that $N_\varphi = N_\theta$. Indeed, for a surface of revolution whose curvatures are continuous at the apex, we have $r_\varphi = r_\theta$ at the apex. It is, therefore, intuitively plausible that the result $N_\varphi = N_\theta$ is general for such shells since one cannot distinguish between the θ and φ directions at the apex. Equations 4.30b and 4.30c then tell us that

$$N_\varphi = N_\theta = -\frac{qr_\theta}{2} = -\frac{qr_\varphi}{2} \quad \text{at} \quad \varphi = 0. \tag{4.33e}$$

The results on pressurized membrane shells are valid for closed shells, or for open shells whose edges are supported in such a manner that no bending effects are introduced at the supports.

It is now interesting, as an introduction to the analysis of composite shells of revolution, to consider an isotropic cylindrical vessel that is capped at one end by a hemispherical head and at the other end by a hemiellipsoidal head as shown in Fig. 4.8.

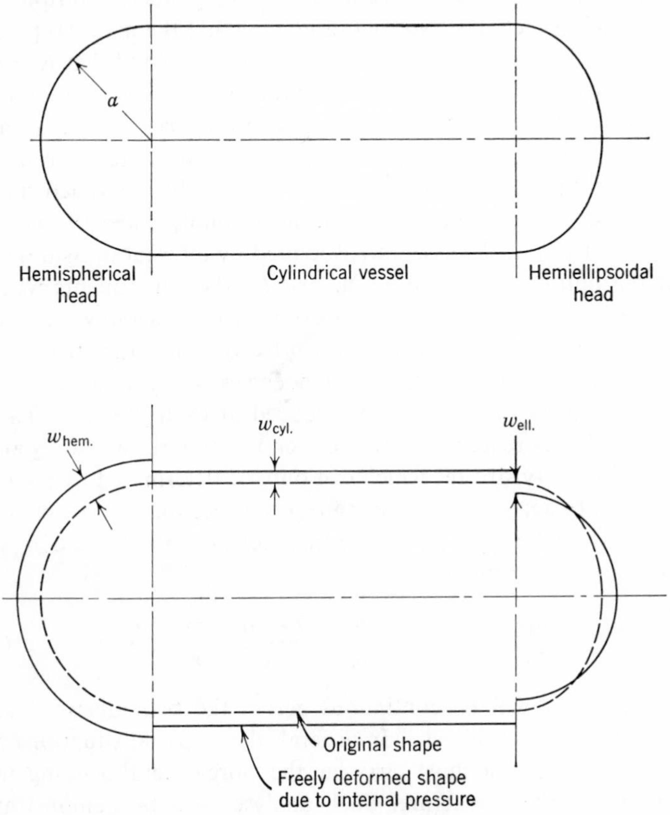

Figure 4.8 Geometry of a typical composite pressure vessel.

We have shown with Eqs. 4.31b that, under the influence of a uniform temperature rise T_0 and an internal pressure p, the transverse displacement of a cylindrical membrane shell would, if the shell were free to deform, be given by

$$w_{\text{cyl}} = \frac{pa^2}{2Eh_c}(2 - \nu) + a\alpha_t T_0. \tag{4.34a}$$

Similarly, we have shown with Eqs. 4.32e and 4.33c that the transverse displacements at the edges of a hemisphere and a hemiellipsoid are given by

$$w_{\text{hem}} = \frac{pR^2}{2Eh_h}(1 - \nu) + R\alpha_t T_0, \tag{4.34b}$$

$$w_{\text{ell}} = \frac{pa^2}{2Eh_e}\left(2 - \frac{a^2}{b^2} - \nu\right) + a\alpha_t T_0, \tag{4.34c}$$

where h_c, h_h, and h_e are the thicknesses of the cylinder, hemisphere, and hemiellipsoid, respectively. Now let us assume that the material properties of all of the components of the assembly are identical and that $R = a$. The foregoing equations then indicate that if the pressure were zero, and if the entire assembly were subjected to the temperature rise T_0, the transverse displacements of the components would be continuous across each of the two junctions if the assembly were separated and allowed to deform freely. Thus, no bending would be induced in the assembly under this condition. On the other hand, if the assembly is loaded by internal pressure, with or without the uniform temperature change T_0, the components would not deform the same amounts at their junctions if the assembly were cut and the components were allowed to deform freely. Since the structure must remain continuous in spite of such tendencies, an axial moment and a transverse shearing force would be induced at each junction. These so-called discontinuity reactions introduce bending into the assembly and give rise to discontinuity stresses which can only be determined by an analysis which takes into account the bending resistance of the components. However, in the special case in which the thicknesses of the three components are related by the formulas

$$\frac{h_h}{h_c} = \frac{1 - \nu}{2 - \nu}, \qquad \frac{h_e}{h_c} = \frac{2 - (a^2/b^2) - \nu}{2 - \nu}, \tag{4.34d}$$

the displacements will be continuous across the two junctions and no discontinuity stresses will arise. In general, these special situations do not arise in practice and one must carry out the more general bending analysis of a composite shell structure. Such analyses will be demonstrated in Section 5.5.

4.3*b* Membrane Shells of Revolution under Arbitrary Loads

When the external loads which act upon a membrane shell of revolution are arbitrary functions of the polar angle θ, Eqs. 4.27 must be solved without further simplification. It is most convenient to solve such problems by expanding the applied loads and the dependent variables in Fourier series with respect to the independent variable θ.

We thus assume that the external loads and the temperature can be expanded in Fourier series of the type

$$
\begin{aligned}
q_\varphi &= \sum_{n=0}^{\infty} q_{\varphi n}(\varphi)\cos n\theta + \sum_{n=1}^{\infty} \bar{q}_{\varphi n}(\varphi)\sin n\theta,\\
q_\theta &= \sum_{n=1}^{\infty} q_{\theta n}(\varphi)\sin n\theta + \sum_{n=0}^{\infty} \bar{q}_{\theta n}(\varphi)\cos n\theta,\\
q &= \sum_{n=0}^{\infty} q_n(\varphi)\cos n\theta + \sum_{n=1}^{\infty} \bar{q}_n(\varphi)\sin n\theta,\\
T &= \sum_{n=0}^{\infty} T_n(\varphi)\cos n\theta + \sum_{n=1}^{\infty} \bar{T}_n(\varphi)\sin n\theta
\end{aligned}
\tag{4.35a}
$$

where the coefficients are known functions of φ. The first and second sums in each of these expansions represent those portions of the arbitrary applied surface loads which are, respectively, symmetric and antisymmetric with respect to the generator passing through $\theta = 0$. To be consistent with the foregoing expansions, we assume further that the stress resultants can be expanded in the form

$$
\begin{aligned}
N_\varphi &= \sum_{n=0}^{\infty} N_{\varphi n}(\varphi)\cos n\theta + \sum_{n=1}^{\infty} \bar{N}_{\varphi n}(\varphi)\sin n\theta,\\
N_\theta &= \sum_{n=0}^{\infty} N_{\theta n}(\varphi)\cos n\theta + \sum_{n=1}^{\infty} \bar{N}_{\theta n}(\varphi)\sin n\theta,\\
N_{\varphi\theta} &= \sum_{n=1}^{\infty} N_{\varphi\theta n}(\varphi)\sin n\theta + \sum_{n=0}^{\infty} \bar{N}_{\varphi\theta n}(\varphi)\cos n\theta,
\end{aligned}
\tag{4.35b}
$$

where the coefficients are to be determined. The first and second sums in these and all subsequent expansions represent the symmetric and antisymmetric contributions to the solution. In view of Eq. 4.26, however, we notice that

$$
\{N_{\theta n}, \bar{N}_{\theta n}\} = -r_\theta\{q_n, \bar{q}_n\} - \frac{r_\theta}{r_\varphi}\{N_{\varphi n}, \bar{N}_{\varphi n}\}. \tag{4.35c}
$$

Once the coefficients in the expansions of the stress resultants have been determined, the displacements can be determined as follows: first, we expand the strains in the series

$$
\begin{aligned}
\epsilon_\varphi{}^0 &= \sum_{n=0}^{\infty} \epsilon_{\varphi n}(\varphi)\cos n\theta + \sum_{n=1}^{\infty} \bar{\epsilon}_{\varphi n}(\varphi)\sin n\theta,\\
\epsilon_\theta{}^0 &= \sum_{n=0}^{\infty} \epsilon_{\theta n}(\varphi)\cos n\theta + \sum_{n=1}^{\infty} \bar{\epsilon}_{\theta n}(\varphi)\sin n\theta,\\
\gamma_{\varphi\theta}{}^0 &= \sum_{n=1}^{\infty} \gamma_n(\varphi)\sin n\theta + \sum_{n=0}^{\infty} \bar{\gamma}_n(\varphi)\cos n\theta.
\end{aligned}
\tag{4.35d}
$$

The coefficients of the strain series are related to the coefficients of the force and temperature expansions by equations of the type 4.8. Thus

$$\epsilon_{\varphi n} = \frac{1}{E_\varphi h} (N_{\varphi n} - \nu_{\theta\varphi} N_{\theta n}) + \alpha_{t\varphi} T_n,$$

$$\epsilon_{\theta n} = \frac{1}{E_\theta h} (N_{\theta n} - \nu_{\varphi\theta} N_{\varphi n}) + \alpha_{t\theta} T_n, \tag{4.35e}$$

$$\gamma_n = N_{\varphi\theta n} / G_{\varphi\theta} h,$$

for the symmetric contribution to the solution. An identical set of equations relates the barred coefficients of the antisymmetric contribution. The displacements are now expanded in the following series:

$$u_\varphi = \sum_{n=0}^{\infty} u_{\varphi n}(\varphi) \cos n\theta + \sum_{n=1}^{\infty} \bar{u}_{\varphi n}(\varphi) \sin n\theta,$$

$$u_\theta = \sum_{n=1}^{\infty} u_{\theta n}(\varphi) \sin n\theta + \sum_{n=0}^{\infty} \bar{u}_{\theta n}(\varphi) \cos n\theta, \tag{4.35f}$$

$$w = \sum_{n=0}^{\infty} w_n(\varphi) \cos n\theta + \sum_{n=1}^{\infty} \bar{w}_n(\varphi) \sin n\theta.$$

Finally, the coefficients of the displacement series are related to the coefficients of the strain series by use of the strain-displacement relations (Eqs. 4.13). For the symmetric contributions this gives, for example,

$$r_\varphi \epsilon_{\varphi n} = \frac{du_{\varphi n}}{d\varphi} + w_n,$$

$$\epsilon_{\theta n} r_\theta \sin \varphi = n u_{\theta n} + u_{\varphi n} \cos \varphi + w_n \sin \varphi, \tag{4.35g}$$

$$\gamma_n r_\theta \sin \varphi = \frac{r_\theta}{r_\varphi} \sin \varphi \frac{du_{\theta n}}{d\varphi} - u_{\theta n} \cos \varphi - n u_{\varphi n}.$$

By rearrangement of the first two of the above, we find that

$$w_n = r_\varphi \epsilon_{\varphi n} - \frac{du_{\varphi n}}{d\varphi},$$

$$u_{\theta n} = \frac{1}{n} \left[\sin \varphi \frac{du_{\varphi n}}{d\varphi} - u_{\varphi n} \cos \varphi + (\epsilon_{\theta n} r_\theta - \epsilon_{\varphi n} r_\varphi) \sin \varphi \right], \tag{4.35h}$$

and when these are substituted into the third of Eqs. 4.35g, it takes the form

$$\frac{r_\theta}{r_\varphi} \sin^2 \varphi \frac{d^2 u_{\varphi n}}{d\varphi^2} - \cos \varphi \sin \varphi \frac{du_{\varphi n}}{d\varphi} + \left(\frac{r_\theta}{r_\varphi} \sin^2 \varphi + \cos^2 \varphi - n^2 \right) u_{\varphi n}$$

$$= n \gamma_n r_\theta \sin \varphi - \frac{r_\theta}{r_\varphi} \sin^2 \varphi \frac{d}{d\varphi} (r_\theta \epsilon_{\theta n} - r_\varphi \epsilon_{\varphi n})$$

$$+ \left(1 - \frac{r_\theta}{r_\varphi} \right) (r_\theta \epsilon_{\theta n} - r_\varphi \epsilon_{\varphi n}) \cos \varphi \sin \varphi \tag{4.35i}$$

(Handwritten margin notes:)
$\varepsilon_\varphi = \frac{1}{r_\varphi} \left(\frac{\partial u_\varphi}{\partial \varphi} + w \right)$

$\varepsilon_\theta = \frac{1}{r} \left(\frac{\partial u_\theta}{\partial \theta} + u_\varphi \cos\varphi + w \sin\varphi \right)$

$\gamma_{\varphi\theta} = \frac{1}{r_\varphi} \frac{\partial u_\theta}{\partial \varphi} - \frac{1}{r} \left(u_\theta \cos\varphi - \frac{\partial u_\varphi}{\partial \theta} \right)$

solve for $u_{\varphi n}$

for the symmetric contribution. A similar equation holds for the antisymmetric contribution.

To illustrate the use of the preceding method, let us consider a problem in which the applied loads and temperature are symmetric with respect to the generator passing through $\theta = 0$ and derive the solution corresponding to the nth terms of the symmetric contribution to each expansion. Upon substitution of the nth symmetric terms into Eqs. 4.27, we obtain the equations

$$\begin{aligned} \frac{dN_{\varphi n}}{d\varphi} + \left(1 + \frac{r_\varphi}{r_\theta}\right) \cot \varphi N_{\varphi n} + \frac{n r_\varphi N_{\varphi\theta n}}{r_\theta \sin \varphi} &= -r_\varphi(q_{\varphi n} + q_n \cot \varphi), \\ \frac{dN_{\varphi\theta n}}{d\varphi} + 2\frac{r_\varphi}{r_\theta} N_{\varphi\theta n} \cot \varphi + \frac{n N_{\varphi n}}{\sin \varphi} &= -r_\varphi \left(q_{\theta n} + \frac{n q_n}{\sin \varphi}\right). \end{aligned} \tag{4.36a}$$

Thus, the dependence of the equation system upon θ has been eliminated. As could be expected when the loads are independent of $\theta (n = 0)$, the foregoing equations are decoupled and reduce to Eqs. 4.28a and 4.28b. As an example, let us apply the analysis to a spherical membrane shell for which $r_\varphi = r_\theta = R$. In this case, Eqs. 4.36a reduce to

$$\begin{aligned} \frac{dN_{\varphi n}}{d\varphi} + 2N_{\varphi n} \cot \varphi + \frac{n N_{\varphi\theta n}}{\sin \varphi} &= -R(q_{\varphi n} + q_n \cot \varphi), \\ \frac{dN_{\varphi\theta n}}{d\varphi} + 2N_{\varphi\theta n} \cot \varphi + \frac{n N_{\varphi n}}{\sin \varphi} &= -R\left(q_{\theta n} + \frac{n q_n}{\sin \varphi}\right). \end{aligned} \tag{4.37a}$$

These equations can be cast into a form which admits a convenient solution by defining the variables

$$S_n = N_{\varphi n} + N_{\varphi\theta n}, \qquad T_n = N_{\varphi n} - N_{\varphi\theta n}, \tag{4.37b}$$

and then adding Eqs. 4.37a and subtracting Eqs. 4.37a in turn to give the new equations

$$\begin{aligned} \frac{dS_n}{d\varphi} + \left(2 \cot \varphi + \frac{n}{\sin \varphi}\right) S_n &= -R\left(q_{\varphi n} + q_{\theta n} + \frac{\cos \varphi + n}{\sin \varphi} q_n\right), \\ \frac{dT_n}{d\varphi} + \left(2 \cot \varphi - \frac{n}{\sin \varphi}\right) T_n &= -R\left(q_{\varphi n} - q_{\theta n} + \frac{\cos \varphi - n}{\sin \varphi} q_n\right). \end{aligned} \tag{4.37c}$$

Each of these equations is a case of Eq. 4.23c and, therefore, formula 4.23d can be used to give the solutions

$$\begin{aligned} S_n = \frac{\cot^n (\varphi/2)}{\sin^2 \varphi} \bigg[A_n - R \int \bigg(q_{\varphi n} &+ q_{\theta n} \\ &+ \frac{\cos \varphi + n}{\sin \varphi} q_n\bigg) \sin^2 \varphi \tan^n (\varphi/2)\, d\varphi\bigg], \end{aligned} \tag{4.37d}$$

$$T_n = \frac{\tan^n(\varphi/2)}{\sin^2\varphi}\left[B_n - R\int\left(q_{\varphi n} - q_{\theta n} + \frac{\cos\varphi - n}{\sin\varphi}q_n\right)\sin^2\varphi\cot^n(\varphi/2)\,d\varphi\right],$$

where A_n and B_n are arbitrary constants. In view of Eqs. 4.37b, we then find that

$$\begin{aligned}
N_{\varphi n} &= \frac{1}{2\sin^2\varphi}[A_n\cot^n(\varphi/2) + B_n\tan^n(\varphi/2)] \\
&\quad - \frac{\cot^n(\varphi/2)}{2\sin^2\varphi}R\int\left(q_{\varphi n} + q_{\theta n} + \frac{n+\cos\varphi}{\sin\varphi}q_n\right)\sin^2\varphi\tan^n(\varphi/2)\,d\varphi \\
&\quad - \frac{\tan^n(\varphi/2)}{2\sin^2\varphi}R\int\left(q_{\varphi n} - q_{\theta n} + \frac{\cos\varphi - n}{\sin\varphi}q_n\right)\sin^2\varphi\cot^n(\varphi/2)\,d\varphi, \\
N_{\varphi\theta n} &= \frac{1}{2\sin^2\varphi}[A_n\cot^n(\varphi/2) - B_n\tan^n(\varphi/2)] \qquad (4.37e) \\
&\quad - \frac{\cot^n(\varphi/2)}{2\sin^2\varphi}R\int\left(q_{\varphi n} + q_{\theta n} + \frac{\cos\varphi + n}{\sin\varphi}q_n\right)\sin^2\varphi\tan^n(\varphi/2)\,d\varphi \\
&\quad + \frac{\tan^n(\varphi/2)}{2\sin^2\varphi}R\int\left(q_{\varphi n} - q_{\theta n} + \frac{\cos\varphi - n}{\sin\varphi}q_n\right)\sin^2\varphi\cot^n(\varphi/2)\,d\varphi,
\end{aligned}$$

and $N_{\theta n}$ can be found from Eq. 4.35c. In the preceding equations, we observe that the portions which involve the integrals represent the particular solutions which are associated with the surface loads, while the portions involving the arbitrary constants A_n and B_n constitute the complementary solutions which are used to satisfy the edge conditions.

Now let us suppose that we have a hemispherical dome loaded by its own weight and supported by k columns which are equally spaced around the edge $\varphi = \pi/2$ (as shown in Fig. 4.9 for the case $k = 4$). In this case, we may recall from Eqs. 4.29a that the dead load has the components

$$q = P\cos\varphi, \qquad q_\varphi = P\sin\varphi, \qquad q_\theta = 0, \qquad (4.38a)$$

where P is the weight of the shell per unit area of its reference surface. Thus, we find that as far as the surface loads are concerned the loads are independent of θ and, therefore, $n = 0$. The particular solution is then

$$N_{\varphi 0} = \frac{-PR}{1+\cos\varphi}, \qquad N_{\theta 0} = PR\left(\frac{1}{1+\cos\varphi} - \cos\varphi\right), \qquad N_{\varphi\theta 0} = 0, \quad (4.38b)$$

from the integrals in Eqs. 4.37e. As we should expect these are identical to our previous solution of the dead load case as given by Eqs. 4.29b and 4.29c. For this portion of the solution, we have set $A_0 = B_0 = 0$ in order to suppress the solution $(\sin^2\varphi)^{-1}$ which is singular at the apex ($\varphi = 0$) of the dome.

To account for the edge loads imparted to the shell by the columns upon

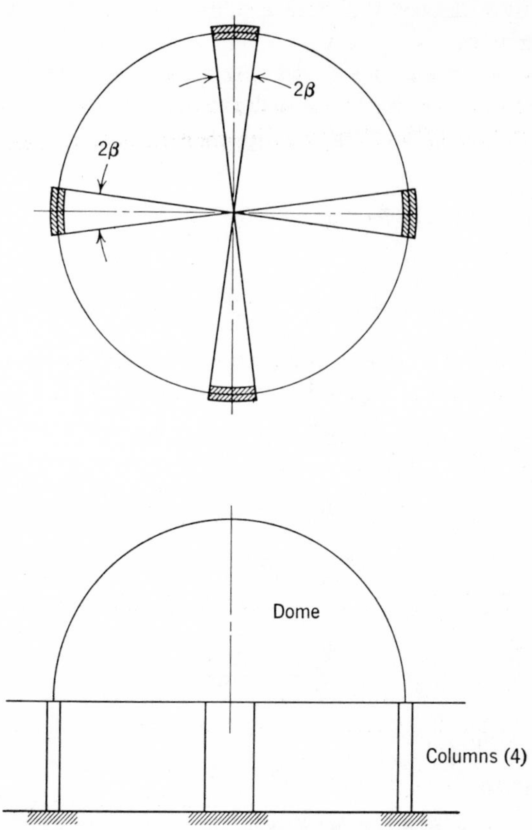

Figure 4.9 Hemispherical shell on four supports.

which it is mounted, we notice that $q_n = q_{\varphi n} = q_{\theta n} = 0$ for $n \geqslant 1$ and find from Eqs. 4.37e that

$$N_{\varphi n} = \frac{B_n \tan^n (\varphi/2)}{2 \sin^2 \varphi} = -N_{\theta n} = -N_{\varphi\theta n}, \qquad n \geqslant 1 \quad (4.38c)$$

where we have set $A_n = 0$ in order to suppress the solution $\cot^n (\varphi/2)$ which is singular at the apex of the dome. The general solution is then

$$N_\varphi = \frac{-PR}{1 + \cos \varphi} + \sum_{n=k,\,2k,\,\ldots}^{\infty} \frac{B_n}{2} \frac{\tan^n (\varphi/2)}{\sin^2 \varphi} \cos n\theta,$$

$$N_{\varphi\theta} = -\sum_{n=k,\,2k,\,\ldots}^{\infty} \frac{B_n}{2} \frac{\tan^n (\varphi/2)}{\sin^2 \varphi} \sin n\theta, \qquad (4.38d)$$

$$N_\theta = PR\left(\frac{1}{1 + \cos \varphi} - \cos \varphi\right) - \sum_{n=k,\,2k,\,\ldots}^{\infty} \frac{B_n}{2} \frac{\tan^n (\varphi/2)}{\sin^2 \varphi} \cos n\theta,$$

where we have defined the index n so as to indicate the periodicity of the supporting reactions.

We now determine the B_n so that at $\varphi = \pi/2$ the force N_φ vanishes between the supports and takes on the value $-P(2\pi R^2)/(2\beta R)k = -P\pi R/\beta k$ over the supports. Mathematically, these boundary conditions are expressed as

$$\begin{aligned} N_\varphi &= -P\pi R/\beta k, & 0 \leqslant \theta \leqslant \beta, \\ &= 0, & \beta \leqslant \theta \leqslant (2\pi/k - \beta), \\ &= -P\pi R/\beta k, & (2\pi/k - \beta) \leqslant \theta \leqslant 2\pi/k, \end{aligned} \tag{4.38e}$$

at $\varphi = \pi/2$, where 2β indicates the angle over which each support extends. In terms of the first of Eqs. 4.38d, these conditions are expressed as

$$\begin{aligned} \sum_{n=k,\,2k,\ldots}^{\infty} \frac{B_n}{2} \cos n\theta &= PR(1 - \pi/\beta k), & 0 \leqslant \theta \leqslant \beta \\ &= PR, & \beta \leqslant \theta \leqslant (2\pi/k - \beta), \\ &= PR(1 - \pi/\beta k), & (2\pi/k - \beta) \leqslant \theta \leqslant 2\pi/k. \end{aligned} \tag{4.38f}$$

It then follows, by use of the methods of Fourier analysis, that

$$\frac{B_n}{2} = -\frac{2PR}{\beta} \sin \beta n \tag{4.38g}$$

and the final solution is

$$\begin{aligned} N_\varphi &= \frac{-PR}{1 + \cos\varphi} - \frac{2PR}{\beta \sin^2 \varphi} \sum_{n=k,\,2k,\ldots}^{\infty} \frac{\sin \beta n}{n} \tan^n (\varphi/2) \cos n\theta, \\ N_\theta &= PR\left(\frac{1}{1 + \cos\varphi} - \cos\varphi\right) \\ &\quad + \frac{2PR}{\beta \sin^2 \varphi} \sum_{n=k,\,2k,\ldots}^{\infty} \frac{\sin \beta n}{n} \tan^n (\varphi/2) \cos n\theta, \\ N_{\varphi\theta} &= \frac{2PR}{\beta \sin^2 \varphi} \sum_{n=k,\,2k,\ldots}^{\infty} \frac{\sin \beta n}{n} \tan^n (\varphi/2) \sin n\theta. \end{aligned} \tag{4.38h}$$

Although this solution satisfies the conditions which have been prescribed by Eqs. 4.38e at the edge $\varphi = \pi/2$, it leads, as can be seen from the last of Eqs. 4.38h, to a nonvanishing edge shearing force $N_{\varphi\theta}$. In an actual application, the latter would have to vanish and, therefore, the solution 4.38h would not satisfy the actual boundary conditions that exist in the problem. A more satisfactory solution could only be obtained by taking bending effects into consideration. The solution 4.38h is, however, expected to be fairly accurate away from the edge of the dome.

4.4 CLOSURE

In this chapter we have shown that, in the analysis of membrane shells, the equations of equilibrium can be solved for the stress resultants directly. After finding the strains in such shells by use of the stress–strain laws, the displacements can be found by suitable integrations of the strain-displacement equations. We demonstrated that the solution procedure is quite simple when applied to membrane shells of revolution whose reference surfaces have straight generators, and that the procedure is only slightly more complicated when the generators are curved. In our consideration of membrane shells whose reference surfaces have curved generators under loads which are arbitrary functions of the polar angle, we used the method of Fourier expansions to eliminate the dependence of the solution upon θ. This method will be applied again and again in problems of shells under loads that are arbitrary functions of θ. As a result, we shall have frequent cause to return to this first encounter with the method in our later work.

Although we showed that the neglect of bending effects greatly simplifies the process of obtaining a solution, we also found that it introduces certain inconsistencies at the edge of the shell when it is not supported in the required manner. The latter point was illustrated for both single and multicomponent shells. The results are, however, expected to be valid at points that are removed from the edges of the shells and this will be confirmed when we consider the analysis of shells with bending resistance. At that time, we shall return to the results obtained here for the purpose of bringing out more fully the range of applicability of the present results.

This ends, for the time being, our consideration of membrane shells. We shall point out additional membrane solutions when we take up the determination of displacements in shells of revolution with bending resistance in Chapters 5 and 6. Then, in Chapter 8, we shall consider the free-vibration analysis of membrane shells of revolution.

We have illustrated the analysis of membrane shells of revolution for cylindrical, conical, spherical, and ellipsoidal shells. For additional exposure to the analysis of membrane shells, the reader is invited to work out the exercises that are given at the end of this chapter and to consult the supplementary references in which a wide variety of additional results are given.

SUPPLEMENTARY REFERENCES

Flügge, W., *Stresses in Shells*, Berlin: Springer Verlag, Chapters 2, 3, 4 (1962).

Timoshenko, S., and Woinowsky-Krieger, W., *Theory of Plates and Shells*, New York: McGraw-Hill, 2nd ed., Chapter 14 (1959).

Haas, A. M., *Thin Concrete Shells*, New York: John Wiley and Sons, Volume I, (1962).

EXERCISES

4.1 Determine the stress resultants and displacements in a liquid filled cylindrical membrane shell of elliptical cross section.

4.2 Derive a solution for a circular cylindrical membrane shell subjected to constant shearing forces ($N_{\varphi\theta}$) distributed around the circumference at its ends.

4.3 Determine the stress resultants in a cylindrical membrane shell of oval cross section whose radius is given by

$$\frac{1}{r} = \frac{1}{r_0}\left(1 + \xi \cos \frac{4\pi s}{L_0}\right)$$

under a uniform internal pressure load. Here ξ is a noncircularity parameter, L_0 is the perimeter of the oval, and r_0 is the radius of a cylinder which has the same perimeter L_0 as the oval.

4.4 Derive the fundamental equations of a flat circular membrane.

4.5 Determine the stress resultants in cylindrical, spherical and conical membrane shells of revolution subjected to an axial inertia load.

4.6 Determine the stress resultants in pressurized membrane shells of revolution whose reference surfaces are in the following form,

(a) A toroid of circular cross section.
(b) A paraboloid.

4.7 Determine the stress resultants in an ogival membrane shell of revolution which is loaded by its own weight. An ogival shell is one whose reference surface is formed by rotating a circular arc about an axis which does not correspond to a diameter as shown in Fig. 4.10.

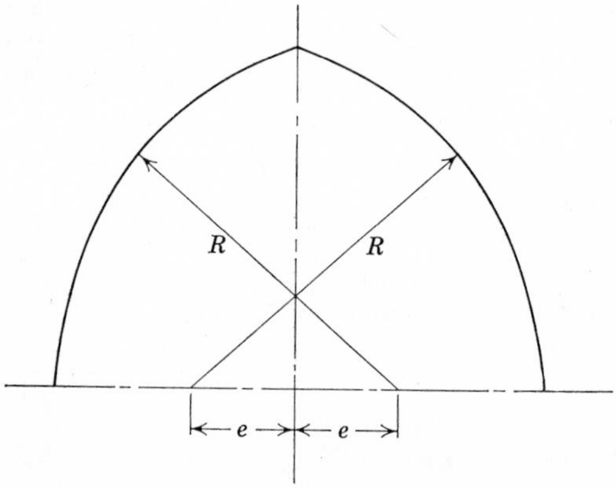

Figure 4.10 Geometry of an ogival shell.

4.8 Determine the displacements in the conical shell shown in Fig. 4.4.

4.9 Determine the stress resultants and displacements which arise in the hemispherical membrane shell loaded by its own weight and mounted as shown in Fig. 4.11.

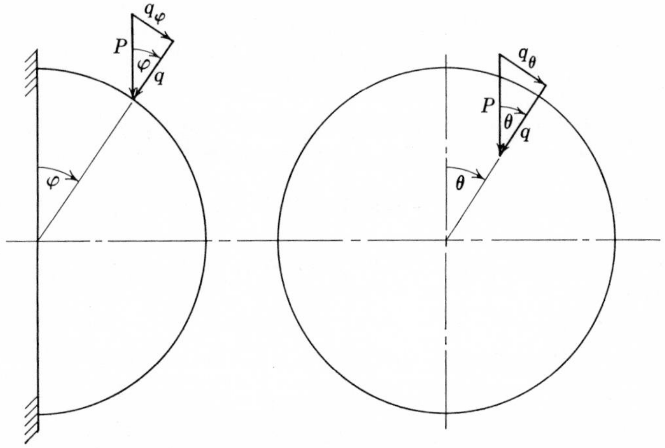

Figure 4.11 Spherical shell loaded by its own weight.

4.10 An alternate method of solution in an analysis of membrane shells of revolution consists of substituting Eqs. 4.13 into Eqs. 4.12 and then using the resulting expressions in Eqs. 4.11. Carry this procedure out for an isotropic spherical membrane shell and reduce the system to a single differential equation in one of the displacements. Give the general solution of the resulting equation.

5

Shells of Revolution with Bending Resistance under Loads that Are Independent of the Polar Angle

5.1 INTRODUCTION

We have shown, in the previous chapter, that the neglect of bending effects leads to fairly simple solutions in the analysis of various shell configurations. These solutions were, however, shown to be of limited validity when they were applied to segments of shells because of the inconsistencies that are introduced at boundaries by the membrane assumption. Closely allied to these difficulties, but not mentioned in the preceding treatment, are the bending effects that are introduced into a shell by the loads themselves. In particular, we have in mind discontinuous surface loads such as concentrated point and line loads and moments, bands of pressure, and so on. While the membrane state of stress may exist under certain load and support conditions, it does not exist under arbitrary conditions. For this reason, the most valid analysis of a shell is, in the general case, one in which bending effects are taken into account. Consequently, our concern in the rest of this book will be the analysis of shells with bending resistance. In particular, we shall focus our attention on shells of revolution.

There exists a large class of problems that are associated with the nuclear, aerospace, and petrochemical industries in which shells of revolution are subjected to loads that are independent of the polar angle. Examples of such loads are axial inertia loads, centrifugal loads, internal pressure, axial gradients in temperature, and so on. Such loads permit certain simplifications to be made in the resulting analysis and for this reason it is appropriate to enter our discussion of shells with bending resistance by taking up, first, the special category of shells under the influence of static loadings which are independent of the polar angle. Shells of revolution under loads which are arbitrary functions of the polar angle will be covered in the next chapter. The solutions which are to be demonstrated in this and the next chapter will be obtained by exact analytical procedures. Since these methods break down for the more complicated shell configurations, we shall, in Chapters 7 and 10, take up the analysis of shells by approximate analytical and numerical techniques, respectively.

To begin the discussion, let us write the fundamental equations which describe the static behavior of a shell of revolution with bending resistance under loads which are independent of the polar angle. In doing this we notice, as we did in Chapter 4, that in a shell of revolution $A_1 = R_1 = r_\varphi$, $A_2 = R_0 = r = r_\theta \sin\varphi$, and $R_2 = r_\theta$, all geometric quantities are independent of θ and the Gauss condition is given by Eq. 4.10. Consequently, all of the shell variables are independent of θ and, starting with the relationships between the strains and displacements, we obtain (see Eqs. 2.19):

$$\epsilon_\varphi{}^0 = \frac{1}{r_\varphi}\left(\frac{du_\varphi}{d\varphi} + w\right), \qquad \epsilon_\theta{}^0 = \frac{1}{r_\theta}(u_\varphi \cot\varphi + w), \qquad \gamma_{\varphi\theta}{}^0 = 0. \tag{5.1}$$

As could be expected, these expressions are identical to those given for membrane shells of revolution under similar loadings by Eqs. 4.28g. When bending effects are to be considered, however, we are also interested in the relationships between the rotations and the displacements which are given by (see Eqs. 2.16):

$$\beta_\varphi = \frac{1}{r_\varphi}\left(u_\varphi - \frac{dw}{d\varphi}\right), \qquad \beta_\theta = 0, \tag{5.2}$$

and in the relationships between the changes in curvature and the displacements as given by (see Eqs. 2.19):

$$\kappa_\varphi = \frac{1}{r_\varphi}\frac{d\beta_\varphi}{d\varphi}, \qquad \kappa_\theta = \frac{1}{r_\theta}\beta_\varphi \cot\varphi, \qquad \tau = 0. \tag{5.3}$$

With these expressions for the strains and changes in curvature, the expressions for the stress resultants and couples reduce from Eqs. 2.24 to the following set:

$$\begin{aligned} N_\varphi &= K_\varphi\left[\frac{1}{r_\varphi}\left(\frac{du_\varphi}{d\varphi} + w\right) + \frac{\nu_{\varphi\theta}}{r_\theta}(u_\varphi \cot\varphi + w) - (\alpha_{t\varphi} + \nu_{\varphi\theta}\alpha_{t\theta})T_0\right], \\ N_\theta &= K_\theta\left[\frac{1}{r_\theta}(u_\varphi \cot\varphi + w) + \frac{\nu_{\theta\varphi}}{r_\varphi}\left(\frac{du_\varphi}{d\varphi} + w\right) - (\alpha_{t\theta} + \nu_{\theta\varphi}\alpha_{t\varphi})T_0\right], \\ N_{\varphi\theta} &= N_{\theta\varphi} = 0, \end{aligned} \tag{5.4}$$

$$
\begin{aligned}
M_\varphi &= D_\varphi\left[\frac{1}{r_\varphi}\frac{d\beta_\varphi}{d\varphi} + \frac{\nu_{\varphi\theta}}{r_\theta}\beta_\varphi \cot\varphi - (\alpha_{t\varphi} + \nu_{\varphi\theta}\alpha_{t\theta})T_1\right],\\
M_\theta &= D_\theta\left[\frac{1}{r_\theta}\beta_\varphi \cot\varphi + \frac{\nu_{\theta\varphi}}{r_\varphi}\frac{d\beta_\varphi}{d\varphi} - (\alpha_{t\theta} + \nu_{\theta\varphi}\alpha_{t\varphi})T_1\right],\\
M_{\varphi\theta} &= M_{\theta\varphi} = 0
\end{aligned}
\tag{5.5}
$$

where

$$
T_0 = \frac{1}{h}\int_\zeta T\,d\zeta, \qquad T_1 = \frac{12}{h^3}\int_\zeta T\zeta\,d\zeta, \tag{5.6}
$$

$$
\begin{aligned}
\{K_\varphi, K_\theta\} &= \{E_\varphi, E_\theta\}h/(1 - \nu_{\varphi\theta}\nu_{\theta\varphi}),\\
\{D_\varphi, D_\theta\} &= \{E_\varphi, E_\theta\}h^3/12(1 - \nu_{\varphi\theta}\nu_{\theta\varphi}),
\end{aligned}
\tag{5.7}
$$

and we have assumed that the shell is composed of a single homogeneous orthotropic layer whose properties are independent of the thickness coordinate ζ. More general materials can also be considered; however, the resulting manipulations become extremely cumbersome while changing the analysis only slightly.

To complete the presentation of the fundamental equations of a shell of revolution under loads that are independent of the polar angle, we add the equations of static equilibrium which, in view of the preceding results, reduce from Eqs. 2.71 to

$$
\begin{aligned}
&\frac{d}{d\varphi}(rN_\varphi) - N_\theta r_\varphi \cos\varphi + rQ_\varphi + rr_\varphi q_\varphi = 0,\\
&\frac{d}{d\varphi}(rQ_\varphi) - \left(\frac{N_\varphi}{r_\varphi} + \frac{N_\theta}{r_\theta}\right) rr_\varphi - rr_\varphi q = 0,\\
&\frac{d}{d\varphi}(rM_\varphi) - M_\theta r_\varphi \cos\varphi - rr_\varphi Q_\varphi = 0
\end{aligned}
\tag{5.8}
$$

where we have assumed that $q_\theta = 0$. Solutions of the foregoing system must satisfy the following boundary conditions (see Eqs. 2.80):

$$
\begin{aligned}
N_\varphi &= \bar{N}_\varphi \quad &\text{or}\quad u_\varphi &= \bar{u}_\varphi,\\
Q_\varphi &= \bar{Q}_\varphi \quad &\text{or}\quad w &= \bar{w},\\
M_\varphi &= \bar{M}_\varphi \quad &\text{or}\quad \beta_\varphi &= \bar{\beta}_\varphi
\end{aligned}
\tag{5.9}
$$

on an edge of constant φ. Since we shall be concerned with shells that are closed with respect to the coordinate θ, these are the only conditions that are to be applied.

When we considered the analysis of membrane shells, we found that the equilibrium equations could be solved for the stress resultants without further manipulation and that the displacements could then be obtained from these forces, via the stress–strain relations, by suitable integrations of the strain-displacement equations. This approach cannot be applied in the analysis of shells with bending resistance because the number of unknown quantities in the equilibrium equations exceeds the number of equilibrium equations.

It is most convenient in the class of problems that is under consideration here to reduce the equations of equilibrium to two differential equations which relate the rotation β_φ and the transverse shearing force Q_φ. This reduction, which was proposed by H. Reissner[1] and generalized by E. Meissner[2] will now be described. The resulting equations will then be used in the solution of problems involving cylindrical, conical, spherical, and composite shells.

The derivation begins with the substitution of the expressions for the stress couples from Eqs. 5.5 into the third equilibrium equation (Eq. 5.8). This gives the result

$$\begin{aligned} \frac{r_\theta}{r_\varphi}\frac{d^2\beta_\varphi}{d\varphi^2} &+ \left[\frac{r_\theta}{r_\varphi}\cot\varphi + \frac{d}{d\varphi}\left(\frac{r_\theta}{r_\varphi}\right) + \frac{r_\theta}{r_\varphi}\frac{1}{D_\varphi}\frac{dD_\varphi}{d\varphi}\right]\frac{d\beta_\varphi}{d\varphi} \\ &- \left[\frac{r_\varphi D_\theta}{r_\theta D_\varphi}\cot^2\varphi + \nu_{\varphi\theta} - \nu_{\varphi\theta}\cot\varphi\frac{1}{D_\varphi}\frac{dD_\varphi}{d\varphi}\right]\beta_\varphi \\ = \frac{(r_\theta Q_\varphi)r_\varphi}{D_\varphi} &+ r_\theta(\alpha_{t\varphi} + \nu_{\varphi\theta}\alpha_{t\theta})\frac{dT_1}{d\varphi} \\ &+ T_1 r_\varphi \cot\varphi\left[\alpha_{t\varphi} + \nu_{\varphi\theta}\alpha_{t\theta} - (\alpha_{t\theta} + \nu_{\theta\varphi}\alpha_{t\varphi})\frac{D_\theta}{D_\varphi}\right] \end{aligned} \tag{5.10}$$

where we have allowed Young's modulus and the thickness to vary with meridional position and where we have used the identity

$$\frac{r_\theta}{r_\varphi}\cot\varphi + \frac{d}{d\varphi}\left(\frac{r_\theta}{r_\varphi}\right) = \cot\varphi - \frac{r_\theta}{r_\varphi^{\,2}}\frac{dr_\varphi}{d\varphi}. \tag{5.10a}$$

Equation 5.10 represents the first of the equations that we are seeking here. The second equation is obtained as follows.

In Section 4.3 we found that, in a membrane shell of revolution under loads that are independent of the polar angle, the following relationships exist between the displacements and the stress resultants (see Eqs. 4.28i):

$$\begin{aligned} \frac{du_\varphi}{d_\varphi} - u_\varphi\cot\varphi &= \frac{N_\varphi}{E_\varphi h}(r_\varphi + \nu_{\theta\varphi}r_\theta) - \frac{N_\theta}{E_\theta h}(r_\theta + \nu_{\varphi\theta}r_\varphi) \\ &\quad + T_0(r_\varphi\alpha_{t\varphi} - r_\theta\alpha_{t\theta}) \end{aligned} \tag{5.11a}$$

$$w + u_\varphi\cot\varphi = \frac{r_\theta}{E_\theta h}(N_\theta - \nu_{\varphi\theta}N_\varphi) + r_\theta\alpha_{t\theta}T_0.$$

[1] Reissner, H., "Spannungen in Kugelschalen," *Müller-Breslau Festschrift*, Leipzig: Kröner (1912), pp. 181–193..

[2] Meissner, E., "Das Elastizitätsproblem fur dünne Schalen von Ringflächen-, Kugel-, und Kegel-form," *Physik. Zeit.*, **14**, 343–349 (1913).

Since the strain equations from which the foregoing expressions were derived apply to shells of revolution under loads which are independent of θ regardless of the inclusion or neglect of bending effects, we may use them for our present purposes. Consequently, we may recall further that we obtained the following solutions of the above equations (see Eqs. 4.28j, 4.28k, and 4.28l):

$$u_\varphi = \sin\varphi \left[C_2 + \int_{\varphi_0}^{\varphi} \frac{F(\varphi)\,d\varphi}{\sin\varphi}\right],$$

$$w = \frac{r_\theta}{E_\theta h}(N_\theta - \nu_{\varphi\theta}N_\varphi) + r_\theta\alpha_{t\theta}T_0 - \cos\varphi\left[C_2 + \int_{\varphi_0}^{\varphi}\frac{F(\varphi)\,d\varphi}{\sin\varphi}\right], \quad (5.11b)$$

$$F(\varphi) = \frac{N_\varphi}{E_\varphi h}(r_\varphi + \nu_{\theta\varphi}r_\theta) - \frac{N_\theta}{E_\theta h}(r_\theta + \nu_{\varphi\theta}r_\varphi) + T_0(\alpha_{t\varphi}r_\varphi - \alpha_{t\theta}r_\theta).$$

We have pointed out earlier that the constant C_2 represents the *axial* displacement of a reference point on the shell. Since this is a rigid body displacement we may, without loss of generality, take $C_2 = 0$. Consequently, the displacement expressions become

$$u_\varphi = \sin\varphi \int \frac{F(\varphi)\,d\varphi}{\sin\varphi},$$
$$w = \frac{r_\theta}{E_\theta h}(N_\theta - \nu_{\varphi\theta}N_\varphi) + r_\theta\alpha_{t\theta}T_0 - \cos\varphi \int\frac{F(\varphi)\,d\varphi}{\sin\varphi}. \quad (5.11c)$$

Now we differentiate the second of Eqs. 5.11a with respect to φ, subtract the result from the product of the first of Eqs. 5.11a with cot φ, take into account the expression for β_φ from Eqs. 5.2, and obtain the result

$$r_\varphi\beta_\varphi = F(\varphi)\cot\varphi - \frac{d}{d\varphi}\left[\frac{r_\theta}{E_\theta h}(N_\theta - \nu_{\varphi\theta}N_\varphi) + r_\theta\alpha_{t\theta}T_0\right]. \quad (5.11d)$$

This equation will become the second of the two equations that we are seeking here as soon as N_φ and N_θ can be expressed in terms of Q_φ. To do this, we first rearrange the second of the equilibrium equations (Eq. 5.8) and obtain the result

$$r_\varphi N_\theta = \frac{1}{\sin\varphi}\left[\frac{d}{d\varphi}(rQ_\varphi) - rN_\varphi - rr_\varphi q\right]. \quad (5.11e)$$

This expression is now used to eliminate N_θ from the first of the equilibrium equations 5.8 to provide the following expression:

$$N_\varphi = Q_\varphi\cot\varphi - \frac{1}{r\sin\varphi}\left[C_1 + \int_{\varphi_0}^{\varphi} rr_\varphi(q\cos\varphi + q_\varphi\sin\varphi)\,d\varphi\right]. \quad (5.11f)$$

It is interesting to observe that Eqs. 5.11e and 5.11f reduce, as could be expected, to Eqs. 4.26 and 4.28c of the theory of membrane shells under similar load conditions when the transverse shearing force Q_φ is neglected. For simplicity, let us write

$$N_\varphi = Q_\varphi \cot \varphi - F_1(\varphi) \tag{5.11g}$$

where

$$F_1(\varphi) = \frac{1}{r \sin \varphi}\left[C_1 + \int_{\varphi_0}^{\varphi} r r_\varphi (q \cos \varphi + q_\varphi \sin \varphi)\, d\varphi\right] \tag{5.11h}$$

and C_1 represents the net axial component of any end loads that are applied to the shell. Now, in view of Eq. 5.11e,

$$N_\theta = \frac{1}{r_\varphi}\frac{d(r_\theta Q_\varphi)}{d\varphi} + \frac{r_\theta}{r_\varphi} F_1(\varphi) - q r_\theta. \tag{5.11i}$$

In the present formulation Eqs. 5.11g and 5.11i take the place of Eqs. 5.4. They are now used to eliminate N_φ and N_θ from Eq. 5.11d in order to obtain the expression

$$\begin{aligned} &\frac{r_\theta}{r_\varphi}\frac{d^2(r_\theta Q_\varphi)}{d\varphi^2} + \left[\frac{r_\theta}{r_\varphi}\cot\varphi + \frac{d}{d\varphi}\left(\frac{r_\theta}{r_\varphi}\right) - \frac{r_\theta}{r_\varphi}\frac{1}{E_\theta h}\frac{d(E_\theta h)}{d\varphi}\right]\frac{d(r_\theta Q_\varphi)}{d\varphi} \\ &\qquad - \left[\frac{r_\varphi E_\theta}{r_\theta E_\varphi}\cot^2\varphi - \nu_{\varphi\theta} - \frac{\nu_{\varphi\theta}\cot\varphi}{E_\theta h}\frac{d(E_\theta h)}{d\varphi}\right](r_\theta Q_\varphi) \\ &\qquad = -E_\theta h r_\varphi \beta_\varphi + G(\varphi), \end{aligned} \tag{5.12}$$

where

$$\begin{aligned} G(\varphi) = &-\frac{d}{d\varphi}\left[\frac{r_\theta^{\,2}}{r_\varphi}F_1 + r_\theta \nu_{\varphi\theta} F_1 - q r_\theta^{\,2}\right] \\ &+ \left[\frac{r_\theta^{\,2}}{r_\varphi}F_1 + \nu_{\varphi\theta} r_\theta F_1 - q r_\theta^{\,2}\right]\frac{1}{E_\theta h}\frac{d(E_\theta h)}{d\varphi} \\ &- \cot\varphi\left[\frac{E_\theta}{E_\varphi}(r_\varphi + \nu_{\theta\varphi} r_\theta)F_1 + (r_\theta + \nu_{\varphi\theta} r_\varphi)\left(F_1\frac{r_\theta}{r_\varphi} - q r_\theta\right)\right] \\ &- E_\theta h\left[\frac{d}{d\varphi}(\alpha_{t\theta} r_\theta T_0) - T_0(r_\varphi \alpha_{t\varphi} - r_\theta \alpha_{t\theta})\cot\varphi\right]. \end{aligned} \tag{5.12a}$$

Equations 5.10 and 5.12 govern the behavior of a thin shell of revolution with bending resistance in which the thickness, principal radii of curvature, temperature, surface load, and thermal expansion coefficients may vary with position along a generator of the reference surface of the shell but not around a latitude circle. However, for simplicity, the Poisson's ratios have been assumed to be independent of both meridional and circumferential position.

In order to illustrate the solution of Eqs. 5.10 and 5.12, let us consider orthotropic shells of revolution whose thickness may be a function of meridional position but whose elastic and thermal properties are independent of position. In this case, it is useful to define the new dependent variables

$$U = r_\theta Q_\varphi, \qquad W = h^2 \beta_\varphi \tag{5.13a}$$

and, in view of the assumptions which have just been made,

from 5.7 (*by assuming material constants are independent of position*)

$$\frac{1}{D_\varphi} \frac{dD_\varphi}{d\varphi} = \frac{3}{h} \frac{dh}{d\varphi}, \qquad \frac{1}{E_\theta h} \frac{d(E_\theta h)}{d\varphi} = \frac{1}{h} \frac{dh}{d\varphi} = \frac{1}{k_\theta} \frac{dk_\theta}{d\varphi} \tag{5.13b}$$

Thus, Eqs. 5.10 and 5.12 take the new form

$$L(W) - 2f(\varphi)W = 12(1 - \nu_{\varphi\theta}\nu_{\theta\varphi}) \frac{U}{E_\varphi} + H(\varphi),$$

$$L(U) = -E_\theta W + G_1(\varphi) \tag{5.14a}$$

where we have defined the differential operator

$$L(\ldots) = \frac{r_\theta h}{r_\varphi^2} \frac{d^2(\ldots)}{d\varphi^2} + \left[\frac{r_\theta h}{r_\varphi^2} \cot\varphi + \frac{h}{r_\varphi} \frac{d}{d\varphi} \left(\frac{r_\theta}{r_\varphi} \right) - \frac{r_\theta}{r_\varphi^2} \frac{dh}{d\varphi} \right] \frac{d(\ldots)}{d\varphi}$$

$$- \left[\frac{E_\theta h}{r_\theta E_\varphi} \cot^2\varphi - \nu_{\varphi\theta} \frac{h}{r_\varphi} - \frac{\nu_{\varphi\theta} \cot\varphi}{r_\varphi} \frac{dh}{d\varphi} \right] (\ldots) \tag{5.14b}$$

and,

$$f(\varphi) = \frac{\nu_{\varphi\theta} h}{r_\varphi} + \left[\frac{r_\theta}{r_\varphi} \cot\varphi + \frac{d}{d\varphi} \left(\frac{r_\theta}{r_\varphi} \right) - \nu_{\varphi\theta} \cot\varphi \right] \frac{1}{r_\varphi} \frac{dh}{d\varphi} + \frac{r_\theta}{r_\varphi^2} \frac{d^2 h}{d\varphi^2}, \tag{5.14c}$$

$$H(\varphi) = \frac{h^3}{r_\varphi} \left\{ (\alpha_{t\varphi} + \nu_{\varphi\theta}\alpha_{t\theta}) r_\theta \frac{dT_1}{d\varphi} \right.$$

$$\left. + T_1 r_\varphi \cot\varphi \left[\alpha_{t\varphi} + \nu_{\varphi\theta}\alpha_{t\theta} - (\alpha_{t\theta} + \nu_{\theta\varphi}\alpha_{t\theta}) \frac{E_\theta}{E_\varphi} \right] \right\}, \tag{5.14d}$$

$$G_1(\varphi) = G(\varphi) \frac{h}{r_\varphi}. \tag{5.14e}$$

Elimination of each variable in Eqs. 5.14 leads to the differential equations

by eliminating W

$$LL(U) - 2fL(U) + 12(1 - \nu_{\varphi\theta}\nu_{\theta\varphi}) \frac{E_\theta}{E_\varphi} U$$

$$= L(G_1) - 2G_1 f - HE_\theta,$$

by eliminating U

$$LL(W) - 2L(fW) + 12(1 - \nu_{\varphi\theta}\nu_{\theta\varphi}) \frac{E_\theta}{E_\varphi} W$$

$$= \frac{G_1 h^3}{D_\varphi} + L(H). \tag{5.15a}$$

Either of these equations can be solved for one of the dependent variables and then the appropriate equation of the set 5.14a can be solved for the other dependent variable. In doing this, we shall obtain solutions which can be represented as follows:

$$U = U^c + U^p, \qquad W = W^c + W^p, \tag{5.15b}$$

where the superscripts c and p refer to the complementary and the particular solutions, respectively. Of these, the particular solution is used to account for the distributed load and temperature terms appearing in Eqs. 5.15a, while the complementary solution is used to satisfy the boundary conditions.

It is most convenient to discuss these solutions separately. Therefore, let us first focus our attention upon the complementary solutions of Eqs. 5.15a and take up the discussion of the particular solutions when specific shells are discussed later on. The complementary solutions satisfy the equations

$$\begin{aligned} LL(U^c) - 2fL(U^c) + 12(1 - \nu_{\varphi\theta}\nu_{\theta\varphi})\frac{E_\theta}{E_\varphi}\,U^c &= 0, \\ LL(W^c) - 2L(fW^c) + 12(1 - \nu_{\varphi\theta}\nu_{\theta\varphi})\frac{E_\theta}{E_\varphi}\,W^c &= 0. \end{aligned} \tag{5.15c}$$

Under some conditions, each of these fourth order differential equations can be split into two second order differential equations. To determine these conditions, let us assume that the split is possible and that the solution of the first of Eqs. 5.15c also satisfies the equation

$$L(U^c) + \lambda^2 U^c = 0 \tag{5.15d}$$

where λ is an undetermined constant parameter. From this we find, upon application of the operator L, that

$$LL(U^c) = -\lambda^2 L(U^c) = \lambda^4 U^c, \tag{5.15e}$$

and with these results we find that the first of Eqs. 5.15a reduces to

$$\left[\lambda^4 + 2\lambda^2 f + 12(1 - \nu_{\varphi\theta}\nu_{\theta\varphi})\frac{E_\theta}{E_\varphi}\right] U^c = 0. \tag{5.15f}$$

Since we are not interested in the trivial solution $U^c = 0$, the foregoing condition tells us that the quantity in brackets must vanish. From the fact that the first and third quantities are constants, we conclude that the quantity in brackets can only vanish if f is also a constant, that is,

$$f = \frac{\nu_{\varphi\theta}h}{r_\varphi} + \left[\left(\frac{r_\theta}{r_\varphi} - \nu_{\varphi\theta}\right)\cot\varphi + \frac{d}{d\varphi}\left(\frac{r_\theta}{r_\varphi}\right)\right]\frac{1}{r_\varphi}\frac{dh}{d\varphi} + \frac{r_\theta}{r_\varphi{}^2}\frac{d^2h}{d\varphi^2} = \text{const.} \tag{5.15g}$$

It is useful, for the study of this criterion, to write it in terms of the distance x along a generator rather than the angle φ by making the change of variable $dx = r_\varphi \, d\varphi$. Thus, the splitting criterion becomes

$$f = \frac{\nu_{\varphi\theta} h}{r_\varphi} + \left[\left(\frac{r_\theta}{r_\varphi} - \nu_{\varphi\theta}\right) \cot \varphi + \frac{dr_\theta}{dx} - \frac{r_\theta}{r_\varphi}\frac{dr_\varphi}{dx}\right] \frac{dh}{dx} + r_\theta \frac{d^2 h}{dx^2} = \text{const.} \tag{5.15h}$$

If a circular cylindrical shell is under consideration, we have $r_\theta = a$, $r_\varphi \to \infty$, and $\varphi = \pi/2$. Thus, Eq. 5.15h reduces to

$$f = a \frac{d^2 h}{dx^2} = \text{const.} \tag{5.15i}$$

The splitting criterion is, therefore, satisfied by wall thickness distributions which are at most second degree functions of x.

If a conical shell is under consideration, $r_\theta = x \tan \alpha$, $r_\varphi \to \infty$, and $\varphi = \pi/2 - \alpha$ where α is the angle which the generators make with the axis of the shell. Now the splitting criterion reduces to

$$f = \left[(1 - \nu_{\varphi\theta}) \frac{dh}{dx} + x \frac{d^2 h}{dx^2}\right] \tan \alpha = \text{const.} \tag{5.15j}$$

and is satisfied for conical shells with wall thickness distributions which are, at most, linear functions of x.

If shells with curved generators are of interest, we notice that it is not likely that the splitting condition will be satisfied, in general. However, if the thickness is constant, we find that

$$f = \frac{\nu_{\varphi\theta} h}{r_\varphi} = \text{const.} \tag{5.15k}$$

Unless $\nu_{\varphi\theta} = 0$, this tells us that the criterion will be satisfied only when the meridional radius of curvature is a constant. This will only be true for cylindrical, conical, spherical, and toroidal shells of revolution. All other shells of constant thickness would, therefore, require the solution of the original fourth order equations.

Now that we have shown that the splitting condition is satisfied in some practical cases, we return to the determination of the parameter λ. From the vanishing of the brackets of Eq. 5.15f, we find that λ satisfies the equation

$$\begin{Bmatrix} \lambda_1^2 \\ \lambda_2^2 \end{Bmatrix} = -f \pm \left[f^2 - 12(1 - \nu_{\varphi\theta}\nu_{\theta\varphi}) \frac{E_\theta}{E_\varphi}\right]^{1/2}. \tag{5.15l}$$

If we note from Eq. 5.15g that f is of the same order of magnitude as h/r_φ, and if we assume that E_θ and E_φ are of the same order of magnitude, it will be evident, since we are dealing with thin shells, that λ_1^2 and λ_2^2 will be complex conjugates. Thus, it is appropriate to rewrite Eq. 5.15l in the form

$$\lambda_1^2 = \bar{\lambda}_2^2 = \lambda^2 = -f + i\left[12(1 - \nu_{\varphi\theta}\nu_{\theta\varphi})\frac{E_\theta}{E_\varphi} - f^2\right]^{1/2}. \quad (5.15m)$$

When the splitting criterion is satisfied, the first of Eqs. 5.15c can be reduced to the pair of equations (see Eq. 5.15d):

$$L(U^c) + \lambda^2 U^c = 0, \qquad L(U^c) + \bar{\lambda}^2 U^c = 0. \quad (5.15n)$$

These equations will each have two independent complex solutions and the solutions of one equation will be the complex conjugates of the solutions of the other. Thus, if we designate the solutions of the first of Eqs. 5.15n as

$$U_1^c = S_1 - iS_2, \qquad U_2^c = S_3 - iS_4, \quad (5.15o)$$

where the S_i are real functions, then the solutions of the second of Eqs. 5.15n can be written as

$$U_3^c = S_1 + iS_2 = \bar{U}_1^c, \qquad U_4^c = S_3 + iS_4 = \bar{U}_2^c. \quad (5.15p)$$

The complete general solution of the set 5.15n or, equivalently, Eq. 5.15c, is then given by

$$U^c = C_1U_1^c + C_2U_2^c + \bar{C}_1\bar{U}_1^c + \bar{C}_2\bar{U}_2^c, \quad (5.15q)$$

where C_1 and C_2 are complex arbitrary constants. If we let

$$C_1 = \frac{A_1 + iA_2}{2}, \qquad C_2 = \frac{A_3 + iA_4}{2}, \quad (5.15r)$$

where the A_i are real arbitrary constants, then the solution 5.15q can be expressed as

$$U^c = A_1S_1 + A_2S_2 + A_3S_3 + A_4S_4, \quad (5.15s)$$

where all quantities are real. This solution is, of course, identical to that which would have been obtained from the solution of the first of Eqs. 5.15c. No matter how U^c is obtained, we may now determine W^c by using the second of Eqs. 5.14a and noting that we are, for the time being, considering only the complementary solution. Thus, we find that

$$E_\theta W^c = -L(U^c) = \lambda^2(C_1U_1^c + C_2U_2^c) + \bar{\lambda}^2(\bar{C}_1\bar{U}_1^c + \bar{C}_2\bar{U}_2^c) \quad (5.15t)$$

If we define,

$$\mu_1^2 = Re\lambda^2 = -f, \qquad \mu_2^2 = Im\lambda^2 = \left[12(1 - \nu_{\varphi\theta}\nu_{\theta\varphi})\frac{E_\theta}{E_\varphi} - f^2\right]^{1/2} \quad (5.15u)$$

then we can write

$$E_\theta W^c = (\mu_1{}^2 A_1 - \mu_2{}^2 A_2)S_1 + (\mu_1{}^2 A_2 + \mu_2{}^2 A_1)S_2 + (\mu_1{}^2 A_3 - \mu_2{}^2 A_4)S_3 + (\mu_1{}^2 A_4 + \mu_2{}^2 A_3)S_4. \quad (5.15w)$$

The functions U_i and, therefore, S_i represent the general solutions of Eqs. 5.15n. Until the operator L is specified by applying the development to a particular shell, no more can be said about these functions. Examples of these solutions will be given presently.

Equations 5.9 indicate that, in the general case of two edges, solutions to problems of the type that are under consideration here must satisfy six boundary conditions. Our general solution 5.15s will satisfy four of these conditions while Eqs. 5.11b and 5.11h will satisfy two more for the required total of six. It should be remembered, however, that we have already satisfied a boundary condition on the axial displacement by setting $C_2 = 0$. Thus, five conditions remain to be satisfied. If the shell which is under consideration is subjected only to loads applied at its edges, then the complementary solutions which have been developed in the preceding discussion are complete. If the shell is also subjected to distributed surface loadings, then a suitable particular solution must be added to take into account the inhomogeneous portions of Eqs. 5.15a. Such solutions will be considered when specific problems involving cylindrical, conical, and spherical shells are taken up.

5.2 CIRCULAR CYLINDRICAL SHELLS

As a first illustration of the foregoing development, let us consider the analysis of a cylindrical shell of circular cross section whose thickness and elastic properties are independent of position. In this case we have (see Fig. 4.1): $r_\theta = a$, $\varphi = \pi/2$, $r_\varphi \to \infty$, and $dx = r_\varphi\, d\varphi$. Consequently, Eqs. 5.14b, 5.14c, and 5.15m reduce to

$$L(\ldots) = ha\,\frac{d^2(\ldots)}{dx^2}, \qquad f(x) = 0,$$
$$\lambda^2 = 2i\left[3\,\frac{E_s}{E_x}(1 - \nu_{xs}\nu_{sx})\right]^{1/2}. \quad (5.16a)$$

The expressions for the stress resultants, stress couples, and displacements in the circular cylindrical shell are given by

$$N_x = -F_1(x), \qquad N_s = a\left(\frac{dQ_x}{dx} - q\right),$$

$$M_x = D_x\left[\frac{d\beta_x}{dx} - (\alpha_{tx} + \nu_{xs}\alpha_{ts})T_1\right],$$

$$M_s = D_s\left[\nu_{sx}\frac{d\beta_x}{dx} - (\alpha_{ts} + \nu_{sx}\alpha_{tx})T_1\right],$$

$$F_1(x) = C_1 + \int_{x_0}^{x} q_x\,dx, \tag{5.16b}$$

$$u_x = \int_{x_0}^{x} F(x)\,dx,$$

$$w = \frac{a(N_s - \nu_{xs}N_x)}{E_s h} + \alpha_{ts}aT_0,$$

$$F(x) = \frac{N_x - \nu_{sx}N_s}{E_x h} + \alpha_{tx}T_0,$$

where

$$Q_x = Q_x{}^p + Q_x{}^c, \qquad \beta_x = \beta_x{}^p + \beta_x{}^c, \tag{5.16c}$$

and we have replaced the subscripts φ and θ with x and s, respectively.

In view of the decomposition of solutions 5.16c into complementary and particular portions, it is well to take up the determination of these contributions separately. Thus, in the next section we shall consider the complementary solution of the problem of a circular cylindrical shell. This will be followed by a discussion of the derivation of particular solutions corresponding to various external loadings and by some typical examples in the analysis of circular cylindrical shells.

5.2*a* Circular Cylindrical Shells under Edge Loadings

In the analysis of cylindrical shells that are subjected only to edge loads, we are concerned with the determination of the complementary solutions $Q_x{}^c$ and $\beta_x{}^c$. To do this, we employ the method of analysis which was associated with Eqs. 5.15c in the introduction to this chapter. These equations take the following form for the circular cylindrical shell:

$$\frac{d^2Q_x{}^c}{dx^2} \pm 2i\mu^2 Q_x{}^c = 0 \tag{5.17a}$$

where

$$\mu^2 = \left[3\frac{E_s}{E_x}\frac{(1 - \nu_{xs}\nu_{sx})}{a^2h^2}\right]^{1/2}. \tag{5.17b}$$

We assume solutions of these equations in the form

$$Q_x{}^c = C\exp(\kappa x) \tag{5.17c}$$

where C and κ are constants. When these are substituted into Eqs. 5.17a, the result is

$$\kappa = \pm\mu(1 \pm i). \tag{5.17d}$$

In view of Eqs. 5.15o, the solution functions can be written in the form

$$U_1^c = S_1 - iS_2 = e^{-\mu(1-i)x} = e^{-\mu x}(\cos\mu x + i\sin\mu x),$$
$$U_2^c = S_3 - iS_4 = e^{\mu(1-i)x} = e^{\mu x}(\cos\mu x - i\sin\mu x). \quad (5.17e)$$

Thus,

$$S_1 = e^{-\mu x}\cos\mu x, \qquad S_2 = -e^{-\mu x}\sin\mu x,$$
$$S_3 = e^{\mu x}\cos\mu x, \qquad S_4 = e^{\mu x}\sin\mu x. \quad (5.17f)$$

Therefore, the final solution is, according to Eqs. 5.15s and 5.15w,

$$Q_x^c = e^{-\mu x}(B_1\cos\mu x + B_2\sin\mu x) + e^{\mu x}(B_3\cos\mu x + B_4\sin\mu x),$$
$$\beta_x^c = \frac{1}{2\mu^2 D_x}[e^{-\mu x}(B_2\cos\mu x - B_1\sin\mu x) + e^{\mu x}(B_3\sin\mu x - B_4\cos\mu x)], \quad (5.17g)$$

where we have arbitrarily replaced $-B_2$ with $+B_2$.

It is interesting to point out here that solutions 5.17g are of the same nature as the general solutions of the problem of a beam on an elastic foundation.[3] To bring out fully the behavior of the solutions 5.17g, we have plotted in Figs. 5.1 and 5.2 the four functions S_i. It is evident from Figs. 5.1 and 5.2 and from Eqs. 5.17g that the functions that involve the negative exponential decay very rapidly and that the functions that involve

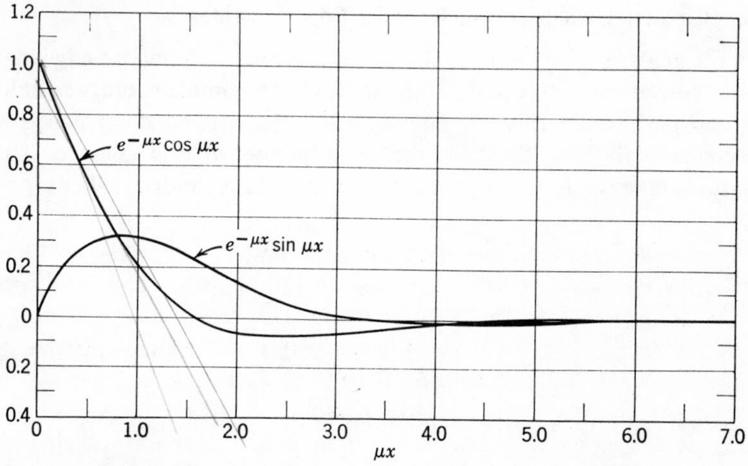

Figure 5.1 Solution functions for circular cylindrical shells.

[3] See, Hetényi, M., *Beams on Elastic Foundation*, Ann Arbor, Mich.: The University of Michigan Press (1946).

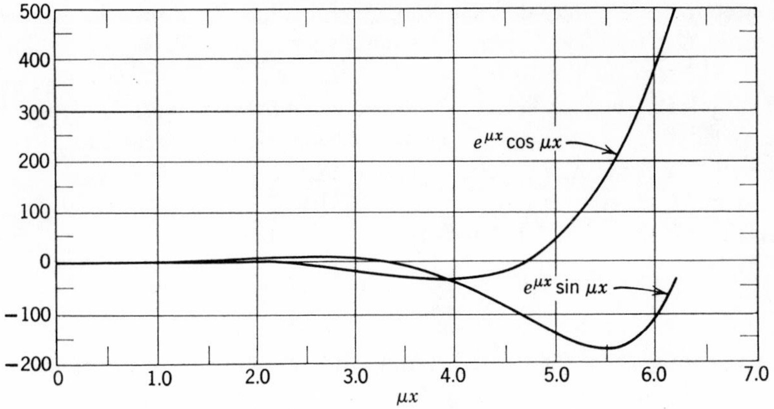

Figure 5.2 Solution functions for circular cylindrical shells.

the positive exponential grow very rapidly as μx increases. Therefore, when a "very long" cylindrical shell is under consideration, the functions that involve the positive exponentials must be suppressed in order that the shell variables will remain finite as μx grows without bound. For a very long (semi-infinite) cylindrical shell, we thus set $B_3 = B_4 = 0$ and the solution reduces to

$$Q_x{}^c = (B_1 \cos \mu x + B_2 \sin \mu x)\, e^{-\mu x},$$
$$\beta_x{}^c = \frac{1}{2\mu^2 D_x}(B_2 \cos \mu x - B_1 \sin \mu x)\, e^{-\mu x}. \qquad (5.17\text{h})$$

The rapid decay of the functions containing the negative exponential allows us to define a decay length L_c beyond which the effect of the complementary solutions, that is, the effect of the edge conditions is not felt, as

$$L_c = \pi/\mu. \qquad (5.17\text{i})$$

This definition is based upon the fact that when $\mu L_c = \pi$, the value of exp $(-\mu L_c)$ has already dropped to 0.043. The concept of a decay length permits us to conclude further that if the shell is of length $2L_c$, or greater, then any forces that are applied at the two ends will have a negligible effect upon each other. This localized nature of the edge conditions is known as the edge, or boundary layer, effect and is common to all shells (as we shall see later). Indeed, if forces are applied at both ends of a cylindrical shell and if the shell is of length greater than $2L_c$, the effect of the end conditions will not be felt sensibly at the middle of the shell and the solution there will be, approximately,

$$Q_x = Q_x{}^p, \qquad \beta_x = \beta_x{}^p. \qquad (5.17\text{j})$$

Consequently, we may define a long cylindrical shell as one whose length exceeds $2L_c$. For such shells, the simplified solutions 5.17h can be safely used, while for shells of length less than $2L_c$ the full solutions 5.17g should be used. If the shell is free at one end and loaded at the other, then only one decay length is, so to speak, involved. Therefore, such shells can be considered long if they are of length greater than L_c.

To make the expression for the decay length more meaningful, let us substitute μ from Eq. 5.17b into Eq. 5.17i to obtain the result

$$L_c = \pi\left[\frac{a^2h^2}{3(1 - \nu_{xs}\nu_{sx})}\frac{E_x}{E_s}\right]^{1/4} \tag{5.17k}$$

Thus, it is seen that the decay length is a function of the radius, thickness, and elastic properties of the cylinder. If $E_x > E_s$, the decay length is greater for an orthotropic cylinder than for an isotropic one. If $E_s < E_x$, the isotropic cylinder has a greater decay length than the orthotropic cylinder. We may obtain an idea of the magnitude of the decay length in a typical case by considering an isotropic cylindrical shell which has the dimensions $a = 20$ in., $h = 1$ in. With these dimensions, Eq. 5.17k gives the result $L_c = 3.4$ in. when ν^2 is neglected with respect to unity. Thus, if loads are applied at both edges then they will not interact if the shell is longer than 6.8 in., and if loads are applied at only one end they will not be felt at the other end if the shell is longer than 3.4 in.

5.2*b* Circular Cylindrical Shells under Distributed Loadings

Now let us consider the determination of the particular solutions $Q_x{}^p$ and $\beta_x{}^p$ which are associated with various types of surface loads. In this case, we are interested in solutions of the inhomogeneous Eqs. 5.14a which for the circular cylindrical shell take the form

$$\begin{aligned}\frac{d^2\beta_x{}^p}{dx^2} &= \frac{Q_x{}^p}{D_x} + (\alpha_{tx} + \nu_{xs}\alpha_{ts})\frac{dT_1}{dx},\\ \frac{d^2Q_x{}^p}{dx^2} &= -\frac{E_sh}{a^2}\beta_x{}^p - \frac{1}{a}\frac{d}{dx}(\nu_{xs}F_1 - qa) - \frac{E_sh}{a}\frac{d}{dx}(\alpha_{ts}T_0).\end{aligned} \tag{5.18a}$$

Before we consider the solution of these equations for the most general types of loadings, it is well to point out that when the shell is under the influence of an internal pressure $q = -p$ and/or a uniform temperature change which is independent of x, the above equations reduce to the homogeneous case and, therefore, $Q_x{}^p = \beta_x{}^p = 0$. The effect of the pressure and temperature are, however, brought into the solution through the contributions (see Eqs. 5.16b):

$$N_s{}^p = pa, \qquad N_x{}^p = 0, \tag{5.18b}$$

$$M_x{}^p = -D_x(\alpha_{tx} + \alpha_{ts}\nu_{xs})T_1, \qquad M_s{}^p = -D_s(\alpha_{ts}$$

$$u_x{}^p = -\frac{\nu_{sx}pax}{E_xh} + \alpha_{tx}T_0x, \qquad w^p = \frac{pa^2}{E_sh} + a$$

where we have set $C_1 = 0$ because the shell is assum loads. It is important to realize that, with the ex moment T_1 which is incompatible with the mem going expressions are identical to those which were loadings by the membrane theory (see Eqs. 4.19d). Thus, we may conclu in connection with our remarks concerning the edge effect, that, at points which are sufficiently far from the ends of the cylindrical shell, the solution approaches (see Eq. 5.17j) the solution which would have been obtained had all bending effects been neglected.

For more general loadings, Eqs. 5.18a can be solved by the method of Fourier expansions wherein the known inhomogeneous portions of those equations are represented by the series

$$\begin{aligned} (\alpha_{tx} + \nu_{xs}\alpha_{ts})\frac{dT_1}{dx} &= \sum_{n=0}^{\infty} a_n \cos\frac{n\pi x}{l}, \\ -\frac{1}{a}\frac{d}{dx}(\nu_{xs}F_1 - qa) - \frac{E_sh}{a}\alpha_{ts}\frac{dT_0}{dx} &= \sum_{n=0}^{\infty} b_n \cos\frac{n\pi x}{l}, \end{aligned} \tag{5.18d}$$

and the particular solutions are represented by the series

$$\begin{aligned} Q_x{}^p &= \sum_{n=0}^{\infty} A_n \cos\frac{n\pi x}{l}, \\ \beta_x{}^p &= \sum_{n=0}^{\infty} B_n \cos\frac{n\pi x}{l}. \end{aligned} \tag{5.18e}$$

Here l is the length of the shell, a_n and b_n are known coefficients which are obtained from the applied loadings and temperatures by the methods of Fourier analysis, and A_n and B_n are unknown coefficients.

For shells which extend to infinity, the above series must be replaced by Fourier integrals over the parameter ω_n which replaces $n\pi x/l$. For simplicity, we shall assume that the length of the cylindrical shell is finite and, therefore, A_n and B_n can be obtained by substituting the expansions 5.18d and 5.18e into Eqs. 5.18a. This gives

$$A_n = -\frac{a_n(E_sh/a^2) + b_n(n\pi/l)^2}{(n\pi/l)^4 + 4\mu^4}, \qquad B_n = -\frac{a_n(n\pi/l)^2 - b_n/D_x}{(n\pi/l)^4 + 4\mu^4}. \tag{5.18f}$$

The particular solutions can now be obtained by substituting these coefficients into the series 5.18e, and their contributions to the rest of the shell variables can be determined by using Eqs. 5.16b. In choosing Fourier e series for the expansions 5.18d and 5.18e, we have assumed that the ernal loadings and temperatures are even functions of the coordinate x. Other functional dependencies can be accommodated by Fourier sine series, or generalized Fourier series, as the situation warrants.

5.2c Examples

As an example of the use of the preceding solutions, we shall now analyze a short circular cylindrical shell, subjected to an internal pressure and a

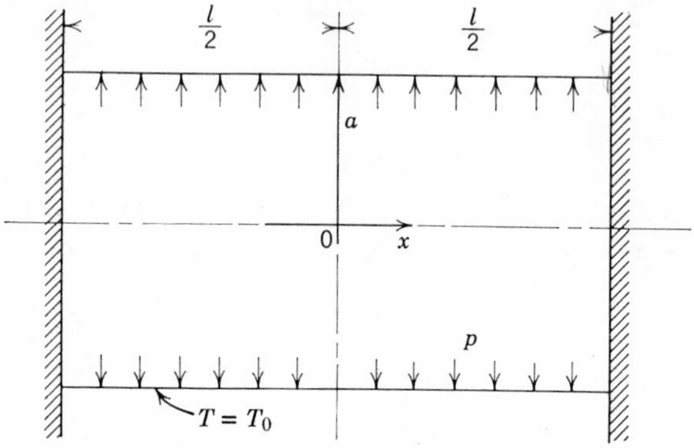

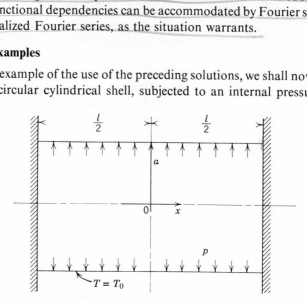

Figure 5.3 Pressurized, uniformly heated, circular cylindrical shell with clamped ends.

uniform temperature rise, which is clamped at its ends as shown in Fig. 5.3. If we note that for this particular type of loading $Q_x{}^p = \beta_x{}^p = 0$, we may write the complete solution in the following alternate form:

$$\begin{aligned} Q_x &= A_1 \cos \mu x \cosh \mu x + A_2 \sin \mu x \sinh \mu x \\ &\qquad + A_3 \sin \mu x \cosh \mu x + A_4 \cos \mu x \sinh \mu x, \\ \beta_x &= \frac{-1}{2\mu^2 D_x}(A_2 \cos \mu x \cosh \mu x - A_1 \sin \mu x \sinh \mu x \\ &\qquad - A_4 \sin \mu x \cosh \mu x + A_3 \cos \mu x \sinh \mu x). \end{aligned} \tag{5.19a}$$

For the clamped ends, we write the boundary conditions which these solutions must satisfy as (see Eqs. 5.9):

$$w = \beta_x = 0 \quad \text{at} \quad x = \pm\, l/2, \tag{5.19b}$$

where we have taken the center of the span of the shell to be the origin. For the application of the boundary conditions to the transverse displacement, we now note, from Eqs. 5.16b, that with $q = -p$,

$$w = \frac{1}{4\mu^4 D_x}\frac{dQ_x}{dx} + \frac{pa^2}{E_s h} + a\alpha_{ts} T_0, \tag{5.19c}$$

or

$$w = \frac{1}{4\mu^3 D_x}[A_1(\cos\mu x \sinh\mu x - \cosh\mu x \sin\mu x) + A_2(\sin\mu x \cosh\mu x + \sinh\mu x \cos\mu x) + A_3(\sin\mu x \sinh\mu x + \cosh\mu x \cos\mu x) + A_4(\cos\mu x \cosh\mu x - \sinh\mu x \sin\mu x)] + \frac{pa^2}{E_s h} + a\alpha_{ts}T_0. \tag{5.19d}$$

In the determination of the arbitrary constants, we notice from the symmetry of the loading that the displacements must be symmetric and the slopes must be antisymmetric with respect to the center of the cylinder. Thus, we may immediately note that

$$A_1 = A_2 = 0. \tag{5.19e}$$

The other arbitrary constants can now be found by applying the boundary conditions (Eqs. 5.19b) at either end of the shell. This gives the result

$$\{A_3, A_4\} = -4\mu^3 D_x\left(\frac{pa^2}{E_s h} + a\alpha_{ts}T_0\right)\frac{\{\sin\delta\cosh\delta, \cos\delta\sinh\delta\}}{\sinh\delta\cosh\delta + \sin\delta\cos\delta} \tag{5.19f}$$

where $\delta = \mu l/2$. The rest of the shell variables are given by the expressions

$$\begin{aligned}
w &= \left(\frac{pa^2}{E_s h} + a\alpha_{ts}T_0\right) \\
&\quad\times\left\{1 - \frac{(\sin\delta\cosh\delta + \cos\delta\sinh\delta)\cosh\mu x\cos\mu x}{\sinh\delta\cosh\delta + \sin\delta\cos\delta} - \frac{(\sin\delta\cosh\delta - \cos\delta\sinh\delta)\sinh\mu x\sin\mu x}{\sinh\delta\cosh\delta + \sin\delta\cos\delta}\right\}, \\
\beta_x &= -2\mu\left(\frac{pa^2}{E_s h} + a\alpha_{ts}T_0\right) \\
&\quad\times\left\{\frac{\cos\delta\sinh\delta\sin\mu x\cosh\mu x - \sin\delta\cosh\delta\cos\mu x\sinh\mu x}{\sinh\delta\cosh\delta + \sin\delta\cos\delta}\right\}, \\
M_x &= -2\mu^2 D_x\left(\frac{pa^2}{E_s h} + a\alpha_{ts}T_0\right) \\
&\quad\times\left\{\frac{(\sin\delta\cosh\delta + \cos\delta\sinh\delta)\sin\mu x\sinh\mu x}{\sinh\delta\cosh\delta + \sin\delta\cos\delta} + \frac{(\cos\delta\sinh\delta - \sin\delta\cosh\delta)\cosh\mu x\cos\mu x}{\sinh\delta\cosh\delta + \sin\delta\cos\delta}\right\}, \\
Q_x &= -4\mu^3 D_x\left(\frac{pa^2}{E_s h} + a\alpha_{ts}T_0\right) \\
&\quad\times\left\{\frac{\sin\delta\cosh\delta\sin\mu x\cosh\mu x + \cos\delta\sinh\delta\cos\mu x\sinh\mu x}{\sinh\delta\cosh\delta + \sin\delta\cos\delta}\right\}, \\
M_s &= \nu_{xs}M_x, \qquad N_s = \frac{E_s h}{a}w - E_s\alpha_{ts}hT_0, \qquad N_x = 0,
\end{aligned} \tag{5.19g}$$

odd x odd = even

which follow from Eqs. 5.16b. Notice that, in the present problem, we have assumed that there are no external axial loads applied to the shell and that, therefore, $N_x = C_1 = 0$. Also, the temperature rise has been assumed to be uniform so that $T_0 \neq 0$, $T_1 = 0$.

It is interesting to indicate the values of the dependent variables at the midpoint of the cylinder. Thus, we find, by setting $x = 0$ in Eqs. 5.19g, that

$$\begin{aligned}
w(0) &= \left(\frac{pa^2}{E_s h} + a\alpha_{ts}T_0\right)\left(1 - \frac{\sin\delta\cosh\delta + \cos\delta\sinh\delta}{\sinh\delta\cosh\delta + \sin\delta\cos\delta}\right),\\
M_x(0) &= -2\mu^2 D_x\left(\frac{pa^2}{E_s h} + a\alpha_{ts}T_0\right)\left(\frac{\cos\delta\sinh\delta - \sin\delta\cosh\delta}{\sinh\delta\cosh\delta + \sin\delta\cos\delta}\right),\\
N_s(0) &= pa - (pa + E_s h\alpha_{ts}T_0)\left(\frac{\sin\delta\cosh\delta + \cos\delta\sinh\delta}{\sinh\delta\cosh\delta + \sin\delta\cos\delta}\right),\\
\beta_x(0) &= Q_x(0) = N_x(0) = 0,\\
M_s(0) &= \nu_{xs}M_x(0).
\end{aligned} \tag{5.19h}$$

If we allow the length of the shell to grow without bound, we find that the fractions involving the trigonometric and hyperbolic functions of δ approach zero and the results approach the limits

$$\lim_{l\to\infty}\begin{Bmatrix} w(0) \\ M_x(0) \\ N_s(0) \end{Bmatrix} = \begin{Bmatrix} \dfrac{pa^2}{E_s h} + a\alpha_{ts}T_0 \\ 0 \\ pa \end{Bmatrix}. \tag{5.19i}$$

These values coincide, as we would expect from Eqs. 5.17j, with the particular solution 5.18c for the present loadings. They also agree, as we have already pointed out in connection with Eqs. 5.18c, with the results which would have been obtained for this problem by a solution based on the membrane approximation (see Eqs. 4.19d).

In Figs. 5.4 and 5.5, the radial displacement and axial bending moment, respectively (as obtained from Eqs. 5.19g) have been plotted as a function of axial position for isotropic cylindrical shells of the type shown in Fig. 5.3. For these calculations, we have chosen $E_x = E_s = E$, $\nu_{xs} = \nu_{sx} = \nu$, $a/h = 20$, and four values of the ratio of length to radius. These results illustrate the edge effect to which we have referred previously. Indeed, as the length of the shell is increased at constant radius and thickness, the particular solution or, equivalently, the solution obtained from the membrane approximation has a progressively greater region of applicability. The same conclusion would hold if, on the other hand, the radius were to be increased while the length and the ratio of the radius to the thickness were to be held at fixed values. Although the data which are plotted in

Figs. 5.4 and 5.5 involve isotropic cylindrical shells, we may deduce from them the behavior of similarly loaded orthotropic cylindrical shells by recalling our remarks concerning the effect of orthotropy on the decay length (see Eq. 5.17k).

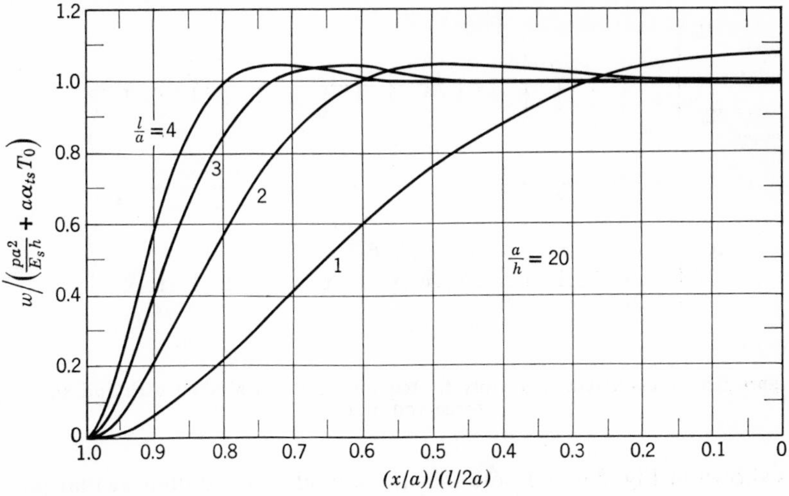

Figure 5.4 Radial displacement distributions for the shell shown in Fig. 5.3.

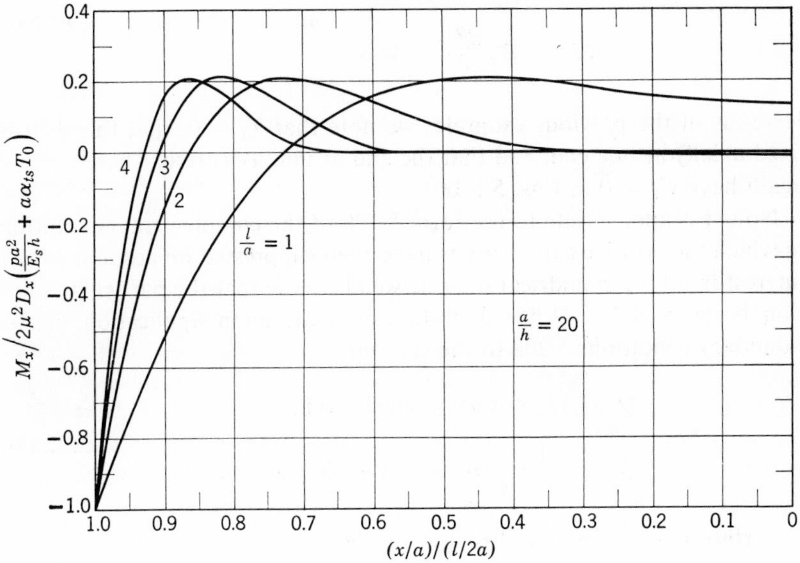

Figure 5.5 Axial moment distributions for the shell shown in Fig. 5.3.

Now let us consider the analysis of a long cylindrical shell which is subjected to a uniform internal pressure, a uniform temperature rise T_0, a distributed end moment M_0, and a distributed end shearing force H_0, as shown in Fig. 5.6. In this case, we take the origin at the left end of the shell

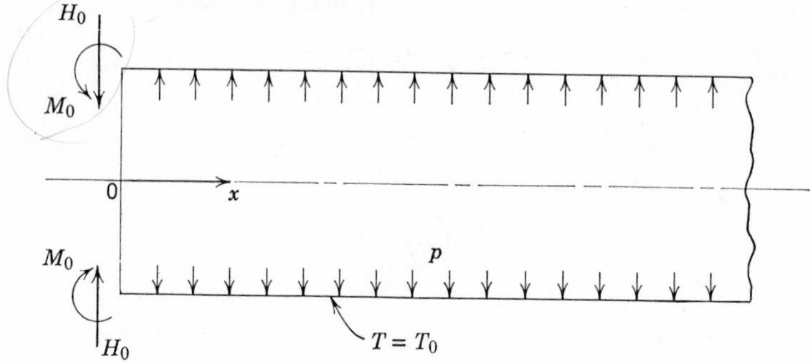

Figure 5.6 Pressurized, uniformly heated long cylindrical shell with end shearing force and moment.

as shown in Fig. 5.6 and note that the boundary conditions at that point can be expressed as

$$\left.\begin{aligned} Q_x &= H_0 \\ M_x &= D_x \frac{d\beta_x}{dx} = M_0 \end{aligned}\right\} \quad \text{at} \quad x = 0. \tag{5.20a}$$

Here, as in the previous example, we note that $T_1 = 0$, that the shell is fixed axially at one end, and that the end at infinity is free. Therefore, we again have $C_1 = 0$ in Eqs. 5.16b.

Now it is appropriate to use form 5.17h of the complementary solution in which the positive exponentials have been suppressed on account of our interest in a long cylindrical shell. If we also note that the particular solution is again $\beta_x{}^p = Q_x{}^p = 0$, it follows that, upon application of the boundary conditions 5.20a to the solution

$$\begin{aligned} Q_x &= (B_1 \cos \mu x + B_2 \sin \mu x)\, e^{-\mu x}, \\ \beta_x &= \frac{1}{2\mu^2 D_x} (B_2 \cos \mu x - B_1 \sin \mu x)\, e,^{-\mu x} \end{aligned} \tag{5.20b}$$

the arbitrary constants can be shown to be

$$B_1 = H_0, \qquad B_2 = -H_0 - 2\mu M_0. \tag{5.20c}$$

As a result we find, from Eqs. 5.16b, that the quantities which describe the behavior of the shell which is under consideration are given by:

$$
\begin{aligned}
w &= \frac{pa^2}{E_s h} + a\alpha_{ts}T_0 - \frac{e^{-\mu x}}{2\mu^3 D_x}[H_0 \cos \mu x - \mu M_0(\sin \mu x - \cos \mu x)],\\
\beta_x &= \frac{-e^{-\mu x}}{2\mu^2 D_x}[H_0 (\cos \mu x + \sin \mu x) + 2\mu M_0 \cos \mu x],\\
M_x &= \frac{e^{-\mu x}}{\mu}[H_0 \sin \mu x + \mu M_0(\cos \mu x + \sin \mu x)],\\
Q_x &= e^{-\mu x}[H_0(\cos \mu x - \sin \mu x) - 2\mu M_0 \sin \mu x],\\
M_s &= \nu_{xs} M_x,\\
N_s &= E_s h\left(\frac{w}{a} - \alpha_{ts}T_0\right), \qquad N_x = 0.
\end{aligned}
\tag{5.20d}
$$

At a point which is far from the left end of the shell we find, from the foregoing, that

$$
\lim_{x\to\infty}\begin{Bmatrix} w(x)\\ \beta_x(x)\\ M_x(x)\\ Q_x(x)\\ N_s(x)\end{Bmatrix} = \begin{Bmatrix} pa^2/E_s h + a\alpha_{ts}T_0\\ 0\\ 0\\ 0\\ pa\end{Bmatrix}. \tag{5.20e}
$$

These results are, according to earlier remarks, expected to be valid at points beyond one decay length from the end of the shell. As could be expected, they agree with the limiting values which we obtained in the analysis of the short cylindrical shell (see Eqs. 5.19i).

The functions of x which multiply the end shearing force and moment in each of Eqs. 5.20d are referred to as influence functions. That is, they give the influence of H_0 and M_0 on a given variable at a given position x. If $x = 0$ we have, for example,

$$
\begin{aligned}
w(0) &= \left(\frac{a^2}{E_s h}\right)p + (a\alpha_{ts})T_0 - \left(\frac{1}{2\mu^3 D_x}\right)H_0 - \left(\frac{1}{2\mu^2 D_x}\right)M_0,\\
\beta_x(0) &= -\left(\frac{1}{2\mu^2 D_x}\right)H_0 - \left(\frac{1}{\mu D_x}\right)M_0.
\end{aligned}
\tag{5.20f}
$$

The quantities in parentheses are referred to as edge influence coefficients. These indicate the influence of H_0, M_0, p, and T_0 on the deflection and slope at the edge of the shell. It will be shown presently that the concept of influence coefficients is extremely useful in the analysis of composite shells of revolution.

We have illustrated the analysis of cylindrical shells under loads that are independent of the polar angle θ by solving some problems involving single layer shells of constant thickness. We leave it to the reader to discover, through the Exercises, that cylindrical shells of layered construction or of a single layer with linearly varying thickness can also be treated by exact analytical methods.

5.3 CONICAL SHELLS

As another illustration, we take up the analysis of a conical shell of constant thickness whose elastic properties are independent of position. Since the generators of the reference surface of such a shell are straight, it is again appropriate to make the change of variable $dx = r_\varphi\, d\varphi$. Now, since the generators are inclined at an angle α with the axis of the shell, we have $\varphi = \pi/2 - \alpha$ and $r_\theta = x \tan \alpha$ (see Fig. 4.3). With these definitions, we find from the general development of Section 5.1 that

$$L(\ldots) = h \tan \alpha \left[x \frac{d^2(\ldots)}{dx^2} + \frac{d(\ldots)}{dx} - \frac{E_\theta}{E_x} \frac{(\ldots)}{x} \right],$$
$$f(x) = 0, \qquad \lambda^2 = i \left[12(1 - \nu_{x\theta}\nu_{\theta x}) \frac{E_\theta}{E_x} \right]^{1/2}, \tag{5.21a}$$

and the expressions for the stress resultants, stress couples and displacements in the conical shell are given by

$$N_x = Q_x \tan \alpha - F_1(x),$$
$$N_\theta = \left[\frac{d(xQ_x)}{dx} - qx \right] \tan \alpha,$$
$$M_x = D_x \left[\frac{d\beta_x}{dx} + \frac{\nu_{x\theta}\beta_x}{x} - (\alpha_{tx} + \nu_{x\theta}\alpha_{t\theta})T_1 \right],$$
$$M_\theta = D_\theta \left[\frac{\beta_x}{x} + \nu_{\theta x} \frac{d\beta_x}{dx} - (\alpha_{t\theta} + \nu_{\theta x}\alpha_{tx})T_1 \right],$$
$$F_1(x) = \frac{1}{x \cos \alpha} \left[\int_{x_0}^{x} x(q \sin \alpha + q_x \cos \alpha)\, dx + C_1 \right], \tag{5.21b}$$
$$u_x = \int F(x)\, dx,$$
$$w = \left[\frac{x}{E_\theta h} (N_\theta - \nu_{x\theta} N_x) + x\alpha_{t\theta} T_0 - u_x \right] \tan \alpha,$$
$$F(x) = \frac{N_x - \nu_{\theta x} N_\theta}{E_x h} + \alpha_{tx} T_0,$$

where

$$Q_x = Q_x{}^c + Q_x{}^p, \qquad \beta_x = \beta_x{}^c + \beta_x{}^p, \tag{5.21c}$$

and we have replaced the subscripts φ and θ of the general development with x and θ, respectively.

5.3*a* Conical Shells under Edge Loadings

To determine the complementary solutions Q_x^c and β_x^c that are used in the satisfaction of the boundary conditions in analyses of conical shells, we employ the method which was outlined in Section 5.1. Thus, we find that Eqs. 5.15n take the following form for the conical shell:

$$\frac{d^2(xQ_x^c)}{dx^2} + \frac{1}{x}\frac{d(xQ_x^c)}{dx} + \left(\pm\frac{i\mu_c^2}{x} - \frac{1}{x^2}\frac{E_\theta}{E_x}\right)(xQ_x^c) = 0, \quad (5.22a)$$

where

$$\mu_c^2 = \left[12(1 - \nu_{x\theta}\nu_{\theta x})\frac{E_\theta \cot^2\alpha}{E_x h^2}\right]^{1/2}. \quad (5.22b)$$

To bring Eqs. 5.22a into a form which is amenable to solution, we make the change of variable

$$y = 2\mu_c\sqrt{x} \quad (5.22c)$$

as a result of which

$$y^2\frac{d^2(xQ_x^c)}{dy^2} + y\frac{d(xQ_x^c)}{dy} - \left(\mp iy^2 + 4\frac{E_\theta}{E_x}\right)(xQ_x^c) = 0. \quad (5.22d)$$

These equations are each a form of Bessel's equation and have the solution (see Eq. 5.15s):

$$xQ_x^c = (A_1S_1 + A_2S_2 + A_3S_3 + A_4S_4) \quad (5.22e)$$

where the S_i are the Kelvin functions[4] of order e, or

$$\begin{aligned} S_1 &= \mathrm{ber}_e\, y, \qquad S_3 = \mathrm{ker}_e\, y, \\ S_2 &= \mathrm{bei}_e\, y, \qquad S_4 = \mathrm{kei}_e\, y, \\ e &= 2(E_\theta/E_x)^{1/2}. \end{aligned} \quad (5.22f)$$

The solution for the rotation is then, according to Eq. 5.15w,

$$\beta_x^c = -\frac{\tan\alpha}{E_\theta h^2}\left[12(1 - \nu_{\theta x}\nu_{x\theta})\frac{E_\theta}{E_x}\right]^{1/2}(A_2S_1 - A_1S_2 + A_4S_3 - A_3S_4). \quad (5.22g)$$

To demonstrate the behavior of the solution functions, let us consider an isotropic conical shell. In this case, we have $e = 2$ and the solutions are the Kelvin functions of order two. By means of recursion formulas, these functions can be expressed in terms of the more commonly available Kelvin functions of the zero-th and first orders. Thus, we note that [4]

$$S_1 = \mathrm{ber}_2\, y = -\mathrm{ber}\, y + \frac{\sqrt{2}}{y}(\mathrm{bei}_1\, y - \mathrm{ber}_1\, y),$$

[4] See, for example, Abramowitz, M., and Stegun, I. A., *Handbook of Mathematical Functions*, National Bureau of Standards Series No. 55, Washington, D. C.: The U.S. Government Printing Office (1965), pp. 379–385.

$$S_2 = \text{bei}_2\, y = -\text{bei}\, y - \frac{\sqrt{2}}{y}(\text{bei}_1\, y + \text{ber}_1\, y),$$

$$S_3 = \text{ker}_2\, y = -\text{ker}\, y + \frac{\sqrt{2}}{y}(\text{kei}_1\, y - \text{ker}_1\, y), \quad (5.22\text{h})$$

$$S_4 = \text{kei}_2\, y = -\text{kei}\, y - \frac{\sqrt{2}}{y}(\text{kei}_1\, y + \text{ker}_1\, y).$$

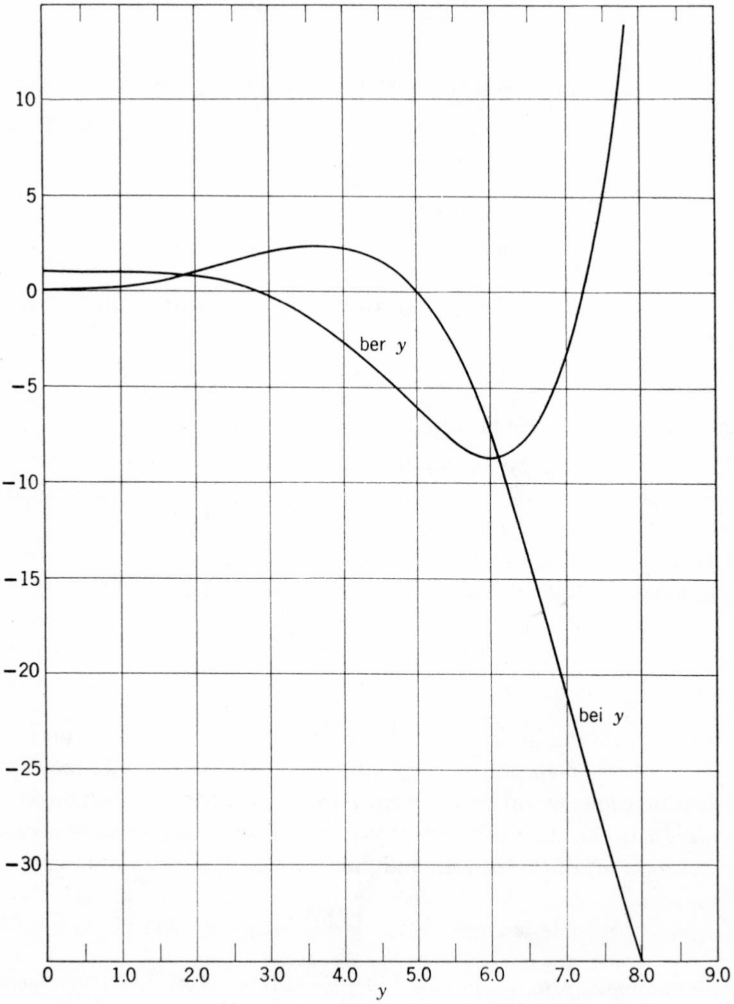

5.7a

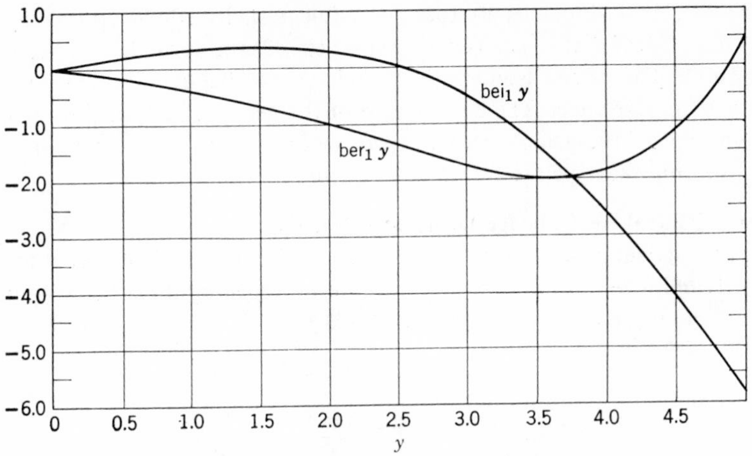

5.7b

Figure 5.7 Solution functions for conical shells.

For purposes of illustration, we have plotted the Kelvin functions of zero-th and first order in Figs. 5.7 and 5.8. These plots indicate that $\text{ber}_2\, y$ and $\text{bei}_2\, y$ will become unbounded as y approaches infinity, while $\text{ker}_2\, y$ and $\text{kei}_2\, y$ will become unbounded as y approaches zero. The plots also show that there is an edge effect in the behavior of a conical shell with bending resistance. This permits us to argue, as we did in the case of the cylindrical shell, that if a frustum of a conical shell is sufficiently long the boundary conditions that are applied at its two ends will not interact. In such shells, the analysis of bending effects near the "small" end can be carried out with sufficient accuracy by taking $A_1 = A_2 = 0$, while the analysis of bending effects near the "large" end can be carried out with $A_3 = A_4 = 0$. If the shell is closed at $x = 0$, then the solutions S_3 and S_4 must be suppressed by setting $A_3 = A_4 = 0$. At points which are sufficiently removed from any edge, the bending effects which are introduced at the edge will not be felt and the complete solution will approach

$$Q_x = Q_x{}^p, \qquad \beta_x = \beta_x{}^p. \tag{5.22i}$$

In order to define a decay length for an isotropic conical shell, for example, we make use of the fact that, in Figs. 5.7 and 5.8, the peaks in each curve extend over a distance $2\mu_c\sqrt{x} \cong \sqrt{8}\pi$. Thus, if we substitute the definition of μ_c from Eq. 5.22b into this relationship, we find that the distance x_c to which the width of the peaks corresponds is, approximately,

$$x_c = \frac{\pi^2 h \tan \alpha}{\sqrt{3(1 - \nu^2)}}, \tag{5.22j}$$

for an isotropic conical shell.

This relationship tells us that for conical shells which approach flat circular plates (that is, shells with α close to $\pi/2$) the decay length becomes very long. This is consistent with the behavior of flat circular plates which display no edge effect. The dependence of the decay length on the angle of inclination of the generators will be brought out further when the results of a specific example are discussed in Section 5.3*c*.

5.3*b* Conical Shells under Distributed Loadings

The particular solutions $Q_x{}^p$ and $\beta_x{}^p$ which are used to account for distributed loadings on a conical shell are governed by the following equations which are obtained from Eqs. 5.14a:

$$L(xQ_x{}^p) = [G_1(x) - E_\theta h^2 \beta_x{}^p] \frac{1}{\tan \alpha}$$
$$L(\beta_x{}^p) = (xQ_x{}^p) \frac{h \tan \alpha}{D_x} + \frac{H(x)}{h^2} \tag{5.23a}$$

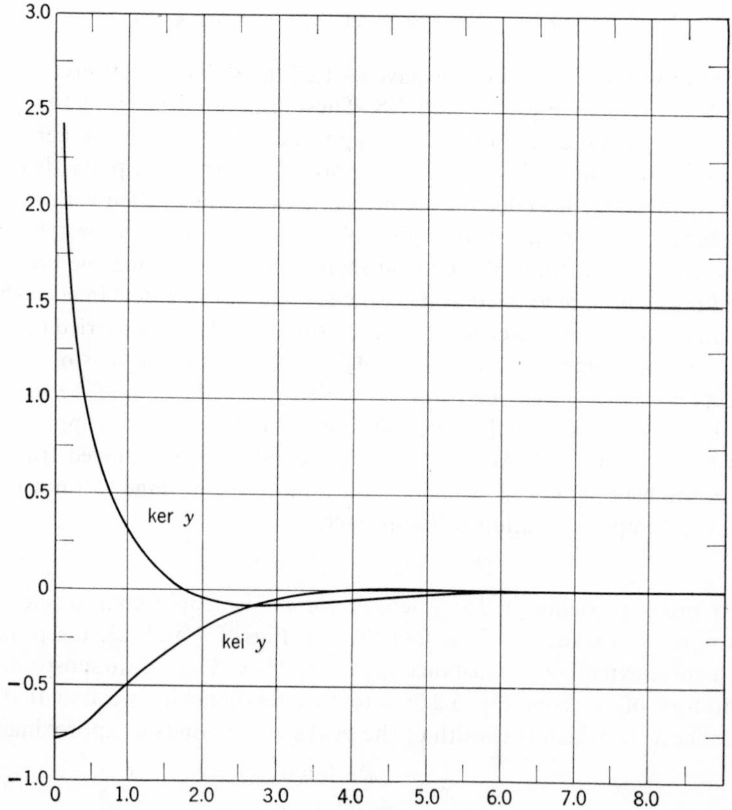

5.8a

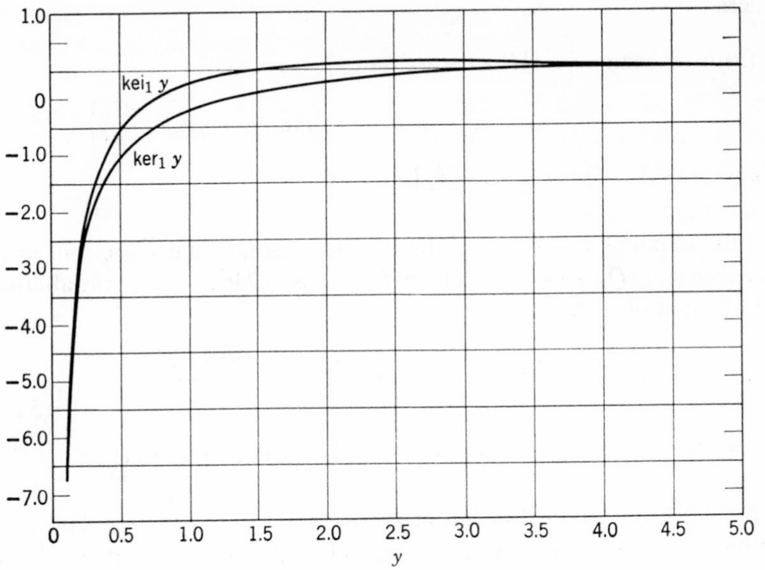

5.8b

Figure 5.8 Solution functions for conical shells.

where

$$G_1(x) = -h \tan\alpha \left\{\frac{d}{dx}[F_1 x \nu_{x\theta} - qx^2 \tan\alpha] + \frac{E_\theta}{E_x} F_1 - \nu_{x\theta} x q \tan\alpha \right.$$
$$\left. + E_\theta h \left[\alpha_{t\theta} \frac{d}{dx}(xT_0) - \alpha_{tx} T_0\right]\right\}, \tag{5.23b}$$

$$H(x) = h^3 \tan\alpha \left\{(\alpha_{tx} + \nu_{x\theta}\alpha_{t\theta}) x \frac{dT_1}{dx}\right.$$
$$\left. + T_1[\alpha_{tx} + \nu_{x\theta}\alpha_{t\theta} - (\alpha_{t\theta} + \nu_{\theta x}\alpha_{tx}) \frac{E_\theta}{E_x}\right\}.$$

Solutions of the foregoing equations are readily obtained when one is concerned with certain loadings acting upon an isotropic conical shell. In this case, we let $E_x = E_\theta = E$, $\nu_{x\theta} = \nu_{\theta x} = \nu$, $\alpha_{tx} = \alpha_{t\theta} = \alpha_t$, and, as a consequence, Eqs. 5.23a and 5.23b reduce to

$$L(xQ_x{}^p) = [G_1(x) - Eh^2\beta_x{}^p] \frac{1}{\tan\alpha}, \tag{5.23c}$$

$$L(\beta_x{}^p) = (xQ_x{}^p) \frac{h \tan\alpha}{D} + \frac{H(x)}{h^2}$$

where

$$G_1(x) = -h \tan \alpha \left\{ \frac{d}{dx} [F_1 x\nu - qx^2 \tan \alpha] + F_1 - \nu xq \tan \alpha + E\alpha_t hx \frac{dT_0}{dx} \right\}, \quad (5.23d)$$

$$H(x) = h^3 \tan \alpha \left[\alpha_t(1 + \nu)x \frac{dT_1}{dx} \right].$$

For the solutions which we are about to demonstrate, it is more convenient to eliminate $(xQ_x{}^p)$ and $\beta_x{}^p$, in turn, from Eqs. 5.23c to obtain the alternate set of equations (see Eqs. 5.15a):

$$LL(\beta_x{}^p) + 12(1 - \nu^2)\beta_x{}^p = \frac{hG_1(x)}{D} + \frac{L[H(x)]}{h^2}$$

$$LL(xQ_x{}^p) + 12(1 - \nu^2)(xQ_x{}^p) = \frac{1}{\tan \alpha} \{L[G_1(x)] - H(x)E\}. \quad (5.23e)$$

If the isotropic conical shell is under the influence of an internal pressure, we have $T_0 = T_1 = q_x = 0$, $q = -p$, and, in the absence of external axial loads, $C_1 = 0$. Thus,

$$F_1(x) = -\frac{px \tan \alpha}{2}, \qquad G_1(x) = -\frac{3}{2} pxh \tan^2 \alpha, \qquad H(x) = 0. \quad (5.24a)$$

In this case, Eqs. 5.23e take the form

$$LL(\beta_x{}^p) + 12(1 - \nu^2)\beta_x{}^p = -\frac{3}{2} \frac{pxh^2 \tan^2 \alpha}{D},$$

$$LL(xQ_x{}^p) + 12(1 - \nu^2)(xQ_x{}^p) = 0, \quad (5.24b)$$

and it follows that

$$Q_x{}^p = 0, \qquad \beta_x{}^p = -\frac{3}{2} \frac{px \tan^2 \alpha}{Eh}. \quad (5.24c)$$

Thus, it is seen that, unlike those of a cylindrical shell, the generators of a conical shell rotate under the influence of an internal pressure. The contributions of the pressure load and Eqs. 5.24c to the stress resultants, the stress couples, and the displacements are, therefore,

$$N_x{}^p = \frac{px}{2} \tan \alpha, \qquad N_\theta{}^p = px \tan \alpha,$$

$$M_x{}^p = M_\theta{}^p = -\frac{ph^2 \tan^2 \alpha}{8(1 - \nu)}, \quad (5.24d)$$

$$u_x{}^p = \frac{px^2 \tan \alpha}{4Eh}(1 - 2\nu), \qquad w^p = \frac{3px^2 \tan^2 \alpha}{4Eh}.$$

This solution is identical, with the exception of the moments, to the solution which was previously obtained (see Eqs. 4.24e) for this case by the membrane approximation. The contribution of $M_\theta{}^p$ and $M_x{}^p$ is, however, negligible for very thin shells, as will be shown presently.

Now suppose that the isotropic conical shell is subjected to an axial load caused by its own weight. In this case, $T_0 = T_1 = 0$, $q_x = P\cos\alpha$, and $q = P\sin\alpha$ where P is the axial force per unit of area of the reference surface. From these data, we find that, in the absence of other external axial loads,

$$\begin{aligned} F_1(x) &= Px/2\cos\alpha, \qquad H(x) = 0, \\ G_1(x) &= -\frac{Pxh\sin\alpha}{\cos^2\alpha}\left[(2+\nu)\cos^2\alpha - \tfrac{3}{2}\right], \end{aligned} \tag{5.25a}$$

and Eqs. 5.23e become

$$\begin{aligned} LL(\beta_x{}^p) + 12(1-\nu^2)\beta_x{}^p &= -\frac{Pxh^2\sin\alpha}{D\cos^2\alpha}\left[(2+\nu)\cos^2\alpha - \tfrac{3}{2}\right], \\ LL(xQ_x{}^p) + 12(1-\nu^2)(xQ_x{}^p) &= 0. \end{aligned} \tag{5.25b}$$

These equations have the solutions

$$Q_x{}^p = 0, \qquad \beta_x{}^p = -\frac{Px\sin\alpha}{Eh\cos^2\alpha}\left[(2+\nu)\cos^2\alpha - \tfrac{3}{2}\right]. \tag{5.25c}$$

The contributions of Eqs. 5.25c and the axial load to the shell variables are, therefore,

$$\begin{aligned} N_x{}^p &= -Px/2\cos\alpha, \qquad N_\theta{}^p = -Px\sin\alpha\tan\alpha, \\ M_x{}^p &= M_\theta{}^p = -\frac{Ph^2\sin\alpha}{12(1-\nu)\cos^2\alpha}\left[(2+\nu)\cos^2\alpha - \tfrac{3}{2}\right], \\ u_x{}^p &= \frac{-Px^2}{2Eh\cos\alpha}\left(\tfrac{1}{2} - \nu\sin^2\alpha\right), \\ w^p &= \frac{Px^2\tan\alpha}{2Eh\cos\alpha}\left[\nu + \tfrac{1}{2} - (2+\nu)\sin^2\alpha\right]. \end{aligned} \tag{5.25d}$$

Now let us consider an isotropic shell under the influence of a temperature that is linearly distributed both across its thickness and along its generators. If we represent the temperature distribution by the function

$$T(\zeta, x) = (\vartheta_0 + x\bar{\vartheta}_0) + \zeta(\vartheta_1 + x\bar{\vartheta}_1) \tag{5.26a}$$

where the ϑ_i and $\bar{\vartheta}_i$ are constants, we find that

$$T_0 = \vartheta_0 + x\bar{\vartheta}_0, \qquad T_1 = \vartheta_1 + x\bar{\vartheta}_1, \tag{5.26b}$$

and

$$\begin{aligned} F_1(x) &= 0, \qquad G_1(x) = -Eh^2x\alpha_t\bar{\vartheta}_0\tan\alpha, \\ H(x) &= (1+\nu)xh^3\alpha_t\bar{\vartheta}_1\tan\alpha. \end{aligned} \tag{5.26c}$$

With these load functions, the governing equations for the particular solutions are

$$LL(\beta_x{}^p) + 12(1 - \nu^2)\beta_x{}^p = -12(1 - \nu^2)\alpha_t x\bar{\vartheta}_0 \tan\alpha,$$
$$LL(xQ_x{}^p) + 12(1 - \nu^2)(xQ_x{}^p) = -Eh^3(1 + \nu)\alpha_t x\bar{\vartheta}_1 \tag{5.26d}$$

and it follows that

$$Q_x{}^p = -D\alpha_t(1 + \nu)\bar{\vartheta}_1, \qquad \beta_x{}^p = -\alpha_t x\bar{\vartheta}_0 \tan\alpha. \tag{5.26e}$$

The contributions of the thermal loading to the stress resultants, stress couples, and displacements are, therefore,

$$N_x{}^p = N_\theta{}^p = -D\alpha_t(1 + \nu)\bar{\vartheta}_1 \tan\alpha,$$
$$M_x{}^p = M_\theta{}^p = -D\alpha_t(1 + \nu)(\bar{\vartheta}_0 \tan\alpha + \vartheta_1 + x\bar{\vartheta}_1),$$
$$u_x{}^p = -\frac{h^2 x\alpha_t}{12}\bar{\vartheta}_1 \tan\alpha + \alpha_t\left(x\vartheta_0 + \frac{x^2}{2}\bar{\vartheta}_0\right), \tag{5.26f}$$
$$w^p = \frac{\alpha_t x^2}{2}\bar{\vartheta}_0 \tan\alpha.$$

Particular solutions for orthotropic conical shells of constant thickness can also be found. For this purpose, it is most convenient to use Eqs. 5.23a which, in their extended form, are given by

$$x\frac{d^2\beta_x{}^p}{dx^2} + \frac{d\beta_x{}^p}{dx} - \frac{1}{x}\frac{E_\theta}{E_x}\beta_x{}^p = \frac{(xQ_x{}^p)}{D_x} + \frac{H(x)}{h^3\tan\alpha},$$
$$x\frac{d^2(xQ_x{}^p)}{dx^2} + \frac{d(xQ_x{}^p)}{dx} - \frac{1}{x}\frac{E_\theta}{E_x}(xQ_x{}^p) = \left[\frac{G_1(x)}{h} - E_\theta h\beta_x{}^p\right]\frac{1}{\tan^2\alpha}, \tag{5.27a}$$

Now we make the change of variable $y = 2x^{1/2}$ by means of which the expressions take the form

$$\frac{d^2\beta_x{}^p}{dy^2} + \frac{1}{y}\frac{d\beta_x{}^p}{dy} - \frac{4}{y^2}\frac{E_\theta}{E_x}\beta_x{}^p = \frac{(xQ_x{}^p)}{D_x} + \frac{H(y)}{h^3\tan\alpha},$$
$$\frac{d^2(xQ_x{}^p)}{dy^2} + \frac{1}{y}\frac{d(xQ_x{}^p)}{dy} - \frac{4}{y^2}\frac{E_\theta}{E_x}(xQ_x{}^p) = \left[\frac{G_1(y)}{h} - E_\theta h\beta_x{}^p\right]\frac{1}{\tan^2\alpha}. \tag{5.27b}$$

The particular solutions of these equations can be found by making use of the fact that $J_e(\lambda_n y)$, the Bessel function of the first kind and order $e = 2(E_\theta/E_x)^{1/2}$, satisfies the equation[5]

$$\frac{d^2 J_e}{dy^2} + \frac{1}{y}\frac{dJ_e}{dy} + \left(\lambda_n{}^2 - \frac{e^2}{y^2}\right)J_e = 0. \tag{5.27c}$$

[5] See, for example, Abramowitz and Stegun, loc. cit., p. 358.

Thus, we may expand the inhomogeneous portions of Eqs. 5.27b in series of the Bessel functions of the first kind as follows:

$$\begin{aligned} G_1(y)/h \tan^2 \alpha &= \sum_n a_n J_e(\lambda_n y), \\ H(y)/h^3 \tan \alpha &= \sum_n b_n J_e(\lambda_n y), \end{aligned} \tag{5.27d}$$

where the a_n and b_n are given by

$$\begin{Bmatrix} a_n \\ b_n \end{Bmatrix} = \frac{2}{[J_{e+1}(\lambda_n)]^2} \int_0^1 \begin{Bmatrix} G_1(y)/\tan \alpha \\ H(y)/h^2 \end{Bmatrix} \frac{y J_e(\lambda_n y)\, dy}{h \tan \alpha}. \tag{5.27e}$$

Here we have assumed that the length of a generator of the shell has been defined in such a manner that the variable y lies in the range $0 \leqslant y \leqslant 1$. The expansions also rely upon the fact that the λ_n are the roots of the equation

$$J_e(\lambda_n) = 0, \qquad n = 1, 2, \ldots \tag{5.27f}$$

Now we assume that $(xQ_x{}^p)$ and $\beta_x{}^p$ can be expanded in similar series which take the form

$$xQ_x{}^p = \sum_n A_n J_e(\lambda_n y), \qquad \beta_x{}^p = \sum_n B_n J_e(\lambda_n y), \tag{5.27g}$$

where the A_n and B_n are arbitrary coefficients which can be found by substituting the expansions 5.27d and 5.27g into Eqs. 5.27b and recalling Eq. 5.27c. Thus,

$$\begin{aligned} A_n &= \frac{-\lambda_n{}^2 a_n - b_n E_\theta h \cot \alpha}{\mu_c{}^4 + \lambda_n{}^4}, \\ B_n &= \frac{a_n \cot \alpha / D_x - \lambda_n{}^2 b_n}{\mu_c{}^4 + \lambda_n{}^4}, \end{aligned} \tag{5.27h}$$

and the remaining variables that are of interest can be found by substituting Eqs. 5.27h into the expansions 5.27g and then using Eqs. 5.21b.

5.3*c* Example

To illustrate the use of the solutions which we developed in Sections 5.3*a* and 5.3*b*, let us now consider an isotropic conical shell which is closed at $x = 0$, clamped at its edge $x = l$, and subjected to an internal pressure load as shown in Fig. 5.9. In carrying out the analysis, it is convenient to define a dimensionless length s such that $x = sl$, where l is the length of a generator of the shell. With this definition, the previously defined variable y (see Eq. 5.22c) takes the form

$$y = 2\bar{\mu}_c \sqrt{s}, \qquad 0 \leqslant s \leqslant 1 \tag{5.28a}$$

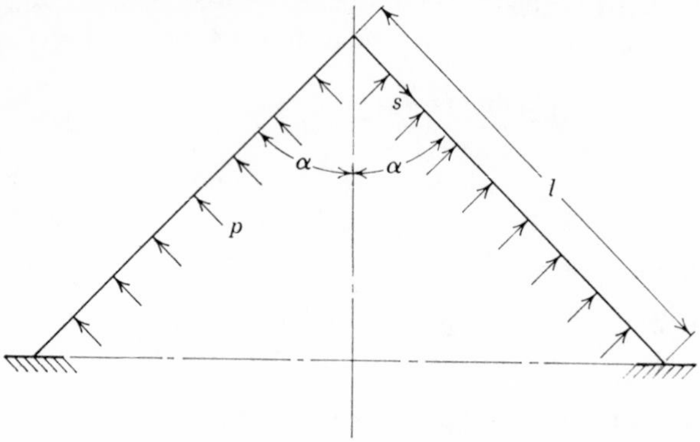

Figure 5.9 Pressurized conical shell with clamped edge.

where

$$\bar{\mu}_c{}^4 = 12(1 - \nu^2)\left(\frac{l}{h}\right)^2 \cot^2 \alpha \tag{5.28b}$$

for the isotropic shell. Since the shell is closed at its apex, we set $A_3 = A_4 = 0$ in solutions 5.22e and 5.22g in order to suppress those functions which would, if they were retained, cause the solutions to become unbounded at the apex. Thus, in terms of the variable s, the complete solution is given by

$$slQ_x = A_1 \operatorname{ber}_2 (2\bar{\mu}_c\sqrt{s}) + A_2 \operatorname{bei}_2 (2\bar{\mu}_c\sqrt{s}),$$

$$\beta_x = -\frac{\tan\alpha}{Eh^2}\sqrt{12(1-\nu^2)}\,[A_2 \operatorname{ber}_2 (2\bar{\mu}_c\sqrt{s}) - A_1 \operatorname{bei}_2 (2\bar{\mu}_c\sqrt{s})] - \frac{3}{2}\frac{psl\tan^2\alpha}{Eh}. \tag{5.28c}$$

At the clamped edge, the boundary conditions are most conveniently expressed in the form

$$\beta_x = u_r = 0 \tag{5.28d}$$

where u_r is the deflection perpendicular to the axis of the shell. An expression for u_r is given by

$$u_r = \epsilon_\theta sl \sin\alpha = \frac{sl\sin\alpha}{Eh}(N_\theta - \nu N_x), \tag{5.28e}$$

or

$$u_r = \frac{sl\sin\alpha}{Eh}\left[\frac{d(slQ_x)}{dsl} - \frac{\nu(slQ_x)}{sl} + \frac{psl}{2}(2-\nu)\right]\tan\alpha. \tag{5.28f}$$

Conditions 5.28d then yield the following expressions for the arbitrary constants:

$$\begin{aligned} B_1 &= \frac{1}{\Delta}\left[\frac{3(h/l)}{\sqrt{12(1-\nu^2)}}(J_2' - \nu J_2)\tan\alpha - (2-\nu)J_1\right], \\ B_2 &= \frac{-1}{\Delta}\left[J_2(2-\nu) + \frac{3(h/l)}{\sqrt{12(1-\nu^2)}}(J_1' - \nu J_1)\tan\alpha\right], \end{aligned} \tag{5.28g}$$

where

$$\begin{aligned} B_1 &= 2A_1/pl^2, \qquad B_2 = 2A_2/pl^2, \\ J_1 &= \mathrm{ber}_2\,(2\bar{\mu}_c), \qquad J_1' = \mathrm{ber}_2'\,(2\bar{\mu}_c), \\ J_2 &= \mathrm{bei}_2\,(2\bar{\mu}_c), \qquad J_2' = \mathrm{bei}_2'\,(2\bar{\mu}_c), \\ \Delta &= J_2(J_2' - \nu J_2) + J_1(J_1' - \nu J_1), \end{aligned} \tag{5.28h}$$

and a prime refers to a derivative with respect to s. The stress resultants and couples in the shell are now obtained from Eqs. 5.21b. This gives the following:

$$\begin{aligned} N_x &= \frac{pl\tan\alpha}{2}\left\{s + \frac{1}{s}[B_1\,\mathrm{ber}_2\,(2\bar{\mu}_c\sqrt{s}) + B_2\,\mathrm{bei}_2\,(2\bar{\mu}_c\sqrt{s})]\right\}, \\ N_\theta &= \frac{pl\tan\alpha}{2}\{2s + B_1\,\mathrm{ber}_2'\,(2\bar{\mu}_c\sqrt{s}) + B_2\,\mathrm{bei}_2'\,(2\bar{\mu}_c\sqrt{s})\}, \\ M_x &= \frac{pl^2\tan\alpha}{2}\left\{\frac{(h/l)}{\sqrt{12(1-\nu^2)}}\left[B_1\left(\mathrm{bei}_2'\,(2\bar{\mu}_c\sqrt{s})\right.\right.\right. \\ &\qquad \left. + \frac{\nu}{s}\,\mathrm{bei}_2\,(2\bar{\mu}_c\sqrt{s})\right) - B_2\left(\mathrm{ber}_2'\,(2\bar{\mu}_c\sqrt{s})\right. \\ &\qquad \left.\left.\left. + \frac{\nu}{s}\,\mathrm{ber}_2\,(2\bar{\mu}_c\sqrt{s})\right)\right] - \frac{(h/l)^2}{4(1-\nu)}\right\}, \\ M_\theta &= \frac{pl^2\tan\alpha}{2}\left\{\frac{(h/l)}{\sqrt{12(1-\nu^2)}}\left[B_1\left(\frac{1}{s}\,\mathrm{bei}_2\,(2\bar{\mu}_c\sqrt{s})\right.\right.\right. \\ &\qquad \left. + \nu\,\mathrm{bei}_2'\,(2\bar{\mu}_c\sqrt{s})\right) - B_2\left(\frac{1}{s}\,\mathrm{ber}_2\,(2\bar{\mu}_c\sqrt{s})\right. \\ &\qquad \left.\left.\left. + \nu\,\mathrm{ber}_2'\,(2\bar{\mu}_c\sqrt{s})\right)\right] - \frac{(h/l)^2}{4(1-\nu)}\right\}, \end{aligned} \tag{5.28i}$$

where we have set $C_1 = 0$ to indicate that there are no external axial loads.

The results of the foregoing analysis are given in Figs. 5.10 to 5.13 where Eqs. 5.28i are plotted as a function of the angle α and the position along a generator for clamped, pressurized conical caps with $l/h = 50$. These

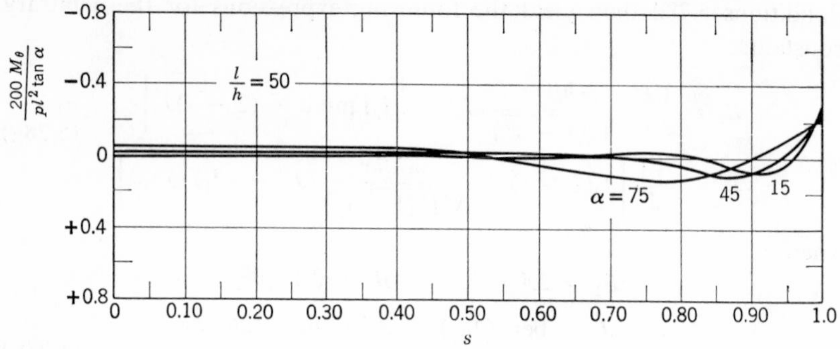

Figure 5.10 Circumferential moment distributions for the shell shown in Fig. 5.9.

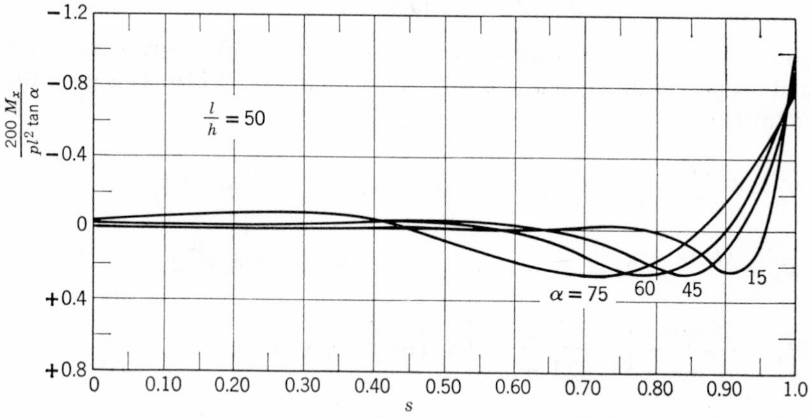

Figure 5.11 Axial moment distributions for the shell shown in Fig. 5.9.

figures indicate the localized nature of the bending effects which are introduced at the clamped edge. Indeed, at points which are more than a certain distance from the edge, the stress resultants and stress couples take on the values which were obtained for pressurized conical membrane shells in Section 4.2*b* (see Eqs. 4.24e). Furthermore, it is seen that the effects of bending make an appreciable contribution only to M_x and to N_θ while M_θ and N_x differ only slightly from the membrane state. In accordance with Eq. 5.22j, Figs. 5.10 to 5.13 also show that the decay length of a conical shell increases as α increases. Thus, we see that the bending effects are felt over a greater distance when the shell is almost flat than when it is almost a cylinder.

The solution that we have presented here is representative of the analyses of conical shells which have appeared in the literature. As a brief review, we note that solutions of the type described here were first

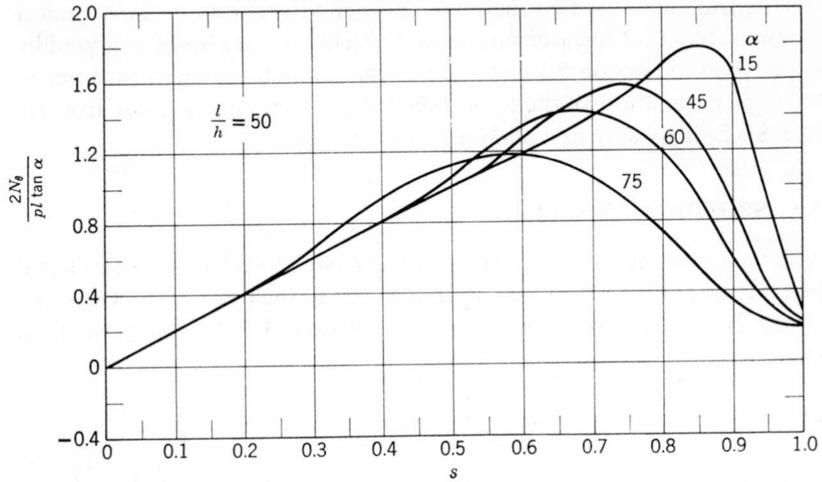

Figure 5.12 Circumferential force distributions for the shell shown in Fig. 5.9.

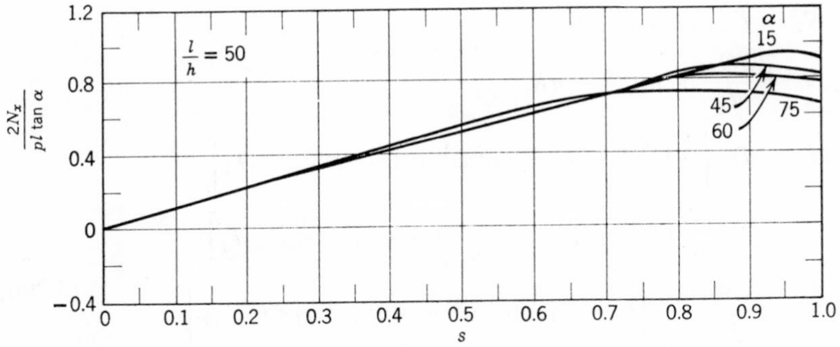

Figure 5.13 Axial force distributions for the shell shown in Fig. 5.9.

carried out for conical shells of constant thickness by Dubois[6] and later by Watts and Lang[7] who considered a cylindrical pressure vessel capped by a conical shell. Taylor and Wenk[8] considered edge effects in long conical frustums, Huth[9] considered thermal stresses due to aerodynamic heating

[6] Dubois, F., "Uber die Festigkeit der Kegelschale," Dissertation, E. T. H. Zurich (1917).

[7] Watts, G. W., and Lang, H. A., "Stresses in a Pressure Vessel with a Conical Head," *Trans. A.S.M.E.*, **74**, 315–326 (1952).

[8] Taylor, C. E., and Wenk, E., Jr., "Analysis of Stresses in the Conical Elements of Shell Structures," *Proc. 2nd U.S. Nat'l. Cong. Appl. Mech. A.S.M.E.*, 323–331 (1955).

[9] Huth, J. H., "Thermal Stresses in Conical Shells," *J. Aerosp. Sci.*, **20**, 613–616 (1953).

and Baltrukonis[10] studied the interaction of edge effects in short conical frustums. Shells of linearly varying wall thickness can also be analyzed by the method of Section 5.1 and, indeed, the solution functions turn out to be simpler than those of the conical shell of constant thickness (see Exercise 5.7). Such shells were first analyzed by Honegger.[11]

5.4 SPHERICAL SHELLS

As a final illustration of the method of analysis which has been developed here, let us examine the behavior of a spherical shell whose thickness and elastic properties are independent of position. In this case, we have $r_\varphi = r_\theta = R$,

$$L(\ldots) = \frac{h}{R}\left[\frac{d^2(\ldots)}{d\varphi^2} + \cot\varphi\,\frac{d(\ldots)}{d\varphi} - \left(\frac{E_\theta}{E_\varphi}\cot^2\varphi - \nu_{\varphi\theta}\right)(\ldots)\right],$$

$$f(\varphi) = \frac{\nu_{\varphi\theta}h}{R}, \qquad \lambda^2 = \frac{-\nu_{\varphi\theta}h}{R} + i\left[12(1-\nu_{\varphi\theta}\nu_{\theta\varphi})\frac{E_\theta}{E_\varphi} - \frac{\nu_{\varphi\theta}{}^2h^2}{R^2}\right]^{1/2}, \tag{5.29a}$$

and the stress resultants, stress couples, and displacements are given by

$$N_\varphi = Q_\varphi\cot\varphi - F_1(\varphi),$$

$$N_\theta = \frac{dQ_\varphi}{d_\varphi} + F_1(\varphi) - qR,$$

$$M_\varphi = D_\varphi\left[\frac{1}{R}\left(\frac{d\beta_\varphi}{d\varphi} + \nu_{\varphi\theta}\beta_\varphi\cot\varphi\right) + (\alpha_{t\varphi} + \nu_{\varphi\theta}\alpha_{t\theta})T_1\right],$$

$$M_\theta = D_\theta\left[\frac{1}{R}\left(\beta_\varphi\cot\varphi + \nu_{\theta\varphi}\frac{d\beta_\varphi}{d\varphi}\right) + (\alpha_{t\theta} + \nu_{\theta\varphi}\alpha_{t\varphi})T_1\right],$$

$$F_1(\varphi) = \frac{R}{\sin^2\varphi} - \left[C_1 + \int_{\varphi_0}^{\varphi}(q_\varphi\sin\varphi + q\cos\varphi)\sin\varphi\,d\varphi\right], \tag{5.29b}$$

$$u_\varphi = \sin\varphi\int\frac{F(\varphi)\,d\varphi}{\sin\varphi},$$

$$w = R\left[\frac{N_\theta - \nu_{\varphi\theta}N_\varphi}{E_\theta h} + \alpha_{t\theta}T_0\right] - u_\varphi\cot\varphi,$$

$$F(\varphi) = \frac{RN_\varphi}{E_\varphi h}(1+\nu_{\theta\varphi}) - \frac{RN_\theta}{E_\theta h}(1+\nu_{\varphi\theta}) + RT_0(\alpha_{t\varphi} - \alpha_{t\theta}),$$

where

$$Q_\varphi = Q_\varphi{}^c + Q_\varphi{}^p, \qquad \beta_\varphi = \beta_\varphi{}^c + \beta_\varphi{}^p. \tag{5.29c}$$

---

[10] Baltrukonis, J. H., "Influence Coefficients for Edge Loaded, Thin, Conical Frustums," *J. Appl. Mech.*, **26**, 241–245 (1959).

[11] Honegger, E., "Festigkeitsberechnung von Kegelschalen mit linear veranderlicher Wandstärke," Dissertation, E. T. H. Zurich (1919).

5.4*a* Spherical Shells under Edge Loadings

For a spherical shell, the complementary solutions satisfy the equations (see Eqs. 5.15n):

$$\frac{d^2Q_\varphi{}^c}{d\varphi^2} + \cot\varphi\,\frac{dQ_\varphi{}^c}{d\varphi} - \frac{E_\theta}{E_\varphi}\cot^2\varphi\, Q_\varphi{}^c \pm 2i\mu_s{}^2 Q_\varphi{}^c = 0, \qquad (5.30a)$$

where

$$\mu_s{}^2 = \left[3(1 - \nu_{\varphi\theta}\nu_{\theta\varphi})\frac{E_\theta}{E_\varphi}\frac{R^2}{h^2} - \frac{\nu_{\varphi\theta}{}^2}{4}\right]^{1/2}. \qquad (5.30b)$$

By means of the change of variables[1]

$$x = \sin^2\varphi, \qquad Q_\varphi{}^c = z\sin\varphi \qquad (5.30c)$$

the foregoing differential equations are transformed into

$$x^2(x-1)\frac{d^2z}{dx^2} + (\tfrac{5}{2}x - 2)x\frac{dz}{dx} + \left[\left(2 - \frac{E_\theta}{E_\varphi} \mp 2i\mu_s{}^2\right)x + \left(\frac{E_\theta}{E_\varphi} - 1\right)\right]\frac{z}{4} = 0. \qquad (5.30d)$$

These equations may be compared to a standard form of the hypergeometric equation as given by[12]

$$x^2(x-1)\frac{d^2z}{dx^2} + [(a+b+1)x + (\alpha+\beta-1)]x\frac{dz}{dx} + (abx - \alpha\beta)z = 0. \qquad (5.30e)$$

From this, it is readily apparent that our Eqs. 5.30d are hypergeometric equations with

$$\begin{aligned} a &= \tfrac{1}{4}[3 + (1 + 4m^2 \pm 8i\mu_s{}^2)^{1/2}],\\ b &= \tfrac{1}{4}[3 - (1 + 4m^2 \pm 8i\mu_s{}^2)^{1/2}],\\ \alpha &= -\tfrac{1}{2}(1 - m),\\ \beta &= -\tfrac{1}{2}(1 + m), \qquad m = (E_\theta/E_\varphi)^{1/2}. \end{aligned} \qquad (5.30f)$$

We have deleted the other signs in front of the radicals in these definitions because these would yield no new information. The complementary solution can, therefore, be written as[12] (see Eq. 5.15s):

$$U^c = RQ_\varphi{}^c = A_1S_1 + A_2S_2, \qquad (5.30g)$$

where

$$\begin{aligned} S_1 &= \sin^m\varphi\; Re\, F(a+\alpha, b+\alpha, \alpha-\beta+1, \sin^2\varphi),\\ S_2 &= \sin^m\varphi\; Im\, F(a+\alpha, b+\alpha, \alpha-\beta+1, \sin^2\varphi) \end{aligned} \qquad (5.30h)$$

and $F(a+\alpha, b+\alpha, \alpha-\beta+1, \sin^2\varphi)$ is a hypergeometric function. In the completely general solution, we should have to add two additional

[12] See, for example, Solution 2.260 in Kamke, E., *Differential-Gleichungen Lösungsmethoden und Lösungen*, New York: Chelsea, (1959).

functions, A_3S_3 and A_4S_4. These solutions,[13] are singular at $\varphi = 0, \pi$ and, consequently, would have to be suppressed when considering shells which are closed at $\varphi = 0, \pi$. If, however, we restrict our attention to spherical caps that are indeed closed at $\varphi = 0$, then the solution 5.30g is the complete solution for Q_φ^c and, in view of Eq. 5.15w,

$$\beta_\varphi{}^c = \frac{-1}{E_\theta hR}[(2\mu_s{}^2A_2 + \nu_{\varphi\theta}A_1)S_1 + (\nu_{\varphi\theta}A_2 - 2\mu_s{}^2A_1)S_2]. \quad (5.30i)$$

The hypergeometric functions which appear in the foregoing solutions are evaluated by using their series representation[12]

$$F(a, b, c, z) = \frac{\Gamma(c)}{\Gamma(a)\Gamma(b)} \sum_{n=0}^{\infty} \frac{\Gamma(a+n)\Gamma(b+n)}{\Gamma(c+n)} \frac{z^n}{n!}, \quad (5.30j)$$

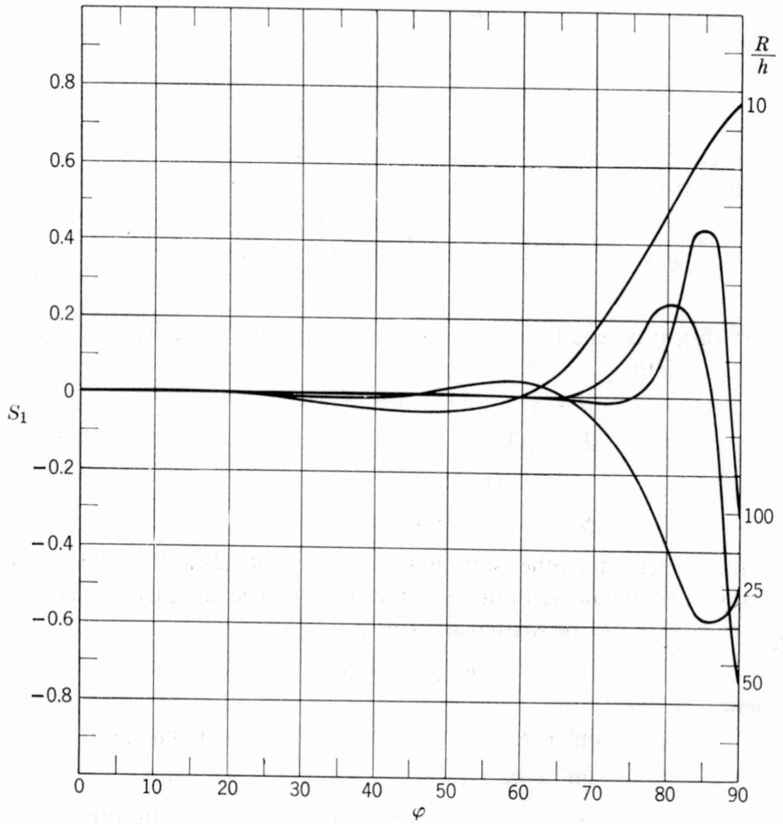

Figure 5.14 Solution functions for spherical shells.

[13] For their determination see, Ince, E. L., *Ordinary Differential Equations*, New York: Dover, Chapter 7, 16 (1956).

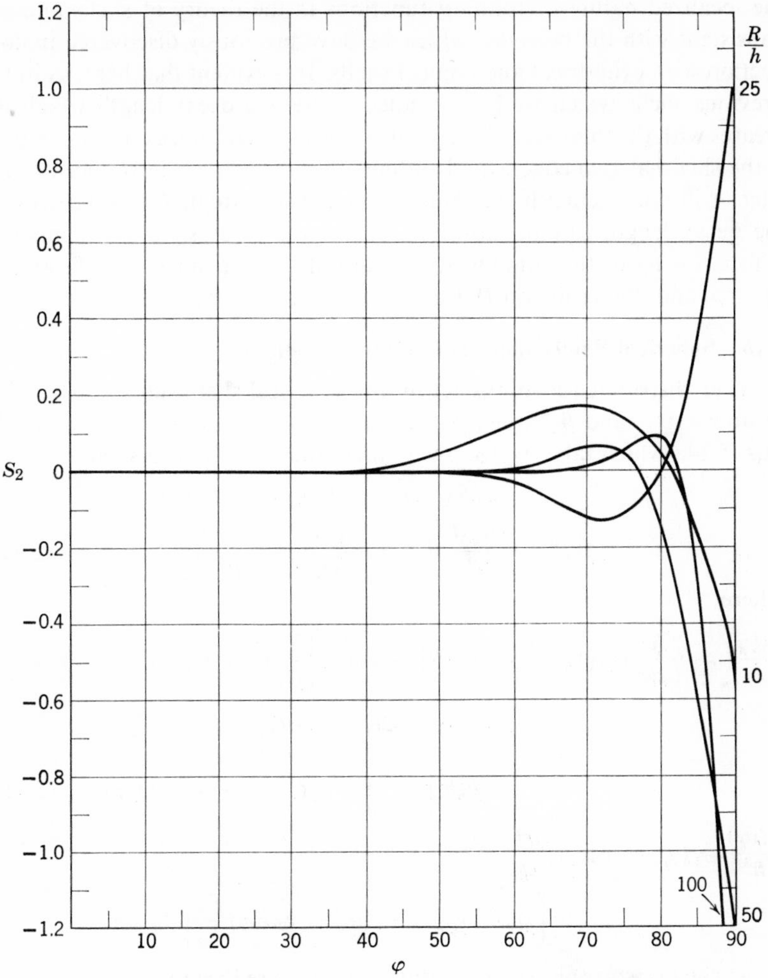

Figure 5.15 Solution functions for spherical shells.

where $\Gamma(\ldots)$ is the Gamma function. The circle of convergence of this series is $|z| = 1$. When $z = 1$ the series will converge absolutely if $Re(c - a - b) > 0$. In view of Eqs. 5.30f, we find that $Re(c - a - b) = \frac{1}{2}$. Therefore, the series converges absolutely for $z = 1$ or, in our case, for $\varphi = \pi/2$. The speed of convergence is, however, closely linked to the value of μ_s and, consequently, to the ratio of the radius to the thickness.

To illustrate the behavior of the solutions, we have plotted S_1 and S_2 for isotropic spherical shells in Figs. 5.14 and 5.15. These curves, which are appropriate for spherical shells that are closed at $\varphi = 0$, indicate once more the localized nature of solution functions in the theory of shells and are consistent with the behavior which we have previously discovered in connection with cylindrical and conical shells. It is evident that here, as in the previous shells which we have studied, there is a decay length which decreases with the thickness of the shell. We may, therefore, expect again that, if the shell has two edges, the bending effects which are introduced at the edges will not interact if the shell is of sufficient extent. An expression for the decay length cannot, however, be derived in as simple a manner as before, owing to the complicated nature of the dependence of S_1 and S_2 upon μ_s and, therefore, on R, h and the elastic properties of the shell.

5.4*b* Spherical Shells under Distributed Loadings

When distributed loadings act on the spherical shell, suitable particular solutions $Q_\varphi{}^p$ and $\beta_x{}^p$ must be derived. Such solutions are governed by Eqs. 5.14a which take the following form for the spherical shell:

$$L(RQ_\varphi{}^p) = -E_\theta h^2 \beta_\varphi{}^p + G_1(\varphi),$$

$$L(\beta_\varphi{}^p) - \frac{2\nu_{\varphi\theta} h}{R}\beta_\varphi{}^p = \frac{RQ_\varphi{}^p h}{D_\varphi} + \frac{H(\varphi)}{h^2}, \tag{5.31a}$$

where

$$\frac{G_1(\varphi)}{h} = -\frac{d}{d\varphi}[F_1(1+\nu_{\varphi\theta}) - qR] - \cot\varphi\left[\frac{E_\theta}{E_\varphi}(1+\nu_{\theta\varphi})F_1 + (1+\nu_{\varphi\theta})(F_1 - qR)\right] - E_\theta h\left[\alpha_{t\theta}\frac{dT_0}{d\varphi} - T_0(\alpha_{t\varphi} - \alpha_{t\theta})\cot\varphi\right], \tag{5.31b}$$

$$\frac{H(\varphi)}{h^3} = (\alpha_{t\varphi} + \nu_{\varphi\theta}\alpha_{t\theta})\frac{dT_1}{d\varphi} + \left[\alpha_{t\varphi} + \nu_{\varphi\theta}\alpha_{t\theta} - (\alpha_{t\theta} + \nu_{\theta\varphi}\alpha_{t\varphi})\frac{E_\theta}{E_\varphi}\right]T_1\cos\varphi.$$

If the shell is isotropic, the preceding equations reduce to

$$L(RQ_\varphi{}^p) = -Eh^2\beta_\varphi{}^p + G_1(\varphi),$$

$$L(\beta_\varphi{}^p) - \frac{2\nu h}{R}\beta_\varphi{}^p = \frac{RQ_\varphi{}^p h}{D} + \frac{H(\varphi)}{h^2} \tag{5.31c}$$

where

$$\frac{G_1(\varphi)}{h} = -\frac{d}{d\varphi}[F_1(1+\nu) - qR] - (1+\nu)\cot\varphi(2F_1 - qR) - Eh\alpha_t\frac{dT_0}{d\varphi}, \tag{5.31d}$$

$$\frac{H(\varphi)}{h^3} = (1+\nu)\alpha_t\frac{dT_1}{d\varphi},$$

and when $Q_\varphi{}^p$ and $\beta_x{}^p$ are in turn eliminated from Eqs. 5.31c, we obtain the new set:

$$LL(Q_\varphi{}^p) - \frac{2\nu h}{R} L(Q_\varphi{}^p) + 12(1 - \nu^2)Q_\varphi{}^p$$
$$= \frac{L[G_1(\varphi)]}{R} - \frac{2\nu h}{R^2} G_1(\varphi) - \frac{EH(\varphi)}{R}, \tag{5.31e}$$

$$LL(\beta_\varphi{}^p) - \frac{2\nu h}{R} L(\beta_\varphi{}^p) + 12(1 - \nu^2)\beta_\varphi{}^p$$
$$= \frac{G_1 h}{D} + \frac{L[H(\varphi)]}{h^2}.$$

As a first example, let us consider the case of internal pressure for which $q = -p$, $q_\varphi = T_0 = T_1 = 0$, and

$$F_1(\varphi) = -\frac{pR}{2}, \qquad H(\varphi) = 0, \qquad G_1(\varphi) = 0. \tag{5.32a}$$

With these values, Eqs. 5.31e become homogeneous and, consequently,

$$Q_\varphi{}^p = \beta_\varphi{}^p = 0. \tag{5.32b}$$

The effect of the internal pressure is, however, brought into the system through Eqs. 5.29b, which give

$$N_\varphi{}^p = N_\theta{}^p = \frac{pR}{2},$$
$$M_\varphi{}^p = M_\theta{}^p = 0, \tag{5.32c}$$
$$u_\varphi{}^p = 0, \qquad w^p = \frac{pR^2}{2Eh}(1 - \nu),$$

where we have assumed that no additional external axial loads act upon the shell (that is, $C_1 = 0$). These solutions coincide with results obtained earlier for spherical shells under internal pressure by the membrane theory (see Eqs. 4.32a and 4.32e).

As a second example, let us consider the case of a spherical shell under the action of its own weight. Here we have $T_0 = T_1 = 0$, $q_\varphi = P \sin \varphi$, $q = P \cos \varphi$, and

$$F_1(\varphi) = PR/(1 + \cos \varphi),$$
$$H(\varphi) = 0, \qquad G_1(\varphi) = -PRh(2 + \nu) \sin \varphi, \tag{5.33a}$$

where we have assumed that no additional axial loads act on the shell and P is the weight of the shell per unit of area of its reference surface. For this case, Eqs. 5.31e take the form

$$LL(Q_\varphi{}^p) - \frac{2\nu h}{R} L(Q_\varphi{}^p) + 12(1 - \nu^2)\, Q_\varphi{}^p = Ph^2(2 + \nu)(1 + \nu) \sin \varphi / R,$$

$$LL(\beta_\varphi{}^p) - \frac{2\nu h}{R} L(\beta_\varphi{}^p) + 12(1 - \nu^2)\beta_\varphi{}^p = -\frac{12PR}{Eh}(2 + \nu)(1 - \nu^2) \sin \varphi. \tag{5.33b}$$

From these, it follows that the particular solutions for the dead load are

$$Q_\varphi{}^p = \frac{PR(1 + \nu)(2 + \nu) \sin \varphi}{(1 - \nu^2)(1 + 12R^2/h^2)},$$
$$\beta_\varphi{}^p = -\frac{12PR(1 + \nu)(2 + \nu) \sin \varphi.}{Eh(1 + 12R^2/h^2)} \tag{5.33c}$$

The contributions of these solutions and of the load to the other shell variables are:

$$N_\varphi{}^p = PR\left[\frac{(1 + \nu)(2 + \nu) \cos \varphi}{(1 - \nu^2)(1 + 12R^2/h^2)} - \frac{1}{1 + \cos \varphi}\right],$$

$$N_\theta{}^p = PR\left[\frac{(1 + \nu)(2 + \nu) \cos \varphi}{(1 - \nu^2)(1 + 12R^2/\mathrm{h}^2)} + \frac{1}{1 + \cos \varphi} - \cos \varphi\right],$$

$$M_\varphi{}^p = M_\theta{}^p = -\frac{Ph^2(1 + \nu)(2 + \nu) \cos \varphi}{(1 - \nu)(1 + 12R^2/h^2)}, \tag{5.33d}$$

$$u_\varphi{}^p = -\frac{PR^2}{Eh}(1 + \nu) \sin \varphi \left[\frac{1}{1 + \cos \varphi} - \log (1 + \cos \varphi)\right],$$

$$w^p = \frac{pR^2}{Eh}\left[\frac{(2 + \nu) \cos \varphi}{1 + 12R^2/h^2} + \frac{1 + \nu}{1 + \cos \varphi} - \cos \varphi\right] - u_\varphi{}^p \cot \varphi.$$

It is interesting to observe that these solutions will approach the solutions obtained by the membrane approximation for this load case when the shell is very thin, that is, as $R/h \to \infty$ (see Eqs. 4.29b, 4.29c, 4.29e, and 4.29f).

Now suppose that the shell undergoes a temperature change that is linear across its thickness but independent of position. If we take the temperature change to be $T = \vartheta_0 + \zeta\vartheta_1$, where ϑ_0 and ϑ_1 are constants, it follows that $q_\varphi = q = F_1 = 0$, $T_0 = \vartheta_0$, and $T_1 = \vartheta_1$. With these results, we find from Eqs. 5.31d that $G_1(\varphi) = H(\varphi) \equiv 0$. The particular solutions for this type of thermal loading are

$$Q_\varphi{}^p = \beta_\varphi{}^p = 0 \tag{5.34a}$$

and it follows that

$$N_\varphi{}^p = N_\theta{}^p = 0, \qquad u_\varphi{}^p = 0, \qquad w^p = R\alpha_t\vartheta_0,$$
$$M_\varphi{}^p = M_\theta{}^p = D\alpha_t(1 + \nu)\vartheta_1. \tag{5.34b}$$

Particular solutions for more general mechanical and thermal surface loads can also be found for isotropic spherical shells of constant thickness. For this purpose, it is best to use Eqs. 5.31a, which for the present case take the form,

$$\begin{aligned}\frac{d^2Q_\varphi{}^p}{d\varphi^2} + \cot\varphi\frac{dQ_\varphi{}^p}{d\varphi} - (\cot^2\varphi - \nu)Q_\varphi{}^p &= -Eh\beta_\varphi{}^p + \frac{G_1(\varphi)}{h},\\ \frac{d^2\beta_\varphi{}^p}{d\varphi^2} + \cot\varphi\frac{d\beta_\varphi{}^p}{d\varphi} - (\cot^2\varphi + \nu)\beta_\varphi{}^p &= \frac{Q_\varphi{}^pR^2}{D} + \frac{H(\varphi)R}{h^3}.\end{aligned} \tag{5.35a}$$

The particular solutions of these equations can be found by observing that $P_n{}^1(\cos\varphi)$, the associated Legendre function of the first kind, satisfies the equation[14]

$$\frac{d^2P_n{}^1}{d\varphi^2} + \cot\varphi\frac{dP_n{}^1}{d\varphi} - [\cot^2\varphi + 1 - n(n+1)]P_n{}^1 = 0, \tag{5.35b}$$

where n is an integer. Now let us expand the loading terms in Eqs. 5.35a in the following series of associated Legendre functions of the first kind:

$$\begin{aligned}G_1(\varphi)/h &= \sum_{n=1}^{\infty} a_nP_n{}^1(\cos\varphi),\\ H(\varphi)R/h^3 &= \sum_{n=1}^{\infty} b_nP_n{}^1(\cos\varphi),\end{aligned} \tag{5.35c}$$

where the a_n and b_n are known coefficients which are obtained from the definitions

$$\begin{Bmatrix} a_n \\ b_n \end{Bmatrix} = \frac{2n+1}{2}\frac{(n-1)!}{(n+1)!}\int_{-1}^{+1}\begin{Bmatrix} G_1(\varphi)/h \\ H(\varphi)R/h^3 \end{Bmatrix} P_n{}^1(\cos\varphi)\,d(\cos\varphi). \tag{5.35d}$$

Now we expand the particular solutions in similar series, as follows:

$$Q_\varphi{}^p = \sum_{n=1}^{\infty} A_nP_n{}^1(\cos\varphi), \qquad \beta_\varphi{}^p = \sum_{n=1}^{\infty} B_nP_n{}^1(\cos\varphi). \tag{5.35e}$$

Here A_n and B_n are as yet unknown coefficients which are determined by substituting expansions 5.35c and 5.35e into Eqs. 5.35a. This gives, in view of Eq. 5.35b,

$$\begin{aligned}A_n &= \frac{a_n[1 - \nu - n(n+1)] - Ehb_n}{[1 - n(n+1)]^2 - \nu^2 + 12(1-\nu^2)R^2/h^2},\\ B_n &= \frac{a_nR^2/D + b_n[1 + \nu - n(n+1)]}{[1 - n(n+1)]^2 - \nu^2 + 12(1-\nu^2)R^2/h^2}.\end{aligned} \tag{5.35f}$$

After these coefficients are substituted into the expansions 5.35e for the

---

[14] See, for example, Abramowitz and Stegun, loc. cit., p. 332.

particular solutions, the rest of the shell variables can be found by using Eqs. 5.29b.

The use of the associated Legendre functions in the derivation of particular solutions for spherical shells suggests that the complementary solutions could also have been expressed in terms of these functions. Indeed, this is true for the isotropic case because of identities that exist between the hypergeometric functions and the Legendre functions (see Exercise 5.14).

5.4c Example

As an illustration, let us now solve the problem of an isotropic hemispherical cap of constant thickness that is clamped at its edge and loaded by an internal pressure p as shown in Fig. 5.16. In this case, the radial displacement u_r (see Eq. 5.28e), which we introduced in our discussion of

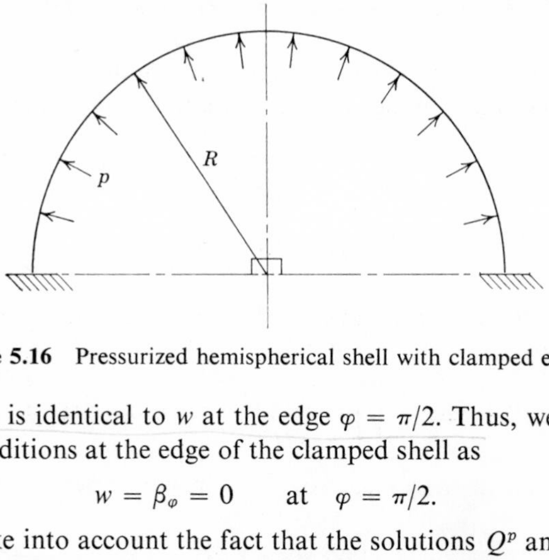

Figure 5.16 Pressurized hemispherical shell with clamped edge.

conical shells, is identical to w at the edge $\varphi = \pi/2$. Thus, we express the boundary conditions at the edge of the clamped shell as

$$w = \beta_\varphi = 0 \quad \text{at} \quad \varphi = \pi/2. \tag{5.36a}$$

Now if we take into account the fact that the solutions Q^p and $\beta_\varphi{}^p$ vanish for the case of internal pressure, we may express the edge conditions in the equivalent form

$$\frac{dQ_\varphi{}^c}{d\varphi} = -\frac{pR(1-\nu)}{2}, \qquad \beta_\varphi{}^c = 0 \quad \text{at} \quad \varphi = \pi/2 \tag{5.36b}$$

where we have used Eqs. 5.29b and the fact that $\cot \pi/2 = 0$. When conditions 5.36a are applied to the general solution 5.30g, 5.30i, and 5.30j, we obtain the following expressions for the arbitrary constants:

$$B_1 = B_2\left(\frac{2\mu_s{}^2J_1 + \nu J_2}{2\mu_s{}^2J_2 - \nu J_1}\right), \qquad B_i = \frac{2A_i}{pR^2},$$
$$B_2 = \frac{-(1-\nu)(2\mu_s{}^2J_2 - \nu J_1)}{J_1'(2\mu_s{}^2J_1 + \nu J_2) + J_2'(2\mu_s{}^2J_2 - \nu J_1)}, \tag{5.36c}$$

where

$$J_1 = S_1(\pi/2), \qquad J_2 = S_2(\pi/2),$$
$$J_1' = \frac{dS_1(\pi/2)}{d\varphi}, \qquad J_2' = \frac{dS_2(\pi/2)}{d\varphi}. \tag{5.36d}$$

The stress resultants and couples which act in the shell can now be written as

$$N_\varphi = \frac{pR}{2}\{[B_1S_1(\varphi) + B_2S_2(\varphi)]\cot\varphi + 1\},$$

$$N_\theta = \frac{pR}{2}\{B_1S_1'(\varphi) + B_2S_2'(\varphi) + 1\},$$

$$M_\varphi = \frac{-ph^2}{24(1-\nu^2)}\{(\nu B_1 + 2\mu_s{}^2B_2)[S_1'(\varphi) + \nu\cot\varphi S_1(\varphi)] + (\nu B_2 - 2\mu_s{}^2B_1)[S_2'(\varphi) + \nu\cot\varphi S_2(\varphi)]\}, \tag{5.36e}$$

$$M_\theta = \frac{-ph^2}{24(1-\nu^2)}\{(\nu B_1 + 2\mu_s{}^2B_2)[\nu S_1'(\varphi) + S_1(\varphi)\cot\varphi] + (\nu B_2 - 2\mu_s{}^2B_1)[\nu S_2'(\varphi) + S_2(\varphi)\cot\varphi]\},$$

where a prime denotes a derivative with respect to φ.

The results of the analysis are given in Figs. 5.17 to 5.19 where N_θ, M_φ, and M_θ are plotted as functions of meridional position and of the ratio R/h for isotropic hemispherical shells loaded as shown in Fig. 5.16. No curves are given for N_φ since in the calculations it was found that $N_\varphi \approx pR/2$ throughout the shell. These curves confirm our earlier conclusion that

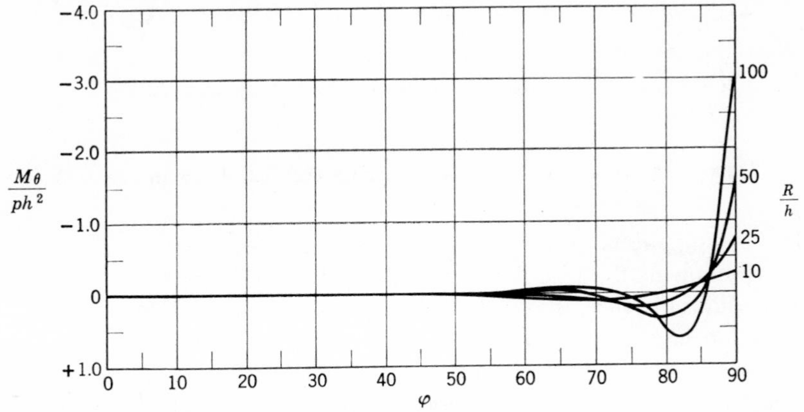

Figure 5.17 Circumferential moment distribution for the shell shown in Fig. 5.16.

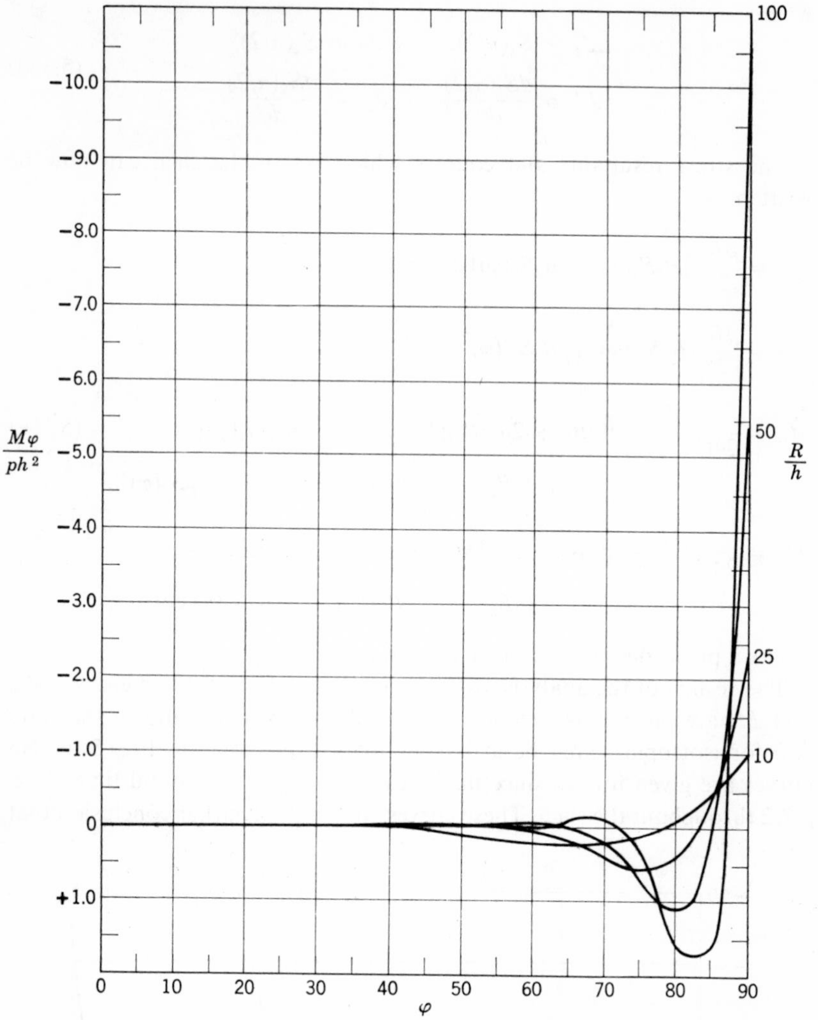

Figure 5.18 Axial moment distributions for the shell shown in Fig. 5.16.

the bending effects which are introduced at the edge make a significant contribution to the results only within a short distance from the edge. Beyond this distance, the results approach the values which were obtained in Section 4.3*a* by means of the theory of membrane shells. It is again seen, as it was in our previous examples, that the region over which the bending effects make a significant contribution to the solution decreases as the thickness of the shell is reduced.

However, this shell has a higher peak.

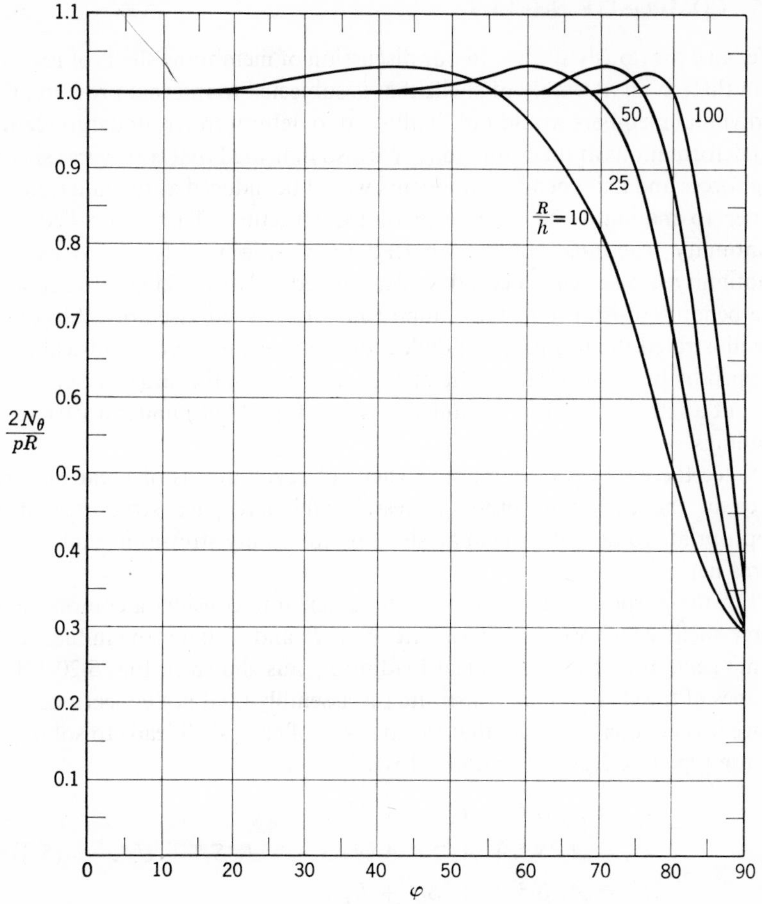

Figure 5.19 Circumferential force distributions for the shell shown in Fig. 5.16.

Extensive calculations of the type whose results have been given here were first carried out by Bolle.[15] Later analyses of a similar nature were carried out by Watts and Lang[16] and Galletly.[17,18]

---

[15] Bolle, L., "Festigkeitsberechnung von Kugelschalen," Dissertation, E. T. H. Zurich (1916), also *Schweiz. Bauzeit*, **66**, 105–108 (1915).

[16] Watts, G. W., and Lang, H. A., "Stresses in a Pressure Vessel with a Hemispherical Head," *Trans. A.S.M.E.*, **75**, 83–89 (1953).

[17] Galletly, G. D., "Influence Coefficients for Hemispherical Shells with Small Openings at the Vertex," *J. Appl. Mech.*, **22**, 20–24 (1955).

[18] Galletly, G. D., "Influence Coefficients for Open-Crown Hemispheres," *Trans. A.S.M.E.*, **82A**, 73–81 (1960).

5.5 COMPOSITE SHELLS

We have previously shown, in our discussion of membrane shells of revolution that, in an assembly of shells that is subjected to internal pressure, the individual members would not, if allowed to deform freely, undergo identical deformations at their junctions. We also indicated that transverse shearing forces and axial bending moments would be induced at the junctions in order to maintain the continuity of the structure. These so-called discontinuity reactions would then lead to what were referred to as discontinuity stresses which could be determined only by taking into account the bending resistance of the components of the shell assembly. Although we illustrated the mismatch of deflections in a pressurized cylindrical shell capped by hemispherical and hemiellipsoidal heads, the situation exists in all but a few special shell combinations (see Eqs. 4.34d) under a variety of loadings.

Since the analysis of composite shells of revolution is of great importance in the design of pressure vessels and aerospace structures, it is appropriate to describe the analysis of discontinuity stresses in such structures here.

For the purpose of illustration, it is sufficient to consider a composite of three shells which we shall designate as A, B, and C under the influence of some general thermomechanical loading F_{TM} as shown in Fig. 5.20a. The shapes of the shells which constitute the assembly need not concern us here since it is adequate to note that the analysis of each shell leads to solutions of the type (see Eqs. 5.15b and 5.15s):

$$\begin{aligned} U_a &= A_1{}^a S_1{}^a + A_2{}^a S_2{}^a + U_a{}^p, \\ U_b &= A_1{}^b S_1{}^b + A_2{}^b S_2{}^b + A_3{}^b S_3{}^b + A_4{}^b S_4{}^b + U_b{}^p, \\ U_c &= A_1{}^c S_1{}^c + A_2{}^c S_2{}^c + U_c{}^p, \end{aligned} \tag{5.37a}$$

where the letters a, b, c identify the solutions and arbitrary constants for Shells A, B, and C, respectively. In writing Eqs. 5.37a, we have accounted for the fact that Shell A is closed at its apex, Shell B is of arbitrary length, and Shell C is of such a length that any bending effects that are introduced at its lower end are not felt at its upper end.

The analysis of this three shell combination thus involves the determination of eight arbitrary constants and proceeds as follows. We cut the composite at the two junctions between the three shells and allow the individual members to deform freely under the load F_{TM} (Fig. 5.20b). Since the free deflections of the shells are not equal across each junction, we restore the continuity of the structure by introducing the "discontinuity" reactions $M_m{}^n$ and $H_m{}^n$ at each junction as shown in Fig. 5.20c. Here $n = a, b, c$ identifies the shell and $m = 1, 2$ identifies the edge at which the moment

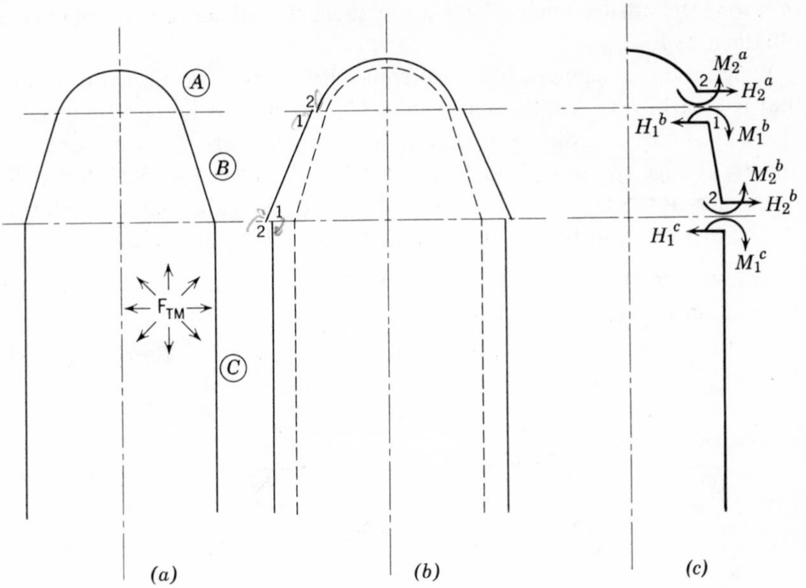

Figure 5.20 Typical three element composite shell.

and shearing force act. The eight arbitrary constants are now determined by applying the continuity conditions

$$M_2^a = M_1^b, \qquad H_2^a = H_1^b, \qquad \beta_2^a = \beta_1^b, \qquad \delta_2^a = \delta_1^b \quad (5.37b)$$

between Shell *A* and Shell *B* and

$$M_2^b = M_1^c, \qquad H_2^b = H_1^c, \qquad \beta_2^b = \beta_1^c, \qquad \delta_2^b = \delta_1^c \quad (5.37c)$$

between Shell *B* and Shell *C*. Here β_m^n and δ_m^n denote, respectively, the rotation and radial displacement at edge *m* of shell *n*. In writing conditions 5.37b and 5.37c, we have also implied that no external moments or shearing forces are applied at the junctions. When conditions 5.37b and 5.37c are applied to the solutions 5.37a, we obtain eight simultaneous linear equations which can be solved for the eight arbitrary constants. Once these are known, any desired quantity can be calculated in any of the shells.

5.5*a* Influence Coefficients

Some economies can be introduced in the analysis of composite shells of revolution by the use of existing tables of influence coefficients. These quantities represent contributions to the various shell variables from unit values of edge moments, edge shearing forces, internal pressure, and so on as we have already indicated in connection with Eqs. 5.20f in the analysis of a long cylindrical shell. For a given shell, the influence coefficients are obtained as follows:

We consider a segment of an isotropic shell of revolution, for example, that is of arbitrary length and profile. The segment is loaded by internal pressure and by an edge moment and a horizontal edge shearing force M_1 and H_1 at edge 1 and M_2 and H_2 at edge 2 as shown in Fig. 5.21. Since the shape has not been specified, it is sufficient to indicate that the solution can be expressed in the form (see Eqs. 5.15b, 5.15s, and 5.15w):

$$\begin{aligned} r_\theta Q_\varphi &= A_1S_1 + A_2S_2 + A_3S_3 + A_4S_4 + r_\theta Q_\varphi{}^p, \\ Eh^2\beta_\varphi &= A_1(\mu_1{}^2S_1 + \mu_2{}^2S_2) + A_2(\mu_1{}^2S_2 - \mu_2{}^2S_1) \\ &\quad + A_3(\mu_1{}^2S_3 + \mu_2{}^2S_4) + A_4(\mu_1{}^2S_4 - \mu_2{}^2S_3) + Eh^2\beta_\varphi{}^p \end{aligned} \tag{5.37d}$$

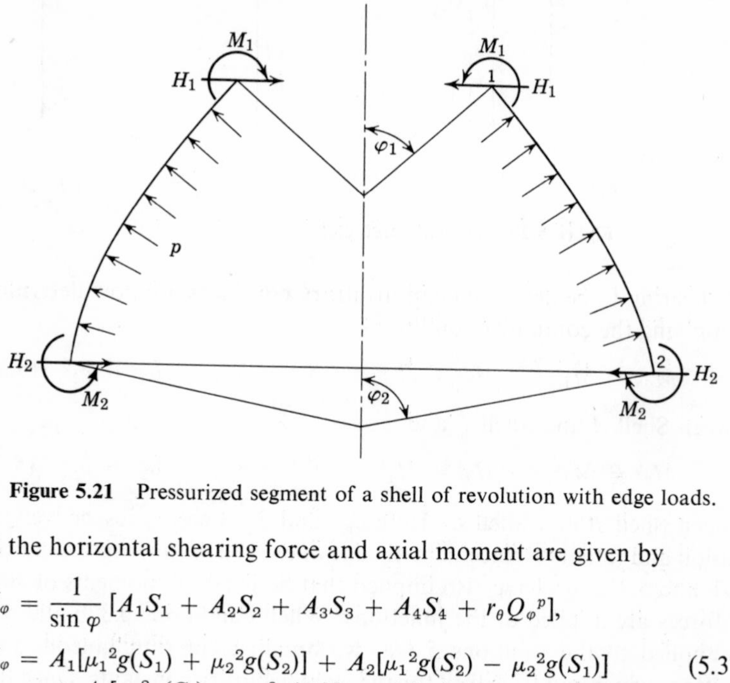

Figure 5.21 Pressurized segment of a shell of revolution with edge loads.

and the horizontal shearing force and axial moment are given by

$$\begin{aligned} r_\theta H_\varphi &= \frac{1}{\sin\varphi}[A_1S_1 + A_2S_2 + A_3S_3 + A_4S_4 + r_\theta Q_\varphi{}^p], \\ M_\varphi &= A_1[\mu_1{}^2g(S_1) + \mu_2{}^2g(S_2)] + A_2[\mu_1{}^2g(S_2) - \mu_2{}^2g(S_1)] \\ &\quad + A_3[\mu_1{}^2g(S_3) + \mu_2{}^2g(S_4)] + A_4[\mu_1{}^2g(S_4) - \mu_2{}^2g(S_3)] \\ &\quad + Eh^2g(\beta_\varphi{}^p) \end{aligned} \tag{5.37e}$$

where

$$g(\ldots) = \frac{h}{12(1-\nu^2)}\left[\frac{1}{r_\varphi}\frac{d(\ldots)}{d\varphi} + \frac{\nu(\ldots)\cot\varphi}{r_\theta}\right].$$

When the boundary conditions

$$\begin{aligned} H_\varphi &= H_1, \qquad M_\varphi = M_1 \qquad \text{at} \quad \varphi = \varphi_1 \\ H_\varphi &= H_2, \qquad M_\varphi = M_2 \qquad \text{at} \quad \varphi = \varphi_2 \end{aligned} \tag{5.37f}$$

are applied to Eqs. 5.37e, we obtain four linear equations with constant coefficients which can be written in the form

$$\begin{Bmatrix} M_1 \\ M_2 \\ H_1 \\ H_2 \end{Bmatrix} = \{a\} \begin{Bmatrix} A_1 \\ A_2 \\ A_3 \\ A_4 \end{Bmatrix} + \{b\}p. \tag{5.37g}$$

Here $\{a\}$ and $\{b\}$ are, respectively, a four by four matrix of the coefficients of the arbitrary constants and a four element column matrix of the coefficients of the pressure as obtained by evaluating Eqs. 5.37e at the end points of the shell. The column matrix of arbitrary constants is now determined by multiplying Eq. 5.37g by the inverse of $\{a\}$, that is,

$$\begin{Bmatrix} A_1 \\ A_2 \\ A_3 \\ A_4 \end{Bmatrix} = \{a\}^{-1} \begin{Bmatrix} M_1 \\ M_2 \\ H_1 \\ H_2 \end{Bmatrix} + \{a\}^{-1}\{b\}p. \tag{5.37h}$$

We are now able to express any of the shell variables as a function of the edge moments, edge shearing forces, and internal pressure which have been applied to the shell. Indeed, if we denote a general shell variable at a location φ by the symbol Y_φ, we can write

$$Y_\varphi = {}_MY_{\varphi 2}M_2 + {}_HY_{\varphi 2}H_2 + {}_MY_{\varphi 1}M_1 + {}_HY_{\varphi 1}H_1 + {}_pY_\varphi p, \tag{5.37i}$$

where ${}_MY_{\varphi i}M_i$ and ${}_HY_{\varphi i}H_i$ identify the contribution to Y_φ from a moment and a shearing force, respectively, acting at edge i, and ${}_pY_\varphi p$ denotes the contribution from the internal pressure to Y_φ. The functions ${}_MY_{\varphi i}$, ${}_HY_{\varphi i}$, and ${}_pY_\varphi$ are called influence functions and when a particular location is fixed by specifying the value of φ, they are known as influence coefficients. If the shell is "long" or if it is closed at one end, the foregoing development leads, instead, to equations of the type

$$Y_\varphi = {}_MY_\varphi M + {}_HY_\varphi H + {}_pY_\varphi p, \tag{5.37j}$$

where M and H are the edge moment and shearing force, respectively.

For the purpose of analysing composite shells, it is of importance to have at hand expressions for the rotation and the radial displacement at the edges of a given shell segment. Thus, Eq. 5.37i leads to equations of the type

$$\begin{aligned}
\delta_2{}^i &= {}_M\delta_{22}{}^iM_2 + {}_H\delta_{22}{}^iH_2 + {}_M\delta_{21}{}^iM_1 + {}_H\delta_{21}{}^iH_1 + {}_p\Delta_2{}^ip, \\
\beta_2{}^i &= {}_M\theta_{22}{}^iM_2 + {}_H\theta_{22}{}^iH_2 + {}_M\theta_{21}{}^iM_1 + {}_H\theta_{21}{}^iH_1 + {}_p\theta_2{}^ip, \\
\delta_1{}^i &= {}_M\delta_{12}{}^iM_2 + {}_H\delta_{12}{}^iH_2 + {}_M\delta_{11}{}^iM_1 + {}_H\delta_{11}{}^iH_1 + {}_p\Delta_1{}^ip, \\
\beta_1{}^i &= {}_M\theta_{12}{}^iM_2 + {}_H\theta_{12}{}^iH_2 + {}_M\theta_{11}{}^iM_1 + {}_M\theta_{11}{}^iH_1 + {}_p\theta_1{}^ip,
\end{aligned} \tag{5.37k}$$

at edges 1 and 2 of the shell. Here the superscript i identifies the shell and ${}_M\delta_{mn}{}^i M_n$ refers to the contribution of M_n at edge n to the displacement at edge m and so on. The quantities ${}_M\delta_{mn}{}^i$, ${}_H\delta_{mn}{}^i$, ${}_M\theta_{mn}{}^i$, ${}_H\theta_{mn}{}^i$, and so on, are called the edge influence coefficients and are found for a particular shell by applying unit edge moments, horizontal shearing forces, and internal pressure one at a time. If the shell is "long" or closed at one end, Eqs. 5.37k reduce to

$$\begin{aligned} \delta^i &= {}_M\delta^i M + {}_H\delta^i H + {}_p\Delta^i p, \\ \beta^i &= {}_M\theta^i M + {}_H\theta^i H + {}_p\theta^i p. \end{aligned} \tag{5.37l}$$

To demonstrate the use of the edge influence coefficients let us return to the assembly of three shells which we considered earlier. The edge deflections and rotations of the component shells can now be written as

$$\begin{aligned} \delta_2{}^a &= {}_M\delta_2{}^a M_1 + {}_H\delta_2{}^a H_1 + {}_p\Delta_2{}^a p, \\ \beta_2{}^a &= {}_M\theta_2{}^a M_1 + {}_H\theta_2{}^a H_1 + {}_p\theta_2{}^a p, \end{aligned} \tag{5.37m}$$

for edge 2 of Shell A;

$$\begin{aligned} \delta_1{}^b &= {}_M\delta_{12}{}^b M_2 + {}_H\delta_{12}{}^b H_2 + {}_M\delta_{11}{}^b M_1 + {}_H\delta_{11}{}^b H_1 + {}_p\Delta_1{}^b p, \\ \beta_1{}^b &= {}_M\theta_{12}{}^b M_2 + {}_H\theta_{12}{}^b H_2 + {}_M\theta_{11}{}^b M_1 + {}_H\theta_{11}{}^b H_1 + {}_p\theta_1{}^b p, \end{aligned} \tag{5.37n}$$

for edge 1 of Shell B;

$$\begin{aligned} \delta_2{}^b &= {}_M\delta_{22}{}^b M_2 + {}_H\delta_{22}{}^b H_2 + {}_M\delta_{21}{}^b M_1 + {}_H\delta_{21}{}^b H_1 + {}_p\Delta_2{}^b p, \\ \beta_2{}^b &= {}_M\theta_{22}{}^b M_2 + {}_H\theta_{22}{}^b H_2 + {}_M\theta_{21}{}^b M_1 + {}_H\theta_{21}{}^b H_1 + {}_p\theta_2{}^b p, \end{aligned} \tag{5.37o}$$

for edge 2 of Shell B, and

$$\begin{aligned} \delta_1{}^c &= {}_M\delta_1{}^c M_2 + {}_H\delta_1{}^c H_2 + {}_p\Delta_1{}^c p, \\ \beta_1{}^c &= {}_M\theta_1{}^c M_2 + {}_H\theta_1{}^c H_2 + {}_p\theta_1{}^c p, \end{aligned} \tag{5.37p}$$

for edge 1 of Shell C, where we have assumed that the moments and shearing forces are continuous across each of the junctions, that is, $M_2{}^a = M_1{}^b = M_1$, $H_2{}^a = H_1{}^b = H_1$, $M_2{}^b = M_1{}^c = M_2$, and $H_2{}^b = H_1{}^c = H_2$.

The continuity conditions at the junctions between the shells can now be stated simply as

$$\begin{aligned} \beta_2{}^a &= \beta_1{}^b, \qquad \delta_2{}^a = \delta_1{}^b, \\ \beta_2{}^b &= \beta_1{}^c, \qquad \delta_2{}^b = \delta_1{}^c, \end{aligned} \tag{5.37q}$$

These conditions, when applied to Eqs. 5.37m to 5.37p, lead to four simultaneous linear equations in the four unknown reactions H_1, H_2, M_1, and M_2. Once these quantities are known, it is possible, by using equations of the type of Eq. 5.37i, to find any shell variable Y_φ at any position in any of the shells. The amount of manipulation that the analyst faces is thus considerably reduced when the edge influence coefficients are employed. Whereas the analysis of our three shell composite previously led to eight equations in eight arbitrary constants, the use of influence coefficients has cut this to four equations in four unknown reactions.

The success of the method depends solely upon the availability of influence coefficients for the shells which we may have occasion to analyse. If these are not available for the shells that are involved, we have the choice of proceeding with the former method or calculating our own influence coefficients. A great deal of progress has been made in this area, and we find that the literature contains information on influence coefficients for most of the geometrical shapes which one might encounter in practice. Thus, we find that Galletly has calculated influence coefficients for hemispherical shells with openings at the apex,[17,18] ellipsoidal shells with openings at the apex,[19] toroidal shell segments with positive curvature,[20] and toroidal shell segments with negative curvature.[21] Influence coefficients were given by Taylor and Wenk[8] for long conical shells whose edges do not interact and by Baltrukonis[10] for short conical shells. Watts and Lang gave influence coefficients for hemispherical[16] and conical[7] caps, while Baker and Cline[22] considered spherical, ellipsoidal, and paraboloidal caps. Influence coefficients for cylindrical shells can be found by analyses of the type given in Section 5.2 (see, for example, Eqs. 5.20f for the long cylindrical shell).

The previously cited tabulations all involve isotropic shells of constant thickness and are predominantly concerned with edge influence coefficients for each particular case. In the interest of brevity, the interior influence coefficients of the type represented by Eq. 5.37i are generally not published. In this connection, consider the fact that for the case of the toroidal shell segments Galletly's original tabulation[20,21] of edge and interior influence coefficients required ten volumes which covered almost a foot of space on the shelf![23]

It is also interesting to point out that, of the cited tabulations, only those involving the conical and the spherical shells are derived from analytical

[19] Galletly, G. D., "Bending of 2:1 and 3:1 Open-Crown Ellipsoidal Shells," *Welding Research Council Bulletin No.* 54 (1959).
[20] Galletly, G. D., "Edge Influence Coefficients for Toroidal Shells of Positive Gaussian Curvature," *Trans. A.S.M.E.*, **82B**, 60–68 (1960).
[21] Galletly, G. D., "Edge Influence Coefficients for Toroidal Shells of Negative Gaussian Curvature," *Trans. A.S.M.E.*, **82B**, 69–77 (1960).
[22] Baker, B. R., and Cline, G. B., Jr., "Influence Coefficients for Thin Smooth Shells of Revolution Subjected to Symmetric Loads," *J. Appl. Mech.* **29**, 335–339 (1962).
[23] The unabridged versions are on file at the Libraries of the A.S.M.E., A.S.C.E., and I.Mech.E.

solutions. The rest of the results were obtained by numerical integration of the governing equations on a digital computer. Such solutions will be covered in Chapter 10.

5.5*b* Example

The use of influence coefficients in the solution of problems involving composite shell structures as encountered in the pressure vessel industry, for example, has been illustrated in the previously cited investigations of Watts and Lang who considered cylindrical shells capped by hemispherical,[16] conical,[7] and flat heads,[24] and by Galletly[25,26] who studied cylindrical vessels capped by heads composed of toroidal and spherical segments (torispherical).

For our present purposes, it is interesting to illustrate the use of influence coefficients by outlining the analysis of a pressurized long cylindrical shell with a hemispherical head[16] as shown in Fig. 5.22. In terms of the edge influence coefficients, the rotation and the radial displacement of each shell at their junction are given by (see Eqs. 5.37l):

$$\begin{aligned} \frac{ET}{pd^2}\,\delta_0{}^c &= {}_M\delta^c\left(\frac{M_0}{pd^2}\right) + {}_H\delta^c\left(\frac{H_0}{pd}\right) + {}_p\Delta^c, \\ \frac{ET^2}{\beta^2 d^3 pt}\,\beta_0{}^c &= {}_M\theta^c\left(\frac{M_0}{pd^2}\right) + {}_H\theta^c\left(\frac{H_0}{pd}\right), \end{aligned} \tag{5.38a}$$

for the long cylindrical shell, and

$$\begin{aligned} \frac{ET}{pd^2}\,\delta_0{}^h &= {}_M\delta^h\left(\frac{M_0}{pd^2}\right) - {}_H\delta^h\left(\frac{H_0}{pd}\right) + {}_p\Delta^h, \\ \frac{ET^2}{\beta^2 d^3 pt}\,\beta_0{}^h &= -{}_M\theta^h\left(\frac{M_0}{pd^2}\right) + {}_H\theta^h\left(\frac{H_0}{pd}\right), \end{aligned} \tag{5.38b}$$

for the hemispherical head, where the dimensions are given in Fig. 5.22. Here we have indicated, with a subscript zero, the radial deflection, rotation, moment, and shearing force at the junction of the shells. The abbreviated forms of the solutions in each shell are employed because we are assuming that the cylindrical shell is long and that the hemispherical shell is closed at its apex. The edge influence coefficients can be derived from our

---

[24] Watts, G. W., and Lang, H. A., "The Stresses in a Pressure Vessel with a Flat Head Closure," *Trans. A.S.M.E.*, **74**, 1083–1091 (1952).

[25] Galletly, G. D., "Torispherical Shells—A Caution to Designers," *Trans. A.S.M.E.*, **81B**, 51–62 (1959).

[26] Galletly, G. D., "Influence Coefficients and Pressure Vessel Analysis," *Trans. A.S.M.E.*, **82B**, 259–269 (1960).

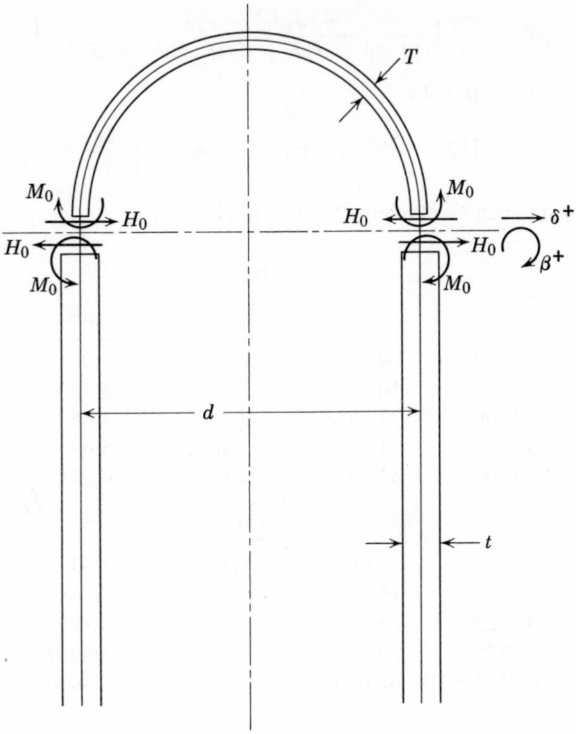

Figure 5.22 Cylindrical shell with hemispherical head.

treatment of cylindrical and spherical shells in the present chapter. From these solutions, it follows that for the cylindrical shell

$$
\begin{aligned}
{}_M\delta^c &= \frac{1}{2}\frac{T}{t}(\beta d)^2, \qquad {}_M\theta^c = \left(\frac{T}{t}\right)^2 \beta d,\\
{}_H\delta^c &= \frac{1}{2}\frac{T}{t}(\beta d), \qquad {}_H\theta^c = \frac{1}{2}\left(\frac{T}{t}\right)^2,\\
{}_p\Delta^c &= \frac{T}{t}\frac{(2-\nu)}{8},\\
\beta d &= [12(1-\nu^2)(d/t)^2]^{1/4},
\end{aligned}
\tag{5.38c}
$$

and for the hemispherical shell

$$
\begin{aligned}
{}_M\delta^h &= m_1 {}_H\theta^h,\\
{}_H\delta^h &= \left[\frac{m_2}{2}\frac{(J_1')^2 + (J_2')^2}{\nu(J_1J_2' - J_2J_1') + m_2(J_1J_1' + J_2J_2')}\right],\\
{}_M\theta^h &= \frac{m_1m_2}{2}\left[\frac{J_1^2 + J_2^2}{\nu(J_1J_2' - J_2J_1') + m_2(J_1J_1' + J_2J_2')}\right],
\end{aligned}
\tag{5.38d}
$$

$$_H\theta^h = \frac{m_1}{4}\left[\frac{J_1J_2' - J_2J_1'}{\nu(J_1J_2' - J_2J_1') + m_2(J_1J_1' + J_2J_2')}\right],$$

$$_p\Delta^h = 0.0875,$$

$$m_1 = [12(1 - \nu^2)(d/T)^2]^{1/2}, \qquad m_2 = \left[\frac{m_1^2}{4} - \nu^2\right]^{1/2},$$

Table 5.1 Influence Coefficients for Cylindrical Shells

d/t	$_p\Delta^c$	$_M\delta^c$	$_H\delta^c$	$_M\theta^c$	$_H\theta^c$
		$T/t = 0.8$			
3.20	0.1700	4.2298	1.3007	2.0812	0.3200
8.00	0.1700	10.5745	2.0567	3.2906	0.3200
16.00	0.1700	21.1491	2.9085	4.6537	0.3200
24.00	0.1700	31.7236	3.5622	5.6996	0.3200
32.00	0.1700	42.2981	4.1133	6.5813	0.3200
		$T/t = 1.0$			
4.00	0.2125	6.6091	1.8178	3.6357	0.5000
10.00	0.2125	16.5227	2.8743	5.7485	0.5000
20.00	0.2125	33.0454	4.0648	8.1296	0.5000
30.00	0.2125	49.5681	4.9784	9.9567	0.5000
40.00	0.2125	66.0908	5.7485	11.4970	0.5000
		$T/t = 1.2$			
4.80	0.2550	9.5171	2.3896	5.7351	0.7200
12.00	0.2550	23.7927	3.7783	9.0679	0.7200
24.00	0.2550	47.5854	5.3433	12.8240	0.7200
36.00	0.2550	71.3781	6.5442	15.7061	0.7200
48.00	0.2550	95.1708	7.5566	18.1359	0.7200
		$T/t = 1.6$			
6.40	0.3400	16.9193	3.6790	11.7730	1.2800
16.00	0.3400	42.2981	5.8171	18.6147	1.2800
32.00	0.3400	84.5963	8.2266	26.3251	1.2800
48.00	0.3400	126.8944	10.0755	32.2416	1.2800
64.00	0.3400	169.1926	11.6342	37.2294	1.2800
		$T/t = 2.0$			
8.00	0.4250	26.4363	5.1416	20.5665	2.0000
20.00	0.4250	66.0908	8.1296	32.5185	2.0000
40.00	0.4250	132.1817	11.4970	45.9881	2.0000
60.00	0.4250	198.2725	14.0809	56.3237	2.0000
80.00	0.4250	264.3634	16.2593	65.0370	2.0000

Table 5.2 Influence Coefficients for Hemispherical Shells

d/T	${}_M\delta^h$	${}_H\delta^h$	${}_p\Delta^h$	${}_M\theta^h$	${}_H\theta^h$
4.00	6.9690	1.8200	0.0875	3.6608	0.5272
10.00	16.7131	2.8631	0.0875	5.7319	0.5058
20.00	33.2457	4.0574	0.0875	8.1196	0.5030
30.00	49.7670	4.9729	0.0875	9.9470	0.5020
40.00	66.2900	5.7438	0.0875	11.4886	0.5015

where J_1, J_2, J_1', and J_2' are given by Eqs. 5.36d. All of these quantities reflect the assumptions that the shells are isotropic and that their thickness and properties are independent of position. The influence coefficients as defined above are listed for the cylindrical shell in Table 5.1 and for the hemispherical shell in Table 5.2.

The discontinuity moment and shearing force can now be determined by enforcing the continuity of the radial deflection and the rotation across the junction as follows:

$$\delta_0^c = \delta_0^h: \quad {}_M\delta^c\left(\frac{M_0}{pd^2}\right) + {}_H\delta^c\left(\frac{H_0}{pd}\right) + {}_p\Delta^c = {}_M\delta^h\left(\frac{M_0}{pd^2}\right) - {}_H\delta^h\left(\frac{H_0}{pd}\right) + {}_p\Delta^h, \tag{5.38e}$$

$$\beta_0^c = \beta_0^h: \quad {}_M\theta^c\left(\frac{M_0}{pd^2}\right) + {}_H\theta^c\left(\frac{H_0}{pd}\right) = -{}_M\theta^h\left(\frac{M_0}{pd^2}\right) + {}_H\theta^h\left(\frac{H_0}{pd}\right).$$

These equations have been solved for all of the combinations of T/t which are given in Table 5.1, using the data listed in both Tables 5.1 and 5.2. The results of these calculations are given in Figs. 5.23 and 5.24 where (M_0/pd^2) and (H_0/pd) are plotted as functions of T/t and d/t, respectively. It is interesting to note that as the thickness of the cylindrical shell decreases, the discontinuity moment and shearing force decrease as well, and this indicates that the assembly is approaching the membrane state of stress. The decrease is, however, more drastic for the discontinuity moment than for the discontinuity shearing force. As far as the stresses that are associated with these discontinuity reactions are concerned, it was found[16] that in the range of the parameters studied here the peak stress in the assembly occurred in the cylindrical portion and exceeded the result obtained by the membrane theory by only three percent. This tells us that pressure vessels

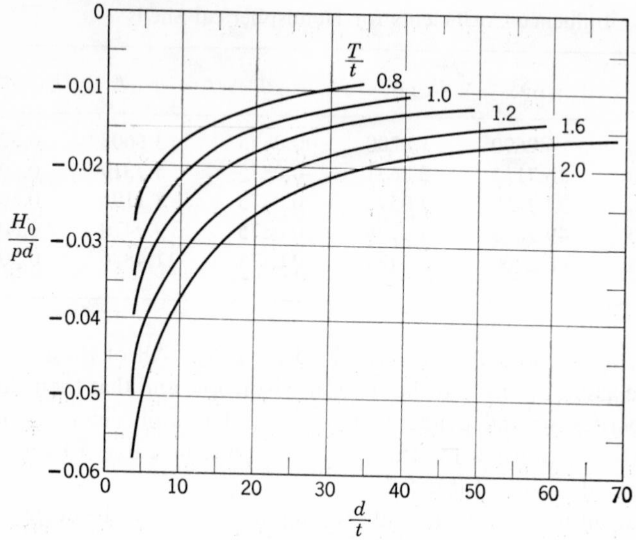

Figure 5.23 Shearing force at junction of shells shown in Fig. 5.22.

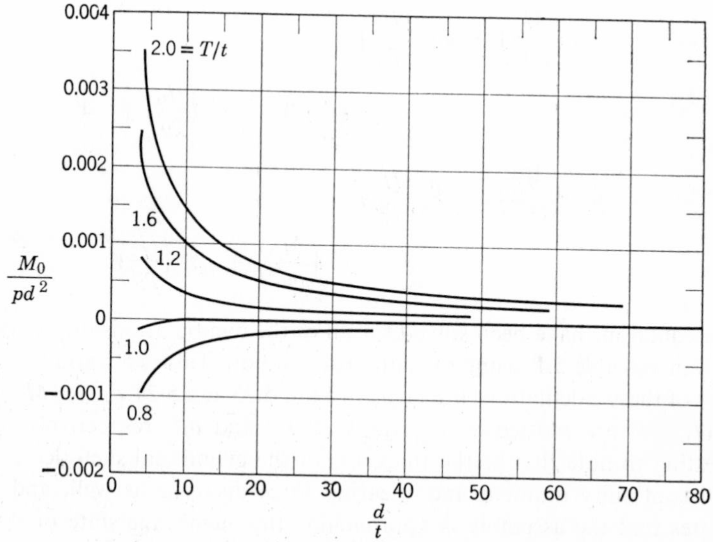

Figure 5.24 Moment at junction of shells shown in Fig. 5.22.

with hemispherical heads can be adequately designed, in the range considered, by use of the membrane theory. The conclusion is not, however, valid for pressure vessel heads in general, as was amply demonstrated in Galletly's analysis of a pressure vessel failure.[25]

5.6 CLOSURE

In this chapter, we have derived an exact analytical method of solution for problems which concern shells of revolution with bending resistance under loads that are independent of the polar angle. We have illustrated the method for cylindrical, conical, and spherical shells whose thickness and elastic properties are independent of meridional position.

The results which were obtained in the course of these calculations indicate that in thin elastic shells, regardless of their shape, the bending effects are highly localized in nature. Indeed, we have found that the bending effects which are introduced at a boundary, for example, make a significant contribution to the overall results of the analysis only within a certain distance from the boundary. The magnitude of this distance, which we have referred to as the decay length, is a function of the elastic properties, the radius, and the thickness of the shell. In particular, we have found that the decay length is directly proportional to the square root of the thickness of the shell. Beyond this distance, the solutions were found to approach the solutions which were obtained for each case by the membrane theory of Chapter 4. Therefore, we may conclude that as a shell becomes thinner the bending effects become more localized and the solutions which would be obtained by the membrane theory become applicable over an increasingly greater region of the shell away from the sources of bending.

The relative simplicity of the solutions that have been demonstrated here is a direct result of the fact that the curvatures of the generators of the reference surfaces of the cylindrical, conical, and spherical shells that have been treated are either zero or a constant. When the curvatures of the generators are functions of position, as is the case in ellipsoidal, paraboloidal, and other shells of revolution, then the method of solution which has been employed here becomes prohibitively difficult. The complications which attend the solution of problems which involve such shells have, therefore, motivated the development of approximate analytical methods (that will be described at length in Chapter 7). More recently, the advent of the digital computer has given impetus to the solution of problems in the theory of thin elastic shells by approximate numerical methods. These methods, which will be described in Part IV, are particularly useful in the analysis of composite shells with arbitrary generators, variable thickness, variable material properties, and so on. Indeed, when such methods are programmed for a high speed digital computer, one can analyze any problem which falls within the framework of any theory of thin elastic shells.

The method of solution which we have developed here is based upon a reduction to two differential equations involving the rotation β_φ and the transverse shearing force Q_φ and is appropriate only in the solution of problems involving shells of revolution under loads which are independent of the polar angle. In the next chapter, when we consider shells of revolution under arbitrary loads, we shall use two other basic approaches, each of which includes as a special case an approach to the solution of the class of problems which we have considered here.

Before we proceed, however, it is well to take this occasion to make an evaluation of the theory of Chapter 2 as it pertains to the static analysis of shells. For this purpose let us, therefore, consider the problem of a circular cylindrical shell of infinite length subjected to periodically spaced bands of constant pressure along its length, as shown in Fig. 5.25. This particular problem can be solved exactly within the framework of the theory of elasticity. We shall outline such a solution here and will adopt it as a standard against which we will compare the results obtained for the same problem by the use of two theories of thin elastic shells;[27] that is, the theory which we have adopted in this text and the higher-order theory of Reissner–Naghdi.

5.6*a* Solution Based upon the Theory of Elasticity

In the problem under consideration, the stress state is independent of circumferential position. Consequently, the equilibrium equations of elasticity reduce to[28]

$$\frac{\partial \sigma_r}{\partial r} + \frac{\partial \sigma_{rx}}{\partial x} + \frac{\sigma_r - \sigma_\theta}{r} = 0, \qquad \frac{\partial \sigma_{rx}}{\partial r} + \frac{\partial \sigma_x}{\partial x} + \frac{\sigma_{rx}}{r} = 0, \tag{5.39a}$$

and the strain-displacement relations become

$$\epsilon_r = \frac{\partial W}{\partial r}, \qquad \epsilon_\theta = \frac{W}{r}, \qquad \epsilon_x = \frac{\partial U}{\partial x}, \qquad \gamma_{rx} = \frac{\partial W}{\partial x} + \frac{\partial U}{\partial r}, \tag{5.39b}$$

where we have used the original notation adopted for the displacements in Section 2.4. Equations 5.39a are identically satisfied if the stresses are expressed in terms of a stress function ψ as follows:

$$\sigma_r = \frac{\partial}{\partial x}\left(\nu \nabla^2 \psi - \frac{\partial^2 \psi}{\partial r^2}\right),$$

[27] Klosner, J. M., and Levine, H. S., "Further Comparison of Elasticity and Shell Theory Solutions," *AIAA Journal*, **4**, 467–480 (1966).

[28] See, for example, Timoshenko, S., and Goodier, J. N., *Theory of Elasticity*, New York: McGraw-Hill, 2nd ed., Chapter 13 (1951).

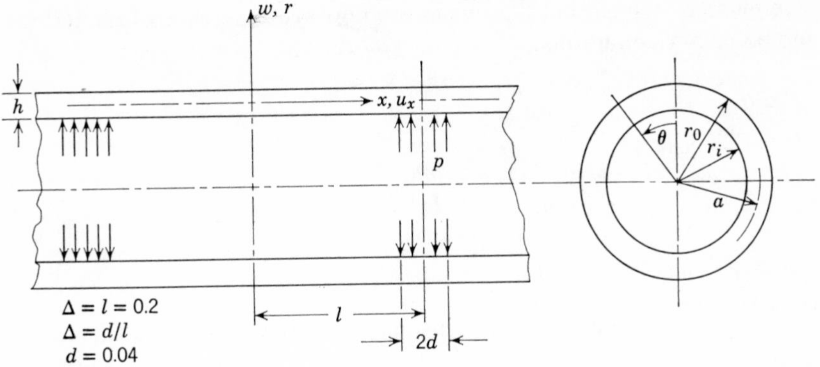

Figure 5.25 Long circular cylindrical shell loaded by periodically-spaced pressure bands.

$$\sigma_\theta = \frac{\partial}{\partial x}\left(\nu\nabla^2\psi - \frac{1}{r}\frac{\partial\psi}{\partial r}\right),$$

$$\sigma_x = \frac{\partial}{\partial x}\left[(2 - \nu)\nabla^2\psi - \frac{\partial^2\psi}{\partial x^2}\right], \tag{5.39c}$$

$$\sigma_{rx} = \frac{\partial}{\partial r}\left[(1 - \nu)\nabla^2\psi - \frac{\partial^2\psi}{\partial x^2}\right],$$

provided that

$$\nabla^2\nabla^2\psi = 0 \tag{5.39d}$$

where

$$\nabla^2(\ldots) = \frac{\partial^2(\ldots)}{\partial r^2} + \frac{1}{r}\frac{\partial(\ldots)}{\partial r} + \frac{\partial^2(\ldots)}{\partial x^2}. \tag{5.39e}$$

The displacements are expressed in terms of the stress function ψ by using Hooke's law to find the strains from the stresses and then using the strain-displacement equations to give the results

$$EW = -(1 + \nu)\frac{\partial^2\psi}{\partial r\,\partial x},$$

$$EU = (1 + \nu)\left[(1 - 2\nu)\nabla^2\psi + \frac{\partial^2\psi}{\partial r^2} + \frac{1}{r}\frac{\partial\psi}{\partial r}\right], \tag{5.39f}$$

where U is the axial displacement. It is interesting to note, as a comparison to the theory of thin elastic shells, that Eqs. 5.39a to 5.39f embody no additional assumptions beyond those on the homogeneity and isotropy of the material and the smallness of the displacements. The mathematical statement of the elasticity problem is completed by means of the following boundary conditions:

$$\sigma_{rx} = \sigma_r = 0 \quad \text{at} \quad r = r_0,$$

$$\sigma_{rx} = 0,$$

$$\sigma_r = -\frac{pd}{l} - \frac{2p}{\pi}\sum_{m=1}^{\infty}\frac{(-1)^m}{m}\sin\frac{m\pi d}{l}\cos\frac{m\pi x}{l} \quad \text{at} \quad r = r_i, \tag{5.39g}$$

$$N_x = \int_{r_i}^{r_0}\sigma_x\,dr = 0.$$

These conditions represent the vanishing of the shearing and normal stress at the outside surface of the shell, the vanishing of the shearing stress and the Fourier expansion of the applied radial stress at the inner surface, and the vanishing of the axial stress resultant.

By use of the method of separation of variables, a solution of the biharmonic equation 5.39d can be found in the form

$$\psi = \frac{p\,d/l}{(r_0/r_i)^2 - 1}\left[\frac{x^3(2-\nu)}{3(1+\nu)} - x\ln r - \frac{r^2x(1-\nu)}{2(1+\nu)}\right] + \sum_{m=1}^{\infty}[A_mI_0(\xi_m) + \xi_mB_mI_1(\xi_m) + C_mK_0(\xi_m) + D_m\xi_mK_1(\xi_m)]\sin\frac{m\pi x}{l} \tag{5.39h}$$

with $\xi_m = m\pi r/l$. In the above, the first square bracketed expression satisfies the "zero-th" contribution to the boundary conditions; that is, $\sigma_r(r_0) = \sigma_{rx}(r_0) = \sigma_{rx}(r_i) = 0$ and $\sigma_r(r_i) = -pd/l$, and the series represents that portion which satisfies the conditions $\sigma_r(r_0) = \sigma_{rx}(r_0) = \sigma_{rx}(r_i) = 0$ and

$$\sigma_r(r_i) = -\frac{2p}{\pi}\sum_{m=1}^{\infty}\frac{(-1)^m}{m}\sin\frac{m\pi d}{l}\cos\frac{m\pi x}{l}, \tag{5.39i}$$

from which the arbitrary constants A_m, B_m, C_m, and D_m can be found for every m. In the solution, I_0, I_1, K_0, and K_1 are the modified Bessel functions of the zero-th and first order and of the first and second kind. Once the coefficients have been found the formal solution for the stress function is complete and the stresses and displacements can be found by use of Eqs. 5.39c and 5.39f. Results based on this solution will be given in Section 5.6*d*.

5.6*b* Solution Based upon Love's Postulates

The problem under consideration can be solved within the framework of Love's postulates by using the method of Section 5.2.

In this case, we note that $T_0 = T_1 = q_x = q_s = 0$ and that the radial pressure is given by

$$q = -\frac{pd}{l} - \frac{2p}{\pi}\sum_{m=1}^{\infty}\frac{(-1)^m}{m}\sin\frac{m\pi d}{l}\cos\frac{m\pi x}{l}. \tag{5.40a}$$

Owing to the periodicity of the applied load, it is only necessary to consider a cylindrical shell having a length equal to one half of the load cycle as shown in Fig. 5.25. Thus, we shall require that the solution must display the following symmetry conditions which serve as boundary conditions at the ends $x = 0$ and $x = l$:

$$\begin{aligned} \beta_x &= 0 \quad \text{at} \quad x = 0, l, \\ Q_x &= 0 \quad \text{at} \quad x = 0, l. \end{aligned} \tag{5.40b}$$

The particular solution that corresponds to the load q satisfies the equations

$$\begin{aligned} \frac{d^2\beta_x{}^p}{dx^2} &= \frac{Q_x{}^p}{D}, \\ \frac{d^2 Q_x{}^p}{dx^2} &= -\frac{Eh}{a^2}\beta_x{}^p + \frac{dq}{dx}. \end{aligned} \tag{5.40c}$$

Consequently, Eqs. 5.18d to 5.18f yield the solutions

$$\begin{aligned} Q_x{}^p &= -\frac{2p}{l}\sum_{m=1}^{\infty}\frac{(-1)^m(m\pi/l)^2}{(m\pi/l)^4 + 4\mu^4}\sin\frac{m\pi d}{l}\sin\frac{m\pi x}{l}, \\ \beta_x{}^p &= \frac{2p}{Dl}\sum_{m=1}^{\infty}\frac{(-1)^m}{(m\pi/l)^4 + 4\mu^4}\sin\frac{m\pi d}{l}\sin\frac{m\pi x}{l} \end{aligned} \tag{5.40d}$$

and so on. Since the solution 5.40d satisfies the conditions 5.40b, the particular solution is the complete solution of the problem. Results that are based upon this solution will be given presently.

5.6c Solution Based on a Shell Theory that Incorporates Transverse Shear and Normal Stress Effects

It is well to include in our comparison of results obtained for the problem under consideration a solution which is based upon a shell theory which incorporates transverse shear and normal stress effects. For this purpose, we adopt the theory of Reissner–Naghdi to which we referred in Chapter 3,[29] although we did not give a derivation of it. For our present purposes, it is sufficient to set down, therefore, the following relationships

[29] See footnotes 11 and 12 of Chapter 3.

for the nonvanishing stress resultants and couples as given by the Reissner–Naghdi theory:

$$N_x = K\left[\frac{du_x}{dx} + \nu\frac{w}{a} + \frac{h^2}{12a}\left\{1 + \frac{3\nu^2}{2(1-\nu)}\right\}\frac{d\beta_x}{dx}\right] + \frac{\nu}{1-\nu}\frac{hp^-}{2},$$

$$N_\theta = K\left[\nu\frac{du_x}{dx} + \frac{w}{a} - \frac{\nu h^2(1+2\nu)}{24a(1-\nu)}\frac{d\beta_x}{dx}\right] + \frac{\nu}{1-\nu}\frac{hp^-}{2},$$

$$M_x = D\left\{\frac{d\beta_x}{dx} + \frac{1}{a}\frac{du_x}{dx} - \frac{\nu}{a(1-\nu)}\right.$$
$$\left.\times\left[\nu\left(\frac{du_x}{dx} + \frac{w}{a}\right) + \frac{1}{5}\left(\nu\frac{du_x}{dx} + \frac{w}{a}\right)\right]\right\} - \frac{\nu h^2 p^-}{10(1-\nu)},$$

$$M_\theta = D\left\{\nu\frac{d\beta_x}{dx} - \frac{w}{a^2} - \frac{\nu}{a(1-\nu)}\right. \tag{5.41a}$$
$$\left.\times\left[\frac{du_x}{dx} + \frac{w}{a} + \frac{1}{5}\left(\nu\frac{du_x}{dx} + \frac{w}{a}\right)\right]\right\} - \frac{\nu h^2 p^-}{10(1-\nu)},$$

$$Q_x = \frac{5}{6}Gh\left\{\frac{dw}{dx} + \beta_x - \frac{\nu h^2}{40(1-\nu)}\frac{d}{dx}\left[(1+\nu)\frac{d\beta_x}{dx} + \frac{1}{a}\left(\frac{du_x}{dx} - \frac{w}{a}\right)\right.\right.$$
$$\left.\left. - \frac{\nu}{1-\nu}\left\{\frac{1+\nu}{a}\left(\frac{du_x}{dx} + \frac{w}{a}\right) + \frac{2}{5a}\left(\nu\frac{du_x}{dx} + \frac{w}{a}\right)\right\}\right]\right\}$$
$$+ \frac{3h^2\nu^2}{50Eh(1-\nu)}\frac{dp^-}{dx},$$

where p^- is the internal pressure load as given by Eqs. 5.39g. We shall also have need for the equilibrium equations of the Reissner–Naghdi theory. These are identical to the first five of Eqs. 3.42, and for the problem under consideration they reduce, in the absence of axial loads, to the set

$$N_x = 0,$$

$$\frac{dQ_x}{dx} - \frac{N_\theta}{a} - p^-\left(1 - \frac{h}{2a}\right) = 0, \tag{5.41b}$$

$$\frac{dM_x}{dx} - Q_x = 0.$$

The quantity $(1 - h/2a)$ accounts for the fact that in this higher order theory the internal loading is *not* replaced by its static equivalent on the reference surface. To solve the problem under consideration, we substitute N_x, Q_x, N_θ, and M_x from Eqs. 5.41a into Eqs. 5.41b to give three equations which relate u_x, β_x, and w. These can then be decoupled by algebraic manipulation to give the set of equations

$$I_1 \frac{d^4 w}{dx^4} + I_2 \frac{d^2 w}{dx^2} + I_3 w = F_1(p^-),$$

$$\left(J_1 \frac{d^4}{dx^4} + J_2 \frac{d^2}{dx^2}\right) \beta_x = \left(J_3 \frac{d^3}{dx^3} + J_4 \frac{d}{dx}\right) w + F_2(p^-), \qquad (5.41c)$$

$$\left(K_1 \frac{d^4}{dx^4} + K_2 \frac{d^2}{dx^2}\right) u_x = \left(K_3 \frac{d^3}{dx^3} + K_4 \frac{d}{dx}\right) w + F_3(p^-),$$

where the I's, J's, and K's are known constant coefficients which depend on the geometry and elastic properties of the shell, and the F's are known functions which involve derivatives of p^- as well as the geometry and elastic properties of the shell. For the sake of simplicity, we shall not give these here (see the Exercises). Since the load p^- is given by Eqs. 5.39g, the displacements and rotation can be expressed as

$$w = w_0 + \sum_{m=1}^{\infty} w_m \cos \frac{m\pi x}{l},$$

$$u_x = u_0 x + \sum_{m=1}^{\infty} u_{xm} \sin \frac{m\pi x}{l}, \qquad (5.41d)$$

$$\beta_x = \sum_{m=1}^{\infty} \beta_{xm} \sin \frac{m\pi x}{l}.$$

The coefficients of these series are obtained by substitution of Eqs. 5.41d into Eqs. 5.41c. The forms 5.41d also satisfy the boundary conditions 5.40b and, therefore, constitute the complete solution of the problem. Numerical results that are based upon these expressions will be given in the next section.

5.6*d* Discussion of Results

The solutions which we have outlined here were used in the calculation of numerical results for cylindrical shells, loaded as shown in Fig. 5.25, having $r_i/r_0 = 0.70$ and 0.93 and $l/2a = d/l = 0.2$ with $\nu = 0.3$.[30]

To make an assessment of the results, let us first consider the transverse shear and normal stresses which act in the cylindrical shell. We have emphasized previously that, in the theory based upon Love's postulates, these stresses are considered to be negligible in comparison to the other stresses which act in the shell. The Reissner–Naghdi and the exact solutions are not limited in this way. Thus, it is interesting to find out if the Reissner–Naghdi theory approximates closely the transverse shear and normal stress distributions obtained by the exact solution and if, at the same time, the

[30] Klosner, J. M., and Levine, H. S., loc. cit.

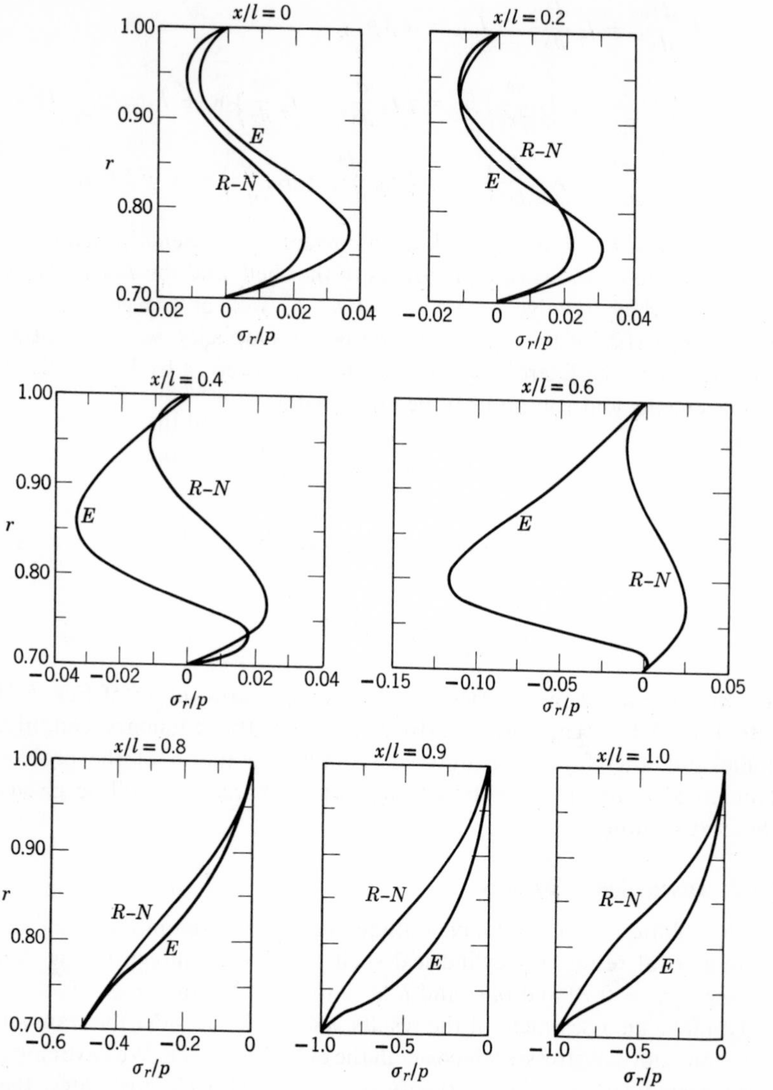

Figure 5.26 Transverse normal stress distributions for the shell shown in Fig. 5.25 with $r_i/r_o = 0.70$.

transverse shear and normal stresses can, indeed, be neglected in comparison to the other stresses in a thin shell.

To answer the first of these questions, we have plotted in Figs. 5.26 to 5.29 the transverse shear and normal stress distributions through the shell wall at several axial positions as obtained by the Reissner–Naghdi theory

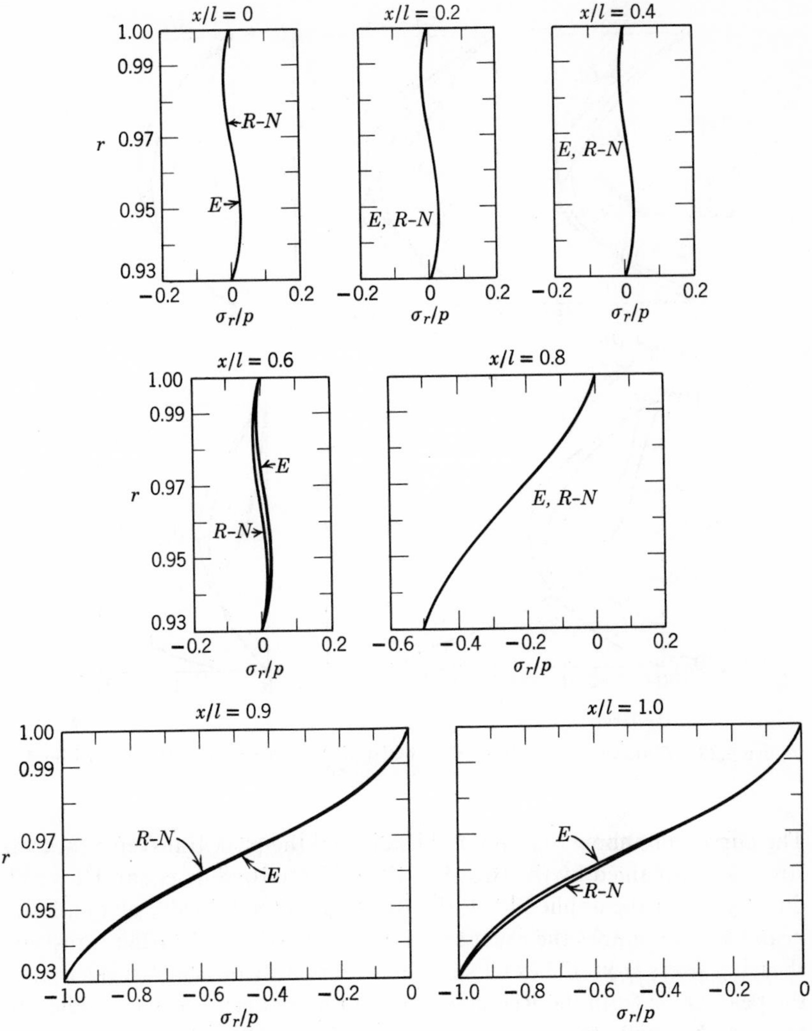

Figure 5.27 Same as Fig. 5.26 for $r_i/r_o = 0.93$.

$(R - N)$ and the elasticity solution (E). Although the theory of Chapter 2 does not predict any transverse normal stresses, it does predict a parabolic distribution of transverse shearing stress. Therefore, we have included in Figs. 5.28 and 5.29 the results based upon Love's postulates and have identified these with an L. The curves indicate that the Reissner–Naghdi theory predicts the exact transverse normal stresses very well over most of the axial positions considered, especially for the thinner of the two shells.

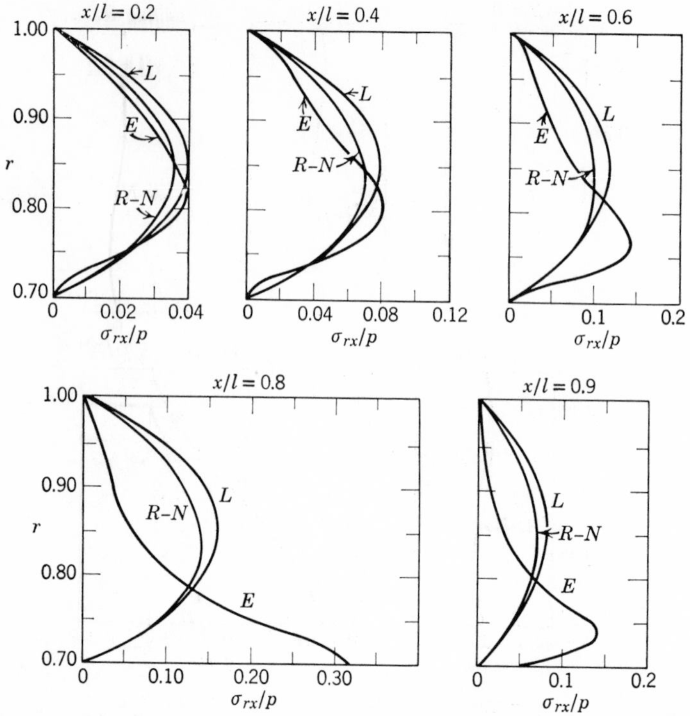

Figure 5.28 Transverse shearing stress distributions for the shell shown in Fig. 5.25 with $r_i/r_0 = 0.70$.

The curves also show that in the thicker shell the peak transverse shearing stresses as obtained by the two shell theories are roughly equal. However, directly under the applied load, the Reissner–Naghdi theory gives a lower peak value than does the exact solution. Furthermore, the peak transverse shearing stress from the exact solution occurs near the inner surface while the peak value from the Reissner–Naghdi theory occurs at the middle surface of the shell. In the case of the thinner shell, the magnitudes and locations of the peak values as obtained from all of the solutions are just about equal.

Now let us consider the question of the relative magnitude of the transverse stresses when they are compared to the other stresses in the cylindrical shell. For this purpose, in Figs. 5.30 to 5.33 we have plotted the axial and the circumferential stress distributions in the two shells under consideration. From an examination of Figs. 5.26 to 5.33, we may conclude first of all that the transverse shear and normal stresses as obtained by the Reissner–Naghdi solution and the exact solution are an order of magnitude

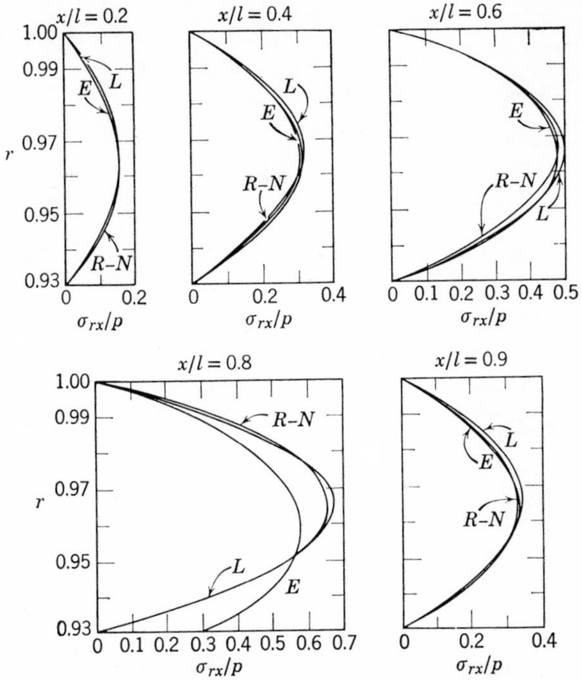

Figure 5.29 Same as Fig. 5.28 for $r_i/r_0 = 0.93$.

smaller than the other stresses in the shell, except directly under the pressure bands. Under the pressure bands, the transverse normal stresses are roughly equal to the other stresses in the thicker shell; however, in the thinner shell they are about one-third of the largest of the other stresses.

We may also recall, in regard to the basic assumptions that were set forth in Chapter 2, that the axial and circumferential stresses were assumed to be linearly distributed while the transverse shearing stresses were assumed to be parabolically distributed over the thickness of the shell. Figures 5.28 to 5.33 show that these assumptions are confirmed by the exact solution for the thinner shell. As could be expected, however, the assumption is not confirmed for the thicker shell.

Finally, it is important to reach some conclusions regarding the accuracy of the results obtained by the shell theories. As far as the circumferential stresses are concerned, Figs. 5.30 and 5.31 show that, for the thicker shell, there is considerable scatter in the results although the Reissner–Naghdi theory seems to give results which come closer to the exact results. For the thinner shell, both shell theories lead to results which approximate the exact results very well.

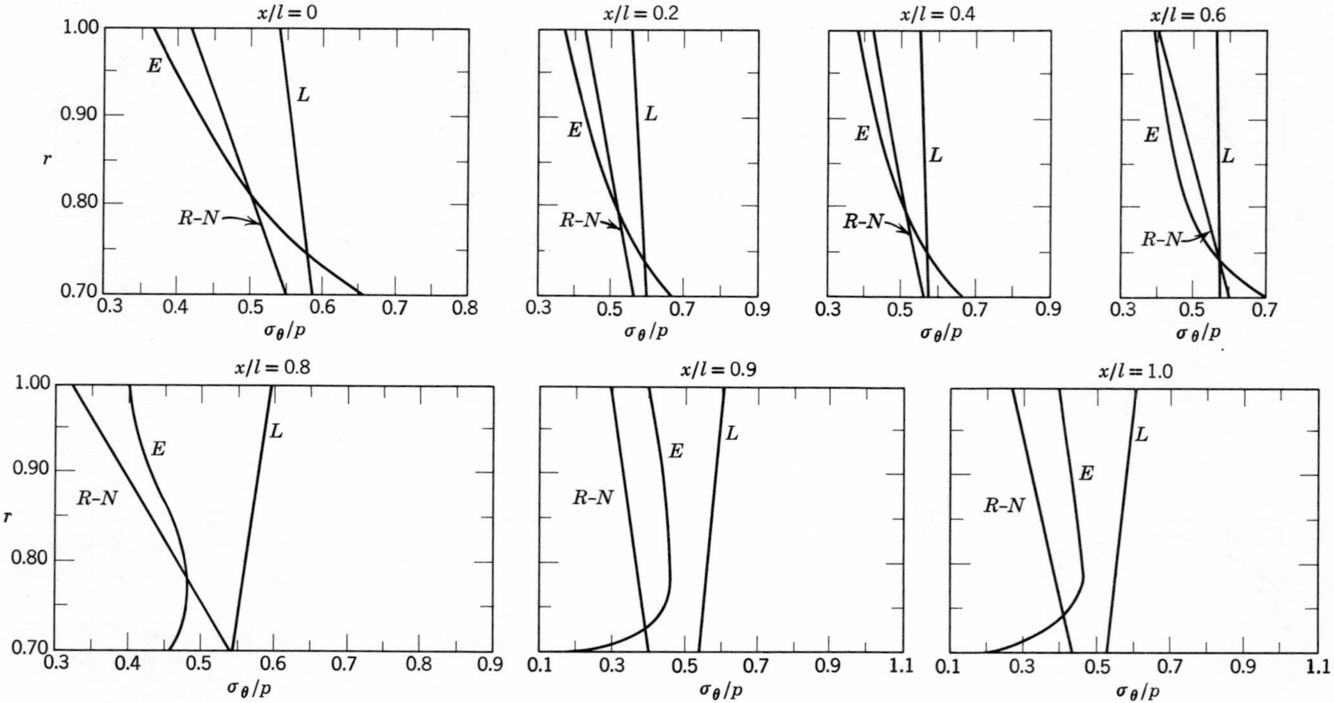

Figure 5.30 Circumferential normal stress distributions for the shell shown in Fig. 5.26 with $r_i/r_0 = 0.70$.

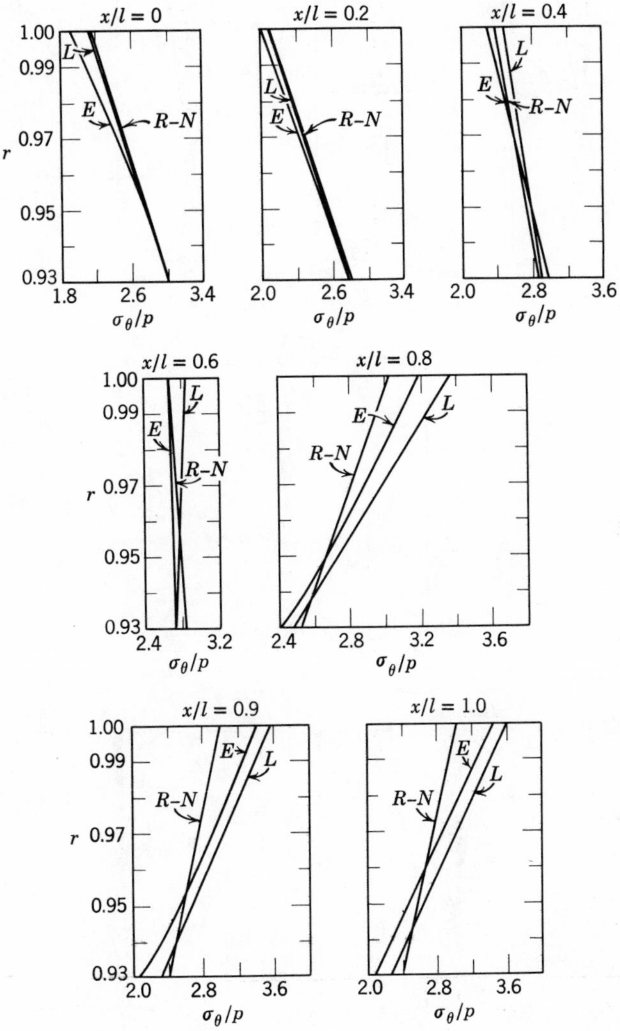

Figure 5.31 Same as Fig. 5.30 for $r_i/r_0 = 0.93$.

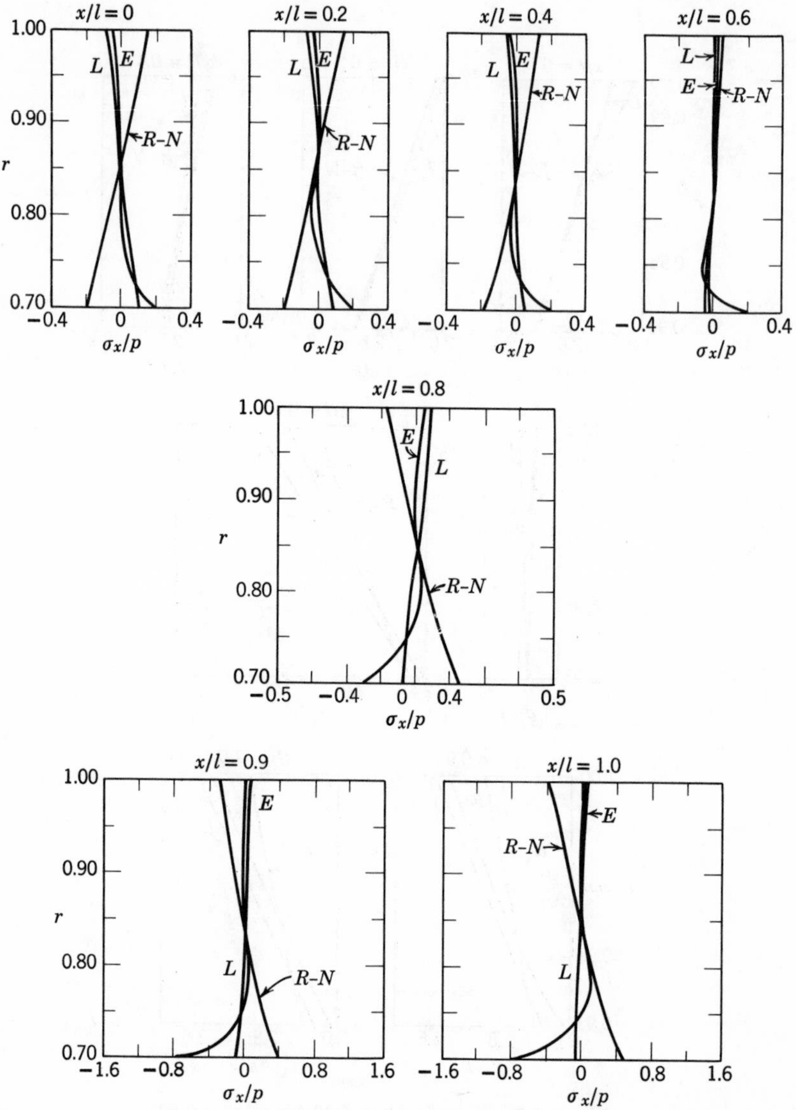

Figure 5.32 Axial normal stress distributions for the shell shown in Fig. 5.25 with $r_i/r_o = 0.70$.

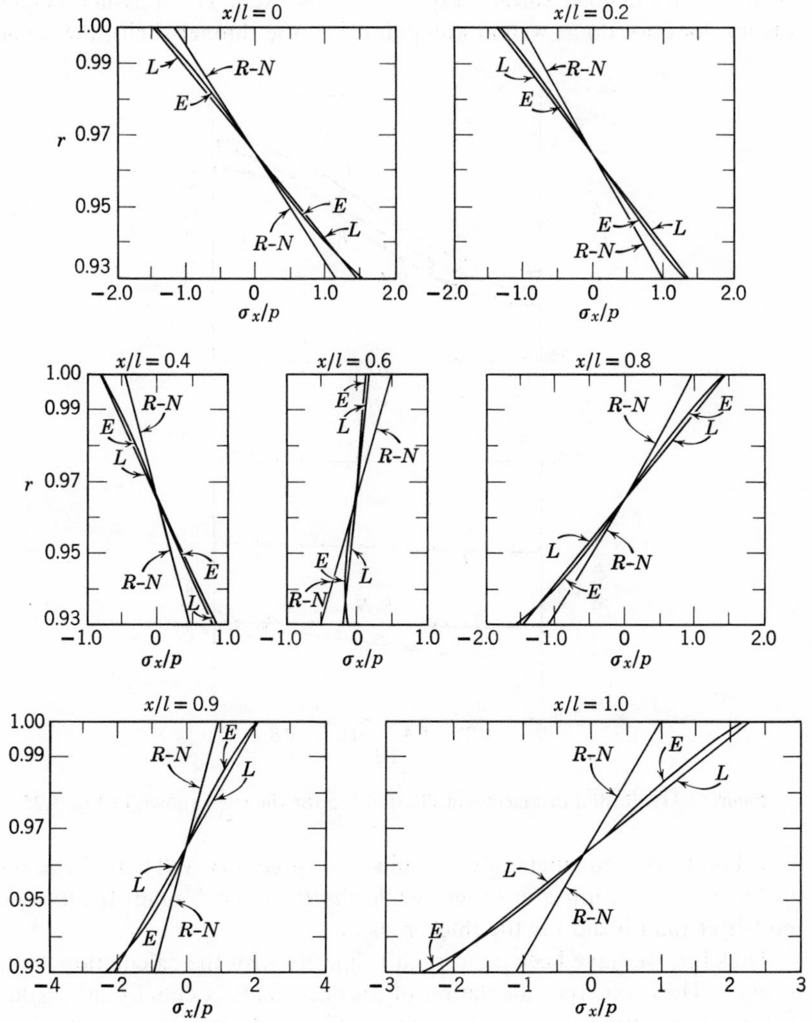

Figure 5.33 Same as Fig. 5.32 for $r_i/r_0 = 0.93$.

Although we have postulated a vanishing axial stress resultant in all of the solutions studied here, the axial normal stresses do not vanish and their values are plotted in Figs. 5.32 and 5.33. The theory based on Love's postulates matches the exact results quite well on the outer surface of the thicker shell but on the inner surface it does not do as well. The Reissner–Naghdi theory does not do as well at any point. For the thinner shells, the theory

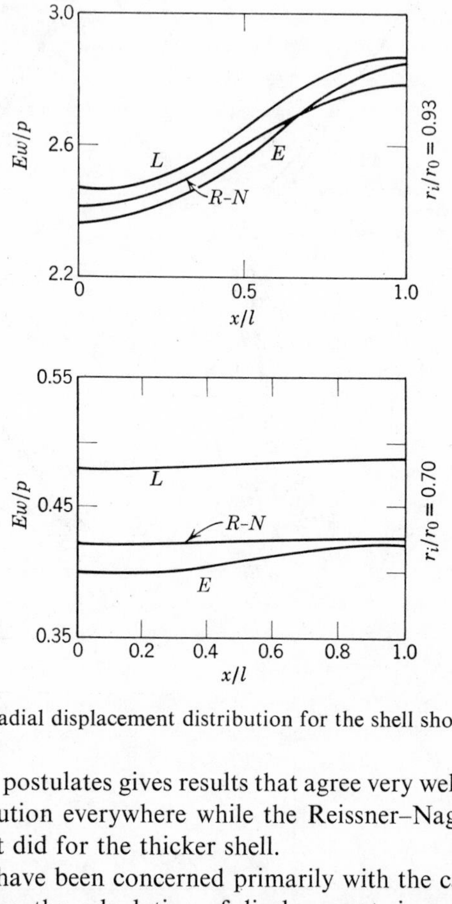

Figure 5.34 Radial displacement distribution for the shell shown in Fig. 5.25.

based on Love's postulates gives results that agree very well with the results of the exact solution everywhere while the Reissner–Naghdi theory does no better than it did for the thicker shell.

Thus far, we have been concerned primarily with the calculation of the stresses. However, the calculation of displacements is equally interesting, and for this purpose, we have plotted in Fig. 5.34 the transverse displacement of the middle surface for the two shells. It is obvious from these data that the Reissner–Naghdi theory gives the best estimate of the exact results.

Three major conclusions can be drawn from the results which have been presented here.

First, it has been shown that the use of a higher-order theory such as the

Reissner–Naghdi theory does not necessarily lead to a better prediction of the *stresses* obtained by the exact solution than does a simpler theory which is based on Love's postulates.[31]

Second, in the calculation of the *radial displacements of the middle surface*, the Reissner–Naghdi theory gives the best estimation of the exact results.

Third, the exact results for the thinner shell confirm the validity of Love's postulates on the preservation of the normal element and the vanishing of the transverse normal and shearing stresses. That is, the distributions of the axial normal stress and the circumferential normal stress are linear across the wall of the thinner shell, the transverse normal stress is negligible except under an applied load, and the transverse shearing stress is small in comparison to the other stresses and is parabolically distributed across the shell wall.

EXERCISES

5.1 Derive a solution for a pressurized short cylindrical shell composed of a single orthotropic layer which is subjected to a moment M_1 and a shearing force Q_1 at one end and to a moment M_2 and a shearing force Q_2 at the other.

5.2 Derive a solution for a long cylindrical shell composed of a single orthotropic layer which is rigidly clamped at one end and subjected to a temperature distribution which is a linear function of the axial coordinate x.

5.3 Derive a general solution for a vertical tank which is rigidly clamped at its bottom, is filled with liquid, and has a thickness which is a linear function of the axial coordinate x.

5.4 An assembly of two semi-infinite cylindrical shells made of identical materials but having unequal thicknesses is rotating at a constant angular velocity ω. Derive expressions for the moment M_0 and the shearing force Q_0 at the junction of the cylinders when
(a) Their middle surface is continuous.
(b) Their inner surface is continuous.

5.5 Consider an assembly of two semi-infinite isotropic cylindrical pipes made of two different materials, but having the same dimensions and subjected to a uniform temperature rise T_0. Derive expressions for the moment

[31] Similar conclusions regarding the calculation of stresses were reached by Kraus, H., in "A Comparison of Measured and Calculated Stresses in Pressure Vessels," *Trans. A.S.M.E.* (to appear). There, experimental data were compared to numerical results obtained by computer programs based on the Love theory and on a higher-order theory (see Chapter 10).

and shearing force which is induced at the junction of the shells and show that the maximum axial stress

$$\sigma_{xi} = \frac{N_{xi}}{h} \pm \frac{6M_{xi}}{h^2}$$

occurs at

$$\bar{x}_i = \frac{1}{\mu} \operatorname{arc\,cot} \left(\frac{2E_i}{E_1 + E_2} \right)$$

in the pipe i where $i = 1, 2$ and E_i is the Young's modulus. Assume that Poisson's ratio is the same for both pipes.

5.6 Analyse a circular cylindrical shell composed of two orthotropic layers. Investigate the decay length of such a shell and compare the result to the decay length of a cylindrical shell composed of a single layer whose thickness is equal to the combined thickness of the two layer shell.

5.7 Obtain a general solution of the problem of an orthotropic conical shell when its elastic properties are independent of position but the thickness varies as kx along the generators.

5.8 Derive a solution for a frustum of an orthotropic conical shell whose large end is clamped and whose small end is subjected to a uniformly distributed axial load V lb/in. but otherwise free.

5.9 Derive particular solutions and their contributions to the various shell variables for a conical shell of constant thickness and elastic properties subjected to

(a) Hydrostatic pressure.

(b) Centrifugal forces due to rotation about the axis at constant angular velocity.

5.10 Derive the complete solution of the problem of a closed spherical shell which is rotating at constant angular velocity about its axis.

5.11 Investigate the splitting criterion $f(\varphi)$ = constant for an ellipsoidal shell of constant thickness. Write Eqs. 5.15n for such a shell.

5.12 Repeat 5.11 for a paraboloidal shell of constant thickness.

5.13 Repeat 5.11 for a toroidal shell of constant thickness.

5.14 Derive solutions of the counterparts of Eqs. 5.30a for an isotropic spherical shell in terms of Legendre functions.

5.15 Carry out the details of the solution that has been given in Section 5.6c.

6

Shells of Revolution with Bending Resistance under Arbitrary Loads

6.1 INTRODUCTION

There are two basic procedures which will be followed in the exact analytical solution of problems involving shells of revolution with bending resistance subjected to an arbitrary system of loads. In the first of these, the fundamental equations of the theory are reduced to three differential equations which relate the displacements u_φ, u_θ, and w. In the second, a stress function is introduced and the governing equations are reduced to two differential equations which relate the stress function, F, and the transverse displacement, w. Once either of the reductions has been accomplished, the shell variables are expanded in Fourier series with respect to the polar coordinate θ, using as a basis the knowledge that when the shell is traversed once around a latitude circle all of the variables must return to their original values; that is, the variables must be single valued and periodic in the interval $0 \leqslant \theta \leqslant 2\pi$. By means of these expansions, which we have previously employed in our treatment of membrane shells of revolution under arbitrary loads (see Section 4.3*b*), the dependence of the shell variables upon the polar angle θ is removed from consideration. The problem is thus reduced to the solution of a set of ordinary differential equations (three in one method and two in the other) in which the independent variable is the coordinate of axial position. Problems which involve shells of revolution under loads that are independent of the polar angle, as treated in the previous chapter, are a special case of the present class of problems. Their solution represents the "zero-th" term in the expansions which are to be employed here. Furthermore, since $u_\theta \equiv 0$ in such problems, they lead, in either of the methods to be used here, to the solution of only two simultaneous ordinary differential equations.

To begin the discussion, let us then present the fundamental equations which describe the static behavior of a shell of revolution with bending resistance under an arbitrary system of loads. In doing this, we again note, as we have already done in Chapters 4 and 5, that in a shell of revolution $A_1 = R_1 = r_\varphi$, $A_2 = R_0 = r = r_\theta \sin\varphi$, and $R_2 = r_\theta$. With these definitions, the equations of static equilibrium are given by

$$\frac{\partial(rN_\varphi)}{\partial\varphi} + r_\varphi \frac{\partial N_{\varphi\theta}}{\partial\theta} - N_\theta r_\varphi \cos\varphi + rQ_\varphi + rr_\varphi q_\varphi = 0,$$

$$\frac{\partial(rN_{\varphi\theta})}{\partial\varphi} + r_\varphi \frac{\partial N_\theta}{\partial\theta} + N_{\varphi\theta} r_\varphi \cos\varphi + r_\varphi Q_\theta \sin\varphi + rr_\varphi q_\theta = 0,$$

$$\frac{\partial(rQ_\varphi)}{\partial\varphi} + r_\varphi \frac{\partial Q_\theta}{\partial\theta} - \left(\frac{N_\varphi}{r_\varphi} + \frac{N_\theta}{r_\theta}\right) rr_\varphi - rr_\varphi q = 0, \tag{6.1}$$

$$\frac{\partial(rM_\varphi)}{\partial\varphi} + r_\varphi \frac{\partial M_{\varphi\theta}}{\partial\theta} - M_\theta r_\varphi \cos\varphi - rr_\varphi Q_\varphi = 0,$$

$$\frac{\partial(rM_{\varphi\theta})}{\partial\varphi} + r_\varphi \frac{\partial M_\theta}{\partial\theta} + M_{\varphi\theta} r_\varphi \cos\varphi - rr_\varphi Q_\theta = 0,$$

where we have taken into account the fact that in a shell of revolution all geometric quantities are independent of θ, and where we have made use of the Gauss condition (Eq. 4.10).

The strains are related to the displacements by

$$\epsilon_\varphi{}^0 = \frac{1}{r_\varphi}\left(\frac{\partial u_\varphi}{\partial\varphi} + w\right), \qquad \epsilon_\theta{}^0 = \frac{1}{r}\left(\frac{\partial u_\theta}{\partial\theta} + u_\varphi \cos\varphi + w \sin\varphi\right),$$
$$\gamma_{\varphi\theta}{}^0 = \frac{r}{r_\varphi}\frac{\partial}{\partial\varphi}\left(\frac{u_\theta}{r}\right) + \frac{1}{r}\frac{\partial u_\varphi}{\partial\theta}. \tag{6.2}$$

The changes in the curvature and the twist are related to the rotations by

$$\kappa_\varphi = \frac{1}{r_\varphi}\frac{\partial\beta_\varphi}{\partial\varphi}, \qquad \kappa_\theta = \frac{1}{r}\left(\frac{\partial\beta_\theta}{\partial\theta} + \beta_\varphi \cos\varphi\right),$$
$$\tau = \frac{r}{r_\varphi}\frac{\partial}{\partial\varphi}\left(\frac{\beta_\theta}{r}\right) + \frac{1}{r}\frac{\partial\beta_\varphi}{\partial\theta}, \tag{6.3}$$

and the rotations are expressed in terms of the displacements by

$$\beta_\varphi = \frac{1}{r_\varphi}\left(u_\varphi - \frac{\partial w}{\partial\varphi}\right), \qquad \beta_\theta = \frac{1}{r}\left(u_\theta - \frac{\partial w}{\partial\theta}\right). \tag{6.4}$$

Finally, the stress resultants and stress couples are related to the strains and changes of curvature by

$$\begin{aligned}
N_\varphi &= K[\epsilon_\varphi{}^0 + \nu\epsilon_\theta{}^0 - (1+\nu)\alpha_t T_0], \\
N_\theta &= K[\epsilon_\theta{}^0 + \nu\epsilon_\varphi{}^0 - (1+\nu)\alpha_t T_0], \\
N_{\varphi\theta} &= N_{\theta\varphi} = Gh\gamma_{\varphi\theta}{}^0, \\
M_\varphi &= D[\kappa_\varphi + \nu\kappa_\theta - (1+\nu)\alpha_t T_1] \\
M_\theta &= D[\kappa_\theta + \nu\kappa_\varphi - (1+\nu)\alpha_t T_1], \\
M_{\varphi\theta} &= M_{\theta\varphi} = Gh^3\tau/12,
\end{aligned} \tag{6.5}$$

where

$$T_0 = \frac{1}{h}\int_\zeta T\, d\zeta, \qquad T_1 = \frac{12}{h^3}\int_\zeta T\zeta\, d\zeta, \tag{6.5a}$$

and

$$\{K, D\} = \{h, h^3/12\}E/(1 - \nu^2). \tag{6.5b}$$

Solutions of the foregoing system of equations must satisfy the following boundary conditions:

$$\begin{aligned}
N_\varphi &= \overline{N}_\varphi &\quad \text{or} \quad u_\varphi &= \bar{u}_\varphi \\
T_{\varphi\theta} &= \overline{T}_{\varphi\theta} &\quad \text{or} \quad u_\theta &= \bar{u}_\theta \\
V_\varphi &= \overline{V}_\varphi &\quad \text{or} \quad w &= \overline{w} \\
M_\varphi &= \overline{M}_\varphi &\quad \text{or} \quad \beta_\varphi &= \bar{\beta}_\varphi
\end{aligned} \tag{6.6}$$

on an edge of constant φ. Since we shall be concerned predominantly with shells that are closed with respect to the coordinate θ, these are the only boundary conditions which we shall have occasion to use.

In writing the system of equations which describes the behavior of a shell of revolution under arbitrary loads, in particular Eqs. 6.5, we have assumed that the shell is composed of a single isotropic layer whose properties are independent of the thickness coordinate ζ. More general materials can be considered; however, the resulting manipulations become extremely cumbersome while changing the fundamentals only slightly. We prefer to carry out the solution of problems involving arbitrarily loaded shells of revolution composed of orthotropic, layered materials, for instance, by means of the numerical procedures which will be described in Part IV.

Our concern in the present chapter will be the demonstration of the solution procedure which we have described in our opening remarks in this section. This will be done for cylindrical shells of circular and noncircular cross section and for spherical shells. Owing to the analytical complications which would otherwise arise, our attention will be restricted to shells whose thickness and elastic properties are independent of position. More general configurations are again left to be treated by the numerical techniques of Part IV.

6.2 CYLINDRICAL SHELLS

The basic equations which describe the static behavior of cylindrical shells with bending resistance under arbitrary loads are derived from the system of equations which has been presented in Section 6.1 by using, as we did in Chapters 4 and 5, the change of variable $dx = r_\varphi \, d\varphi$, and replacing the variables φ and θ of the general formulation by x and s, respectively, for the cylindrical shell (see Fig. 4.1). Thus, the equations of equilibrium take the form

$$\begin{aligned}
\frac{\partial N_x}{\partial x} + \frac{\partial N_{sx}}{\partial s} + q_x &= 0,\\
\frac{\partial N_{xs}}{\partial x} + \frac{\partial N_s}{\partial s} + \frac{Q_s}{r} + q_s &= 0,\\
\frac{\partial Q_x}{\partial x} + \frac{\partial Q_s}{\partial s} - \frac{N_s}{r} - q &= 0,\\
\frac{\partial M_x}{\partial x} + \frac{\partial M_{sx}}{\partial s} - Q_x &= 0,\\
\frac{\partial M_{xs}}{\partial x} + \frac{\partial M_s}{\partial s} - Q_s &= 0,
\end{aligned} \tag{6.7}$$

and the strains, rotations, changes in curvature, and the displacements are related by the expressions

$$\epsilon_x{}^0 = \frac{\partial u_x}{\partial x}, \qquad \epsilon_s{}^0 = \frac{\partial u_s}{\partial s} + \frac{w}{r}, \qquad \gamma_{xs}{}^0 = \frac{\partial u_s}{\partial x} + \frac{\partial u_x}{\partial s}, \tag{6.8a}$$

$$\beta_x = -\frac{\partial w}{\partial x}, \qquad \beta_s = \frac{u_s}{r} - \frac{\partial w}{\partial s}, \tag{6.8b}$$

$$\begin{aligned}
\kappa_x &= \frac{\partial \beta_x}{\partial x} = -\frac{\partial^2 w}{\partial x^2}, \qquad \kappa_s = \frac{\partial \beta_s}{\partial s} = \frac{\partial}{\partial s}\left(\frac{u_s}{r} - \frac{\partial w}{\partial s}\right),\\
\tau &= \frac{\partial \beta_s}{\partial x} + \frac{\partial \beta_x}{\partial s} = \frac{1}{r}\frac{\partial u_s}{\partial x} - 2\frac{\partial^2 w}{\partial x \, \partial s}.
\end{aligned} \tag{6.8c}$$

Equations 6.7 and 6.8c can be brought into a simpler form by means of the following arguments which were first advanced by Donnell.[1]

First, in connection with the equations of equilibrium, it can be argued that the transverse shearing force Q_s makes a negligible contribution to the equilibrium of forces in the circumferential direction, an assumption which can be expected to improve in accuracy as the ratio of the radius to the

[1] Donnell, L. H., "Stability of Thin Walled Tubes Under Torsion," N.A.C.A. Report No. 479 (1933).

thickness of the shell increases. Therefore, the term Q_s/r in the second of Eqs. 6.7 can be neglected and the equations of equilibrium of the cylindrical shell are reduced to the set

$$\frac{\partial N_x}{\partial x} + \frac{\partial N_{sx}}{\partial s} + q_x = 0,$$
$$\frac{\partial N_{sx}}{\partial x} + \frac{\partial N_s}{\partial s} + q_s = 0, \tag{6.9}$$
$$\frac{\partial^2 M_x}{\partial x^2} + 2\frac{\partial^2 M_{xs}}{\partial x\,\partial s} + \frac{\partial^2 M_s}{\partial s^2} - \frac{N_s}{r} - q = 0,$$

from which Q_s and Q_x have been eliminated by means of the fourth and fifth equilibrium equations.

Secondly, in connection with the relationships between the changes of curvature and twist and the displacements, it is reasoned that these quantities are negligibly affected by the "stretching" displacement u_s. Consequently, it is assumed that the changes in curvature and twist of a thin cylindrical shell can be expressed as

$$\kappa_x = -\frac{\partial^2 w}{\partial x^2}, \qquad \kappa_s = -\frac{\partial^2 w}{\partial s^2}, \qquad \tau = -2\frac{\partial^2 w}{\partial x\,\partial s}. \tag{6.10}$$

These expressions are identical to the corresponding equations of the theory of plates.[2] Indeed, the two assumptions which have been made here are equivalent to the statement that the behavior of a thin cylindrical shell of small curvature and that of a thin plate are similar, the main exception being the presence of N_s/r in the third equilibrium equation and the presence of w/r in the definition of the circumferential normal strain. The assumptions regarding the contributions of the shearing-stress resultant Q_s and the circumferential displacement u_s have no effect on the analysis of cylindrical shells under loads that are independent of the polar angle θ (as considered in Section 5.2) because $u_s = Q_s \equiv 0$ in such problems.

Owing to their relative simplicity we shall, in this discussion, adopt Eqs. 6.9 and 6.10 as part of the fundamental equations of arbitrarily loaded thin cylindrical shells with bending resistance. Their validity will be discussed in Section 6.2*d*.

In addition to Eqs. 6.8a, 6.9, and 6.10, we also require the relationships between the stress resultants and the strains and between the stress couples and the changes in curvature. These, however, follow directly from Eqs. 6.5 by a change of subscripts. The same is true for the boundary conditions that are to be prescribed on edges of constant x in the cylindrical shell.

[2] See, for example, Timoshenko, S., and Woinowsky-Krieger, S., *Theory of Plates and Shells*, New York: McGraw-Hill, 2nd ed., Chapter 4 (1959).

These follow by a change of subscripts in Eqs. 6.6, and there is no need to repeat them here.

It is now appropriate to carry out the reduction of the governing equations of the cylindrical shell to three equations that relate the displacements u_x, u_s, and w. This is accomplished by substituting the curvature expressions (Eqs. 6.10) and the strain expressions (Eqs. 6.8a) into the expressions for the stress resultants and stress couples as obtained from Eqs. 6.5. The latter expressions are substituted into the three equilibrium equations (Eqs. 6.9) which then take the form

$$\frac{\partial^2 u_x}{\partial x^2} + \frac{1-\nu}{2}\frac{\partial^2 u_x}{\partial s^2} + \frac{1+\nu}{2}\frac{\partial^2 u_s}{\partial x\,\partial s} + \frac{\nu}{r}\frac{\partial w}{\partial x} = P_x, \tag{6.11a}$$

$$\frac{1-\nu}{2}\frac{\partial^2 u_s}{\partial x^2} + \frac{\partial^2 u_s}{\partial s^2} + \frac{1+\nu}{2}\frac{\partial^2 u_x}{\partial x\,\partial s} + \frac{\partial}{\partial s}\left(\frac{w}{r}\right) = P_s, \tag{6.11b}$$

$$\frac{h^2}{12}\nabla^4 w + \frac{1}{r}\left(\frac{w}{r} + \frac{\partial u_s}{\partial s} + \nu\frac{\partial u_x}{\partial x}\right) = P, \tag{6.11c}$$

where

$$\begin{aligned} P_x &= -\frac{(1-\nu^2)}{Eh} q_x + (1+\nu)\alpha_t \frac{\partial T_0}{\partial x}, \\ P_s &= -\frac{(1-\nu^2)}{Eh} q_s + (1+\nu)\alpha_t \frac{\partial T_0}{\partial s}, \\ P &= -\frac{(1-\nu^2)}{Eh} q + (1+\nu)\alpha_t \left[\frac{T_0}{r} - \frac{h^2}{12}\nabla^2 T_1\right], \end{aligned} \tag{6.11d}$$

and

$$\nabla^4 = \nabla^2(\nabla^2), \qquad \nabla^2(\ldots) = \frac{\partial^2(\ldots)}{\partial x^2} + \frac{\partial^2(\ldots)}{\partial s^2}. \tag{6.11e}$$

We could apply the method of solution which will be developed here to Eqs. 6.11 in their present form. Indeed, if the cylindrical shell which is under consideration is other than circular in cross section, it is best to solve Eqs. 6.11 directly, and this will be done in Section 6.2*c*. However, if we are concerned with circular cylindrical shells (as will be the case in Sections 6.2*a* and 6.2*b*), Eqs. 6.11 can be brought into a still more useful form by means of the following manipulations that were first carried out by Donnell.[1]

First, take two partial derivatives of Eq. 6.11a with respect to x, two partial derivatives of Eq. 6.11a with respect to s, and solve for the mixed fourth partial derivatives of u_s in each case to give

$$\begin{aligned} \frac{\partial^4 u_s}{\partial x^3\,\partial s} &= \frac{2}{1+\nu}\left[\frac{\partial^2 P_x}{\partial x^2} - \frac{\partial^4 u_x}{\partial x^4} - \frac{1-\nu}{2}\frac{\partial^4 u_x}{\partial x^2\,\partial s^2} - \frac{\nu}{a}\frac{\partial^3 w}{\partial x^3}\right], \\ \frac{\partial^4 u_s}{\partial x\,\partial s^3} &= \frac{2}{1+\nu}\left[\frac{\partial^2 P_x}{\partial s^2} - \frac{\partial^4 u_x}{\partial x^2\,\partial s^2} - \frac{1-\nu}{2}\frac{\partial^4 u_x}{\partial s^4} - \frac{\nu}{a}\frac{\partial^3 w}{\partial x\,\partial s^2}\right], \end{aligned} \tag{6.12a}$$

where we have noted that in a circular cylindrical shell $r = a$. Now operate on Eq. 6.11b with $\partial^2/\partial x\, \partial s$ to give

$$\frac{\partial^4 u_s}{\partial x\, \partial s^3} + \frac{1-\nu}{2}\frac{\partial^4 u_s}{\partial x^3\, \partial s} + \frac{1+\nu}{2}\frac{\partial^4 u_x}{\partial x^2\, \partial s^2} + \frac{1}{a}\frac{\partial^3 w}{\partial x\, \partial s^2} - \frac{\partial^2 P_s}{\partial x\, \partial s} = 0. \tag{6.12b}$$

The mixed partial derivatives of u_s can now be eliminated from Eq. 6.12b by using Eqs. 6.12a. This gives

$$\nabla^4 u_x = \frac{1}{a}\frac{\partial^3 w}{\partial x\, \partial s^2} - \frac{\nu}{a}\frac{\partial^3 w}{\partial x^3} + \frac{\partial^2 P_x}{\partial x^2} + \frac{2}{1-\nu}\frac{\partial^2 P_x}{\partial s^2} - \frac{1+\nu}{1-\nu}\frac{\partial^2 P_s}{\partial x\, \partial s}. \tag{6.13a}$$

Now take two partial derivatives of Eq. 6.11b with respect to x and two partial derivatives of Eq. 6.11b with respect to s. Solve each of the resulting expressions for the mixed fourth partial derivative of u_x and substitute the latter into the equation which is obtained by operating on Eq. 6.11a with $\partial^2/\partial x\, \partial s$. This procedure gives

$$\nabla^4 u_s = -\frac{2+\nu}{a}\frac{\partial^3 w}{\partial x^2\, \partial s} - \frac{1}{a}\frac{\partial^3 w}{\partial s^3} + \frac{\partial^2 P_s}{\partial s^2} + \frac{2}{1-\nu}\frac{\partial^2 P_s}{\partial x^2} - \frac{1+\nu}{1-\nu}\frac{\partial^2 P_x}{\partial x\, \partial s}. \tag{6.13b}$$

Finally, take a partial derivative of Eq. 6.13a with respect to x, a partial derivative of Eq. 6.13b with respect to s, and substitute these results into the expression which is obtained by applying ∇^4 to Eq. 6.11c. This gives the following differential equation which governs the transverse deflection w:

$$\frac{h^2}{12}\nabla^8 w + \frac{1-\nu^2}{a^2}\frac{\partial^4 w}{\partial x^4} = \nabla^4 P - \frac{1}{a}\left[\frac{\partial^3 P_s}{\partial s^3} + \nu\frac{\partial^3 P_x}{\partial x^3} + (2+\nu)\frac{\partial^3 P_s}{\partial s\, \partial x^2} - \frac{\partial^3 P_x}{\partial x\, \partial s^2}\right]. \tag{6.13c}$$

The remarkable feature of Eqs. 6.13a, 6.13b, and 6.13c, which are commonly referred to as Donnell's equations, is that the displacements have been decoupled. That is, for any known mechanical or thermal loading, Eq. 6.13c can be solved for w and then u_x and u_s can be obtained as the solutions of Eqs. 6.13a and 6.13b.

Since the system which has been derived is of the eighth order, the solution will have sufficient arbitrariness to satisfy boundary conditions of the type

$$\begin{aligned} N_x &= \bar{N}_x &&\text{or}\quad u_x = \bar{u}_x, \\ T_{xs} &= \bar{T}_{xs} &&\text{or}\quad u_s = \bar{u}_s, \\ V_x &= \bar{V}_x &&\text{or}\quad w = \bar{w}, \\ M_x &= \bar{M}_x &&\text{or}\quad \beta_x = \bar{\beta}_x, \end{aligned} \tag{6.14}$$

on each of two edges of constant x, or

$$\begin{aligned} N_s &= \bar{N}_s & &\text{or} & u_s &= \bar{u}_s, \\ N_{sx} &= \bar{N}_{sx} & &\text{or} & u_x &= \bar{u}_x, \\ V_s &= \bar{V}_s & &\text{or} & w &= \bar{w}, \\ M_s &= \bar{M}_s & &\text{or} & \beta_s &= \bar{\beta}_s, \end{aligned} \tag{6.15}$$

on each of two edges of constant s. When the shell is closed with respect to the coordinate s, the boundary conditions at edges of constant s are replaced by conditions of periodicity.

As in the previous chapter, it is convenient to decompose the solution of Eqs. 6.13a, 6.13b, and 6.13c into particular and complementary components by means of the definitions

$$\begin{aligned} u_x &= u_x^{\,p} + u_x^{\,c}, \\ u_s &= u_s^{\,p} + u_s^{\,c}, \\ w &= w^p + w^c, \end{aligned} \tag{6.16}$$

and so on, where the superscripts p and c refer to the contributions from the distributed surface loadings and edge loadings, respectively. Consequently, we shall again take up, in separate sections, the determination of these contributions to the solution. Here we shall find, owing to the method of solution which will be adopted, that in some cases the particular solution also satisfies the boundary conditions. For these, it will not be necessary to determine an additional complementary solution.

6.2*a* Circular Cylindrical Shells under Arbitrary Edge Loadings

In the absence of surface loadings, Donnell's equations reduce to the set

$$\begin{aligned} &\frac{h^2}{12}\nabla^8 w^c + \frac{1-\nu^2}{a^2}\frac{\partial^4 w^c}{\partial x^4} = 0, \\ &\nabla^4 u_s^{\,c} = -\frac{2+\nu}{a}\frac{\partial^3 w^c}{\partial x^2\,\partial s} - \frac{1}{a}\frac{\partial^3 w^c}{\partial s^3}, \\ &\nabla^4 u_x^{\,c} = -\frac{\nu}{a}\frac{\partial^3 w^c}{\partial x^3} + \frac{1}{a}\frac{\partial^3 w^c}{\partial x\,\partial s^2}. \end{aligned} \tag{6.17a}$$

where, in view of Eqs. 6.16, we are concerned only with the determination of the complementary solutions $u_x^{\,c}$, $u_s^{\,c}$, and w^c. Now we replace s with $a\theta$ and define the following dimensionless variables:

$$y = \frac{x}{a}, \qquad v = \frac{u_s^{\,c}}{a}, \qquad u = \frac{u_x^{\,c}}{a}, \qquad \bar{w} = \frac{w^c}{a}. \tag{6.17b}$$

With these definitions, Eqs. 6.17a become

$$\nabla^8 \overline{w} + 4k^4 \frac{\partial^4 \overline{w}}{\partial y^4} = 0,$$
$$\nabla^4 v = -(2+\nu)\frac{\partial^3 \overline{w}}{\partial y^2\,\partial\theta} - \frac{\partial^3 \overline{w}}{\partial \theta^3}, \tag{6.17c}$$
$$\nabla^4 u = -\nu\frac{\partial^3 \overline{w}}{\partial y^3} + \frac{\partial^3 \overline{w}}{\partial y\,\partial\theta^2},$$

where

$$\nabla^2(\ldots) = \frac{\partial^2(\ldots)}{\partial y^2} + \frac{\partial^2(\ldots)}{\partial \theta^2}, \tag{6.17d}$$

and

$$4k^4 = 12(1-\nu^2)\left(\frac{a}{h}\right)^2 = 4\mu^4 a^4, \tag{6.17e}$$

(see Eq. 5.17b) for an isotropic shell. If we restrict our attention to loads which are applied to edges of constant x, we can assume solutions of Eqs. 6.17c in the form[3]

$$\overline{w} = \sum_j \sum_n A_{nj}\, e^{p_{nj}y} \cos n\theta,$$
$$u = \sum_j \sum_n B_{nj}\, e^{p_{nj}y} \cos n\theta, \tag{6.18a}$$
$$v = \sum_j \sum_n C_{nj}\, e^{p_{nj}y} \sin n\theta,$$

where the number of terms in the summation on j will presently be shown to be eight and the number of terms in the summation on n depends upon a Fourier analysis of the edge conditions. If we substitute the njth terms of these expansions into Eqs. 6.17c, we obtain the following relationships between the arbitrary coefficients:

$$B_{nj} = -\frac{p_{nj}(\nu p_{nj}^2 + n^2)}{(p_{nj}^2 - n^2)^2} A_{nj} = c_{nj}A_{nj},$$
$$C_{nj} = -\frac{n[n^2 - (2+\nu)p_{nj}^2]}{(p_{nj}^2 - n^2)^2} A_{nj} = d_{nj}A_{nj}. \tag{6.18b}$$

The quantity p_{nj} is used to satisfy the first of Eqs. 6.17c, from which we find, upon substitution of $\overline{w}$ from Eqs. 6.18a, that

$$(p_{nj}^2 - n^2)^4 = -4k^4 p_{nj}^4, \qquad j = 1, \ldots, 8. \tag{6.18c}$$

[3] Hoff, N. J., "Boundary Value Problems of the Thin Walled Circular Cylinder," *J. Appl. Mech.*, **21**, 343–350 (1954).

Since this equation has eight roots, it is now clear why there are eight terms to be taken in the summation on j in Eqs. 6.18a. The eight roots are determined as follows:

Take the square root of Eq. 6.18c and obtain

$$(p_{nj}^2 - n^2)^2 = \pm 2ik^2 p_{nj}^2, \tag{6.18d}$$

where $i^2 = -1$. Now take the square root of Eq. 6.18d and obtain the results

$$(p_{nj}^2 - n^2) = \pm(1 + i)kp_{nj}, \tag{6.18e, f}$$

$$(p_{nj}^2 - n^2) = \pm(1 - i)kp_{nj}, \tag{6.18g, h}$$

from which the eight roots p_{nj} can be found. Let us, for example, consider the case where the root p_{nj} is governed by Eq. 6.18e and represent it in the complex form

$$p_{n1} = \alpha_n + i\beta_n, \tag{6.18i}$$

where α_n and β_n are real quantities. Upon substitution of this form into Eq. 6.18e and separation of the real and imaginary parts, we find that

$$a_n b_n - n^2 - kb_n = 0, \tag{6.18j}$$

$$a_n^2 - b_n^2 - 2ka_n = 0, \tag{6.18k}$$

where $a_n = \alpha_n + \beta_n$ and $b_n = \alpha_n - \beta_n$. Elimination of a_n from Eq. 6.18k by use of Eq. 6.18j then yields the equation

$$b_n^4 + k^2 b_n^2 - n^4 = 0, \tag{6.18l}$$

whose solution is

$$b_n^2 = -(k^2/2) + [(k/2)^2 + n^4]^{1/2}. \tag{6.18m}$$

Since α_n and β_n are real quantities, b_n must also be real and, to insure this, we have suppressed the negative square root in Eq. 6.18m. The final values for b_n then are

$$b_n = \pm \Omega_n \tag{6.18n}$$

where

$$\Omega_n = \{-(k^2/2) + [(k/2)^2 + n^4]^{1/2}\}^{1/2}. \tag{6.18o}$$

If, for the time being, we focus our attention on the negative root in Eq. 6.18n, we find that

$$a_n = \frac{n^2 + kb_n}{b_n} = k - \frac{n^2}{\Omega_n}, \tag{6.18p}$$

and, furthermore,

$$\alpha_n = \frac{1}{2}(a_n + b_n) = \frac{1}{2}\left(k - \frac{n^2}{\Omega_n} - \Omega_n\right) \equiv -\alpha_{n2},$$
$$\beta_n = \frac{1}{2}(a_n - b_n) = \frac{1}{2}\left(k - \frac{n^2}{\Omega_n} + \Omega_n\right) \equiv \beta_{n2}, \tag{6.18q}$$

where α_{n2} and β_{n2} are arbitrarily defined as shown above. The final form for the root of Eq. 6.18e now is

$$p_{n1} = -\alpha_{n2} + i\beta_{n2}. \tag{6.18r}$$

If we consider the positive root in Eq. 6.18n we find, in a similar fashion, that

$$a_n = k + \frac{n^2}{\Omega_n},$$
$$\alpha_n = \frac{1}{2}\left(k + \frac{n^2}{\Omega_n} + \Omega_n\right) \equiv \alpha_{n1}, \tag{6.18s}$$
$$\beta_n = \frac{1}{2}\left(k + \frac{n^2}{\Omega_n} - \Omega_n\right) \equiv -\beta_{n1},$$

and the root corresponding to this choice is

$$p_{n2} = \alpha_{n1} - i\beta_{n1}. \tag{6.18t}$$

It now follows, by using the same procedure, that the roots of Eq. 6.18f are

$$p_{n3} = -\alpha_{n1} + i\beta_{n1},$$
$$p_{n4} = \alpha_{n2} - i\beta_{n2}, \tag{6.18u}$$

that the roots of Eq. 6.18g are

$$p_{n5} = -\alpha_{n2} - i\beta_{n2},$$
$$p_{n6} = \alpha_{n1} + i\beta_{n1}, \tag{6.18v}$$

and that the roots of Eq. 6.18h are

$$p_{n7} = -\alpha_{n1} - i\beta_{n1},$$
$$p_{n8} = \alpha_{n2} + i\beta_{n2}. \tag{6.18w}$$

It is interesting to note that the eight roots p_{nj} are expressed in terms of the four quantities α_{n1}, β_{n1}, α_{n2}, and β_{n2}.

Upon inspection of the eight roots which we have just found, we find that

$$p_{n1} = -p_{n4} = \bar{p}_{n5},$$
$$p_{n2} = -p_{n3} = \bar{p}_{n6}, \tag{6.18x}$$
$$p_{n5} = -p_{n8} = -\bar{p}_{n4},$$
$$p_{n7} = -p_{n6} = -\bar{p}_{n3},$$

where a bar denotes a complex conjugate. In view of the foregoing we find, from Eqs. 6.18b, the further results:

$$\begin{aligned} c_{n1} &= -c_{n4} = \bar{c}_{n5}, & d_{n1} &= d_{n4} = \bar{d}_{n5}, \\ c_{n2} &= -c_{n3} = \bar{c}_{n6}, & d_{n2} &= d_{n3} = \bar{d}_{n6}, \\ c_{n5} &= -c_{n8} = -\bar{c}_{n4}, & d_{n5} &= d_{n8} = \bar{d}_{n4}, \\ c_{n7} &= -c_{n6} = -\bar{c}_{n3}, & d_{n7} &= d_{n6} = \bar{d}_{n3}. \end{aligned} \tag{6.18y}$$

Having thus obtained the eight roots p_{nj}, we may write the nth terms of the expansions 6.18a as

$$\begin{aligned} \bar{w}_n = {} & e^{\alpha_{n1}y}\,[(A_{n2} + A_{n6})\cos\beta_{n1}y + i(A_{n6} - A_{n2})\sin\beta_{n1}y] \\ & + e^{-\alpha_{n1}y}\,[(A_{n3} + A_{n7})\cos\beta_{n1}y + i(A_{n3} - A_{n7})\sin\beta_{n1}y] \\ & + e^{\alpha_{n2}y}\,[(A_{n4} + A_{n8})\cos\beta_{n2}y + i(A_{n8} - A_{n4})\sin\beta_{n2}y] \\ & + e^{-\alpha_{n2}y}\,[(A_{n1} + A_{n5})\cos\beta_{n2}y + i(A_{n1} - A_{n5})\sin\beta_{n2}y], \end{aligned} \tag{6.19a}$$

$$\begin{aligned} u_n = {} & e^{\alpha_{n1}y}\,[(B_{n2} + B_{n6})\cos\beta_{n1}y + i(B_{n6} - B_{n2})\sin\beta_{n1}y] \\ & + e^{-\alpha_{n1}y}\,[(B_{n3} + B_{n7})\cos\beta_{n1}y + i(B_{n3} - B_{n7})\sin\beta_{n1}y] \\ & + e^{\alpha_{n2}y}\,[(B_{n4} + B_{n8})\cos\beta_{n2}y + i(B_{n8} - B_{n4})\sin\beta_{n2}y] \\ & + e^{-\alpha_{n2}y}\,[(B_{n1} + B_{n5})\cos\beta_{n2}y + i(B_{n1} - B_{n5})\sin\beta_{n2}y], \end{aligned} \tag{6.19b}$$

$$\begin{aligned} v_n = {} & e^{\alpha_{n1}y}\,[(C_{n2} + C_{n6})\cos\beta_{n1}y + i(C_{n6} - C_{n2})\sin\beta_{n1}y] \\ & + e^{-\alpha_{n1}y}\,[(C_{n3} + C_{n7})\cos\beta_{n1}y + i(C_{n3} - C_{n7})\sin\beta_{n1}y] \\ & + e^{\alpha_{n2}y}\,[(C_{n4} + C_{n8})\cos\beta_{n2}y + i(C_{n8} - C_{n4})\sin\beta_{n2}y] \\ & + e^{-\alpha_{n2}y}\,[(C_{n1} + C_{n5})\cos\beta_{n2}y + i(C_{n1} - C_{n5})\sin\beta_{n2}y], \end{aligned} \tag{6.19c}$$

where

$$\begin{aligned} \bar{w} &= \sum_n \bar{w}_n \cos n\theta, \\ u &= \sum_n u_n \cos n\theta, \\ v &= \sum_n v_n \sin n\theta, \end{aligned} \tag{6.19d}$$

and we have replaced the roots by their complex forms. Since the displacements are real functions, it follows that each of the various combinations of the arbitrary constants which appear in Eqs. 6.19a, 6.19b, and 6.19c must also be real. It is well, therefore, to define the following real arbitrary constants:

$$\begin{aligned} F_{n1} &= A_{n2} + A_{n6}, & F_{n2} &= i(A_{n6} - A_{n2}), \\ F_{n3} &= A_{n3} + A_{n7}, & F_{n4} &= i(A_{n3} - A_{n7}), \\ F_{n5} &= A_{n4} + A_{n8}, & F_{n6} &= i(A_{n8} - A_{n4}), \\ F_{n7} &= A_{n1} + A_{n5}, & F_{n8} &= i(A_{n1} - A_{n5}). \end{aligned} \tag{6.20}$$

The B_{nj} and C_{nj} are related to the A_{nj} by Eqs. 6.18b and the F_{nj} by Eqs. 6.20. Consequently, Eqs. 6.19a to 6.19c can be rewritten in terms of the F_{nj} as follows:

$$\begin{aligned}\bar{w}_n = {} & e^{\alpha_{n1}y}\,[F_{n1}\cos\beta_{n1}y + F_{n2}\sin\beta_{n1}y] \\ & \qquad + e^{-\alpha_{n1}y}\,[F_{n3}\cos\beta_{n1}y + F_{n4}\sin\beta_{n1}y], \\ & + e^{\alpha_{n2}y}\,[F_{n5}\cos\beta_{n2}y + F_{n6}\sin\beta_{n2}y] \\ & \qquad + e^{-\alpha_{n2}y}\,[F_{n7}\cos\beta_{n2}y + F_{n8}\sin\beta_{n2}y],\end{aligned} \tag{6.21a}$$

$$\begin{aligned}u_n = {} & e^{\alpha_{n1}y}\,[(g_{n3}F_{n2} - f_{n3}F_{n1})\cos\beta_{n1}y - (g_{n3}F_{n1} + f_{n3}F_{n2})\sin\beta_{n1}y] \\ & + e^{-\alpha_{n1}y}\,[(f_{n3}F_{n3} + g_{n3}F_{n4})\cos\beta_{n1}y + (f_{n3}F_{n4} - g_{n3}F_{n3})\sin\beta_{n1}y] \\ & + e^{\alpha_{n2}y}\,[(g_{n1}F_{n6} - f_{n1}F_{n5})\cos\beta_{n2}y - (f_{n1}F_{n6} + g_{n1}F_{n5})\sin\beta_{n2}y] \\ & + e^{-\alpha_{n2}y}\,[(f_{n1}F_{n7} + g_{n1}F_{n8})\cos\beta_{n2}y \\ & \qquad + (f_{n1}F_{n8} - g_{n1}F_{n7})\sin\beta_{n2}y],\end{aligned} \tag{6.21b}$$

$$\begin{aligned}v_n = {} & e^{\alpha_{n1}y}\,[(f_{n3}'F_{n1} - g_{n3}'F_{n2})\cos\beta_{n1}y + (f_{n3}'F_{n2} + g_{n3}'F_{n1})\sin\beta_{n1}y] \\ & + e^{-\alpha_{n1}y}\,[(f_{n3}'F_{n3} + g_{n3}'F_{n4})\cos\beta_{n1}y + (f_{n3}'F_{n4} - g_{n3}'F_{n3})\sin\beta_{n1}y] \\ & + e^{\alpha_{n2}y}\,[(f_{n1}'F_{n5} - g_{n1}'F_{n6})\cos\beta_{n2}y + (f_{n1}'F_{n6} + g_{n1}'F_{n5})\sin\beta_{n2}y] \\ & + e^{-\alpha_{n2}y}\,[(f_{n1}'F_{n7} + g_{n1}'F_{n8})\cos\beta_{n2}y \\ & \qquad + (f_{n1}'F_{n8} - g_{n1}'F_{n7})\sin\beta_{n2}y],\end{aligned} \tag{6.21c}$$

where

$$\begin{aligned}f_{n1} &= \frac{-1}{2k^2}\left(\nu\beta_{n2} - \frac{n^2\beta_{n2}}{\alpha_{n2}^{\ 2} + \beta_{n2}^{\ 2}}\right), \\ g_{n1} &= \frac{-1}{2k^2}\left(\nu\alpha_{n2} + \frac{n^2\alpha_{n2}}{\alpha_{n2}^{\ 2} + \beta_{n2}^{\ 2}}\right), \\ f_{n3} &= \frac{-1}{2k^2}\left(\nu\beta_{n1} - \frac{n^2\beta_{n1}}{\alpha_{n1}^{\ 2} + \beta_{n1}^{\ 2}}\right), \\ g_{n3} &= \frac{-1}{2k^2}\left(\nu\alpha_{n1} + \frac{n^2\alpha_{n1}}{\alpha_{n1}^{\ 2} + \beta_{n1}^{\ 2}}\right), \\ f_{n1}' &= \frac{-\alpha_{n2}\beta_{n2}n^3}{k^2(\alpha_{n2}^{\ 2} + \beta_{n2}^{\ 2})^2}, \\ g_{n1}' &= \frac{-n}{2k^2}\left(2 + \nu - \frac{n^2(\alpha_{n2}^{\ 2} - \beta_{n2}^{\ 2})}{\alpha_{n2}^{\ 2} + \beta_{n2}^{\ 2}}\right), \\ f_{n3}' &= \frac{-\alpha_{n1}\beta_{n1}n^3}{k^2(\alpha_{n1}^{\ 2} + \beta_{n}^{\ 2})^2}, \\ g_{n3}' &= \frac{-n}{2k^2}\left(2 + \nu - \frac{n^2(\alpha_{n1}^{\ 2} - \beta_{n1}^{\ 2})}{\alpha_{n1}^{\ 2} + \beta_{n1}^{\ 2}}\right).\end{aligned} \tag{6.21d}$$

The general solution of the problem of a circular cylindrical shell subjected to loads at edges of constant x is now complete. It contains eight arbitrary constants which are determined from four boundary conditions at each of the two edges of constant x. It is important to note, however, that the form of the solutions 6.18a implies that the load system is symmetric with respect to the generator passing through $\theta = 0$. If the system were to be antisymmetric with respect to $\theta = 0$, then the deflections would have to be assumed in the form

$$\bar{w} = \sum_n \sum_{j=1}^{8} A_{nj}\, e^{p_{nj}y} \sin n\theta,$$

$$u = \sum_n \sum_{j=1}^{8} B_{nj}\, e^{p_{nj}y} \sin n\theta, \tag{6.22}$$

$$v = \sum_n \sum_{j=1}^{8} C_{nj}\, e^{p_{nj}y} \cos n\theta.$$

In this case, the first of Eqs. 6.18b would remain unchanged while the right-hand side of the second of Eqs. 6.18b would be the negative of its present value. All of the other equations would remain valid except that wherever they appear $\cos n\theta$ and $\sin n\theta$ would have to be replaced by $\sin n\theta$ and $-\cos n\theta$, respectively. General unsymmetrical loads can be handled by suitable combinations of the symmetric and antisymmetric solution systems.

If the shell is closed with respect to the coordinate θ, we have just the right number of arbitrary constants available for the satisfaction of the boundary conditions 6.14 on the edges of constant x. If the shell were a segment having, in addition, two edges of constant θ, then our solution would not be arbitrary enough to also satisfy the boundary conditions 6.15 which would be brought into the problem at such edges. This is an unfortunate limitation of the present method of solution and is not likely to be overcome within the framework of available solution functions.

It is now interesting to show that the present solution contains, as a special case, the general solution of the problem of a cylindrical shell under edge conditions which do not vary with the polar angle θ. We do this by setting $n = 0$ in the present analysis. This yields the results

$$p_0 = \pm(1 \pm i)k,$$
$$\alpha_{01} = \alpha_{02} = \beta_{01} = \beta_{02} = k, \tag{6.23}$$

and

$$\frac{w^c}{a} = e^{ky}\,[(F_{01} + F_{05}) \cos ky + (F_{02} + F_{06}) \sin ky] + e^{-ky}\,[(F_{03} + F_{07}) \cos ky + (F_{04} + F_{08}) \sin ky] \tag{6.24a}$$

$$u_x{}^c\left(\frac{2k}{va}\right) = e^{ky}\,[(F_{02} + F_{06})(\cos ky - \sin ky) - (F_{01} + F_{05})(\cos ky + \sin ky)] \quad (6.24b)$$
$$+\, e^{-ky}\,[(F_{03} + F_{07})(\cos ky - \sin ky) + (F_{04} + F_{08})(\cos ky + \sin ky)]$$
$$u_s{}^c \equiv 0, \quad (6.24c)$$

which, when differences in notation are accounted for, can be shown to be identical to the solution which we obtained earlier for the isotropic cylindrical shell.

We have arbitrarily restricted our attention to the analysis of circular cylindrical shells under the influence of loads applied to edges of constant x. Similar analyses of segments of circular cylindrical shells with loads applied along edges of constant θ can, of course, also be carried out[4] but will not be pursued here. It is sufficient to note that, for such problems, the solutions of Eqs. 6.17c would be assumed in the form

$$\begin{aligned} \overline{w} &= \sum_n \sum_{j=1}^{8} A_{nj}\, e^{p_{nj}\theta} \cos ny, \\ u &= \sum_n \sum_{j=1}^{8} B_{nj}\, e^{p_{nj}\theta} \sin ny, \\ v &= \sum_n \sum_{j=1}^{8} C_{nj}\, e^{p_{nj}\theta} \cos ny, \end{aligned} \quad (6.25)$$

and so on, where $n = m\pi a/l$.

6.2*b* Circular Cylindrical Shells under Arbitrary Distributed Loadings

In the consideration of a circular cylindrical shell under arbitrary distributed loadings, we are faced with the solution of the full, inhomogeneous, Donnell equations (as given by Eqs. 6.13a to 6.13c) with one or more nonvanishing P's. To solve these equations, we employ the method of Fourier expansions, wherein we may, for example, expand the terms containing the distributed loadings in double series of the type

$$\begin{aligned} P_x &= \sum_m \sum_n P_{xmn} \cos\frac{m\pi x}{l} \cos\frac{n\pi s}{s_0}, \\ P_s &= \sum_m \sum_n P_{smn} \sin\frac{m\pi x}{l} \sin\frac{n\pi s}{s_0}, \\ P &= \sum_m \sum_n P_{mn} \sin\frac{m\pi x}{l} \cos\frac{n\pi s}{s_0}, \\ -s_0 &\leqslant s \leqslant s, \qquad o \leqslant x \leqslant l, \end{aligned} \quad (6.26a)$$

[4] See, for example, Hoff, N. J., Kempner, J., and Pohle, F. V., "Line Loads Applied Along Generators of Thin-Walled Circular Cylinders of Finite Length," *Q. Appl. Math.*, **11**, 411–426 (1954).

where $2s_0$ is the length of arc subtended by the shell segment in the s direction. The foregoing choice of the expansions implies that the loading system is symmetric with respect to the generator passing through $\theta = 0$ and with respect to the axial position $x = l/2$. It also implies that the mechanical and thermal loadings can be represented by Fourier expansions of the type

$$q_x = \sum_m \sum_n q_{xmn} \cos \frac{m\pi x}{l} \cos \frac{n\pi s}{s_0},$$

$$q_s = \sum_m \sum_n q_{smn} \sin \frac{m\pi x}{l} \sin \frac{n\pi s}{s_0}, \tag{6.26b}$$

$$q = \sum_m \sum_n q_{mn} \sin \frac{m\pi x}{l} \cos \frac{n\pi s}{s_0},$$

$$T_0 = \sum_m \sum_n T_{0mn} \sin \frac{m\pi x}{l} \cos \frac{n\pi s}{s_0},$$

$$T_1 = \sum_m \sum_n T_{1mn} \sin \frac{m\pi x}{l} \cos \frac{n\pi s}{s_0}. \tag{6.26c}$$

The latter two equations imply, in turn, that the temperature distribution can be represented by the series

$$T = \sum_m \sum_n T_{mn}(\zeta) \sin \frac{m\pi x}{l} \cos \frac{n\pi s}{s_0}, \tag{6.26d}$$

and, in view of Eqs. 6.5a,

$$T_{0mn} = \frac{1}{h} \int_\zeta T_{mn}(\zeta)\, d\zeta, \qquad T_{1mn} = \frac{12}{h^3} \int_\zeta T_{mn}(\zeta)\zeta\, d\zeta. \tag{6.26e}$$

Finally, the coefficients in the expansions 6.26a can be found in terms of the coefficients of the load and temperature series by means of the definitions 6.11d. Thus, we obtain the relationships

$$P_{xmn} = -\frac{(1 - \nu^2)}{Eh} q_{xmn} + (1 + \nu)\alpha_t \left(\frac{m\pi}{l}\right) T_{0mn},$$

$$P_{smn} = -\frac{(1 - \nu^2)}{Eh} q_{smn} - (1 + \nu)\alpha_t \left(\frac{n\pi}{s_0}\right) T_{0mn},$$

$$P_{mn} = -\frac{(1 - \nu^2)}{Eh} q_{mn} + (1 + \nu)\alpha_t \left[\frac{h^2}{12}\left(\frac{m^2\pi^2}{l^2} + \frac{n^2\pi^2}{{s_0}^2}\right) T_{1mn} + \frac{T_{0mn}}{a}\right]. \tag{6.26f}$$

For loads which can be expressed in the form 6.26a, we assume further that the displacements can be expanded in the series

$$
\begin{aligned}
u_x{}^p &= \sum_m \sum_n u_{mn} \cos \frac{m\pi x}{l} \cos \frac{n\pi s}{s_0}, \\
u_s{}^p &= \sum_m \sum_n v_{mn} \sin \frac{m\pi x}{l} \sin \frac{n\pi s}{s_0}, \\
w^p &= \sum_m \sum_n w_{mn} \sin \frac{m\pi x}{l} \cos \frac{n\pi s}{s_0},
\end{aligned}
\tag{6.26g}
$$

where the coefficients are, as yet, unknown. To determine these coefficients in terms of the known coefficients of the loading functions, we substitute Eqs. 6.26a and 6.26g into Eqs. 6.13a to 6.13c with the result

$$
\begin{aligned}
&\left\{\frac{h^2}{12}\left[\left(\frac{m\pi}{l}\right)^2 + \left(\frac{n\pi}{s_0}\right)^2\right]^4 + \frac{(1-\nu^2)}{a^2}\left(\frac{m\pi}{l}\right)^4\right\} w_{mn} \\
&\quad = \left[\left(\frac{m\pi}{l}\right)^2 + \left(\frac{n\pi}{s_0}\right)^2\right]^2 P_{mn} \\
&\qquad + \left[\left(\frac{n\pi}{s_0}\right)^2 + (2+\nu)\left(\frac{m\pi}{l}\right)^2\right]\left(\frac{n\pi}{s_0}\right)\frac{P_{smn}}{a} \\
&\qquad - \left[\nu\left(\frac{m\pi}{l}\right)^2 - \left(\frac{n\pi}{s_0}\right)^2\right]\left(\frac{m\pi}{l}\right)\frac{P_{xmn}}{a}, \\
&\left[\left(\frac{m\pi}{l}\right)^2 + \left(\frac{n\pi}{s_0}\right)^2\right]^2 v_{mn} \\
&\quad = -\left[(2+\nu)\left(\frac{m\pi}{l}\right)^2 + \left(\frac{n\pi}{s_0}\right)^2\right]\left(\frac{n\pi}{s_0}\right)\frac{w_{mn}}{a} \\
&\qquad - \left[\left(\frac{n\pi}{s_0}\right)^2 + \frac{2}{1-\nu}\left(\frac{m\pi}{l}\right)^2\right] P_{smn} - \frac{1+\nu}{1-\nu}\left(\frac{m\pi}{l}\right)\left(\frac{n\pi}{s_0}\right) P_{xmn}, \\
&\left[\left(\frac{m\pi}{l}\right)^2 + \left(\frac{n\pi}{s_0}\right)^2\right]^2 u_{mn} \\
&\quad = -\left[\left(\frac{n\pi}{s_0}\right)^2 - \nu\left(\frac{m\pi}{l}\right)^2\right]\left(\frac{m\pi}{l}\right)\frac{w_{mn}}{a} \\
&\qquad - \left[\left(\frac{m\pi}{l}\right)^2 + \frac{2}{1-\nu}\left(\frac{n\pi}{s_0}\right)^2\right] P_{xmn} - \frac{1+\nu}{1-\nu}\left(\frac{m\pi}{l}\right)\left(\frac{n\pi}{s_0}\right) P_{smn}.
\end{aligned}
\tag{6.27a}
$$

Thus, for every combination of m and n the arbitrary coefficients of the assumed displacement series 6.26g can be found from the foregoing expressions. Although Eqs. 6.26g represent the particular solutions of a given problem, they also satisfy certain interesting boundary conditions.

To show this, we note that in view of Eqs. 6.26g, the other shell variables can be found by means of Eqs. 6.2, 6.3, 6.4, and 6.5 to be the following:

$$\beta_x{}^p = -\sum_m \sum_n w_{mn} \left(\frac{m\pi}{l}\right) \cos \frac{m\pi x}{l} \cos \frac{m\pi s}{s_0},$$

$$\beta_s{}^p = \sum_m \sum_n \left[\frac{v_{mn}}{a} + \left(\frac{n\pi}{s_0}\right) w_{mn}\right] \sin \frac{m\pi x}{l} \sin \frac{n\pi s}{s_0},$$

$$N_x{}^p = K \sum_m \sum_n \left[-\left(\frac{m\pi}{l}\right) u_{mn} + \nu \left(\frac{n\pi}{s_0}\right) v_{mn} + \frac{\nu w_{mn}}{a} - T_{0mn}\alpha_t(1+\nu)\right] \times \sin \frac{m\pi x}{l} \cos \frac{n\pi s}{s_0},$$

$$N_s{}^p = K \sum_m \sum_n \left[\left(\frac{n\pi}{s_0}\right) v_{mn} + \frac{w_{mn}}{a} - \nu \left(\frac{m\pi}{l}\right) u_{mn} - T_{0mn}\alpha_t(1+\nu)\right] \times \sin \frac{m\pi x}{l} \cos \frac{n\pi s}{s_0},$$

$$N_{sx}{}^p = N_{xs}{}^p = \frac{K(1-\nu)}{2} \sum_m \sum_n \left[\left(\frac{m\pi}{l}\right) v_{mn} - \left(\frac{n\pi}{s_0}\right) u_{mn}\right] \times \cos \frac{m\pi x}{l} \sin \frac{n\pi s}{s_0},$$

$$M_x{}^p = D \sum_m \sum_n \left\{\left[\left(\frac{m\pi}{l}\right)^2 + \nu\left(\frac{n\pi}{s_0}\right)^2\right] w_{mn} - T_{1mn}\alpha_t(1+\nu)\right\} \times \sin \frac{m\pi x}{l} \cos \frac{n\pi s}{s_0},$$

$$M_s{}^p = D \sum_m \sum_n \left\{\left[\left(\frac{n\pi}{s_0}\right)^2 + \nu\left(\frac{m\pi}{l}\right)^2\right] w_{mn} - T_{1mn}\alpha_t(1+\nu)\right\} \times \sin \frac{m\pi x}{l} \cos \frac{n\pi s}{s_0},$$

$$M_{sx}{}^p = M_{xs}{}^p = D(1-\nu) \sum_m \sum_n \left(\frac{m\pi}{l}\right)\left(\frac{n\pi}{s_0}\right) w_{mn} \cos \frac{m\pi x}{l} \sin \frac{n\pi s}{s_0},$$

$$Q_x{}^p = D \sum_m \sum_n \left\{\left(\frac{m\pi}{l}\right)\left[\left(\frac{m\pi}{l}\right)^2 + \left(\frac{n\pi}{s_0}\right)^2\right] w_{mn} - \left(\frac{m\pi}{l}\right) T_{1mn}\alpha_t(1+\nu)\right\} \cos \frac{m\pi x}{l} \cos \frac{n\pi s}{s_0},$$

$$Q_s{}^p = -D \sum_m \sum_n \left(\frac{n\pi}{s_0}\right)\left\{\left[\left(\frac{m\pi}{l}\right)^2 + \left(\frac{n\pi}{s_0}\right)^2\right] w_{mn} - T_{1mn}\alpha_t(1+\nu)\right\} \sin \frac{m\pi x}{l} \sin \frac{n\pi s}{s_0}, \qquad (6.27b)$$

where we have used the last two of Eqs. 6.7 for the determination of the transverse shearing-stress resultants.

Now we observe from the foregoing that at the edges $x = 0, l$, we have

$$\beta_s{}^p = N_x{}^p = N_s{}^p = M_x{}^p = M_s{}^p = Q_s{}^p = V_s{}^p = u_s{}^p = w^p \equiv 0, \quad (6.28)$$

and on the edges $s = \pm s_0$ we have

$$\beta_s{}^p = N_{xs}{}^p = N_{sx}{}^p = M_{xs}{}^p = M_{sx}{}^p = Q_s{}^p = V_s{}^p$$
$$= T_{xs}{}^p = T_{sx}{}^p = u_s{}^p \equiv 0. \quad (6.29)$$

Therefore, if we had wanted to specify that the edges $x = 0$ and $x = l$ of a circular cylindrical shell which is closed with respect to the coordinate θ were to be simply supported but free to move axially, that is, $u_s = w = N_x = M_x = 0$, then the solution 6.26g would be complete because it satisfies both the differential equations and the boundary conditions of the problem. In this case, no complementary solution would have to be added. If, instead, the ends of the shell were to be clamped but free to move axially, that is, $\beta_x = u_s = w = N_x = 0$, then the solution 6.26g would not be complete because the boundary conditions would be violated. In this case, a complementary solution of the type developed in Section 6.2*a* would have to be added in order to provide the additional arbitrariness which will permit the satisfaction of the boundary conditions by the combined solution.

We should emphasize that the forms 6.26a and 6.26g imply that certain symmetries, which we have pointed out, exist in the loading and deformation state of the shell. Loads with other symmetries can be handled in the same manner by using other functional forms, while completely arbitrary loadings can be handled by means of generalized Fourier series of the type 4.35 which contain both symmetrical and antisymmetrical components.

6.2*c* Noncircular Cylindrical Shells

As a result of imperfections that are introduced during construction, it often happens that a cylindrical shell whose cross section is intended to be circular attains a noncircular cross section. In other cases, such as in the design of submarine hulls, the cross section is intended to be noncircular. The solution of problems involving such shells follows, in general, the same procedure as did the solution of problems involving cylindrical shells of circular cross section. However, since the radius of the reference surface of a noncircular cylindrical shell is a function of circumferential position, Eqs. 6.11 cannot be rearranged into a form which is analogous to Eqs. 6.13. Hence, they must be solved as they stand once the variation of the radius of curvature has been introduced. A further consequence of the variable radius is that explicit expressions can no longer be obtained for roots of the type p_{nj} associated with the complementary solution of a circular cylindrical shell or for the coefficients of the series expansions which are assumed for the particular solution.

As an illustration let us, therefore, consider the analysis of a cylindrical shell whose cross section is an oval under the influence of a uniform internal pressure. In this case, Eqs. 6.11 reduce to the set

$$\frac{\partial^2 u_x}{\partial x^2} + \frac{1-\nu}{2}\frac{\partial^2 u_x}{\partial s^2} + \frac{1+\nu}{2}\frac{\partial^2 u_s}{\partial x\,\partial s} + \frac{\nu}{r}\frac{\partial w}{\partial x} = 0, \tag{6.30a}$$

$$\frac{1-\nu}{2}\frac{\partial^2 u_s}{\partial x^2} + \frac{\partial^2 u_s}{\partial s^2} + \frac{1+\nu}{2}\frac{\partial^2 u_x}{\partial x\,\partial s} + \frac{\partial}{\partial s}\left(\frac{w}{r}\right) = 0, \tag{6.30b}$$

$$\nabla^4 w + \frac{12}{rh^2}\left(\frac{w}{r} + \frac{\partial u_s}{\partial s} + \nu\frac{\partial u_x}{\partial x}\right) = \frac{p}{D}, \tag{6.30c}$$

where we have taken the internal pressure to be $q = -p$. We let the curvature of the oval cross section of the reference surface of the shell be defined by the expression[5]

$$\frac{1}{r} = \frac{1}{r_0}\left(1 + \xi\cos\frac{4\pi s}{L_0}\right), \tag{6.31}$$

where L_0 is the total perimeter of the oval, r_0 is the radius of a circle which has the same perimeter as the oval, that is, $L_0 = 2\pi r_0$ and ξ is a measure of the "noncircularity" of the oval. The parameter ξ is less than or equal to unity and when it is equal to zero the oval becomes a circle. It is to be emphasized that formula 6.31 does not include ellipses, although ellipses can be constructed which have approximately the same contour as ovals of a given ξ. The form 6.31 is, however, to be preferred because it leads to a more convenient analysis and because, in design and/or construction, one is more likely to come up with an oval than with a mathematically precise elliptical cross section anyway.

Aside from the form of the governing equations 6.30 and the definition of the curvature 6.31, the formal solution procedure is identical to that of our earlier discussion of circular cylindrical shells under arbitrary distributed loads. First, we expand the uniform transverse pressure in the Fourier series

$$p = \sum_{m=1,3,\ldots}^{\infty} \frac{4p_0}{m\pi}\sin\frac{m\pi x}{l}, \tag{6.32a}$$

[5] Romano, F., and Kempner, J., "Stresses in Short Noncircular Cylindrical Shells Under Lateral Pressure," *J. Appl. Mech.*, **29**, 669–674 (1962).

where p_0 is the intensity of the applied pressure load. Next, we expand the displacements in the form (see Eqs. 6.26g of the analysis of circular cylindrical shells):

$$u_x{}^p = \left(\frac{p_0 r_0{}^2}{Eh}\right) \sum_{m=1,3,\ldots}^{\infty} \sum_{n=0,4,8,\ldots}^{\infty} u_{mn} \cos\frac{m\pi x}{l} \cos\frac{n\pi s}{L_0},$$

$$u_s{}^p = \left(\frac{p_0 r_0{}^2}{Eh}\right) \sum_{m=1,3,\ldots}^{\infty} \sum_{n=0,4,8,\ldots}^{\infty} v_{mn} \sin\frac{m\pi x}{l} \sin\frac{n\pi s}{L_0}, \quad (6.32\text{b})$$

$$w^p = \left(\frac{p_0 r_0{}^2}{Eh}\right) \sum_{m=1,3,\ldots}^{\infty} \sum_{n=0,4,8,\ldots}^{\infty} w_{mn} \sin\frac{m\pi x}{l} \cos\frac{n\pi s}{L_0},$$

where, on account of the symmetry of the oval cross section we have used $s_0 = L_0/4$ and have redefined the index n accordingly. In view of Eqs. 6.28, which are valid for the form 6.32b, once differences in notation have been taken into account, we find that the assumed solution 6.32b satisfies the conditions of simple support with axial motion permitted at the ends $x = 0, l$. For the sake of convenience, let us then adopt the latter as the actual boundary conditions in our illustrative problem. The solution 6.32b will, therefore, be the complete solution of our problem.

Before continuing the solution process, it is well to point out that as a result of the assumed forms of w and $1/r$ it follows that

$$\frac{w}{r} = \sum_{m=1,3,\ldots}^{\infty} \sum_{n=0,4,8,\ldots}^{\infty} \frac{1}{2r_0}\left(\frac{p_0 r_0{}^2}{Eh}\right) [2w_{mn} + \xi(1 + \delta_{4n})w_{m,n-4} + \xi w_{m,n+4}] \sin\frac{m\pi x}{l} \cos\frac{n\pi s}{L_0}, \quad (6.32\text{c})$$

where δ_{4n} is the Kronecker delta and $w_{m,-n} = 0$ for $n > 0$. Expressions which relate u_{mn} and v_{mn} to w_{mn} can now be found by substituting Eqs. 6.32b and 6.32c into Eqs. 6.30a and 6.30b. This gives the following result:

$$u_{mn} = \frac{(l/L_0 m)[\nu - (nl/mL_0)^2] \times [2w_{mn} + \xi(1 + \delta_{4n})w_{m,n-4} + \xi w_{m,n+4}]}{[1 + (nl/mL_0)^2]^2},$$

$$v_{mn} = -\frac{(n/m^2)(l/L_0)^2[2 + \nu + (nl/mL_0)^2] \times [2w_{mn} + \xi(1 + \delta_{4n})w_{m,n-4} + \xi w_{m,n+4}]}{[1 + (nl/mL_0)^2]^2}. \quad (6.32\text{d})$$

A relationship for the w_{mn} is now found by substituting Eqs. 6.32a to 6.32d into Eq. 6.30c, from which it follows that

$$\gamma_{mn}^a w_{m,n-8} + \gamma_{mn}^b w_{m,n-4} + \gamma_{mn}^c w_{mn} + \gamma_{mn}^d w_{m,n+4} + \gamma_{mn}^e w_{m,n+8} = \gamma_m \delta_{n0}, \quad (6.32\text{e})$$

where

$$\begin{aligned}
\gamma_{mn}^{a} &= (1 + \delta_{8n})\xi^2\alpha_{m,n-4}, \qquad \gamma_{mn}^{b} = 2(1 + \delta_{4n})\xi(\alpha_{m,n-4} + \alpha_{mn}),\\
\gamma_{mn}^{c} &= \beta_{mn} + 4\alpha_{mn} + \xi^2[(1 + \delta_{4n})\alpha_{m,n-4} + \alpha_{m,n+4}],\\
\gamma_{mn}^{d} &= 2\xi(\alpha_{mn} + \alpha_{m,n+4}), \qquad \gamma_{mn}^{e} = \xi^2\alpha_{m,n+4},\\
\gamma_{m} &= 16/m\pi,\\
\alpha_{mn} &= [1 + (nl/mL_0)^2]^{-2},\\
\beta_{mn} &= \pi^2(h/L_0)^2(L_0/l)^4m^4/12(1 - \nu^2)\alpha_{mn},\\
&\qquad m = 1, 3, \ldots, \quad n = 0, 4, 8, \ldots.
\end{aligned} \tag{6.32f}$$

We have thus obtained a doubly infinite set of simultaneous linear equations for the determination of the w_{mn}. These equations cannot, in general, be solved. It is, therefore, customary to truncate the system at some $m = M$ and $n = N$, say, after which the w_{mn} can be determined by standard methods for the solution of simultaneous linear equations. The number of terms that are to be considered in the solution is strongly dependent upon the parameter ξ; indeed, as ξ decreases fewer terms are required to obtain a reliable result. When ξ goes to zero, Eqs. 6.32e reduce to a single equation from which all of the w_{mn} can be obtained in closed form. The latter situation corresponds to the case when the oval becomes a circle and the resulting solution is, as could be expected, identical to the first of Eqs. 6.27a for the circular cylindrical shell under a distributed pressure load.

Numerical computations[5] which are based upon the foregoing development indicate that results which are accurate to four significant figures can be obtained by truncating the system at $m = 11$ and $n = 36$. This leads to six sets of equations corresponding to the six values of m. Each of these sets involves ten linear equations in ten unknowns, corresponding to the ten values of n that have been selected. Owing to the definitions 6.32f, the coefficients of the terms on the diagonal of each of these sets will be the greatest in magnitude and, therefore, a convergent iterative scheme can be employed to avoid the labor of solving the ten by ten system once for each of the six values of m. The iterative process begins by ignoring all of the terms to the right of the diagonal. In this way, we can obtain the first approximations $w_{m0}^{(1)}$ directly from the first equation in each set, $w_{m4}^{(1)}$ from the second equation, $w_{m8}^{(1)}$ from the third, and so on. Next, we set the values of the terms to the right of the diagonal equal to their values from the first approximation. This permits us to obtain the second approximations $w_{m0}^{(2)}$ from the first equation, $w_{m4}^{(2)}$ from the second equation, $w_{m8}^{(2)}$ from the third equation and so on. The process continues in this manner until the change in results from one approximation to the next is less than some predetermined amount. It was found[5] that two such approximations yielded results which were only 0.1% off the exact result

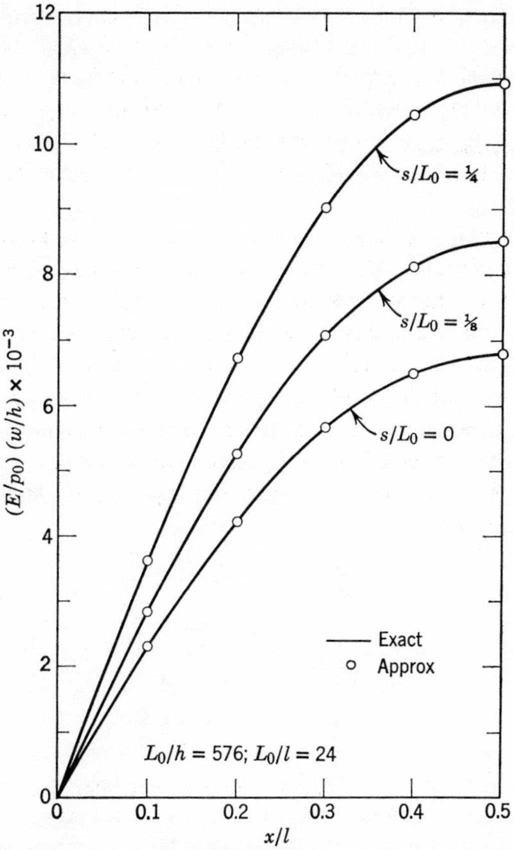

Figure 6.1 Radial displacement distributions for pressurized oval cylindrical shells with simply supported ends.

which was obtained by solving the six full systems of ten by ten linear equations.

Results for the transverse displacement at several positions along the circumference of a cylindrical shell of oval cross section are plotted in Fig. 6.1 as a function of axial position. In examining these data, it is interesting to note that at $s = L_0/8$, $3L_0/8$, $5L_0/8$, and $7L_0/8$ it is found, from Eq. 6.31, that $r = r_0$. Thus, at these positions the radius of the oval is the same as the radius of a circle having the same perimeter as the oval. As a result of this observation, it can be argued[5] that one should be able to approximate the results at a given point on an oval shell by means of an analysis of a circular cylindrical shell having the same load and support conditions as the oval shell and a constant radius which is equal to the local radius of the oval shell at the point in question. In this way, the simpler theory presented in Section 5.2 for the analysis of symmetrically loaded circular cylindrical shells can be used to analyze the uniformly loaded oval shell which was considered here. In Fig. 6.1, therefore, the circles indicate results obtained with this type of approximation, while the solid lines represent the results obtained from the exact, extended method. The plots indicate that the approximate method is, indeed, successful in predicting the results from the exact method.

In the foregoing, the functional dependence of the assumed solution 6.32b made it applicable to simply supported cylindrical shells and for such end conditions no additional complementary solution was required. If, on the other hand, we had wished to solve the preceding problem for the case of clamped edges, for example, then a complementary solution would be required in order that the combination of the two solutions will satisfy the new boundary conditions. Thus, it is well to also consider the solution of Eqs. 6.30 when the surface load is replaced, for example, by loads at edges of constant x. In this case we assume (see Eqs. 6.18a) that the displacements are of the form

$$\begin{aligned} w^c &= \sum_n \sum_j A_{jn}\, e^{p_{nj}x} \cos\frac{n\pi s}{L_0}, \\ u_x{}^c &= \sum_n \sum_j B_{jn}\, e^{p_{nj}x} \cos\frac{n\pi s}{L_0}, \\ u_s{}^c &= \sum_n \sum_j C_{jn}\, e^{p_{nj}x} \sin\frac{n\pi s}{L_0}, \end{aligned} \tag{6.33a}$$

where the dimensionless quantities 6.17b have not been used and the extent of the summation on j will be clarified presently. Upon substitution of these equations, along with Eqs. 6.32c into Eqs. 6.30a and 6.30b, we find that

$$\begin{aligned} B_{jn} &= \frac{\alpha'_{jn}}{2p_{nj}r_0}\left[\nu + \left(\frac{n\pi}{p_{nj}L_0}\right)^2\right][2A_{jn} + \xi(1 + \delta_{4n})A_{j,n-4} + \xi A_{j,n+4}], \\ C_{jn} &= \frac{\alpha'_{jn}}{2r_0}\left[\left(\frac{n\pi}{p_{nj}L_0}\right)^2 - 2 - \nu\right][2A_{jn} + \xi(1 + \delta_{4n})A_{j,n-4} + \xi A_{j,n+4}], \end{aligned} \tag{6.33b}$$

and when these are substituted into Eq. 6.30c with $p = 0$, the result is

$$\beta^a_{nj}A_{j,n-8} + \beta^b_{nj}A_{j,n-4} + \beta^c_{nj}A_{jn} + \beta^d_{nj}A_{j,n+4} + \beta^e_{nj}A_{j,n+8} = 0, \tag{6.33c}$$

where

$$\begin{aligned} &\beta^a_{nj} = \xi^2(1 + \delta_{8n})\alpha'_{j,n-4}, \qquad \beta^b_{nj} = 2\xi(1 + \delta_{4n})(\alpha'_{j,n-4} + \alpha'_{jn}), \\ &\beta^c_{nj} = \beta'_{nj} + 4\alpha'_{jn} + \xi^2[(1 + \delta_{4n})\alpha'_{j,n-4} + \alpha'_{j,n+4}], \\ &\alpha'_{jn} = \left[1 - \left(\frac{n\pi}{p_{nj}L_0}\right)^2\right]^{-2}, \ \beta^d_{nj} = 2\xi(\alpha'_{jn} + \alpha'_{j,n+4}) \\ &\beta'_{nj} = \pi^2(h/L_0)^2(L_0p_{nj}/\pi)^4/12, \ \beta^e_{nj} = \xi^2\alpha'_{j,n+4}. \end{aligned} \tag{6.33d}$$

When differences in notation are accounted for, Eqs. 6.33b and 6.33c are identical to their counterparts, Eqs. 6.32d and 6.32e from the particular solution except for the important fact that Eqs. 6.33c are homogeneous. Therefore, to avoid the trivial solution $A_{jn} = 0$, we must set the determinant of the coefficients of Eqs. 6.33c equal to zero. This leaves us with the formidable task of finding the roots of a determinant which is, in the general case of an infinite sum on n, infinite and has an infinite number of roots p_{nj}. If the shell is circular, then $\xi = 0$ and Eqs. 6.33c reduce to a single equation which is identical to Eq. 6.18c and has eight roots p_{nj} for every value of n. As we have shown in Section 6.2*a*, these roots can be found explicitly. For oval shells with $\xi \neq 0$ it is again, as in the particular solution, appropriate to truncate the system at some value of n and then to find the values of the roots p_{nj} of the resulting determinant. These roots will be finite in number but we shall not pursue them here. Calculations of this type were carried out by Vafakos, Romano, and Kempner.[6]

Thus, we have shown that problems of noncircular cylindrical shells can be solved by the same general methods that we developed for the analysis of circular cylindrical shells. However, the variation of the radius of the noncircular shell prevented the explicit determination of the arbitrary coefficients in the particular solution or the characteristic roots p_{nj} of the complementary solution. Consequently, we had to rely upon approximate techniques, which were described, to obtain a numerical result.

6.2*d* On the Accuracy of Donnell's Equations

Our analysis of arbitrarily loaded cylindrical shells has been based upon the solution of a set of equations that was deduced from the theory of Chapter 2 by using Donnell's assumptions[1] regarding the contribution of the shearing force Q_s to the equilibrium of forces and the contribution of the circumferential displacement u_s to the expressions for the change of curvature and twist. It is, therefore, appropriate, before we close this discussion of cylindrical shells, to make an assessment of the Donnell theory.

To make such an assessment, we must select a standard of comparison against which the results of the Donnell theory are to be measured. For this purpose, we could select a theory based upon Eqs. 6.1 to 6.5 which does not reflect any of Donnell's assumptions. We have pointed out in Chapter 3, however, that the stress resultants and stress couples as obtained from Eqs. 6.5 for cylindrical shells do not satisfy the sixth equation of equilibrium. Therefore, in order to obtain the most significant comparison possible let us adopt as our standard of reference the theory of Flügge–Lur'e–

[6] Vafakos, W. P., Romano, F., and Kempner, J., "Clamped Short Oval Cylindrical Shells Under Hydrostatic Pressure," *J. Aerospace Sci.*, **29**, 1347–1357 (1962).

Byrne which we outlined in Section 3.3*a*. As we have pointed out, the equations of the latter theory satisfy the sixth equation of equilibrium and yield vanishing strains during rigid body displacements for cylindrical shells.

Kempner[7] has shown that the equations of Flügge–Lur'e–Byrne can be reduced to the following form [that is analogous to the Donnell equations (Eqs. 6.13a to 6.13c)] for a circular cylindrical shell:

$$\nabla^4(\nabla^2 + 1)^2 w + 4k^4 \frac{\partial^4 w}{\partial y^4} + 2(1 - \nu)\left[\frac{\partial^6 w}{\partial y^2\, \partial \theta^4} + \frac{\partial^4 w}{\partial y^2\, \partial \theta^2} - \frac{\partial^6 w}{\partial y^6}\right] = \frac{-a^3}{D}\nabla^4 q, \tag{6.34a}$$

$$\nabla^4 u = -\nu \frac{\partial^3 w}{\partial y^3} + \frac{\partial^3 w}{\partial \theta^2\, \partial y} - \frac{1}{12}\left(\frac{h}{a}\right)^2 \times \left[\frac{\partial^5 w}{\partial \theta^4\, \partial y} - \frac{\partial^5 w}{\partial y^5} + \frac{3}{2}(1 - \nu)\frac{1}{12}\left(\frac{h}{a}\right)^2 \frac{\partial^5 w}{\partial \theta^2\, \partial y^3}\right], \tag{6.34b}$$

$$\nabla^4 v = -(2 + \nu)\frac{\partial^3 w}{\partial \theta\, \partial y^2} - \frac{\partial^3 w}{\partial \theta^3} + \frac{1}{12}\left(\frac{h}{a}\right)^2\left[2\frac{\partial^5 w}{\partial \theta\, \partial y^4} + 2\frac{\partial^5 w}{\partial \theta^3\, \partial y^2}\right]. \tag{6.34c}$$

In these equations, we have ignored the quantity $(h/a)^2/12$ in comparison to unity in accordance with our interest in thin shells. Similarly, we have neglected unity in comparison to the large parameter $4k^4$ that was defined by Eq. 6.17e. We have also used the dimensionless variables (with the overbar deleted from w) that were defined by Eqs. 6.17b. For reasons of simplicity, we have restricted our attention to transverse pressure loads only. To facilitate our comparison, it is appropriate to repeat here the corresponding equations of Donnell (see Eqs. 6.13a to 6.13c):

$$\nabla^8 w + 4k^4 \frac{\partial^4 w}{\partial y^4} = -\frac{a^3}{D}\nabla^4 q, \tag{6.34d}$$

$$\nabla^4 u = -\nu \frac{\partial^3 w}{\partial y^3} + \frac{\partial^3 w}{\partial y\, \partial \theta^2}, \tag{6.34e}$$

$$\nabla^4 v = -(2 + \nu)\frac{\partial^3 w}{\partial y^2\, \partial \theta} - \frac{\partial^3 w}{\partial \theta^3}. \tag{6.34f}$$

Obviously, the Donnell equations are considerably simpler than those of Flügge–Lur'e–Byrne.

If we follow the example of Hoff[8] and assume the same type of solution

---

[7] Kempner, J., "Remarks on Donnell's Equations," *J. Appl. Mech.*, **22**, 117–118 (1955).

[8] Hoff, N. J., "The Accuracy of Donnell's Equations," *J. Appl. Mech.*, **22**, 329–334 (1955).

functions for Eqs. 6.34a to 6.34c as we did for Eqs. 6.34d to 6.34f when we solved them in Sections 6.2*a* and 6.2*b*, then it will be possible for us to reduce the assessment of the Donnell theory to a discussion of the roots p that appear in the complementary solutions and of the coefficients that appear in the particular solution for each set of equations. To be specific, we recall here that when the shell is free of surface loading the transverse displacement is assumed in the form

$$w = e^{py}\cos n\theta \qquad (n = 0, 1, 2, \ldots), \tag{6.34g}$$

when loads are applied at edges of constant x (see Eqs. 6.18a) and in the form

$$w = e^{p\theta}\cos ny \qquad (n = m\pi a/l, \quad m = 0, 1, 2, \ldots), \tag{6.34h}$$

when loads are applied at edges of constant θ (see Eqs. 6.25). When the shell is subjected to a radial pressure load that can be expressed in a Fourier series with a general term

$$q = \cos sy \cos n\theta \qquad (s = m\pi a/l, \quad m, n = 0, 1, 2, \ldots), \tag{6.34i}$$

then the radial displacement is expressed as a Fourier series with the general term

$$w = A\cos sy\cos n\theta. \tag{6.34j}$$

By using solution functions of the type 6.34g to 6.34j, Hoff[8] showed that significant errors could occur when Donnell's equations are used. As a result, Morley[9] subsequently proposed the following set of governing equations:

$$\nabla^4(\nabla^2 + 1)^2 w + 4k^4\frac{\partial^4 w}{\partial y^4} = \frac{-a^3}{D}\nabla^4 q, \tag{6.34k}$$

$$\nabla^4 u = -\nu\frac{\partial^3 w}{\partial y^3} + \frac{\partial^3 w}{\partial y\,\partial\theta^2}, \tag{6.34l}$$

$$\nabla^4 v = -(2 + \nu)\frac{\partial^3 w}{\partial x^2\,\partial\theta} - \frac{\partial^3 w}{\partial\theta^3}. \tag{6.34m}$$

The last two of these equations are identical to those of Donnell, while the first differs from the first equation of Flügge–Lur'e–Byrne in that only the square bracketed term in Eq. 6.34a is neglected.

It is now interesting, as a conclusion to this discussion, to make a comparison of the results that are obtained for the roots p and the coefficients A when the functions 6.34g to 6.34j are each substituted, in turn, into Eq.

[9] Morley, L. S. D., "An Improvement of Donnell's Approximation for Thin-Walled Circular Cylinders," *Quart. Journ. Mech. and Applied Math.*, **12**, 89–99 (1959).

Table 6.1[a] Roots when $w = e^{p\theta} \cos ny$

k	n		p_1, p_2	p_3, p_4
		Morley	$0.0506 + 0.0494i$	$0.0025 + 1.0000i$
5	0.01	Flügge	$0.0510 + 0.0490i$	$0.0025 + 1.0000i$
		Donnell	$0.2458 + 0.1017i$	$0.1018 + 0.2455i$
		Morley	$0.5316 + 0.3696i$	$0.1825 + 1.0767i$
5	0.10	Flügge	$0.5330 + 0.3662i$	$0.1812 + 1.0783i$
		Donnell	$0.7824 + 0.3195i$	$0.3241 + 0.7714i$
		Morley	$2.5441 + 0.9801i$	$1.0520 + 2.3704i$
5	1.00	Flügge	$2.5469 + 0.9694i$	$1.0455 + 2.3749i$
		Donnell	$2.6278 + 0.9514i$	$1.0962 + 2.2807i$
		Morley	$12.3921 + 2.0172i$	$7.7414 + 3.2290i$
5	10.00	Flügge	$12.3952 + 1.9456i$	$7.7458 + 3.2942i$
		Donnell	$12.4120 + 2.0142i$	$7.7689 + 3.2180i$
		Morley	$0.1012 + 0.0987i$	$0.0100 + 1.0002i$
10	0.01	Flügge	$0.1014 + 0.0985i$	$0.0100 + 1.0002i$
		Donnell	$0.3476 + 0.1439i$	$0.1440 + 0.3473i$
		Morley	$0.9153 + 0.5133i$	$0.3619 + 1.2982i$
10	0.10	Flügge	$0.9157 + 0.5121i$	$0.3611 + 1.2987i$
		Donnell	$1.1026 + 0.4535i$	$0.4567 + 1.0948i$
		Morley	$3.5360 + 1.4131i$	$1.4640 + 3.4131i$
10	1.00	Flügge	$3.5371 + 1.4097i$	$1.4613 + 3.4146i$
		Donnell	$3.5963 + 1.3903i$	$1.4923 + 3.3506i$
		Morley	$14.5372 + 3.4394i$	$7.0534 + 7.0887i$
10	10.00	Flügge	$14.5388 + 3.4209i$	$7.0534 + 7.1011i$
		Donnell	$14.5535 + 3.4356i$	$7.0711 + 7.0711i$
		Morley	$0.5254 + 0.3741i$	$0.1818 + 1.0812i$
50	0.01	Flügge	$0.5254 + 0.3740i$	$0.1818 + 1.0812i$
		Donnell	$0.7769 + 0.3217i$	$0.3218 + 0.7768i$
		Morley	$2.3723 + 1.0512i$	$0.9808 + 2.5425i$
50	0.10	Flügge	$2.3723 + 1.0511i$	$0.9807 + 2.5426i$
		Donnell	$2.4585 + 1.0169i$	$1.0183 + 2.4550i$
		Morley	$7.7964 + 3.0065i$	$3.2293 + 7.7414i$
50	1.00	Flügge	$7.7965 + 3.2063i$	$3.2290 + 7.7415i$
		Donnell	$7.8237 + 3.1954i$	$3.2409 + 7.7139i$
		Morley	$26.2692 + 9.5168i$	$10.9573 + 22.8158i$
50	10.00	Flügge	$26.2695 + 9.5158i$	$10.9566 + 22.8163i$
		Donnell	$26.2776 + 9.5138i$	$10.9616 + 22.8069i$

[a] By permission of the Clarendon Press, Oxford, England.

6.34a of the Flügge–Lur'e–Byrne theory, Eq. 6.34d of Donnell's approximation, and Eq. 6.34k of Morley's improvement of Donnell's approximation.

When the solution $e^{p\theta} \cos ny$ is substituted into the three governing equations for w in the absence of surface loads, we find that the roots p satisfy the equations

$$(p_F^2 - n^2)^2(p_F^2 - n^2 + 1)^2 + 4k^4n^4 + 2(1 - \nu)n^2(n^4 - p_F^4 - p_F^2) = 0, \quad (6.34\text{n})$$

for the Flügge–Lur'e–Byrne theory,

$$(p_D^2 - n^2)^4 + 4k^4n^4 = 0, \quad (6.34\text{o})$$

for the Donnell theory, and

$$(p_M^2 - n^2)^2(p_M^2 - n^2 + 1)^2 + 4k^4n^4 = 0, \quad (6.34\text{p})$$

for the Morley theory. While it is possible to find explicit expressions for the roots p_D and p_M of Eqs. 6.34o and 6.34p (see Eqs. 6.18r, t, u, v, w) for the Donnell theory, it is not possible to do so for Eq. 6.34n. This is the primary reason for seeking a suitable approximate formulation. To compare the roots obtained from Eqs. 6.34n, o, p, calculations have been carried out[9] for $k = 5$, 10, 50, and several values of the parameter $n = m\pi a/l$. According to Eq. 6.17e, the chosen values of k correspond to $a/h = 15.1$, 60.3, and 1510 when $\nu = 0.3$. The first of these values is near the lower limit that we have proposed for the validity of the theory of thin elastic shells in Chapter 2, while the upper limit represents a shell that is so thin it would hardly fulfill any structural requirements. The results of the calculations are given in Table 6.1 where the first four roots as obtained from each theory are tabulated. (Recall from Section 6.2*a* that the eight roots occur in four complex conjugate pairs). Table 6.1 indicates that the roots obtained from Morley's equations are excellent approximations of the roots obtained from the equations of Flügge–Lur'e–Byrne. The table also shows the substantial errors that occur when the roots are obtained from Donnell's equations for the lower values of n. According to the definition of n, this loss of accuracy occurs when the shell is long in comparison to its radius.

When the solution $e^{py} \cos n\theta$ is substituted into the three governing equations for w, equations in p, n, and k are obtained which are analogous to Eqs. 6.34n, o, p. Calculations of the roots of the resulting equations have also been carried out[9] and are summarized in Table 6.2 for the previous values of k and several integer values of n. Again the roots obtained from Morley's equations match very closely the roots obtained from the

Table 6.2[a] Roots when $w = e^{py} \cos n\theta$

k	n		p_1, p_2	p_3, p_4
		Morley	4.9502 + 5.0502i	— —
5	0	Flügge	4.9854 + 5.0154i	— —
		Donnell	5.0000 + 5.0000i	— —
		Morley	5.0502 + 4.9502i	0
5	1	Flügge	5.0848 + 4.9148i	0
		Donnell	5.1019 + 4.9021i	0.1019 + 0.0979i
		Morley	5.3700 + 4.6764i	0.3669 + 0.3195i
5	2	Flügge	5.4026 + 4.6387i	0.3646 + 0.3220i
		Donnell	5.4261 + 4.6359i	0.4261 + 0.3641i
		Morley	5.9358 + 4.3180i	0.9348 + 0.6800i
5	3	Flügge	5.9607 + 4.2780i	0.9509 + 0.6582i
		Donnell	5.9931 + 4.2893i	0.9931 + 0.7107i
		Morley	6.7075 + 3.9845i	1.7072 + 1.0141i
5	4	Flügge	6.7354 + 3.9374i	1.7001 + 1.0260i
		Donnell	6.7605 + 3.9670i	1.7605 + 1.0330i
		Morley	12.4943 + 3.1249i	7.4947 + 1.8745i
5	10	Flügge	12.5167 + 3.0368i	7.4812 + 1.9264i
		Donnell	12.5194 + 3.1238i	7.5194 + 1.8762i
		Morley	9.9750 + 10.0250i	— —
10	0	Flügge	9.9926 + 10.0076i	— —
		Donnell	10.0000 + 10.0000i	— —
		Morley	10.0250 + 9.9750i	0
10	1	Flügge	10.0425 + 9.9575i	0
		Donnell	10.0502 + 9.9503i	0.0502 + 0.0497i
		Morley	10.1779 + 9.8281i	0.1761 + 0.1701i
10	2	Flügge	10.1950 + 9.8102i	0.1758 + 0.1704i
		Donnell	10.2038 + 9.8042i	0.2038 + 0.1958i
		Morley	10.4413 + 9.5943i	0.4406 + 0.4049i
10	3	Flügge	10.4579 + 9.5761i	0.4430 + 0.4023i
		Donnell	10.4683 + 9.5718i	0.4683 + 0.4282i
		Morley	10.8243 + 9.2922i	0.8240 + 0.7074i
10	4	Flügge	10.8406 + 9.2732i	0.8227 + 0.7088i
		Donnell	10.8522 + 9.2719i	0.8522 + 0.7281i
		Morley	15.2678 + 7.4347i	5.2678 + 2.5652i
10	10	Flügge	15.2808 + 7.4080i	5.2633 + 2.5744i
		Donnell	15.2909 + 7.4293i	5.2909 + 2.5707i
		Morley	49.9950 + 50.0050i	— —
50	0	Flügge	49.9985 + 50.0015i	— —
		Donnell	50.0000 + 50.0000i	— —

Table 6.2—*continued* Roots when $w = e^{py} \cos n\theta$

k	n		p_1, p_2	p_3, p_4
50		Morley	50.0050 + 49.9950i	0
	1	Flügge	50.0085 + 49.9915i	0
		Donnell	50.0100 + 49.9900i	0.0100 + 0.0100i
50		Morley	50.0350 + 49.9650i	0.0347 + 0.0346i
	2	Flügge	50.0385 + 49.9615i	0.0347 + 0.0346i
		Donnell	50.0400 + 49.9600i	0.0400 + 0.0400i
50		Morley	50.0851 + 49.9151i	0.0850 + 0.0847i
	3	Flügge	50.0886 + 49.9116i	0.0850 + 0.0847i
		Donnell	50.0902 + 49.9102i	0.0902 + 0.0898i
50		Morley	50.1555 + 49.8455i	0.1554 + 0.1544i
	4	Flügge	50.1590 + 49.8420i	0.1554 + 0.1544i
		Donnell	50.1605 + 49.8405i	0.1605 + 0.1595i
50		Morley	51.0140 + 49.0255i	1.0140 + 0.9744i
	10	Flügge	51.0174 + 49.0220i	1.0139 + 0.9745i
		Donnell	51.0192 + 49.0208i	1.0192 + 0.9792i

[a] By permission of the Clarendon Press, Oxford, England.

equations of Flügge–Lur'e–Byrne. The roots obtained from Donnell's equations also match these results satisfactorily.

When the shell is subjected to a surface load that can be expressed in the general form 6.34i, the transverse deflection can be expressed in the form 6.34j. When these functions are substituted into the equations which govern w, the resulting expression for the coefficient in the deflection function is

$$A_F = \frac{-(a^3/D)(s^2 + n^2)^2}{(s^2 + n^2)^2(s^2 + n^2 - 1)^2 + 4k^4s^4 + 2(1 - \nu)(s^6 - s^2n^4 + s^2n^2)} \qquad (6.34q)$$

for the Flügge–Lur'e–Byrne theory,

$$A_D = \frac{-(a^3/D)(s^2 + n^2)^2}{(s^2 + n^2)^4 + 4k^4s^4} \qquad (6.34r)$$

for the Donnell theory, and

$$A_M = \frac{-(a^3/D)(s^2 + n^2)^2}{(s^2 + n^2)^2(s^2 + n^2 - 1)^2 + 4k^4s^4} \qquad (6.34s)$$

for the Morley theory. For purposes of comparison, the ratios A_F/A_D and A_F/A_M as calculated[9] for the various values of k, n, and s are given in Table 6.3. It is again obvious that Morley's equations give results that are essentially the same as those obtained from the equations of Flügge–Lur'e–Byrne. Donnell's equations yield results that are in considerable error at the lower values of n.

Table 6.3[a] Coefficients for $w = A \cos sy \cos n\theta$

k	n	s	A_F/A_M	A_F/A_D
5	1	0	—	—
5	2	0	1.0000	1.7778
5	3	0	1.0000	1.2656
5	1	0.5	0.9999	1.0148
5	2	0.5	1.0157	1.4520
5	3	0.5	1.0020	1.2557
5	1	1.0	0.9999	1.0042
5	2	1.0	1.0053	1.0833
5	3	1.0	1.0095	1.1904
5	10	1.0	1.0001	1.0202
10	1	0	—	—
10	2	0	1.0000	1.7778
10	3	0	1.0000	1.2656
10	1	0.5	1.0000	1.0010
10	2	0.5	1.0020	1.0561
10	3	0.5	1.0030	1.1835
10	1	1.0	1.0000	1.0003
10	2	1.0	1.0004	1.0060
10	3	1.0	1.0020	1.0417
10	10	1.0	1.0001	1.0202

[a] By permission of the Clarendon Press, Oxford, England.

As an end to this discussion we may, therefore, make the following conclusions:

When the shell is closed with respect to the coordinate θ and subjected to loads at edges of constant x which lead to solutions in the form $e^{py} \cos n\theta$, the analysis based on Donnell's equations, which was given in Section 6.2*a*, generally leads to a reliable result.

When the shell is open and subjected to loads at edges of constant θ which lead to solutions in the form $e^{p\theta} \cos ny$, Donnell's equations lead to reliable results only for large n, that is, for short shells. For the lower values of n, Morley's equations should be used.

Similarly, in the analysis of cylindrical shells under distributed loads, Donnell's equations lead to reliable results only for short shells. Morley's equations should, again, be used for the longer shells.

As far as cylindrical shells of noncircular cross section are concerned, the accuracy of Donnell's approximation has not as yet been assessed.

However, it should be noted that the Donnell type analysis which was carried out for oval shells in Section 6.2*c* was applied only to short shells. Therefore, the results reported[5,6] in Section 6.2*c* are expected to be valid.

6.3 SHALLOW SPHERICAL SHELLS

We shall take up the analysis of general spherical shells in Section 6.4; however, before doing so it is well to consider here the special case of shallow spherical shells on account of the simplifications which result from the assumption of shallowness.

Generally, a shell is considered to be shallow if, as postulated by E. Reissner,[10] its height, H, is less than one eighth of its base diameter, $2a$ (see Fig. 6.2). If the equation of a meridian of a spherical shell is taken in the form

$$z = (R^2 - r^2)^{1/2} - (R - H), \tag{6.35a}$$

then on the base plane $z = 0$, we have $r = a$ and, therefore,

$$a^2 = 2HR - H^2 \tag{6.35b}$$

for spherical shells in general. For a shallow spherical shell, this equation reduces to

$$a^2 \cong 2HR. \tag{6.35c}$$

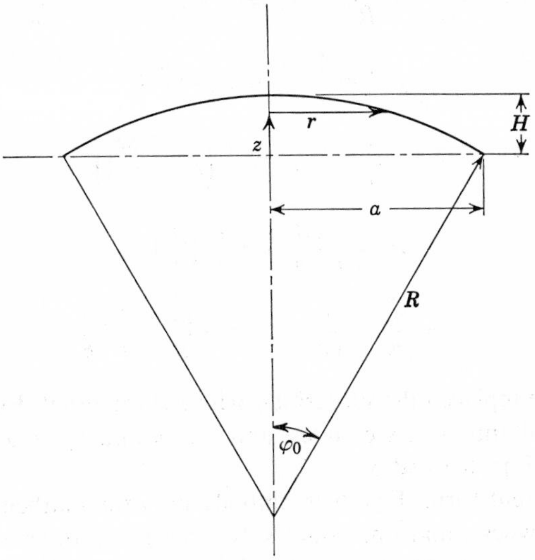

Figure 6.2 Geometry of a shallow spherical shell.

---

[10] Reissner, E., "Stresses and Small Displacements of Shallow Spherical Shells," *J. Math. Phys.*, **25**, 80–85, 279–300 (1946), also **27**, 240 (1948) and **38**, 16–35 (1959).

From this formula we can conclude further that the assumption of shallowness which was stated previously, that is, $H/2a < 1/8$, can be restated as $a/R < \frac{1}{2}$ and, equivalently, as $\varphi_0 < 30°$.

To write the fundamental equations of a shallow spherical shell, we notice that $R_1 = R_2 = R$, $A_1 = R$, $A_2 = r$, and, from the Gauss condition for small angles, $dr \approx R d\varphi$. With these values, the basic equations of the shallow spherical shell take the following form:

$$\frac{\partial(rN_r)}{\partial r} + \frac{\partial N_{r\theta}}{\partial \theta} - N_\theta + \frac{r}{R} Q_r + rq_r = 0,$$

$$\frac{\partial(rN_{r\theta})}{\partial r} + \frac{\partial N_\theta}{\partial \theta} + N_{r\theta} + \frac{r}{R} Q_\theta + rq_\theta = 0,$$

$$\frac{\partial(rQ_r)}{\partial r} + \frac{\partial Q_\theta}{\partial \theta} - \frac{r}{R}(N_r + N_\theta) - rq = 0, \tag{6.36a}$$

$$\frac{\partial(rM_r)}{\partial r} + \frac{\partial M_{r\theta}}{\partial \theta} - M_\theta - rQ_r = 0,$$

$$\frac{\partial(rM_{r\theta})}{\partial r} + \frac{\partial M_\theta}{\partial \theta} + M_{r\theta} - rQ_\theta = 0,$$

$$\epsilon_r^0 = \frac{\partial u_r}{\partial r} + \frac{w}{R}, \qquad \epsilon_\theta^0 = \frac{1}{r}\left(\frac{\partial u_\theta}{\partial \theta} + u_r\right) + \frac{w}{R},$$

$$\gamma_{r\theta}^0 = \frac{1}{r}\frac{\partial u_r}{\partial \theta} + r\frac{\partial}{\partial r}\left(\frac{u_\theta}{r}\right), \tag{6.36b}$$

$$\kappa_r = \frac{\partial \beta_r}{\partial r}, \qquad \kappa_\theta = \frac{1}{r}\left(\beta_r + \frac{\partial \beta_\theta}{\partial \theta}\right),$$

$$\tau = \frac{1}{r}\frac{\partial \beta_r}{\partial \theta} + r\frac{\partial}{\partial r}\left(\frac{\beta_\theta}{r}\right), \tag{6.36c}$$

$$\beta_r = \frac{u_r}{R} - \frac{\partial w}{\partial r}, \qquad \beta_\theta = \frac{u_\theta}{R} - \frac{1}{r}\frac{\partial w}{\partial \theta}, \tag{6.36d}$$

where we have replaced the subscript φ with r throughout. Expressions for the stress resultants, stress couples, and the boundary conditions follow directly from Eqs. 6.5 and 6.6.

In their present form, Eqs. 6.36 embody only the mathematical definition of shallowness, and one could solve those equations as they stand. However, it is possible to make some additional physical arguments which will introduce further simplifications into the analysis of shallow shells. These arguments, which were first enunciated by Reissner,[10] involve the neglect of the contributions of the transverse shearing stress resultants to the equilibrium of forces in the meridional and tangential directions, and the neglect of the contributions of the "stretching" displacements u_θ and u_r to the change of curvature expressions. If, therefore, we adopt these arguments, the first two of Eqs. 6.36a reduce to

$$\begin{aligned} \frac{\partial(rN_r)}{\partial r} + \frac{\partial N_{r\theta}}{\partial \theta} - N_\theta + rq_r &= 0, \\ \frac{\partial(rN_{r\theta})}{\partial r} + \frac{\partial N_\theta}{\partial \theta} + N_{r\theta} + rq_\theta &= 0, \end{aligned} \tag{6.36e}$$

and the expressions for the change of curvature and twist reduce to

$$\begin{aligned} \kappa_r = -\frac{\partial^2 w}{\partial r^2}, \qquad \kappa_\theta &= -\frac{1}{r}\left(\frac{\partial w}{\partial r} + \frac{1}{r}\frac{\partial^2 w}{\partial \theta^2}\right), \\ \tau = -2\frac{\partial}{\partial r}&\left(\frac{1}{r}\frac{\partial w}{\partial \theta}\right). \end{aligned} \tag{6.36f}$$

The latter equations are identical to the change of curvature expressions of a flat circular plate.[11] Thus, it is interesting to observe that Reissner's assumptions regarding shallow spherical shells are identical to Donnell's assumptions for cylindrical shells and lead to an analogous set of basic equations. Indeed, we may note that, as a result of Donnell's assumptions, the cylindrical shell is treated as a curved rectangular plate while, as a result of Reissner's assumptions,[10] the shallow spherical shell is treated as a curved circular plate. Although the system 6.36 which describes the behavior of the shallow spherical shell could be solved by reducing it, first, to three coupled differential equations which relate u_r, u_θ, and w, it is preferable to use this occasion to demonstrate yet another approach to the solution of problems in the analysis of shells; namely, a method which is based upon the introduction of auxiliary functions which simplify the manipulations. In the present situation we notice, upon examination of Eqs. 6.36e, that the equilibrium of the stress resultants is governed by a set of equations which is analogous to those which govern the plane stress problem of elasticity. Guided by this observation, we first assume that the surface loads are derivable from a load potential Ω such that

$$q_r = -\frac{\partial \Omega}{\partial r}, \qquad q_\theta = -\frac{1}{r}\frac{\partial \Omega}{\partial \theta}, \tag{6.37a}$$

and then, in analogy with the plane stress problem, Eqs. 6.36e will be

[11] See, for example, Chapter 3 of the text by Timoshenko and Woinowsky-Krieger to which we referred in footnote 2 of this chapter.

satisfied if the stress resultants are expressed in terms of the load potential and a stress function F as follows:

$$N_\theta = \frac{\partial^2 F}{\partial r^2} + \Omega, \qquad N_r = \frac{1}{r}\frac{\partial F}{\partial r} + \frac{1}{r^2}\frac{\partial^2 F}{\partial \theta^2} + \Omega,$$
$$N_{r\theta} = -\frac{\partial}{\partial r}\left(\frac{1}{r}\frac{\partial F}{\partial \theta}\right). \tag{6.37b}$$

To continue the plane stress analogy, we now note that the strain-displacement equations 6.36b lead to the following compatibility equation:[12]

$$\frac{1}{r^2}\frac{\partial^2 \epsilon_r^{\,0}}{\partial \theta^2} - \frac{1}{r}\frac{\partial \epsilon_r^{\,0}}{\partial r} + \frac{1}{r^2}\frac{\partial}{\partial r}\left(r^2\frac{\partial \epsilon_\theta}{\partial r}\right) - \frac{1}{r^2}\frac{\partial^2(r\gamma_{r\theta}^{\,0})}{\partial r\,\partial \theta} = \frac{\nabla^2 w}{R}, \tag{6.37c}$$

where

$$\nabla^2(\ldots) = \frac{\partial^2(\ldots)}{\partial r^2} + \frac{1}{r}\frac{\partial(\ldots)}{\partial r} + \frac{1}{r^2}\frac{\partial^2(\ldots)}{\partial \theta^2}. \tag{6.37d}$$

Then, substitution of the following strain–stress equations (see Eqs. 4.8):

$$\epsilon_r^{\,0} = \frac{1}{Eh}(N_r - \nu N_\theta) + \alpha_t T_0,$$
$$\epsilon_\theta^{\,0} = \frac{1}{Eh}(N_\theta - \nu N_r) + \alpha_t T_0, \tag{6.37e}$$
$$\gamma_{r\theta}^{\,0} = \frac{1}{Gh}N_{r\theta},$$

into the compatibility equation 6.37c, yields the equation

$$\nabla^4 F - \frac{Eh}{R}\nabla^2 w = -(1-\nu)\nabla^2\Omega - Eh\alpha_t\nabla^2 T_0. \tag{6.37f}$$

A second equation which relates F and w is obtained by eliminating Q_r and Q_θ from the third equation of equilibrium by using the fourth and fifth of Eqs. 6.36a. In this manner, we find that

$$\frac{\partial}{\partial r}\left[\frac{\partial(rM_r)}{\partial r} + \frac{\partial M_{r\theta}}{\partial \theta} - M_\theta\right] + \frac{1}{r}\frac{\partial}{\partial \theta}\left[\frac{\partial(rM_{r\theta})}{\partial r} + \frac{\partial M_\theta}{\partial \theta} + M_{r\theta}\right]$$
$$-\frac{r}{R}(N_r + N_\theta) - rq = 0. \tag{6.38a}$$

[12] Odqvist, F. K. G., "Kompatibilitätsgleichungen bei Zylinder-koordinaten," *Z.A.M.M.*, **14**, 123–124 (1934).

Now we note, from Eqs. 6.5, that the moments are given in terms of the change of curvature expressions (Eqs. 6.36f) by

$$M_r = -D\left[\frac{\partial^2 w}{\partial r^2} + \nu\left(\frac{1}{r}\frac{\partial w}{\partial r} + \frac{1}{r^2}\frac{\partial^2 w}{\partial \theta^2}\right) - \alpha_t(1+\nu)T_1\right],$$

$$M_\theta = -D\left[\frac{1}{r}\frac{\partial w}{\partial r} + \frac{1}{r^2}\frac{\partial^2 w}{\partial \theta^2} + \nu\frac{\partial^2 w}{\partial r^2} - \alpha_t(1+\nu)T_1\right], \qquad (6.38b)$$

$$M_{r\theta} = -D(1-\nu)\frac{\partial}{\partial r}\left(\frac{1}{r}\frac{\partial w}{\partial \theta}\right),$$

and, incidentally, the foregoing expressions, together with the fourth and fifth of Eqs. 6.36a, lead to the additional results:

$$Q_r = -D\frac{\partial}{\partial r}[\nabla^2 w - \alpha_t(1+v)T_1], \qquad Q_\theta = -D\frac{1}{r}\frac{\partial}{\partial \theta}[\nabla^2 w - \alpha_t(1+v)T_1]. \qquad (6.38c)$$

Finally, substitution of Eqs. 6.37b and 6.38b into Eq. 6.38a gives

$$D\nabla^4 w + \frac{1}{R}\nabla^2 F = -q - \frac{2\Omega}{R} - D\alpha_t(1+\nu)\nabla^2 T_1. \qquad (6.38d)$$

Equations 6.37f and 6.38d are the governing equations of the analysis of arbitrarily loaded shallow spherical shells. Once w and F are obtained from a solution of these equations, the stress couples and shearing stress resultants can be obtained by taking the appropriate derivatives (as indicated by Eqs. 6.38b and 6.38c) of w and the stress resultants can be obtained by taking derivatives of the stress function F as indicated by Eqs. 6.37b. The remaining displacements u_r and u_θ can then be found by suitable integrations of Eqs. 6.37e, which follow the same basic scheme which we have used previously (see Eqs. 5.11). Thus, it follows that these displacements are given by

$$u_r = \int\left[\frac{N_r - \nu N_\theta}{Eh} + \alpha T_0 - \frac{w}{R}\right] dr + f(\theta), \qquad (6.39a)$$

$$u_\theta = r\int\left[\frac{N_{r\theta}}{Gh} - \frac{1}{r}\frac{\partial u_r}{\partial \theta}\right]\frac{dr}{r} + rq(\theta), \qquad (6.39b)$$

where $f(\theta)$ and $g(\theta)$ are arbitrary functions of integration. To find a relationship which will be useful in the determination of the latter, we substitute Eqs. 6.39a and 6.39b into the equation for $\epsilon_\theta{}^0$ from Eqs. 6.36b. This gives the result

$$f''(\theta) + f(\theta) + rg'(\theta) = r\epsilon_\theta{}^0 - w\frac{r}{R} - r\frac{\partial}{\partial \theta}\int \gamma_{r\theta}{}^0\frac{dr}{r}$$
$$+ r\frac{\partial}{\partial \theta}\int\frac{dr}{r^2}\frac{\partial}{\partial \theta}\int\left(\epsilon_r{}^0 - \frac{w}{R}\right) dr, \qquad (6.39c)$$

to which we shall return presently. It is interesting, in studying Eqs. 6.37f and 6.38d, to observe that if the curvature $1/R$ of the shell vanishes (as it would in the case of a flat circular plate), the equations reduce to

$$\begin{aligned} \nabla^4 F &= -(1 - \nu)\nabla^2 \Omega - Eh\alpha_t \nabla^2 T_0, \\ \nabla^4 w &= -q/D - \alpha_t(1 + \nu)\nabla^2 T_1. \end{aligned} \tag{6.40}$$

These are the equations which govern the behavior of a flat circular plate.[11] They indicate that the state of stress in the plane of the plate, that is, the stress function F, is independent of the transverse displacement w and vice versa. We have, therefore, shown that the salient effect of the curvature of a shell is the coupling of the stresses in its plane to its transverse displacements.

In the general case of nonvanishing curvature, we are concerned with the solution of Eqs. 6.37f and 6.38d. As in all of our previous work, we shall demonstrate such solutions first for shells subjected to loads at their edges and then for shells subjected to distributed surface loadings. In keeping with this procedure, we note that the solutions of the governing equations can again be decomposed, as follows:

$$\begin{aligned} w &= w^c + w^p, \\ F &= F^c + F^p, \end{aligned} \tag{6.41}$$

where the superscripts c and p identify the complementary and the particular solutions.

6.3*a* Shallow Spherical Shells under Edge Loadings

When the shallow spherical shell is subjected only to loadings that are applied to its edges, we set $\Omega = q = T = 0$ and the governing equations reduce to

$$\begin{aligned} \nabla^4 F^c - \frac{Eh}{R}\nabla^2 w^c &= 0, \\ \nabla^4 w^c + \frac{1}{RD}\nabla^2 F^c &= 0. \end{aligned} \tag{6.42a}$$

If we eliminate F^c, for example, from these equations, we obtain the single equation

$$\nabla^6 w^c + k_s^4 \nabla^2 w^c = 0, \tag{6.42b}$$

$$k_s^4 = \frac{12(1 - \nu^2)}{R^2 h^2}, \tag{6.42c}$$

which can be written in the equivalent form

$$\nabla^2 \psi = 0, \tag{6.42d}$$

$$\psi = \nabla^4 w^c + k_s^4 w^c. \tag{6.42e}$$

If, in addition, we let

$$w^c = \chi - (\psi/k_s^4), \tag{6.42f}$$

we find, upon substitution of this relationship into Eq. 6.42e, that χ is the solution of

$$\nabla^4\chi + k_s^4\chi = 0. \tag{6.42g}$$

To find the stress function, we substitute Eq. 6.42f into the second of Eqs. 6.42a and obtain the relation

$$\nabla^2\phi = 0, \tag{6.42h}$$

$$\phi = \nabla^2\chi + \frac{F^c}{RD}, \tag{6.42i}$$

where we have taken into account Eq. 6.42d. By rearrangement then,

$$F^c = RD(\phi - \nabla^2\chi). \tag{6.42j}$$

In summary, therefore, w^c is obtained as a combination of the harmonic function ψ and the solution χ of Eq. 6.42g, while the stress function F^c is obtained as a combination of another harmonic function ϕ and the solution χ. In view of the form of the operator ∇^2 as given by Eq. 6.37d, it follows, by using the method of separation of variables, for example, that the single valued solutions of Eqs. 6.42d, g, h are

$$\begin{aligned} \phi &= A_{10} + A_{20}\log r + \sum_{n=1}^{\infty}(A_{1n}r^n + A_{2n}r^{-n})\cos n\theta, \\ \psi &= B_{10} + B_{20}\log r + \sum_{n=1}^{\infty}(B_{1n}r^n + B_{2n}r^{-n})\cos n\theta, \\ \chi &= \sum_{n=0}^{\infty}[C_{1n}\,\mathrm{ber}_n\,k_sr + C_{2n}\,\mathrm{bei}_n\,k_sr \\ &\qquad + C_{3n}\,\mathrm{ker}_n\,k_sr + C_{4n}\,\mathrm{kei}_n\,k_sr]\cos n\theta, \end{aligned} \tag{6.43}$$

where we have noted that the Kelvin functions satisfy an equation of the type 5.22d which we encountered in the analysis of conical shells of constant thickness under loads which are independent of the polar angle.

The use of $\cos n\theta$ in the foregoing implies a stress system which is symmetric with respect to $\theta = 0$ and includes as a special case the solution with $n = 0$ which is applicable to shallow spherical shells under edge loadings that are independent of θ. For an antisymmetric system, $\cos n\theta$ would be replaced by $\sin n\theta$ while for a general state of stress, a suitable combination of symmetric and antisymmetric states of stress would be utilized.

It is now appropriate to return to Eqs. 6.39 and to clarify the nature of the arbitrary functions $f(\theta)$ and $g(\theta)$ which appear there. In the absence of external loadings and temperature distributions we find, first, that

$$u_r = -\frac{\psi}{Rk_s^4} - \frac{1+\nu}{Eh}\frac{\partial F}{\partial r} + f(\theta), \tag{6.44a}$$

$$u_\theta = r\int \frac{\partial}{\partial \theta}\left(\frac{\psi}{Rk_s^4}\right)\frac{dr}{r^2} - \frac{1+\nu}{Eh}\frac{1}{r}\frac{\partial F}{\partial \theta} + rg(\theta) + f'(\theta), \tag{6.44b}$$

where we have used Eqs. 6.37b and 6.42f to 6.42j. Now Eq. 6.39c takes the form

$$f''(\theta) + f(\theta) + rg'(\theta) = \frac{1}{Rk_s^4}\left[\int \psi\, dr - r\psi - r\frac{\partial}{\partial \theta}\int \frac{\partial}{\partial \theta}\int \psi \frac{dr}{r^2}\right]. \tag{6.44c}$$

This equation will have solutions of the type

$$f = f_c + f_\psi, \qquad g = g_c + g_\psi, \tag{6.44d}$$

where the subscripts c and ψ refer to the complementary and the particular solutions of Eq. 6.44c. To evaluate f_c and g_c, we note that these are governed by

$$f_c''(\theta) + f_c(\theta) + rg_c'(\theta) = 0. \tag{6.44e}$$

This equation, which is the sum of a pure function of θ and a function of r and θ, can only be satisfied if

$$f_c''(\theta) + f_c(\theta) = 0, \qquad rg_c'(\theta) = 0, \tag{6.44f}$$

and, therefore,

$$f_c = c_1 \cos\theta + c_2 \sin\theta, \qquad g_c = c_3, \tag{6.44g}$$

where c_1, c_2, and c_3 are arbitrary constants. Upon introduction of these terms into Eqs. 6.44a and 6.44b, it becomes evident that f_c and g_c represent rigid body motions which contribute nothing to the state of stress. To find f_ψ and g_ψ, we introduce the function ψ from Eqs. 6.43 into Eq. 6.44c and obtain the equation

$$f_\psi''(\theta) + f_\psi(\theta) + rg_\psi'(\theta) = \frac{-1}{Rk_s^4}[B_{20}r + 2B_{21}\cos\theta], \tag{6.44h}$$

from which we may infer that

$$f_\psi''(\theta) + f_\psi(\theta) = -\frac{2B_{21}}{Rk_s^4}\cos\theta, \tag{6.44i}$$

$$g_\psi'(\theta) = -\frac{B_{20}}{Rk_s^4}, \tag{6.44j}$$

and, finally, it follows that

$$f_\psi(\theta) = -\frac{B_{21}\theta\sin\theta}{Rk_s^4}, \qquad g_\psi(\theta) = -\frac{B_{20}\theta}{Rk_s^4}. \tag{6.44k}$$

Because of the presence of the variable θ, these functions represent multivalued contributions to the displacements u_r and u_θ; that is, when the shell is traversed completely around its circumference the functions f_ψ and g_ψ do not return to their original values. If the shell has a slit running from one edge to the other along a meridian of constant θ, such results cause no special concern. However, if such a slit does not exist, the multivalued functions must be cancelled by adding a suitable multivalued stress system to the solution. Thus, we note that an additional, multivalued solution of Eq. 6.42h which will fill this need is given by

$$\phi^* = A_0 r(\theta \sin\theta - \log r \cos\theta). \tag{6.44l}$$

It can then be shown, by calculating the displacements u_r^* and u_θ^* which are associated with ϕ^*, that the net displacements will be single valued if we take[13]

$$A_0 = -\frac{Eh}{1+\nu}\frac{B_{21}}{Rk_s^4}. \tag{6.44m}$$

The functions ϕ, ψ and χ as given by Eqs. 6.43 contain eight arbitrary constants for each value of n. Thus, the solutions which are constructed from these functions will be arbitrary enough to satisfy four boundary conditions at each of two edges. As in the case of the cylindrical shell, a segment with four edges cannot, therefore, be treated in general because the solution does not possess sufficient arbitrariness to satisfy the sixteen boundary conditions which must be satisfied in such a case. For this reason, we shall restrict ourselves to shallow spherical shells with two edges of constant r, which are closed with respect to the coordinate θ. If, in addition, the shell is closed at $r = 0$, then we must suppress the solutions $\log r$, r^{-n}, $\mathrm{ker}_n\, k_s r$, and $\mathrm{kei}_n\, k_s r$ which are singular at $r = 0$ by setting

$$A_{2n} = B_{2n} = C_{3n} = C_{4n} = 0, \tag{6.45}$$

for all values of n. In view of Eq. 6.44m, this will automatically suppress ϕ^* which is also singular at $r = 0$. As a result, there will be four arbitrary constants left for each value of n in the solution and these can be readily determined from four boundary conditions at the edge $r = a$.

6.3*b* Shallow Spherical Shells under Distributed Loadings

If the shallow spherical shell is subjected to distributed surface loadings and temperatures, we are concerned with the determination of the

---

[13] Notice that Eqs. 6.44 are identical to equations which arise in the analysis of circular rings and curved bars in the plane theory of elasticity. See, for example, Timoshenko, S., and Goodier, J. N., *Theory of Elasticity*, New York: McGraw-Hill, 2nd edition, Chapter 4 (1951).

particular solutions F^p and w^p which satisfy the equations (see Eqs. 6.37f and 6.38d):

$$k_s^{-4}\nabla^6 F^p + \nabla^2 F^p = F_{MT}, \tag{6.46a}$$

where

$$F_{MT} = -R\left[q + \frac{2\Omega}{R} + D\alpha_t(1+\nu)\nabla^2 T_1\right] - [(1-\nu)\nabla^4\Omega + Eh\alpha_t\nabla^4 T_0]k_s^{-4} \tag{6.46b}$$

and

$$w^p = \frac{R}{Eh}[\nabla^2 F^p + (1-\nu)\Omega + Eh\alpha_t T_0]. \tag{6.46c}$$

Notice, in connection with Eq. 6.46c, that we have not included an additional harmonic function as we did in Eq. 6.42f because we are only interested in the particular solutions here.

Now let us assume a solution of Eq. 6.46a in the form

$$F^p = F_0{}^p + k_s^{-4}F_1{}^p + k_s^{-8}F_2{}^p + \cdots, \tag{6.47a}$$

whose coefficients satisfy the set of equations

$$\begin{aligned} \nabla^2 F_0{}^p &= F_{MT}, \\ F_1{}^p &= -\nabla^4 F_0{}^p = -\nabla^2 F_{MT}, \\ F_2{}^p &= -\nabla^4 F_1{}^p = \nabla^6 F_{MT}, \end{aligned} \tag{6.47b}$$

and so on. In this manner, the determination of the particular solution of Eq. 6.46a has been reduced to the solution of the first of Eqs. 6.47b.

As an illustration, let us consider the case of a shallow spherical shell under the influence of an internal pressure and a temperature distribution which are arbitrary functions of radial position but are trigonometric functions of the circumferential position as, for example,

$$\begin{aligned} q &= -p_n(r)\cos n\theta, \\ T_0 &= T_{0n}(r)\cos n\theta, \\ T_1 &= T_{1n}(r)\cos n\theta. \end{aligned} \tag{6.48a}$$

These represent the nth component of a Fourier analysis of a loading, applied to a shell that is closed with respect to θ, which is symmetric with respect to the position $\theta = 0$. If we assume that the stress function and the transverse displacement are similarly defined as

$$\begin{aligned} F_n{}^p &= F_{mn}{}^p(r)\cos n\theta, \\ w^p &= w_n{}^p(r)\cos n\theta, \end{aligned} \tag{6.48b}$$

then the coefficients of the particular solution for the stress function are governed by the solution of the equation

$$\nabla_n^2 F_{0n}{}^p = S_n(r) \equiv Rp_n - RD(1 + \nu)\alpha_t \nabla_n{}^2 T_{1n} - Eh\alpha_t \nabla_n{}^4 T_{0n} k_s{}^{-4}$$

$$\nabla_n{}^2(\ldots) = \frac{d^2}{dr^2}(\ldots) + \frac{1}{r}\frac{d}{dr}(\ldots) - \frac{n^2}{r^2}(\ldots). \tag{6.48c}$$

The particular solution of the foregoing equation can be shown by standard methods, such as variation of parameters,[14] to be

$$F_{0n}{}^p = \frac{1}{2n}\int S_n(\eta)(r^n - \eta^n)(r^{-n} + \eta^{-n})\eta \, d\eta, \tag{6.48d}$$

while the rest of the functions in the expansion 6.47a are given by

$$F_{mn}{}^p = (-1)^m \nabla_n{}^{2(2m-1)} S_n(r). \tag{6.48e}$$

If, as is many times the case, the coefficients of the loading function can be expressed as

$$S_n(r) = T_n r^n, \tag{6.49a}$$

where T_n is a constant, then Eq. 6.48c can be solved directly, with the result

$$F_{0n}{}^p = \frac{T_n r^{n+2}}{4(n + 1)}. \tag{6.49b}$$

Furthermore, it follows from Eq. 6.48e that

$$F_{mn}{}^p = 0, \qquad m \geqslant 1, \tag{6.49c}$$

and, finally

$$F_n{}^p = \frac{T_n r^{n+2}}{4(n + 1)} \cos n\theta,$$
$$w_n{}^p = \frac{RT_n r^n}{Eh} \cos n\theta. \tag{6.49d}$$

The rest of the shell variables follow from Eqs. 6.49d by use of Eqs. 6.37b, 6.38b, 6.39a, and 6.39b.

This will end, for the time being, our discussion of the static analysis of shallow spherical shells. We shall not present the solution of any specific problems at this time; however, in the next section when spherical shells of arbitrary extent are considered, we shall bring out some results concerning the range of validity of the assumption of shallowness.

It is well to emphasize, before turning to the consideration of more

---

[14] See, for example, Sokolnikoff, I. S., and Redheffer, R. M., *Mathematics of Physics and Engineering*, New York: McGraw-Hill, pp. 72–76 (1958).

general spherical shells, that the use of the stress function has allowed us to reduce the analysis of shallow spherical shells to two simultaneous differential equations. This represents a drastic simplification over the procedure which might otherwise have been employed; that is, the procedure in which the governing equations would have been reduced to three simultaneous differential equations which relate the three nonvanishing displacements in an arbitrarily loaded spherical shell.

6.4 NONSHALLOW SPHERICAL SHELLS

We considered the analysis of shallow spherical shells in the preceding section for two basic reasons. First, we wanted to indicate that in such shells certain contributions to the equilibrium of the stress resultants and to the changes in curvature and twist could be neglected. This resulted in a considerable simplification of the governing equations and led to solutions in terms of the Kelvin functions about which more has been known than the solution functions which we are about to derive here for general spherical shells. Second, we wanted to introduce, in a fairly simple manner, a method of solution in which a stress function is defined in order to circumvent the arduous manipulations which might otherwise have been involved. Having made these points we are, therefore, ready to take up the analysis of arbitrarily loaded nonshallow spherical shells.

As before, we begin our treatment by setting down the basic equations of the shell that, if we note that $r_\varphi = r_\theta = R$, take the following form:

$$\frac{\partial}{\partial\varphi}(N_\varphi \sin\varphi) + \frac{\partial N_{\varphi\theta}}{\partial\theta} - N_\theta \cos\varphi + Q_\varphi \sin\varphi + q_\varphi R \sin\varphi = 0,$$

$$\frac{\partial}{\partial\varphi}(N_{\varphi\theta} \sin\varphi) + \frac{\partial N_\theta}{\partial\theta} + N_{\varphi\theta} \cos\varphi + Q_\theta \sin\varphi + q_\theta R \sin\varphi = 0,$$

$$\frac{\partial}{\partial\varphi}(Q_\varphi \sin\varphi) + \frac{\partial Q_\theta}{\partial\theta} - (N_\varphi + N_\theta)\sin\varphi - qR\sin\varphi = 0, \qquad (6.50)$$

$$\frac{\partial}{\partial\varphi}(M_\varphi \sin\varphi) + \frac{\partial M_{\varphi\theta}}{\partial\theta} - M_\theta \cos\varphi - Q_\varphi R \sin\varphi = 0,$$

$$\frac{\partial}{\partial\varphi}(M_{\varphi\theta} \sin\varphi) + \frac{\partial M_\theta}{\partial\theta} + M_{\varphi\theta} \cos\varphi - Q_\theta R \sin\varphi = 0,$$

$$\epsilon_\varphi{}^0 = \frac{1}{R}\left(\frac{\partial u_\varphi}{\partial\varphi} + w\right),$$

$$\epsilon_\theta{}^0 = \frac{1}{R}\left(\csc\varphi \frac{\partial u_\theta}{\partial\theta} + u_\varphi \cot\varphi + w\right), \qquad (6.51)$$

$$\gamma_{\varphi\theta}{}^0 = \frac{1}{R}\left(\frac{\partial u_\theta}{\partial\varphi} - u_\theta \cot\varphi + \csc\varphi \frac{\partial u_\varphi}{\partial\theta}\right),$$

$$\kappa_\varphi = \frac{1}{R}\frac{\partial \beta_\varphi}{\partial \varphi},$$

$$\kappa_\theta = \frac{1}{R}\left(\csc\varphi \frac{\partial \beta_\theta}{\partial \theta} + \beta_\varphi \cot\varphi\right), \tag{6.52}$$

$$\tau = \frac{1}{R}\left(\frac{\partial \beta_\theta}{\partial \varphi} - \beta_\theta \cot\varphi + \csc\varphi \frac{\partial \beta_\varphi}{\partial \theta}\right),$$

$$\beta_\varphi = \frac{1}{R}\left(u_\varphi - \frac{\partial w}{\partial \varphi}\right),$$
$$\beta_\theta = \frac{1}{R}\left(u_\theta - \csc\varphi \frac{\partial w}{\partial \theta}\right), \tag{6.53}$$

and the stress resultants, stress couples, and boundary conditions are given by Eqs. 6.5 and 6.6.[15]

We could solve the foregoing system of equations by a procedure which is similar to the method which we followed in the analysis of cylindrical shells. That is, we could eliminate the stress resultants and couples from the equations of equilibrium and reduce the entire system (by means of Eqs. 6.51, 6.52, and 6.53) to three simultaneous differential equations which govern the three nonvanishing displacements. It is far more convenient, however, to draw upon the experience which was gained in the analysis of shallow spherical shells and to again introduce a stress function which simplifies the manipulations. This was first done for nonshallow spherical shells by Vlasov[16] and later by Berry.[17] The procedure begins[17] with the observation that the changes of curvature and twist can be written in the form

$$\kappa_\varphi = \kappa_\varphi{}^0 + \frac{\epsilon_\varphi{}^0}{R}, \qquad \kappa_\theta = \kappa_\theta{}^0 + \frac{\epsilon_\theta{}^0}{R},$$
$$\tau = \tau^0 + \frac{\gamma_{\varphi\theta}{}^0}{R}, \tag{6.54a}$$

[15] Since $R_1 = R_2$, the stress resultants and couples that are obtained for the spherical shell from Eqs. 6.5 satisfy the sixth equation of equilibrium. Furthermore, they are identical to those which would be obtained from Eqs. 3.27 of the theory of Flügge–Lur'e–Byrne.

[16] Vlasov, V. Z., *General Theory of Shells and its Applications in Engineering*, Moscow–Leningrad: Gozudarstvennoye Izdatel'stvo Techniko-Teoreticheskoy Literatury (1949). NASA Technical Translation TT F-99 (1964).

[17] Berry, J. G., "On Thin Hemispherical Shells Subjected to Concentrated Edge Moments and Forces," *Proc. 3rd Midwest Conf. on Solid Mechanics*, Purdue University Experimental Research Series No. 129, 25–44 (1955).

where

$$\kappa_\varphi{}^0 = -\frac{1}{R^2}\left(\frac{\partial^2 w}{\partial \varphi^2} + w\right),$$

$$\kappa_\theta{}^0 = -\frac{1}{R^2}\left(\csc^2\varphi\,\frac{\partial^2 w}{\partial \theta^2} + \cot\varphi\,\frac{\partial w}{\partial \varphi} + w\right), \tag{6.54b}$$

$$\tau^0 = \frac{2}{R^2}\csc\varphi\left(\cot\varphi\,\frac{\partial w}{\partial \theta} - \frac{\partial^2 w}{\partial \varphi\,\partial \theta}\right),$$

and these expressions permit us to write the stress couples as

$$M_\varphi = D(\kappa_\varphi{}^0 + \nu\kappa_\theta{}^0) + N_\varphi\frac{h^2}{12R} - D\alpha_t(1+\nu)\left(T_1 + \frac{T_0}{R}\right),$$

$$M_\theta = D(\kappa_\theta{}^0 + \nu\kappa_\varphi{}^0) + N_\theta\frac{h^2}{12R} - D\alpha_t(1+\nu)\left(T_1 + \frac{T_0}{R}\right), \tag{6.54c}$$

$$M_{\varphi\theta} = \frac{D(1-\nu)}{2}\tau^0 + N_{\varphi\theta}\frac{h^2}{12R}.$$

Now we substitute these relationships into the moment equilibrium equations. Then, when we take into account the fact that the stress resultants satisfy the first two of Eqs. 6.50, we find that the transverse shearing stress resultants are related to the transverse displacements by the expressions

$$Q_\varphi\left(1 + \frac{1}{\xi}\right) = -\frac{D}{R^3}\frac{\partial}{\partial \varphi}(\nabla^2 w + 2w) - \frac{D}{R}\alpha_t(1+\nu)\frac{\partial}{\partial \varphi}\left(T_1 + \frac{T_0}{R}\right) - \frac{q_\varphi R}{\xi},$$

$$Q_\theta\left(1 + \frac{1}{\xi}\right) = -\frac{D}{R^3}\csc\varphi\,\frac{\partial}{\partial \theta}(\nabla^2 w + 2w) - \frac{D}{R}\alpha_t(1+\nu)\csc\varphi\,\frac{\partial}{\partial \theta}\left(T_1 + \frac{T_0}{R}\right) - \frac{q_\theta R}{\xi}, \tag{6.54d}$$

where

$$\nabla^2(\ldots) = \frac{\partial^2(\ldots)}{\partial \varphi^2} + \cot\varphi\,\frac{\partial(\ldots)}{\partial \varphi} + \csc^2\varphi\,\frac{\partial^2(\ldots)}{\partial \theta^2},$$

$$\xi = \frac{12R^2}{h^2}. \tag{6.54e}$$

In the development which follows, we shall take advantage of the fact that ξ is a very large number in comparison to unity; that is, we shall assume that $(1 + \xi) \approx \xi$ whenever it is appropriate to do so.

The first two equations of equilibrium are satisfied if, in analogy to the treatment in the previous section, we introduce a stress function F and a load potential Ω such that

$$N_\varphi = \frac{1}{R^2}\left[\csc^2\varphi\frac{\partial^2 F}{\partial\theta^2} + \cot\varphi\frac{\partial F}{\partial\varphi} + F + \frac{D}{R}(\nabla^2 w + 2w)\right] + \Omega,$$

$$N_\theta = \frac{1}{R^2}\left[\frac{\partial^2 F}{\partial\varphi^2} + F + \frac{D}{R}(\nabla^2 w + 2w)\right] + \Omega, \tag{6.54f}$$

$$N_{\varphi\theta} = \frac{1}{R^2}\left[\cos\varphi\csc^2\varphi\frac{\partial F}{\partial\theta} - \csc\varphi\frac{\partial^2 F}{\partial\varphi\,\partial\theta}\right],$$

where

$$\frac{\partial\Omega}{\partial\varphi} = \frac{D}{R}\alpha_t(1+\nu)\frac{\partial}{\partial\varphi}\left(T_1 + \frac{T_0}{R}\right) - q_\varphi R,$$

$$\frac{\partial\Omega}{\partial\theta} = \frac{D}{R}\alpha_t(1+\nu)\frac{\partial}{\partial\theta}\left(T_1 + \frac{T_0}{R}\right) - q_\theta R\sin\varphi. \tag{6.54g}$$

When these definitions, together with the expressions for the transverse shearing stress resultants, are substituted into the third equation of equilibrium, we obtain the first of the differential equations which relate F and w:

$$(\nabla^2 + 2)\left(\nabla^2 w + 2w + \frac{R}{D}F\right) = S(\varphi, \theta)$$

$$\equiv -\frac{R^3}{D}\left\{\frac{D}{R}\alpha_t(1+\nu)\nabla^2\left(T_1 + \frac{T_0}{R}\right) + 2\Omega + qR + \frac{R}{\xi}\csc\varphi\left[\frac{\partial}{\partial\varphi}(q_\varphi\sin\varphi) + \frac{\partial q_\theta}{\partial\theta}\right]\right\}. \tag{6.54h}$$

The second differential equation which governs F and w is obtained from the following compatibility relationship which is derived by eliminating u_φ and u_θ from Eqs. 6.51:

$$\frac{\partial}{\partial\varphi}\left(\sin\varphi\frac{\partial\gamma_{\varphi\theta}{}^0}{\partial\theta}\right) = \frac{\partial}{\partial\varphi}\left(\sin^2\varphi\frac{\partial\epsilon_\theta{}^0}{\partial\varphi}\right) + \frac{\partial^2\epsilon_\varphi{}^0}{\partial\theta^2} - \sin\varphi\cos\varphi\frac{\partial\epsilon_\varphi{}^0}{\partial\varphi} + 2\epsilon_\varphi{}^0\sin^2\varphi - \frac{\sin^2\varphi}{R}(\nabla^2 w + 2w). \tag{6.55a}$$

The strains are eliminated from this equation by means of Hooke's law after which the term on the left-hand side of the equation becomes one involving $N_{\varphi\theta}$. To eliminate the latter, we substitute the first and second equilibrium equations into the third and obtain the result

$$-2\frac{\partial}{\partial\varphi}\left(\sin\varphi\,\frac{\partial N_{\varphi\theta}}{\partial\theta}\right)$$
$$=\left\{\frac{R}{\sin\varphi}\left[\frac{\partial}{\partial\varphi}(q_\varphi\sin\varphi)+\frac{\partial q_\theta}{\partial\theta}+q\sin\varphi\right]\right.$$
$$+\frac{\partial^2 N_\varphi}{\partial\varphi^2}+2\cot\varphi\,\frac{\partial N_\varphi}{\partial\varphi}+2N_\theta-\cot\varphi\,\frac{\partial N_\theta}{\partial\varphi}$$
$$\left.+\csc^2\varphi\,\frac{\partial^2 N_\theta}{\partial\theta^2}\right\}\sin^2\varphi. \tag{6.55b}$$

When this is substituted into the compatibility equation from which the strains have been eliminated, we obtain the equation

$$(\nabla^2+2)\left(N_\varphi+N_\theta-\frac{Eh}{R}\,w\right)$$
$$=-(\nabla^2+2)Eh\alpha_t T_0-R(1+\nu)\csc\varphi$$
$$\times\left[\frac{\partial}{\partial\varphi}(q_\varphi\sin\varphi)+\frac{\partial q_\theta}{\partial\theta}+q\sin\varphi\right], \tag{6.55c}$$

and when N_φ and N_θ are eliminated by means of Eqs. 6.54f, the end result of the process is

$$(\nabla^2+2)\left[\frac{1}{R^2}(\nabla^2+2)F+\frac{2D}{R^3}(\nabla^2+2)w-\frac{Eh}{R}\,w\right]=P(\varphi,\theta)$$
$$\equiv-(\nabla^2+2)(Eh\alpha_t T_0+2\Omega)-R(1+\nu)\csc\varphi$$
$$\times\left[\frac{\partial}{\partial\varphi}(q_\varphi\sin\varphi)+\frac{\partial q_\theta}{\partial\theta}+q\sin\varphi\right]. \tag{6.55d}$$

Finally, it is convenient to eliminate F from Eqs. 6.54h and 6.55d and, thereby, to obtain the equations

$$\nabla^6 w+4\nabla^4 w+\xi(1-\nu^2)\nabla^2 w+2\xi(1-\nu^2)w=W,$$
$$W\equiv(\nabla^2+2)S-\frac{R^3}{D}\,P, \tag{6.56a}$$

$$(\nabla^2+2)F=\frac{D}{R}\left[S-(\nabla^2+2)^2 w\right]. \tag{6.56b}$$

We have thus arrived, through Eqs. 6.54h and 6.55d, at the differential equation which governs the transverse deflection w in an arbitrarily loaded spherical shell. It is important, however, to note that if the shallowness assumption is applied to the foregoing development, the equations will not reduce to the equations that we derived previously for the shallow spherical shell because the former equations were derived by neglecting certain contributions to equilibrium and to the changes of curvature. Numerical results obtained by the two treatments for problems that involve spherical shells that meet the shallowness criterion which we cited in Section 6.3 will, presently, be shown to be in good agreement.

In accordance with the custom which we have established in this text, we shall next consider the solution of Eqs. 6.56 for spherical shells of arbitrary extent under edge loadings. After that, we shall consider such shells under the influence of distributed surface loadings.

6.4*a* Nonshallow Spherical Shells under Arbitrary Edge Loadings

In the absence of all loadings except edge loadings, we find that the loading functions $S(\varphi, \theta)$ and $P(\varphi, \theta)$ vanish. The governing equation (6.56a) then reduces to

$$\nabla^6 w^c + c_1 \nabla^4 w^c + c_2 \nabla^2 w^c + c_3 w^c = 0, \tag{6.57a}$$

where

$$\begin{aligned} c_1 &= 4, \\ c_2 &= \xi(1 - \nu^2), \\ c_3 &= 2\xi(1 - \nu^2), \end{aligned} \tag{6.57b}$$

and the superscript c indicates our consideration of the complementary solution of the problem.

Equation 6.57a can be put into the equivalent form

$$(\nabla^2 - r_1)(\nabla^2 - r_2)(\nabla^2 - r_3)w^c = 0, \tag{6.57c}$$

provided that the r_α are the roots of the cubic equation

$${r_\alpha}^3 + c_1 {r_\alpha}^2 + c_2 r_\alpha + c_3 = 0, \qquad \alpha = 1, 2, 3. \tag{6.57d}$$

Formally speaking, therefore, we need only consider solutions which satisfy an equation of the type

$$\frac{\partial^2 w^c}{\partial \varphi^2} + \cot \varphi \frac{\partial w^c}{\partial \varphi} + \csc^2 \varphi \frac{\partial^2 w^c}{\partial \theta^2} - r_\alpha w^c = 0. \tag{6.57e}$$

To solve such an equation, we assume first that we are dealing with a spherical shell which is closed with respect to the coordinate θ and that, therefore, all of the shell variables of the complementary solution can be expressed as Fourier series of the type

$$\begin{Bmatrix} u_\theta \\ N_{\varphi\theta} \\ M_{\varphi\theta} \\ Q_\theta \end{Bmatrix} = \sum_{m=1}^{\infty} \begin{Bmatrix} u_{\theta m} \\ N_{\varphi\theta m} \\ M_{\varphi\theta m} \\ Q_{\theta m} \end{Bmatrix} \sin n\theta$$

$$\begin{Bmatrix} F \\ u_\varphi \\ w \\ N_\varphi \\ N_\theta \\ M_\varphi \\ M_\theta \\ Q_\varphi \end{Bmatrix} = \sum_{m=0}^{\infty} \begin{Bmatrix} F_m \\ u_{\varphi m} \\ w_m \\ N_{\varphi m} \\ N_{\theta m} \\ M_{\varphi m} \\ M_{\theta m} \\ Q_{\varphi m} \end{Bmatrix} \cos m\theta, \tag{6.57f}$$

which imply that the states of stress and deformation are symmetric with respect to the point $\theta = 0$ and we have deleted the superscript c for convenience. As before, antisymmetric states are considered by switching $\sin m\theta$ and $\cos m\theta$ in the foregoing while general states can be handled by utilizing a suitable combination of symmetric and antisymmetric states.

If we use the definition of w^c in Eq. 6.57e, it takes the form

$$\frac{d^2 w_m{}^c}{d\varphi^2} + \cot\varphi \frac{dw_m{}^c}{d\varphi} - (m^2 \csc^2\varphi + r_\alpha) w_m{}^c = 0. \tag{6.57g}$$

The solution of this equation can be deduced if we note that the associated Legendre functions of the first and second kind, that is, $P_\mu{}^m(\cos\varphi)$ and $Q_\mu{}^m(\cos\varphi)$, respectively, satisfy the differential equations[18]

$$\left\{\frac{d^2}{d\varphi^2} + \cot\varphi \frac{d}{d\varphi} - m^2 \csc^2\varphi + \mu(\mu + 1)\right\}\begin{Bmatrix} P_\mu{}^m(\cos\varphi) \\ Q_\mu{}^m(\cos\varphi) \end{Bmatrix} = 0. \tag{6.57h}$$

Thus, the solutions of Eq. 6.57g are

$$w_m{}^c = A_\alpha{}^m P_{\mu_\alpha}{}^m(\cos\varphi) + B_\alpha{}^m Q_{\mu_\alpha}{}^m(\cos\varphi), \tag{6.57i}$$

where, from a comparison of Eqs. 6.57g and 6.57h, we find that

$$\mu_\alpha = -\tfrac{1}{2} + (\tfrac{1}{4} - r_\alpha)^{1/2}, \tag{6.57j}$$

and $A_\alpha{}^m$, $B_\alpha{}^m$ are arbitrary constants. In writing Eq. 6.57j, we have ignored the negative square root because it leads to no new information. The final solution of Eq. 6.57e can then be written as

$$w^c = \sum_{m=0}^{\infty} \sum_{\alpha=1}^{3} [A_\alpha{}^m P_{\mu_\alpha}{}^m(\cos\varphi) + B_\alpha{}^m Q_{\mu_\alpha}{}^m(\cos\varphi)] \cos m\theta. \tag{6.57k}$$

It is now appropriate to mention that the three roots of Eq. 6.57d can be

[18] See, for example, Magnus, W., and Oberhettinger, F., *Formulas and Theorems for the Special Functions of Mathematical Physics*, New York: Chelsea (1949), p. 53.

obtained by using the formulas[19]

$$\begin{aligned} r_1 &= A + B - \frac{c_1}{3}, \\ \begin{Bmatrix} r_2 \\ r_3 \end{Bmatrix} &= -\frac{1}{2}(A + B) - \frac{c_1}{3} \pm \frac{i\sqrt{3}}{2}(A - B), \end{aligned} \tag{6.57l}$$

where

$$\begin{Bmatrix} A \\ B \end{Bmatrix} = \left\{\frac{1}{2}\left[-q \pm \left(\frac{\Delta}{27}\right)^{1/2}\right]\right\}^{1/3}, \tag{6.57m}$$

and

$$\begin{aligned} q &= c_3 - \frac{c_1 c_2}{3} + \frac{2c_1^3}{27}, \\ p &= c_2 - \frac{c_1^2}{3}, \\ \Delta &= 27q^2 + 4p^3. \end{aligned} \tag{6.57n}$$

It is evident that the character of the roots r_α is governed by nature of the discriminant Δ. Indeed, if

$\Delta > 0$: one root is real and two are complex conjugates,

$\Delta = 0$: all roots are real and two are equal,

$\Delta < 0$: all roots are real and unequal.

In our case, we find from Eqs. 6.57b and 6.57n that with $1 + \xi \approx \xi$:

$$\begin{aligned} q &= \tfrac{2}{3}\xi(1 - \nu^2), \\ p &= \xi(1 - \nu^2), \\ \Delta &= 4\xi^3(1 - \nu^2)^3. \end{aligned} \tag{6.57o}$$

Since Δ is clearly a positive, nonzero quantity, we may write the roots of Eq. 6.57d symbolically as

$$r_1 = a_1, \qquad \begin{Bmatrix} r_2 \\ r_3 \end{Bmatrix} = a_2 + ia_3, \tag{6.57p}$$

where a_1, a_2, and a_3 are real numbers. As a further consequence of the foregoing discussion it follows, from Eq. 6.57j, that one of the indices of the Legendre functions will be real while the other two will be complex conjugates. Thus, it is appropriate to observe that if a pair of Legendre functions have indices which are complex conjugates they can be written in the form

$$P^m_{a+ib}(\cos\varphi) = Re[P^m_{a+ib}(\cos\varphi)] \pm iIm[P^m_{a+ib}(\cos\varphi)], \tag{6.57q}$$

and similarly for the Legendre functions of the second kind. Now, guided by the fact that the deflection w^c must be a real quantity we must insure that

[19] See, for example, Sokolnikoff, I. S., and E. S., *Higher Mathematics for Engineers and Physicists*, New York: McGraw-Hill (1941), pp. 86–90.

the right-hand side of Eq. 6.57k will also be real. This is accomplished by defining the arbitrary constants according to the scheme

$$A_2{}^m + A_3{}^m = C_2{}^m, \qquad i(A_2{}^m - A_3{}^m) = C_3{}^m,$$
$$B_2{}^m + B_3{}^m = D_2{}^m, \qquad i(B_2{}^m - B_3{}^m) = D_3{}^m. \tag{6.57r}$$

With this, the solution 6.57k takes the form

$$\begin{aligned} w^c = \sum_{m=0}^{\infty} \{ & C_1{}^m P_{\mu_1}{}^m(\cos\varphi) + D_1{}^m Q_{\mu_1}{}^m(\cos\varphi) + C_2{}^m\, Re[P_{\mu_2}{}^m(\cos\varphi)] \\ & + D_2{}^m\, Re[Q_{\mu_2}{}^m(\cos\varphi)] + C_3{}^m Im[P_{\mu_2}(\cos\varphi)] \\ & + D_3{}^m Im[Q_{\mu_2}{}^m(\cos\varphi)]\} \cos m\theta, \end{aligned} \tag{6.57s}$$

where, for consistency, we have replaced $A_1{}^m$ and $B_1{}^m$ with $C_1{}^m$ and $D_1{}^m$, respectively. Having thus obtained the general solution for the transverse displacement w^c, we obtain the stress function as the solution of the equation

$$(\nabla^2 + 2)F^c = -\frac{D}{R}(\nabla^2 + 2)^2 w^c, \tag{6.58a}$$

that follows from Eq. 6.56b by setting $S(\varphi, \theta) = 0$ in accordance with our present interest in spherical shells under arbitrary edge loadings. The solution of Eq. 6.58a can be expressed as

$$F^c = F_a + F_b, \tag{6.58b}$$

in which the functions F_a and F_b satisfy the equations

$$F_a = -\frac{D}{R}(\nabla^2 + 2)w^c, \tag{6.58c}$$

$$(\nabla^2 + 2)F_b = 0. \tag{6.58d}$$

The function F_a can, therefore, be obtained directly from the solution for w^c by differentiation. This gives, in view of Eqs. 6.57f to 6.57h, and 6.57k:

$$\begin{aligned} F_a = -\frac{D}{R} \sum_{m=0}^{\infty} \sum_{\alpha=1}^{3} & (2 + r_\alpha) \\ & \times [A_\alpha{}^m P_{\mu_\alpha}{}^m(\cos\varphi) + B_\alpha{}^m Q_{\mu_\alpha}{}^m(\cos\varphi)] \cos m\theta, \end{aligned} \tag{6.58e}$$

or, upon using Eqs. 6.57p to 6.57r:

$$\begin{aligned} F_a = -\frac{D}{R} \sum_{m=0}^{\infty} \{ & (2 + a_1)[C_1{}^m P_{\mu_1}{}^m(\cos\varphi) + D_1{}^m Q_{\mu_1}{}^m(\cos\varphi] \\ & + C_2{}^m[(2 + a_2)\, Re\, P_{\mu_2}{}^m(\cos\varphi) - a_3\, Im\, P_{\mu_2}{}^m(\cos\varphi)] \\ & + C_3{}^m[(2 + a_2)\, Im\, P_{\mu_2}{}^m(\cos\varphi) + a_3\, Re\, P_{\mu_2}{}^m(\cos\varphi)] \\ & + D_2{}^m[(2 + a_2)\, Re\, Q_{\mu_2}{}^m(\cos\varphi) - a_3\, Im\, Q_{\mu_2}{}^m(\cos\varphi)] \\ & + D_3{}^m[(2 + a_2)\, Im\, Q_{\mu_2}{}^m(\cos\varphi) \\ & \qquad + a_3\, Re\, Q_{\mu_2}{}^m(\cos\varphi)]\} \cos m\theta. \end{aligned} \tag{6.58f}$$

Equation 6.58d can, in turn, be solved by noting that it is a special case of Eq. 6.57h in which $\mu(\mu + 1) = 2$. Thus $\mu = 1, -2$ and since

$$\begin{Bmatrix} P^m_{-n-1}(\cos\varphi) \\ Q_{-n-1}(\cos\varphi) \end{Bmatrix} = \begin{Bmatrix} P_n^m(\cos\varphi) \\ Q_n^m(\cos\varphi) \end{Bmatrix}, \tag{6.58g}$$

we need only consider the solutions corresponding to $\mu = 1$. Consequently,

$$F_b = \sum_{m=1}^{\infty} [C_4^m P_1^m(\cos\varphi) + D_4^m Q_1^m(\cos\varphi)] \cos m\theta, \tag{6.58h}$$

where C_4^m and D_4^m are two additional arbitrary constants for each value of m and all quantities are real.

The displacement and stress function given by Eqs. 6.57s, 6.58b, 6.58f, and 6.58h constitute the complementary solution of the problem of a spherical shell of arbitrary extent. From these, the rest of the shell variables can be found. The solutions contain eight arbitrary coefficients for each value of m, except $m = 0$, which are used to satisfy four boundary conditions at each of two edges of constant φ. In the event that the shell is closed at $\varphi = 0$, the associated Legendre functions of the second kind, that is $Q_\mu^m(\cos\varphi)$ which are singular at $\varphi = 0$, must be suppressed by setting

$$D_i^m = 0, \qquad i = 1, 2, 3, 4. \tag{6.58i}$$

The remainder of the arbitrary coefficients can then be found from four boundary conditions at the edge of the shell.

If the shell is subjected to a loading which is independent of the circumferential variable θ, the foregoing development is considerably simplified by setting $m = 0$. It turns out (see the Exercises) that F_b is, in this case, identically zero and for this reason the summation in the series 6.58h begins at $m = 1$. In this way, we are concerned, (see Chapter 5) with only six arbitrary coefficients and these can be determined from six boundary conditions, three per edge, which are to be satisfied when the loads are independent of θ.

Since Legendre functions of complex degree have not been widely used until recently, they have not been tabulated. For this reason, it is well to summarize here some pertinent identities involving these functions in order to facilitate the analysis of the behavior of spherical shells. It is most efficient, from the standpoint of numerical calculations, to express the Legendre functions in terms of hypergeometric functions which, in turn, can be calculated from their infinite series expansions. We have already noted this fact in Chapter 5, where we gave the relevant expansion formula in Eq. 5.30j. The calculations are expedited further by using special forms which converge most rapidly in the vicinity of the points $\varphi = 0, \pi/2$, and π as necessary. Thus, near $\varphi = 0$ it is best to use[20]

$$P_\mu(\cos\varphi) = F\left(-\mu, \mu + 1, 1, \sin^2\frac{\varphi}{2}\right). \tag{6.59a}$$

For points near $\varphi = \pi/2$, use[21]

$$P_\mu(\cos\varphi) = \frac{\Gamma[(\mu+1)/2]\cos(\mu\pi/2)}{\pi^{1/2}\Gamma[(\mu/2)+1]} F\left(\frac{\mu+1}{2}, -\frac{\mu}{2}, \frac{1}{2}, \cos^2\varphi\right)$$
$$+ \frac{2x\Gamma[(\mu/2)+1]\sin(\mu\pi/2)}{\pi^{1/2}\Gamma[(\mu+1)/2]} F\left(\frac{\mu}{2}+1, \frac{1}{2} - \frac{\mu}{2}, \frac{3}{2}, \cos^2\varphi\right), \tag{6.59b}$$

and for points near $\varphi = \pi$ use[22]

$$\frac{\pi}{\sin\pi\mu} P_\mu(\cos\varphi) = -2\sum_{r=0}^{\infty} \frac{(-\mu)_r(\mu+1)_r}{(r!)^2}\left(\frac{1+x}{2}\right)^r\left[\sum_{\alpha=1}^{r}\frac{1}{\alpha}\right]$$
$$+ \left[\log\left(\frac{1+x}{1-x}\right) + \psi(\mu) + \psi(-1-\mu) - 2\psi(0)\right]$$
$$\times F\left(-\mu, \mu+1, 1, \frac{x+1}{2}\right) \tag{6.59c}$$

where

$$x = \cos\varphi \tag{6.59d}$$

$$(\mu)_r = \mu(\mu+1)\cdots(\mu+r-2)(\mu+r-1), \tag{6.59e}$$

and $\Gamma(\ldots)$, $\psi(\ldots)$ denote the Gamma function and its logarithmic derivative, respectively.[23] The associated Legendre functions and their derivatives can then be determined from the following recursion formulas:[24]

$$P_\mu{}^1(\cos\varphi) = \frac{\mu+1}{\sin\varphi}[P_{\mu+1}(\cos\varphi) - \cos\varphi P_\mu(\cos\varphi)], \tag{6.59f}$$

$$P_\mu{}^m(\cos\varphi) = -[2(m-1)\cot\varphi P_\mu{}^{m-1}(\cos\varphi)$$
$$+ (\mu - m + 2)(\mu + m - 1)P_\mu{}^{m-2}(\cos\varphi)], \tag{6.59g}$$

$$\frac{d}{d\varphi}P_\mu(\cos\varphi) = P_\mu{}^1(\cos\varphi), \tag{6.59h}$$

---

[20] Magnus and Oberhettinger, loc. cit., p. 56.

[21] Hobson, E. W., *The Theory of Spherical and Ellipsoidal Harmonics*, New York: Chelsea (1955), p. 228.

[22] Kratzer, A., and Franz, W., *Transzendente Funktionen*, Leipzig: Geest und Portig K. G. (1960), p. 146.

[23] Magnus and Oberhettinger, loc. cit., pp. 1–3.

[24] Magnus and Oberhettinger, loc. cit., p. 62.

$$\frac{d}{d\varphi} P_\mu{}^m(\cos\varphi) = -[(\mu - m + 1)(\mu + m)P_\mu{}^{m-1}(\cos\varphi) + m \cot\varphi P_\mu{}^m(\cos\varphi)]. \quad (6.59\text{i})$$

Finally, the Legendre functions of the second kind can be obtained from

$$Q_\mu{}^m(\cos\varphi) = \frac{\pi}{2\sin(\mu + m)\pi}[P_\mu{}^m(\cos\varphi)\cos(\mu + m)\pi - P_\mu{}^m(-\cos\varphi)] \quad (6.59\text{j})$$

while for the special case $\mu = 1$,

$$Q_1(x) = \frac{x}{2}\log\left(\frac{1+x}{1-x}\right) - 1, \quad (6.59\text{k})$$

$$Q_1{}^1(x) = -\tfrac{1}{2}(1 - x^2)^{1/2}\log\left(\frac{1+x}{1-x}\right) - \frac{x}{(1-x^2)^{1/2}}, \quad (6.59l)$$

$$Q_1{}^m(x) = -\left[\frac{2(m-1)x}{(1-x^2)^{1/2}}Q_1{}^{m-1}(x) + m(3-m)Q_1{}^{m-2}(x)\right], \quad (6.59\text{m})$$

$$\frac{d}{d\varphi}Q_1{}^m(x) = (m+1)(m-2)Q_1{}^{m-1}(x) - \frac{mx}{(1-x^2)^{1/2}}Q_1{}^m(x). \quad (6.59\text{n})$$

With formulas 6.59, any desired value which might arise in the analysis of spherical shells can be calculated.

6.4*b* Nonshallow Spherical Shells under Arbitrary Distributed Loadings

In the presence of distributed loadings, we seek the solutions of the equations

$$\nabla^6 w^p + c_1\nabla^4 w^p + c_2\nabla^2 w^p + c_3 w^p = W(\varphi, \theta),$$
$$(\nabla^2 + 2)F^p = \frac{D}{R}[S(\varphi, \theta) - (\nabla^2 + 2)^2 w^p]. \quad (6.60\text{a, b})$$

If, in keeping with our previously established procedure, we restrict our attention to spherical shells that are closed with respect to the coordinate θ, and if we assume that the meridional and the circumferential dependence of the load functions, transverse deflection, stress function, and so on are separable, then the shell variables can be expanded in Fourier series of the type

$$\begin{Bmatrix} F^p(\varphi, \theta) \\ w^p(\varphi, \theta) \\ S(\varphi, \theta) \\ W(\varphi, \theta) \end{Bmatrix} = \sum_{m=0}^{\infty} \begin{Bmatrix} F_m{}^p(\varphi) \\ w_m{}^p(\varphi) \\ S_m(\varphi) \\ W_m(\varphi) \end{Bmatrix} \cos m\theta, \quad (6.60\text{c})$$

and similarly for the remainder of the shell variables (see Eqs. 6.57f). With these series, Eqs. 6.60a and 6.60b are reduced to ordinary differential equations which relate the m—subscripted variables. To solve these equations, in which φ is the independent variable, we assume that the coefficient functions in Eqs. 6.60c can, in turn, be expanded in series of associated Legendre functions of real, integer degree as follows:

$$\begin{Bmatrix} w_m{}^p(\varphi) \\ F_m{}^p(\varphi) \\ S_m(\varphi) \\ W_m(\varphi) \end{Bmatrix} = \sum_{n=1}^{\infty} \begin{Bmatrix} a_{mn} \\ b_{mn} \\ c_{mn} \\ d_{mn} \end{Bmatrix} P_n{}^m(\cos\varphi) \tag{6.60d}$$

in which it is, incidentally, implied that q, q_φ, q_θ, T_0, T_1, and Ω can also be expanded in series of the type 6.60c and 6.60d.

The coefficients of the known loading functions can be found by the usual methods of generalized Fourier analysis that, in the present case of spherical coordinates, lead to the definitions[25]

$$\begin{Bmatrix} c_{mn} \\ d_{mn} \end{Bmatrix} = \frac{2n+1}{2}\frac{(n-m)!}{(n+m)!}\int_{-1}^{+1}\begin{Bmatrix} S_m(\varphi) \\ W_m(\varphi) \end{Bmatrix} P_n{}^m(\cos\varphi)\, d(\cos\varphi). \tag{6.60e}$$

Once these coefficients have been determined, the unknown coefficients in the series expansions of the transverse displacement and the stress function are determined by substituting the series 6.60c and 6.60d into Eqs. 6.60a and 6.60b, and noting that the associated Legendre functions employed here satisfy Eq. 6.57h with $\mu = n$. This leads to the expressions

$$\begin{aligned} a_{mn} &= d_{mn}[c_3 - c_2 n(n+1) + c_1 n^2(n+1)^2 - n^3(n+1)^3]^{-1}, \\ b_{mn} &= \frac{D}{R}[c_{mn} - \{2 - n(n+1)\}^2 a_{mn}). \end{aligned} \tag{6.60g, h}$$

Once these coefficients are known, the formal solution of Eqs. 6.60a and 6.60b is complete and the remainder of the shell variables can be determined by using the appropriate formulas of the arbitrarily loaded spherical shell.

6.4*c* Examples

It is now appropriate to illustrate the use of the solutions which were presented in the foregoing development. As part of this we shall, in addition to clarifying the behavior of spherical shells, compare the results obtained for several problems by the present approach and by the shallow shell approach of Section 6.3. For convenience, all problems considered here will involve edge loaded spherical shells and, therefore, we shall rely

[25] See, for example, Whittaker, E. T., and Watson, G. N., *Modern Analysis*, Cambridge: The University Press, 4th edn. (1952), p. 325.

primarily upon the development of complementary solutions which was described in Section 6.4*a*.

Our first example concerns a hemispherical shell which is subjected to two concentrated moments M_0 which are applied to its edge at opposite ends of a diameter[26] as shown in Fig. 6.3. If the edge $\varphi = \pi/2$ is assumed

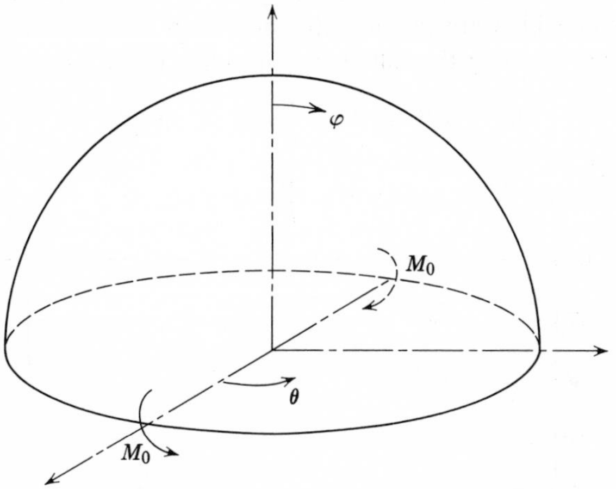

Figure 6.3 Hemispherical shell loaded by concentrated edge moments.

to be free of other loads, the boundary conditions are expressed as (see Eqs. 6.6):

$$N_\varphi = N_{\varphi\theta} + \frac{M_{\varphi\theta}}{R} = Q_\varphi + \frac{1}{R}\frac{\partial M_{\varphi\theta}}{\partial \theta} = 0,$$
$$M_\varphi = \frac{M_0}{\pi R}\left[1 + 2\sum_{m=1}^{\infty} \cos 2m\theta\right], \tag{6.61a}$$

where the two concentrated moments have been expressed as a Fourier series. The solution process begins with the observation that the shell is closed at $\varphi = 0$. Thus, the Legendre functions of the second kind, which are singular at $\varphi = 0$, must be suppressed by setting (see Eqs. 6.58i):

$$D_i^m = 0, \qquad i = 1, 2, 3, 4, \tag{6.61b}$$

while the remaining arbitrary coefficients which appear in the complementary solutions 6.57s, 6.58b, 6.58f, and 6.58h are determined by applying conditions 6.61a. The details of this lengthy manipulation will be omitted since they contribute nothing to the present development. However,

[26] Berry, J. G., loc. cit.

numerical results are given in Figs. 6.4 and 6.5 for a typical hemispherical shell with $R = 6$ in., $h = 0.095$ in., $\nu = 0.30$, and $E = 3 \times 10^7$ psi. The results given in these figures involve the dimensionless stresses

$$\frac{\pi h^2 R}{M_0}\{\sigma_\varphi{}^B, \sigma_\theta{}^B, \tau_{\varphi\theta}{}^B, \sigma_\varphi{}^M, \sigma_\theta{}^M, \tau_{\varphi\theta}{}^M\}, \tag{6.61c}$$

where the superscripts B and M identify the so-called bending and membrane stresses which are in turn obtained from the stress resultants and stress couples by using the following formulas (based upon Eqs. 2.32):

$$\begin{aligned}\{\sigma_\varphi{}^M, \sigma_\theta{}^M, \tau_{\varphi\theta}{}^M\} &= \frac{1}{h}\{N_\varphi, N_\theta, N_{\varphi\theta}\},\\ \{\sigma_\varphi{}^B, \sigma_\theta{}^B, \tau_{\varphi\theta}{}^B\} &= \frac{6}{h^2}\{M_\varphi, M_\theta, M_{\varphi\theta}\}.\end{aligned} \tag{6.61d}$$

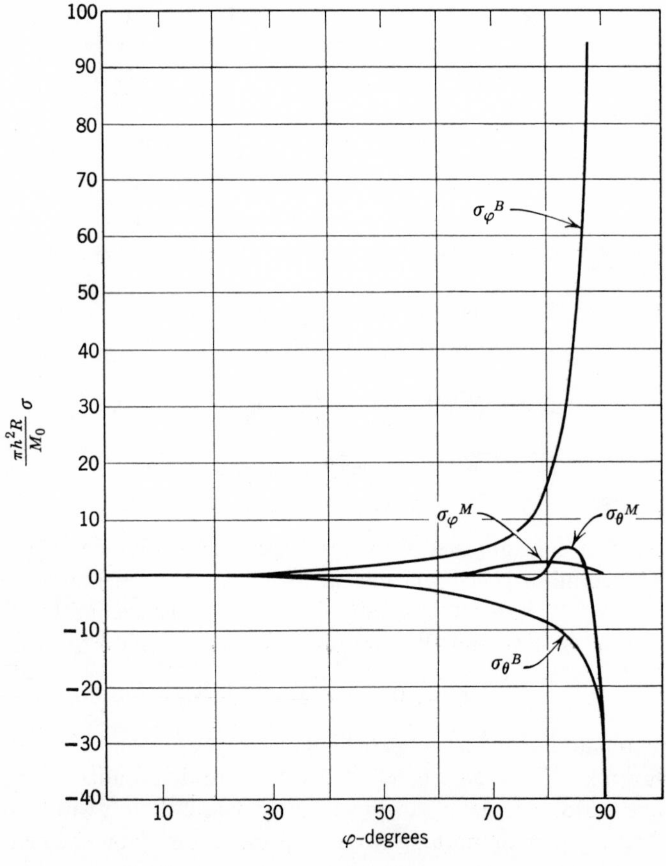

Figure 6.4 Stress distributions along the meridian passing through $\theta = 0$ for the shell shown in Fig. 6.3.

In view of Eqs. 2.32, we should recall that the membrane stresses are constant across the shell wall while the bending stresses are linearly distributed across it. Thus, it should be noted that the bending stresses given above occur at the outside surface ($\zeta = h/2$) of the shell, although their magnitude is equal to the magnitude of the bending stresses on the inside surface ($\zeta = -h/2$).

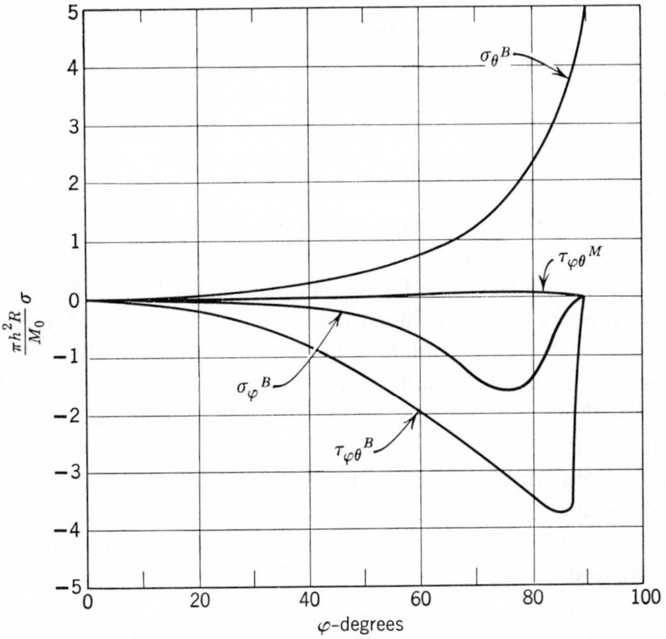

Figure 6.5 Same as Fig. 6.4 for the meridian passing through $\theta = \pi/4$.

In Fig. 6.4, we have plotted the normal bending and membrane stresses as a function of meridional position along the generator passing through $\theta = 0$. The shearing membrane and bending stresses vanish on the generator $\theta = 0$ and are, therefore, not given. The results of Fig. 6.4 indicate the highly localized nature of all of the stresses which quickly decay to negligible values as one moves from the edge toward the apex. It is also evident, as could be expected in this particular problem, that the bending stresses predominate. Indeed, the stress $\sigma_\varphi{}^B$ becomes unbounded at the edge owing to the fact that we are considering concentrated moments. In Fig. 6.5, similar data have been plotted along the generator passing through $\theta = \pi/4$. At this particular location, the shearing stresses do not vanish and have, therefore, been plotted. However, the normal membrane stresses are so small that they have been omitted. We have already demonstrated, in all of our previous examples, that the effects of bending are highly localized as far as the distribution of stresses along the generator of a shell is concerned. The present data are, as could be expected, consistent with this conclusion. However, they reveal, in addition, that the effects of bending are also highly localized as far as the distribution of stresses around a latitude circle is concerned. This is clear from a comparison of the ordinates of Figs. 6.4 and 6.5.

As a second example, we give the results of an analysis which was carried out for a clamped hemispherical shell with $R = 6$ in., $h = 0.095$ in., $\nu = 0.3$, and $E = 3 \times 10^7$ psi which is subjected to a concentrated load $P = 100$ lb. at its apex, by treating it as a nonshallow shell[27] and also as a shallow shell.[28] Although this example concerns a shell which is subjected to a load that is independent of θ, we give the results here because we are primarily interested in clarifying the applicability of the shallow shell treatment. In Table 6.4 we have, therefore, given the normal membrane and bending stresses (see Eqs. 6.61d) as obtained for the cited problem by the two treatments (the shearing stresses vanish because the load is independent of θ). The tabulated data indicate that the results obtained by the two treatments are in very good agreement in the interval $0 \leqslant \varphi \leqslant 24° 33'$ which falls within the region of shallowness which we defined ($0 \leqslant \varphi \leqslant 30°$) in Section 6.3. Furthermore, at the point $\varphi = 24° 33'$, the bending stresses obtained by both analyses have decayed to negligible values, and the membrane stresses are very close to the result $\sigma_\varphi{}^M = -\sigma_\theta{}^M = 162$ psi which is obtained by using Eqs. 4.26 and 4.28c of the membrane theory with $q = q_\varphi = 0$, and $C_1 = P/2\pi$. Thus, it is safe to rely upon the results of the shallow shell approximation in this class of problems.

As a conclusion we may, therefore, say that the nonshallow shell treatment which has been derived in this section gives an exact result, within the scope of Love's postulates, for problems which concern spherical shells of arbitrary extent. The shallow shell treatment of the previous section gives a very good approximation to these results whenever the shallowness assumption is valid. As an example of this, we have shown its success in matching the results of the nonshallow shell analysis in the case of the hemispherical shell which carries a concentrated load at its apex. It should be remembered, however, that the shallow shell approximation was useful because analysts had been more familiar, in the past, with the Kelvin functions that are associated with it than they were with the Legendre functions which arise in the analysis of the nonshallow spherical shell. This deficiency has been removed by the appearance of recent nonshallow shell analyses

[27] Berry, J. G., loc. cit.
[28] Reissner, E., loc. cit.

Table 6.4

φ	$\sigma_\varphi{}^M$		$\sigma_\theta{}^M$	
	s[a]	ns[b]	s	ns
0°	−2289	−2289	−2289	−2281
2°	−2098	−2090	−1816	−1817
4°	−1780	−1771	−1105	−1100
5° 58′	−1426	−1417	−705	−701
7° 58′	−1146	−1125	−33	−36
9° 58′	−893	−880	248	250
12°	−689	−675	391	399
16° 4′	−410	−408	423	430
20° 15′	−253	−251	323	317
24° 33′	−167	−167	209	207

φ	$\sigma_\varphi{}^B$		$\sigma_\theta{}^B$	
	s	ns	s	ns
0°	∞	∞	∞	∞
2°	−4120	−4115	−7653	−7647
4°	−423	−422	−3520	−3510
5° 58′	969	962	−1697	−1694
7° 58′	1225	1225	−682	−685
9° 58′	1179	1172	−220	−215
12°	936	931	−14.6	58
16° 4′	427	425	70.6	87
20° 15′	123	126	38	37
24° 33′	13	12	8.5	8.4

[a] *s*, shallow shell treatment.
[b] *ns*, nonshallow shell treatment.

and, thanks to the digital computer, it is no more difficult to construct a table of Legendre functions than it is to construct one of Kelvin functions. For this reason, it is best to treat with the shallow shell theory only those problems to which it is clearly applicable and to analyze all other spherical shell problems with the nonshallow shell theory.

6.5 CLOSURE

In this chapter, we have described the analysis of shells of revolution, as exemplified by cylindrical, shallow spherical, and nonshallow spherical shells, under arbitrary loads.[29] Our methods were based on two approaches.

[29] An analysis of conical shells which is similar to the analysis which we have given for cylindrical shells is described in Hoff, N. J., "Thin Circular Conical Shells Under Arbitrary Loads," *J. Appl. Mech.*, **22**, 557–562 (1955).

Of these, the first involved the reduction of the shell equations to three equilibrium displacement equations which were then solved for the displacements. The second made use of a stress function by means of which the shell equations were reduced to two equations which relate the stress function and the transverse displacement. As a result of our assumptions that the shell is, in each case, made of an isotropic homogeneous material and that its thickness and elastic properties are independent of position, we were able to solve the governing equations of each class of shells by the classical methods and functions of mathematical physics. Indeed, with this experience behind us we shall be able to solve the free vibration problem for various shells of revolution in Part III by means of a straightforward extension of the complementary solutions which were developed in the present chapter.

Shells in which the assumptions of isotropy, homogeneity, constant thickness, and so on are not in effect are no less interesting in modern practice than the ones which we have covered here. However, the complications which attend the relaxation of those assumptions can, in general, be overcome only by some sort of approximate analysis. For this reason we shall, in the next chapter, describe some approximate analytical techniques which have been found to be useful in the analysis of shells. Then, in Part IV we shall take up the analysis of shells by approximate numerical techniques which have been programmed for use on a digital computer.

EXERCISES

6.1 Solve the problem of an infinitely long circular cylindrical shell subjected at its middle to two concentrated radial loads acting on opposite ends of a diameter.

6.2 Obtain a solution for a simply supported circular cylindrical shell of length L and radius a which is subjected to the following distributed load over an area $2b$ by $2c$ at opposite ends of a diameter at its middle:

$$q = X(x)S(s)p$$

where

$$\begin{aligned} X(x) &= 1, \qquad -b \leqslant x \leqslant b \\ X(x) &= 0, \qquad |x| > b \\ S(s) &= 1, \qquad -c \leqslant s \leqslant c \\ S(s) &= 0, \qquad c < |s| < a\pi/2. \end{aligned}$$

6.3 By performing suitable limiting processes upon the foregoing solution, obtain solutions for a cylindrical shell subjected to:

(a) A constant force applied around the circumference of the shell at its middle.

(b) Two concentrated forces applied at opposite ends of a diameter at the middle of the shell.

(c) Two radial line loads applied along the length of the shell on generators passing through opposite ends of a diameter.

6.4 Derive a solution for a tall circular cylindrical tank standing vertically on four supports. Assume that the lower end of the shell is attached to a rigid ring and that it is filled to the top with a liquid.

6.5 Derive a general solution for a circular cylindrical shell subjected to loads which are independent of s using the displacement approach of Section 6.2. Compare the solution to the one obtained in Section 5.2.

6.6 Set up a general solution for the problem of a simply supported cylindrical shell of elliptical cross section which is subjected to a uniform radial pressure load.

6.7 Set all derivatives with respect to s equal to zero in Eqs. 6.30 and solve the resulting equations for a cylindrical shell whose curvature is given in Eq. 6.31. Apply the solution to a short noncircular cylindrical shell whose ends are simply supported and

(a) Free to move axially.
(b) Restrained from axial motion.

6.8 Show that the presence of a surface load and a temperature distribution has no effect upon the arguments which led to Eqs. 6.44 for the displacements in a shallow spherical shell. Verify Eq. 6.44m.

6.9 Find a particular solution for shallow spherical shell that is rotating about its axis at a constant angular velocity.

6.10 Set up a theory of shallow conical shells.

6.11 Investigate the displacements u_φ and u_θ in a nonshallow spherical shell under arbitrary edge loads. Are they single-valued?

6.12 Consider a nonshallow spherical shell under a system of edge loads which is independent of circumferential position. Derive a general solution, independent of the one given in Section 6.4, by means of an auxiliary stress function. That is, show that the term $m = 0$ is not required in the expansion 6.58h.

6.13 Make the mathematical assumption of shallowness in the development of Section 6.4 and deduce a general solution for the problem of a shallow spherical shell in which the shearing stress contribution to equilibrium, and so on, have not been neglected.

6.14 Derive a new set of governing equations for an arbitrarily loaded cylindrical shell by utilizing a stress function in the manner of Sections 6.3 and 6.4.

6.15 By suitable procedures, reduce the solutions given in Sections 6.2, 6.3, and 6.4 so that they will be appropriate to cylindrical, shallow spherical, and nonshallow spherical *membrane* shells.

7

Approximate Analytical Solutions

7.1 INTRODUCTION

We have seen, in the development of the exact analytical solutions which were carried out in the preceding chapters, that we were able, in each case, to determine the solution in a fairly straightforward manner by using the classical procedures and solution functions of mathematical physics. We pointed out on several occasions, however, that the success of these analyses was directly attributable to the fact that we were dealing throughout the development with shells of constant thickness, principal radii of curvature, and elastic properties. We also indicated that, if any of these requirements were to be relaxed, the possibility of an exact analytical solution would be radically diminished, and an approximate solution would have to be sought.

It is also possible that, in many circumstances, it may simply not be convenient to carry out solutions of the foregoing type even though the problems involved fall into one of the categories which have already been treated. For example, we may not have access to suitable tabulations of the solution functions for specific values of the parameters that arise. When this is the case, we are faced with the necessity of extending or creating a suitable tabulation of the required function; a prospect which may or may not be convenient depending on the availability of computing equipment. Even if the necessary data were to be available in one form or another, we might not have the time to carry out an exact solution of the type which we have described so far. This is invariably the case in any preliminary design or proposal preparation effort.

For these reasons, it is now appropriate for us to take up the development of approximate analytical methods which will permit us, on the one hand, to extend the class of problems for which some sort of analytical solution is available and, on the other hand, to permit more convenient analyses to be carried out for the shells which we have considered up to now.

Actually, we have already taken up two categories of approximate solutions; that is, membrane shells and shallow spherical shells. These treatments were developed on physical grounds and, when applied to shells which satisfied the assumptions upon which they were based, yielded accurate results. This was particularly true of the shallow shell theory. However, as far as the membrane theory was concerned, it was found to lead to significant discrepancies at and near boundaries and sources of bending.

In the present chapter, we shall discuss two approximate analytical procedures which have been useful in the static analysis of shells and are commonly referred to as the Geckeler approximation and asymptotic integration. The former was developed for the analysis of shells of revolution under loadings that are independent of circumferential position while the latter is a general mathematical procedure, which, although it is applicable to arbitrarily loaded shells, will be illustrated in detail for shells under θ-independent loadings.

It will be shown, by means of examples, that these procedures lead to solutions that are very good approximations to the exact solutions which we have developed previously. However, there will still remain cases for which an approximate numerical solution, programmed for a digital computer, provides the only means to accomplish the analysis. Such solutions will be taken up for static problems of shells in Chapter 10.

7.2 THE GECKELER APPROXIMATION

Our first category of approximate analytical solutions arises directly from the analysis of shells of revolution under loads that are independent of circumferential position.[1] We recall that the behavior of such shells is governed in the treatment of Chapter 5 by the following equations:

$$\frac{r_\theta}{r_\varphi}\frac{d^2\beta_\varphi}{d\varphi^2} + \left[\frac{r_\theta}{r_\varphi}\cot\varphi + \frac{d}{d\varphi}\left(\frac{r_\theta}{r_\varphi}\right) + \frac{r_\theta}{r_\varphi}\frac{1}{D_\varphi}\frac{dD_\varphi}{d\varphi}\right]\frac{d\beta_\varphi}{d\varphi} - \left[\frac{r_\varphi}{r_\theta}\frac{D_\theta}{D_\varphi}\cot^2\varphi + \nu_{\varphi\theta} - \nu_{\varphi\theta}\cot\varphi\frac{1}{D_\varphi}\frac{dD_\varphi}{d\varphi}\right]\beta_\varphi = \frac{(r_\theta Q_\varphi)}{D_\varphi}r_\varphi + \frac{r_\varphi H(\varphi)}{h^3}, \tag{7.1a}$$

---

[1] Geckeler, J. W., "Über die Festigkeit achsensymetrischer Schalen," *Forschungsarb. Ingwes.*, Berlin, **276**, 1–52 (1926).

$$\frac{r_\theta}{r_\varphi}\frac{d^2(r_\theta Q_\varphi)}{d\varphi^2} + \left[\frac{r_\theta}{r_\varphi}\cot\varphi + \frac{d}{d_\varphi}\left(\frac{r_\theta}{r_\varphi}\right) - \frac{r_\theta}{r_\varphi}\frac{1}{E_\theta h}\frac{d(E_\theta h)}{d\varphi}\right]\frac{d(r_\theta Q_\varphi)}{d\varphi}$$

$$- \left[\frac{r_\varphi E_\theta}{r_\theta E_\varphi}\cot^2\varphi - \nu_{\varphi\theta} - \nu_{\varphi\theta}\cot\varphi\frac{1}{E_\theta h}\frac{d}{d\varphi}(E_\theta h)\right](r_\theta Q_\varphi)$$

$$= -E_\theta h r_\varphi \beta_\varphi + G(\varphi). \tag{7.1b}$$

In our application of these equations to the analysis of circular cylindrical shells, we found solutions of the form (see Eqs. 5.17g):

$$e^{\pm\bar{\mu}y}\begin{Bmatrix}\cos\bar{\mu}y\\ \sin\bar{\mu}y\end{Bmatrix}, \tag{7.2a}$$

$$\bar{\mu}^4 = 3(1 - \nu_{sx}\nu_{xs})\frac{E_s}{E_x}\left(\frac{a}{h}\right)^2, \tag{7.2b}$$

where, to facilitate the discussion, we have defined a nondimensional axial coordinate y such that $x = ay$. In view of our interest in thin shells, we may observe at this point that $\bar{\mu}$ is a large parameter.

In the analyses of cylindrical, conical, and spherical shells under θ-independent, as well as arbitrary, loadings which we carried out in Chapters 5 and 6, we found that bending effects were significant over only a short distance from their point of introduction. Indeed, we discovered that the behavior of the solution functions for the conical and the spherical shells was essentially the same as that of the exponential-trigonometric solution functions (Eqs. 7.2a) of the cylindrical shell. Guided by this fact let us, therefore, develop an approximate analysis of shells of revolution by assuming that the behavior of all shells is of the type

$$e^{\pm\kappa\xi}\begin{Bmatrix}\cos\kappa\xi\\ \sin\kappa\xi\end{Bmatrix}, \tag{7.3}$$

where κ is a large geometrical parameter and ξ is a dimensionless position coordinate. Now, we observe that each time we differentiate these solution functions with respect to the position coordinate we multiply the expression 7.3 once by the large parameter κ. Thus, if we consider the solutions for β_φ or $r_\theta Q_\varphi$, we find in each case that their second derivatives will be two orders of κ greater than the functions themselves, and so on. Now, if we assume further that r_φ and r_θ are of the same order of magnitude, that the variation of E_φ, E_θ, and h is smooth, and that we are dealing with shells for which $\cot\varphi$ is a small number (that is, φ is near $\pi/2$), then we shall be justified in neglecting, in each of Eqs. 7.1a and 7.1b, the terms involving the functions and their first derivatives in comparison to the terms involving the second derivative. This gives

$$\frac{r_\theta}{r_\varphi^{\,2}}\frac{d^2(r_\theta Q_\varphi)}{d\varphi^2} = -E_\theta h\beta_\varphi + \frac{G(\varphi)}{r_\varphi},$$
$$\frac{r_\theta}{r_\varphi^{\,2}}\frac{d^2\beta_\varphi}{d\varphi^2} = \frac{r_\theta Q_\varphi}{D_\varphi} + \frac{H(\varphi)}{h^3}. \tag{7.4a}$$

Differentiation of the first of these equations twice with respect to φ and retention of only the highest derivative of β_φ and $r_\theta Q_\varphi$ on each side of the result then gives

$$\frac{r_\theta}{r_\varphi^{\,2}}\frac{d^4(r_\theta Q_\varphi)}{d\varphi^4} = -E_\theta h\frac{d^2\beta_\varphi}{d\varphi^2} + \frac{d^2}{d\varphi^2}\left(\frac{G}{r_\varphi}\right). \tag{7.4b}$$

With the second of Eqs. 7.4a, this becomes

$$\frac{d^4(r_\theta Q_\varphi)}{d\varphi^4} + 4\kappa^4(r_\theta Q_\varphi) = \frac{r_\varphi^{\,2}}{r_\theta}\frac{d^2}{d\varphi^2}\left(\frac{G}{r_\varphi}\right) - \frac{E_\theta H r_\varphi^{\,4}}{r_\theta^{\,2}h^2}, \tag{7.4c}$$

where

$$\kappa^4 = 3(1-\nu_{\varphi\theta}\nu_{\theta\varphi})\frac{E_\theta}{E_\varphi}\frac{r_\varphi^{\,4}}{h^2 r_\theta^{\,2}}, \tag{7.4d}$$

is a function of φ. The rest of the shell variables can be obtained from the solution of Eq. 7.4c by the first of Eqs. 7.4a and the methods which have been used in the previous chapters. Equation 7.4c represents a drastic simplification of the original equations which govern the behavior of shells of revolution under the influence of θ-independent loads. It may, however, still prove to be a fairly complicated matter to solve even that equation if the variation of κ with φ is not right. Indeed, the approximation really saves a significant amount of work only if κ is a constant. In such an event, the approximation is equivalent to the replacement of a given shell by a cylindrical shell of appropriate dimensions. Consequently, the approximation has found its greatest utility in the treatment of spherical shells and of those shells which can be broken down into zones over which the geometry is essentially constant. An example of this involves the replacement of a cylindrical shell with linearly varying wall thickness by one with a constant thickness which is equal to the average thickness of the actual shell.

To illustrate the usefulness of the Geckeler approximation, we shall next take up the case of a spherical shell of constant thickness as considered in Section 5.4. We shall show that the resulting solution is far simpler than the one based upon the hypergeometric functions while giving results which are of satisfactory accuracy for engineering purposes. As a further illustration, we shall demonstrate that such a solution greatly facilitates the analysis of complex shell structures as exemplified by a U-tube steam generator for a pressurized water nuclear power plant.

7.2a Application to the Analysis of a Spherical Shell

For a spherical shell of constant thickness, Eqs. 7.4c and 7.4d take the form

$$\frac{d^4 Q_\varphi}{d\varphi^4} + 4\kappa^4 Q_\varphi = \frac{d^2}{d\varphi^2}\left(\frac{G}{R}\right) - \frac{E_\theta HR}{h^2}, \tag{7.5a}$$

where

$$\kappa^4 = 3(1 - \nu_{\varphi\theta}\nu_{\theta\varphi})\frac{E_\theta}{E_\varphi}\left(\frac{R}{h}\right)^2 \tag{7.5b}$$

and (see Eqs. 5.31b):

$$\begin{aligned}\frac{H(\varphi)}{h^3} &= (\alpha_{t\varphi} + \nu_{\varphi\theta}\alpha_{t\theta})\frac{dT_1}{d\varphi} + \left[\alpha_{t\varphi} + \nu_{\varphi\theta}\alpha_{t\theta} - (\alpha_{t\theta} + \nu_{\theta\varphi}\alpha_{t\varphi})\frac{E_\theta}{E_\varphi}\right] T_1 \cos\varphi,\\ \frac{G(\varphi)}{R} &= -\frac{d}{d\varphi}[F_1(1 + \nu_{\varphi\theta}) - qR]\\ &\quad - \cot\varphi\left[\frac{E_\theta}{E_\varphi}F_1(1 + \nu_{\theta\varphi}) + (1 + \nu_{\varphi\theta})(F_1 - qR)\right]\\ &\quad - E_\theta h\left[\alpha_{t\theta}\frac{dT_0}{d\varphi} - T_0(\alpha_{t\varphi} - \alpha_{t\theta})\cot\varphi\right].\end{aligned} \tag{7.5c}$$

Equation 7.5a is equivalent to Eq. 5.17a of the analysis of the circular cylindrical shell and, consequently, its solution can be written as (see Eqs. 5.17g):

$$\begin{aligned}Q_\varphi &= e^{\kappa\varphi}(C_1 \cos\kappa\varphi + C_2 \sin\kappa\varphi)\\ &\quad + e^{-\kappa\varphi}(C_3 \cos\kappa\varphi + C_4 \sin\kappa\varphi) + Q_\varphi{}^p.\end{aligned} \tag{7.5d}$$

Then, in view of the first of Eqs. 7.4a,

$$\begin{aligned}E_\theta h\beta_\varphi &= 2\kappa^2 e^{\kappa\varphi}(C_1 \sin\kappa\varphi - C_2 \cos\kappa\varphi)\\ &\quad + 2\kappa^2 e^{-\kappa\varphi}(C_4 \cos\kappa\varphi - C_3 \sin\kappa\varphi) + E_\theta h\beta_\varphi{}^p,\end{aligned} \tag{7.5e}$$

where

$$E_\theta h\beta_\varphi{}^p = \frac{G(\varphi)}{R} - \frac{d^2 Q_\varphi{}^p}{d\varphi^2}. \tag{7.5f}$$

The rest of the shell variables can be obtained from Eqs. 7.5d and 7.5e by means of Eqs. 5.29b. Obviously, the solutions obtained here are much simpler than the solutions which were derived for this class of problems in Section 5.4 in terms of hypergeometric functions.

As an illustration of this procedure, let us reconsider the clamped, isotropic pressurized hemispherical shell which we analyzed by the exact method of solution in Section 5.4*c*. In this case we find, as before, that $F_1 = -pR/2$ and $H(\varphi) = G(\varphi) = 0$. As a result, we again find, as could be expected, that

$$Q_\varphi{}^p = \beta_\varphi{}^p = 0. \tag{7.6a}$$

The solutions 7.5d and 7.5e are valid for a shell with two edges of constant φ. To make them applicable to a shell which is closed at $\varphi = 0$, we discard the terms with the negative exponential because these decay as φ increases. Thus, the solutions for the problem under consideration take the form

$$\begin{aligned} Q_\varphi &= e^{\kappa\varphi}\,(C_1 \cos\kappa\varphi + C_2 \sin\kappa\varphi), \\ Eh\beta_\varphi &= 2\kappa^2\, e^{\kappa\varphi}\,(C_1 \sin\kappa\varphi - C_2 \cos\kappa\varphi), \end{aligned} \tag{7.6b}$$

and these must satisfy the boundary conditions (see Eqs. 5.36b):

$$Eh\beta_\varphi = 0, \qquad \frac{dQ_\varphi}{d\varphi} = -\frac{pR}{2}(1 - \nu), \tag{7.6c}$$

at the clamped edge $\varphi = \pi/2$. Upon application of these conditions to the general solutions, we find that the arbitrary constants are given as

$$\begin{aligned} C_1 &= -\frac{pR(1-\nu)}{2\kappa}\, e^{-\kappa\pi/2} \cos\kappa\pi/2 = \frac{pR}{2} D_1, \\ C_2 &= -\frac{pR(1-\nu)}{2\kappa}\, e^{-\kappa\pi/2} \sin\kappa\pi/2 = \frac{pR}{2} D_2, \end{aligned} \tag{7.6d}$$

and, in view of Eqs. 5.29b,

$$\begin{aligned} N_\varphi &= \frac{pR}{2}\{1 + e^{\kappa\varphi} \cot\varphi(D_1 \cos\kappa\varphi + D_2 \sin\kappa\varphi)\}, \\ N_\theta &= \frac{pR}{2}\{1 + \kappa\, e^{\kappa\varphi}\,[D_1(\cos\kappa\varphi - \sin\kappa\varphi) \\ &\qquad + D_2(\cos\kappa\varphi + \sin\kappa\varphi)]\}, \\ M_\varphi &= \frac{-ph^2}{24(1-\nu^2)}\, 2\kappa^2\, e^{\kappa\varphi}\,\{\kappa D_2(\cos\kappa\varphi - \sin\kappa\varphi) \\ &\qquad - \kappa D_1(\sin\kappa\varphi + \cos\kappa\varphi) \\ &\qquad + \nu \cot\varphi(D_2 \cos\kappa\varphi - D_1 \sin\kappa\varphi)\}, \\ M_\theta &= \frac{-ph^2}{24(1-\nu^2)}\, 2\kappa^2\, e^{\kappa\varphi}\,\{\cot\varphi(D_2 \cos\kappa\varphi - D_1 \sin\kappa\varphi) \\ &\qquad + \nu\kappa D_2(\cos\kappa\varphi - \sin\kappa\varphi) \\ &\qquad - \nu\kappa D_1(\sin\kappa\varphi + \cos\kappa\varphi)\}. \end{aligned} \tag{7.6e}$$

Results which were obtained with these formulas will be compared to the results of the exact analysis of Section 5.4*c* and to the results of an analysis based on asymptotic integration, which will be given presently, in Section 7.4 (see Table 7.1).

7.2*b* Application to the Analysis of a Composite Shell Structure

In the foregoing, we illustrated the simplifications which could be achieved by the Geckeler approximation when it is applied to a single spherical shell. The full value of the approach can be more aptly demonstrated, however, by applying it to the analysis of a multicomponent shell structure such as the U-tube steam generator for pressurized water nuclear power plants that is shown schematically in Fig. 7.1.[2]

Such a structure is analyzed by the general procedure which was described in Section 5.5. Accordingly, it is first broken up into simpler structural shapes for which stress and deformation equations are available. Figure 7.1 shows the members into which the steam generator is broken for the purposes of the present analysis. According to the diagram, the steam generator is broken up into a long cylinder, a short transition cylinder, a spherical segment, and a tube sheet.

In the analysis of the composite structure, the long cylindrical shell is treated by the method of Section 5.2. The tube sheet is considered as a perforated circular plate surrounded by a solid ring. According to standard practice, the effect of the U-tubes is neglected because their stiffness is small compared to that of the tube sheet. In the tube sheet assembly, the ring is treated by the theory of Timoshenko[3] while the perforated inner plate is treated as a solid circular plate[4] with modified elastic constants E^* and ν^* which account for the presence of the perforations.[5]

The short tapered transition cylinder is analyzed by means of the Geckeler approximation. Thus, it is considered as a short cylindrical shell with a constant thickness that is equal to the average thickness of the actual section. An exact analysis could also be carried out (see Exercise 5.7) in which the transition section is treated as a tapered conical shell. We choose not to pursue the latter approach here.

Finally, the spherical portion of the assembly is also treated by the Geckeler approximation in order to avoid the hypergeometric functions

[2] Kraus, H., "Pressure and Thermal Stresses in U-tube Steam Generators for Nuclear Power Plants," *Bettis Technical Review*, April, 1960, 13–28.

[3] Timoshenko, S., *Strength of Materials, Volume II, Advanced Theory and Problems*, Princeton: D. Van Nostrand, 3rd ed. (1956).

[4] Timoshenko, S., and Woinowsky-Krieger, S., *Theory of Plates and Shells*, New York: McGraw-Hill, 2nd ed., Chapter 3 (1959).

[5] O'Donnell, W. J., and Langer, B. F., "Design of Perforated Plates," *Trans. A.S.M.E.*, **74B**, 307–320 (1962).

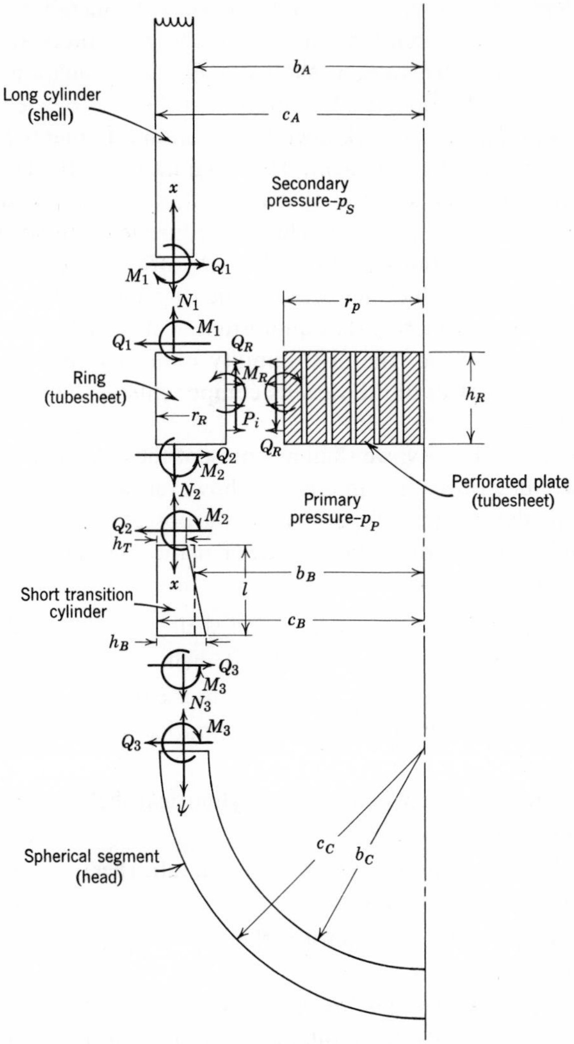

Figure 7.1 Typical steam generator for a nuclear power plant showing loads acting on each part.

(or equivalently, Legendre functions) which would otherwise have to be used.

In accordance with the procedure that was described in Section 5.5, the elements of the heat exchanger assembly are separated at their junctions and are allowed to deform freely under the applied pressure load. Since all of the members behave differently under the load they do not deform equally. Hence, to maintain continuity between the members of the structure, unknown discontinuity moments and shearing forces are introduced at each joint in the structure, as shown in Fig. 7.1. Equations are written which relate the deflection and the rotation at the ends of each component to the pressure and to the unknown discontinuity moments and shearing forces that act on the component. The magnitudes of the latter can then be found from the requirement that the deflection and rotation must be continuous across each junction. This procedure leads to six equations in the six unknown reactions M_1, Q_1, M_2, Q_2, M_3, and Q_3. (The moment M_R and the force Q_R which act between the ring and the circular plate can be eliminated by considering the equilibrium of the plate under the applied pressure loadings). Once the discontinuity moments and shearing forces are known, the stresses in the various components of the structure can be determined.

For the sake of brevity, we shall not present the details of the procedure that we have described. It is interesting, however, to present the results of a sample calculation of this type. For this purpose, the analysis was applied to a steam generator for a nuclear power plant whose dimensions are as follows (see Fig. 7.1):

b_A	Inner radius of long cylindrical shell	22.25	in.
c_A	Outer radius of long cylindrical shell	24.0	in.
b_B	Average inner radius of short cylindrical shell	22.0	in.
c_B	Average outer radius of short cylindrical shell	24.0	in.
h_T	Thickness at top of short cylindrical shell	3.5	in.
h_B	Thickness at bottom of short cylindrical shell	2.0	in.
r_R	Outer radius of ring	24.0	in.
r_P	Radius to outermost perforation in tube sheet	19.594	in.
h_R	Thickness of tube sheet	8.625	in.
l	Length of short cylindrical shell	9.5	in.
ν	Poisson's ratio	0.30	
ν^*	Effective Poisson's ratio for tube sheet	0.49	
E^*/E	Effective Young's modulus ratio for tube sheet	0.18	
p_P	Primary pressure	2200	psi
p_S	Secondary pressure	425	psi
b_C	Inner radius of spherical head	22.0	in.
c_C	Outer radius of spherical head	24.0	in.

The stress and deflection distribution over the tube sheet of the steam generator in the sample problem are shown in Fig. 7.2. The tube sheet deflection is not zero at the edge of the tube sheet because of an additional deflection which is added to the tube sheet deflection by the rotation of the rest of the structure.

The stress distribution (excluding that of the tube sheet that is described in Fig. 7.2) as calculated for the entire structure of the steam generator in

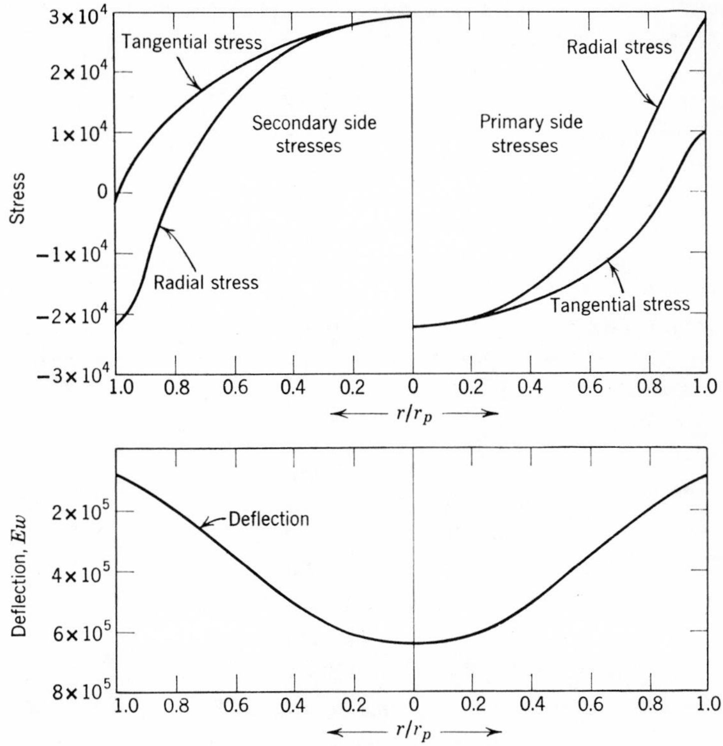

Figure 7.2 Stresses and deflections in the tube sheet of the steam generator shown in Fig. 7.1.

the sample problem is shown in Fig. 7.3. There the stresses are measured outward from and normal to the surface on which they act. Thus, the axial and circumferential stresses on the outer surface are shown on the top half of Fig. 7.3 and are measured outward from the outer surface of the steam generator. Similarly, the axial and circumferential stresses on the inner surface are shown on the bottom half of Fig. 7.3 and are measured outward from the inside surface. This difference in origins for the plots of inner and outer surface stresses accounts for the fact that at the top of the hemisphere, the inner and outer surface stresses, although equal, appear as two different points.

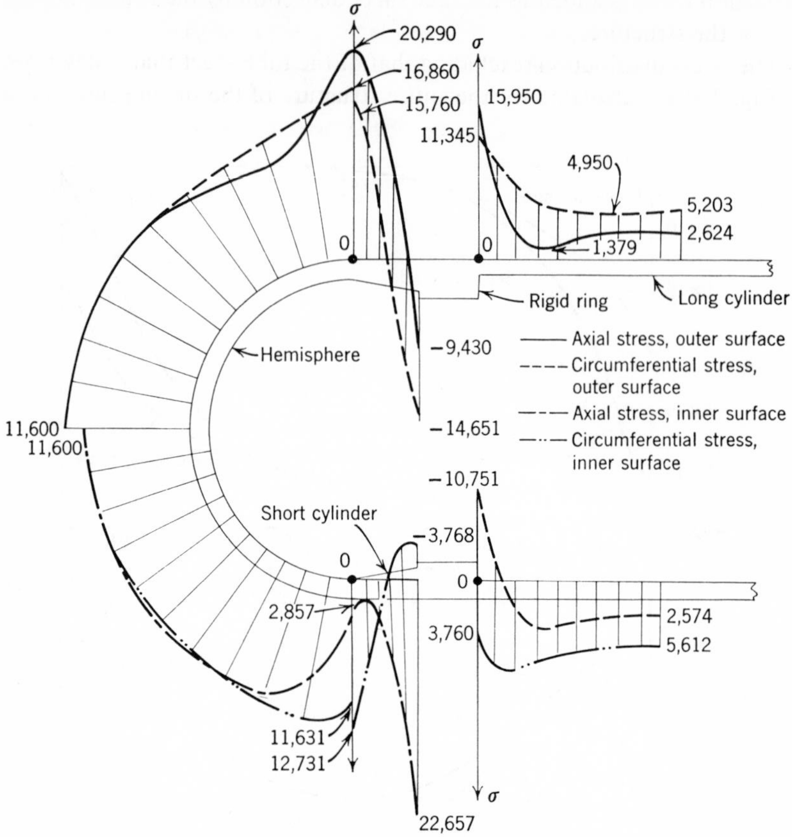

Figure 7.3 Stress distributions in the steam generator shown in Fig. 7.1.

The stress distributions in each member reach their maximum values at the joints in the structure, and the stresses in the hemisphere and long cylinder rapidly reach steady values away from these joints. The maximum stress in the structure, excluding the tube sheet, occurs at the junction of the hemisphere and the short cylinder. However, the greatest stress in the steam generator occurs at the center of the tube sheet.

We have thus demonstrated that the use of approximate solutions of the Geckeler type have made feasible the analysis of a fairly complicated composite shell structure. In these calculations, we have relied on solution functions which are far more convenient to handle than those which would, otherwise, have been required.

Calculations of the foregoing type are often carried out by hand. However, the process can quickly become extremely tedious when, as is the case in the design process, several configurations must be analyzed before the final dimensions are chosen. If a computer is available, the formulas of the procedure can be programmed and then the calculations can be carried out as many times as is necessary without any additional effort. Indeed, the present results were obtained with a program of this type.[2]

Such structures can also be handled by a numerical solution of the fundamental shell equations which has been programmed, without regard to the shape of the shell, for the digital computer. Programs of this type will be discussed in Chapter 10.

7.3 ASYMPTOTIC INTEGRATION

Our second category of approximate analytical solutions arises from the study of second order differential equations which contain a large parameter. Since a rigorous treatment[6] of the method is beyond the scope of our present interests, we choose, instead, to give a heuristic outline of a specific variant of the method which is due to Langer[7] and which was systematically applied to shells of revolution under θ-independent loadings by Naghdi.[8]

Although we shall outline the method for the orthotropic shells of revolution of variable thickness under θ-independent loads which we considered in Chapter 5, it will be evident from the development that it is also applicable to the analysis of the arbitrarily loaded isotropic shells which we considered in Chapter 6.

To begin, we recall from Chapter 5 that the analysis of shells of revolution under θ-independent edge loadings (distributed surface loadings will be discussed presently) could be reduced to the solution of an equation of the type (see Eqs. 5.15n):

$$L(U^c) + \lambda^2 U^c = 0, \tag{7.7a}$$

provided that the splitting criterion $f(\varphi) =$ constant is met (see Eq. 5.15g). If we introduce the definitions of λ^2 and the operator $L(\ldots)$ from Eqs.

---

[6] See, for example, Erdélyi, A., *Asymptotic Expansions*, New York: Dover, Chapter IV (1956).

[7] Langer, R. E., "On the Asymptotic Solution of Ordinary Differential Equations . . .," *Trans. Am. Math. Soc.*, **37**, 397–416 (1935).

[8] Naghdi, P. M., "The Effect of Transverse Shear Deformation on the Bending of Elastic Shells of Revolution," *Q. Appl. Math.*, **15**, 41–52 (1957). Also, Naghdi, P. M., and DeSilva, C. N., "On the Deformation of Elastic Shells of Revolution," *Q. Appl. Math.*, **12**, 369–374 (1954).

5.14b and 5.15m into the foregoing equation, it takes the form

$$U'' + \left[\cot\varphi + \frac{(r_\theta/r_\varphi)'}{(r_\theta/r_\varphi)} - \frac{h'}{h}\right] U'$$
$$- \frac{r_\varphi^{\,2}}{r_\theta h}\left\{\frac{E_\theta h}{E_\varphi r_\theta}\cot^2\varphi - \nu_{\varphi\theta}\frac{h}{r_\varphi}\left(1 + \cot\varphi\,\frac{h'}{h}\right) + f\right.$$
$$\left. - i\left[12(1 - \nu_{\varphi\theta}\nu_{\theta\varphi})\frac{E_\theta}{E_\varphi} - f^2\right]^{1/2}\right\} U = 0, \quad (7.7b)$$

where a prime denotes a derivative with respect to φ. It is well known that a differential equation of the type

$$\frac{d^2y}{dx^2} + p(x)\frac{dy}{dx} + q(x)y = 0, \quad (7.8a)$$

can be cast into the so-called normal form

$$\frac{d^2u}{dx^2} + \gamma(x)u(x) = 0, \quad (7.8b)$$

where

$$\gamma(x) = q(x) - \frac{1}{2}\frac{dp}{dx} - \frac{p^2}{4}, \quad (7.8c)$$

by means of the change of variable

$$u = y\exp\left[\tfrac{1}{2}\int p\,dx\right]. \quad (7.8d)$$

In terms of our Eq. 7.7b, the change of variable is, therefore,

$$Y = U\exp\left\{\tfrac{1}{2}\int\left[\cot\varphi + \frac{(r_\theta/r_\varphi)'}{(r_\theta/r_\varphi)} - \frac{h'}{h}\right]d\varphi\right\}, \quad (7.9a)$$

or, after the integration is carried out,

$$Y = U\left[\frac{r_\theta\sin\varphi}{hr_\varphi}\right]^{1/2}. \quad (7.9b)$$

Then, in view of Eqs. 7.8b and 7.8c, the variable Y satisfies the differential equation

$$Y'' - \left\{\frac{E_\theta r_\varphi^{\,2}}{E_\varphi r_\theta^{\,2}}\cot^2\varphi - \nu_{\varphi\theta}\frac{r_\varphi}{r_\theta}\left(1 + \frac{h'}{h}\cot\varphi\right) + \frac{fr_\varphi^{\,2}}{hr_\theta}\right.$$
$$+ \frac{1}{4}\left[\cot\varphi + \frac{(r_\theta/r_\varphi)'}{(r_\theta/r_\varphi)} - \frac{h'}{h}\right]^2$$
$$+ \frac{1}{2}\left[-\csc^2\varphi + \frac{(r_\theta/r_\varphi)''}{(r_\theta/r_\varphi)} - \frac{(r_\theta/r_\varphi)'^2}{(r_\theta/r_\varphi)^2} - \frac{h''}{h} + \left(\frac{h'}{h}\right)^2\right]$$
$$\left. - i\left[12(1 - \nu_{\varphi\theta}\nu_{\theta\varphi})\frac{E_\theta r_\varphi^{\,4}}{E_\varphi r_\theta^{\,2}h^2} - \left(\frac{fr_\varphi}{r_\theta h}\right)^2\right]^{1/2}\right\} Y = 0. \quad (7.9c)$$

This is the normal form of the governing equation of the problem. It is convenient, before discussing its asymptotic solution, to rewrite it in the more compact form

$$Y'' + [2i\kappa^2\Psi^2(\varphi) + \Lambda(\varphi)]Y = 0, \tag{7.9d}$$

where $2\kappa^2$ and $\Psi^2(\varphi)$ are defined in such a manner that they represent the constant and the variable portions of the radical in Eq. 7.9c and

$$\begin{aligned} -\Lambda(\varphi) = {} & \frac{E_\theta r_\varphi^{\,2}}{E_\varphi r_\theta^{\,2}} \cot^2\varphi - \nu_{\varphi\theta}\frac{r_\varphi}{r_\theta}\left(1 + \frac{h'}{h}\cot\varphi\right) + \frac{f r_\varphi^{\,2}}{h r_\theta} \\ & + \frac{1}{4}\left[\cot\varphi + \frac{(r_\theta/r_\varphi)'}{(r_\theta/r_\varphi)} - \frac{h'}{h}\right]^2 \\ & + \frac{1}{2}\left[\frac{(r_\theta/r_\varphi)''}{(r_\theta/r_\varphi)} - \frac{(r_\theta/r_\varphi)'^2}{(r_\theta/r_\varphi)^2} - \frac{h''}{h} + \left(\frac{h'}{h}\right)^2 - \csc^2\varphi\right]. \end{aligned} \tag{7.9e}$$

It was shown by Langer[7] that, corresponding to Eq. 7.9d, there exists a so-called comparison equation whose solution is asymptotic, with respect to the large parameter κ, to the solution of Eq. 7.9d. The domain of validity of this asymptotic solution depends on the functions in the coefficient of Y. If φ ranges over an interval I_φ which includes a point φ_0 at which $\Lambda(\varphi)$ may have a pole of first or second order, if Ψ^2 contains as a factor the quantity $(\varphi - \varphi_0)^a$ where a is a real nonnegative constant, and if both Λ and Ψ^2 are analytic and bounded in the rest of I_φ, then the asymptotic solution will be valid in the entire interval I_φ including the point φ_0. If Λ and Ψ^2 do not behave in this way, then the solution will be valid in some subinterval of I_φ.

The functions Λ and Ψ^2 can be represented in such a manner that they reflect the foregoing considerations by the forms

$$\begin{aligned} \Lambda(\varphi) &= \frac{A_1}{(\varphi - \varphi_0)^2} + \frac{B_1}{(\varphi - \varphi_0)} + \Lambda_1(\varphi), \\ \Psi^2(\varphi) &= (\varphi - \varphi_0)^a \Psi_1^{\,2}(\varphi), \end{aligned} \tag{7.10a}$$

where A_1 and B_1 are known constants, $\Lambda_1(\varphi)$ is analytic and bounded with respect to κ in I_φ, and $\Psi_1^{\,2}(\varphi)$ is a nonvanishing single-valued analytic function in I_φ, including the point φ_0. With these definitions, it was shown by Langer[7] that the comparison equation

$$y'' + \left[2i\kappa^2\Psi^2(\varphi) + \frac{A_1}{(\varphi - \varphi_0)^2} + \frac{B_1}{\varphi - \varphi_0} + \Omega(\varphi)\right] y = 0, \tag{7.10b}$$

where $\Omega(\varphi)$ is analytic and bounded with respect to κ in I_φ, is satisfied by the functions

$$\begin{Bmatrix} y_1 \\ y_2 \end{Bmatrix} = \Psi^{-1/2}(\varphi)\sigma^{1/2}\begin{Bmatrix} J_\rho(\sigma) \\ Y_\rho(\sigma) \end{Bmatrix}. \tag{7.10c}$$

Since $L(y) + \lambda^2 y = 0$

$L(y) + \bar{\lambda}^2 y = 0$

REF. (5.1)

Here J_ρ and Y_ρ are the Bessel functions of the first and second kind and

$$\rho = 2\mu(1 - 4A_1)^{1/2}, \qquad 2\mu = (a + 2)^{-1},$$
$$\sigma = \omega(2i\kappa^2)^{1/2}, \qquad \omega = \int_{\varphi_0}^{\varphi} \Psi(\eta)\, d\eta. \tag{7.10d}$$

Since the argument σ is imaginary the solutions y_1 and y_2 represent four functions as discussed in Section 5.1. These are the real and the imaginary parts of the Bessel functions that appear in the solution (Eq. 7.10c).

If we let

$$\Lambda_1(\varphi) = \Omega(\varphi) + \Delta(\varphi), \tag{7.10e}$$

where Δ (which can be described as a correction function) is also analytic and bounded with respect to κ in I_φ, then Eq. 7.9d may be written as

$$Y'' + \left[2i\kappa^2\Psi^2(\varphi) + \frac{A_1}{(\varphi - \varphi_0)^2} + \frac{B_1}{(\varphi - \varphi_0)} + \Omega(\varphi)\right] Y = -\Delta(\varphi) Y. \tag{7.10f}$$

Now, since the homogeneous portions of Eq. 7.10f and the comparison equation 7.10b are identical, we may find the particular solution of Eq. 7.10f by the method of variation of parameters. Thus,

$$Y_j = y_j + \int_{\varphi_0}^{\varphi} D_1(\varphi, \eta)\Delta(\eta) Y_j(\eta)\, d\eta, \qquad j = 1, 2,$$
$$D_1(\varphi, \eta) = \Gamma_1^{-1}(y_1, y_2)[y_1(\varphi)y_2(\eta) - y_2(\varphi)y_1(\eta)], \tag{7.10g}$$

where $y_j (j = 1, 2)$ are the homogeneous solutions of Eqs. 7.10b and 7.10f and Γ^{-1} denotes the Wronskian[9] of y_1 and y_2. This integral equation can be solved by iteration, a process which yields the formal solution

$$Y_j = y_j(\varphi) + \sum_{n=1}^{\infty} y_j^{(n)}(\varphi), \tag{7.10h}$$

where

$$y_j^{(n+1)}(\varphi) = \int_{\varphi_0}^{\varphi} D_1(\varphi, \eta)\Delta(\eta) y_j^{(n)}(\eta)\, d\eta,$$
$$y_j^{(0)}(\varphi) = y_j(\varphi). \tag{7.10i}$$

It can be shown[10] that the series 7.10h converges uniformly in the interval I_φ and that, furthermore, the term $y_j(\varphi)$ is dominant in the expansion when the conditions which have been placed earlier upon the development are

[9] See, for example, footnote 14 in Chapter 6.
[10] Erdélyi, A., loc. cit.

satisfied. Thus, we conclude that $y_j(\varphi)$ is asymptotic with respect to κ to the solution Y_j of Eq. 7.10f.

It is interesting to realize, at this point, that the asymptotic solutions which we have just derived all involve Bessel functions of complex argument and of various orders which depend upon the geometry of the specific shell to which the method is applied. The solutions are, of course, applicable to shells of variable thickness and radii of curvature provided only that the splitting criterion (Eq. 5.15g) is satisfied.

The foregoing development was restricted to the determination of complementary solutions for shells of revolution under θ-independent edge loadings. To find an approximate particular solution when the shell is also subjected to a distributed surface loading, we recall, for example, that in every case which we considered in Sections 5.2*b*, 5.3*b*, and 5.4*b*, we found that the particular solutions were identical to the membrane solution of the problem involved and if they were not identical to the membrane solution they approached it as $(R/h)^2$ became large. Based on observations of this type, it has become customary to take the membrane state $Q^p = \beta_\varphi{}^p = 0$ as an approximation to the particular solution of a shell under a distributed loading. The stress resultants $N_\varphi{}^p$ and $N_\theta{}^p$ then take on their membrane values, while $M_\varphi{}^p = M_\theta{}^p = 0$. In a study of this practice as it relates to the determination of a solution by asymptotic integration, Hildebrand[11] concluded that if we take only the leading term of the series 7.10h as an approximate complementary solution, it is indeed consistent to also take $Q^p = \beta_\varphi{}^p = 0$, provided that the intensity of the distributed loading does not vary appreciably over any distance which is of the order $(r_\theta h)^{1/2}$.

The method of asymptotic integration provides a method of attack for all problems of shell analysis. Where exact analytical solutions of the type covered in Chapters 5 and 6 are available, it provides solution forms which are more convenient to use. Where exact analytical solutions cannot be obtained it provides the only analytical approach to the solution. In the latter category we have in mind, particularly, shells whose principal radii of curvature and whose thickness are functions of meridional position. To illustrate the simplifications which are possible when the method of asymptotic integration is used, we shall next reconsider the analysis of a spherical shell of uniform thickness. This will provide a convenient vehicle of comparison between an exact solution of the problem as obtained in Section 5.4*c* and the solution based on Geckeler's approximation which we obtained in Section 7.2*a*. After that, we shall consider the analysis of a toroidal shell, which we have not previously studied.

[11] Hildebrand, F. B., "On Asymptotic Integration in Shell Theory," *Proc. Symp. in Appl. Math.*, New York: McGraw-Hill, **III**, 53–66 (1950).

7.3a Application to the Analysis of a Spherical Shell

To apply the foregoing development to a spherical shell of constant thickness, we set $r_\varphi = r_\theta = R$ and observe that, as a result,

splitting criteria

$$f = \frac{\nu_{\varphi\theta} h}{R}, \qquad \kappa^4 = 3(1 - \nu_{\varphi\theta}\nu_{\theta\varphi}) \frac{E_\theta}{E_\varphi} \left(\frac{R}{h}\right)^2, \quad 7.4d$$

$$\Psi^2 = \left[1 - \frac{E_\varphi}{E_\theta}\left(\frac{h}{R}\right)^2 \frac{\nu_{\varphi\theta}}{12(1 - \nu_{\varphi\theta}\nu_{\theta\varphi})}\right]^{1/2} \approx 1 = \Psi_1^2, \quad (7.11a)$$

$$\Lambda = \frac{1}{2}\csc^2\varphi - \left(\frac{E_\theta}{E_\varphi} + \frac{1}{4}\right)\cot^2\varphi, \quad 7.9e$$

need to solve for Λ

$$Y = RQ_\varphi \left(\frac{\sin\varphi}{h}\right)^{1/2}, \quad a = 0, \qquad 7.9b$$

and Y satisfies the differential equation (see Eq. 7.9d):

$$Y'' + \left[2i\kappa^2 + \frac{1}{2}\csc^2\varphi - \left(\frac{E_\theta}{E_\varphi} + \frac{1}{4}\right)\cot^2\varphi\right] Y = 0. \qquad (7.11b)$$

If we observe that $\Lambda(\varphi)$ can be expanded in the form

$$\Lambda(\varphi) = \frac{1}{2}\left(\frac{1}{\varphi} + \frac{\varphi}{3!} + \frac{7\varphi^3}{3\cdot 5!} + \cdots\right)^2$$
$$- \left(\frac{E_\theta}{E_\varphi} + \frac{1}{4}\right)\left(\frac{1}{\varphi} - \frac{\varphi}{3} - \frac{\varphi^3}{45} + \cdots\right)^2, \qquad (7.11c)$$

then

$$\Lambda(\varphi) = \left(\frac{1}{4} - \frac{E_\theta}{E_\varphi}\right)\frac{1}{\varphi^2} + \Lambda_1(\varphi), \qquad (7.11d)$$

where $\Lambda_1(\varphi)$ is a series of terms involving nonnegative powers of φ. From this we find, upon comparison to Eqs. 7.10a, that

$$\varphi_0 = B_1 = 0, \qquad A_1 = 1/4 - E_\theta/E_\varphi, \qquad (7.11e)$$

and, furthermore, from Eqs. 7.10d,

$$2\mu = \frac{1}{2}, \qquad \rho = \left(\frac{E_\theta}{E_\varphi}\right)^{1/2}, \qquad \omega = \varphi,$$
$$\sigma = (2i\kappa^2)^{1/2}\varphi. \qquad (7.11f)$$

Therefore, the asymptotic solutions are, from Eqs. 7.10c,

Homogeneous part of the sol.

$$\begin{Bmatrix} Y_1 \\ Y_2 \end{Bmatrix} = \sigma^{1/2} \begin{Bmatrix} J_\rho(\sigma) \\ Y_\rho(\sigma) \end{Bmatrix}. \qquad (7.11g)$$

In the present case it is also possible, since the leading term in the coefficient of Y in Eq. 7.11b is a constant which contains the large parameter κ, to

$$J_\nu(x) = x^\nu \sum_{m=0}^{\infty} \frac{(-1)^m x^{2m}}{2^{2m+\nu} \, m! \, \Gamma(\nu+m+1)}$$

$$Y_\nu(x) = \frac{1}{\sin\nu\pi}\left[J_\nu(x)\cos\nu\pi - J_{-\nu}(x)\right]$$

simplify the analysis further. This can be accomplished by restricting our attention, as we did in the case of the Geckeler approximation, to values of φ which are close to $\pi/2$. In this manner, the term $2i\kappa^2$ will be dominant and the equation can be simplified to read

$$Y'' + 2i\kappa^2 Y = 0. \tag{7.12a}$$

This equation is identical to Eq. 5.17a of the analysis of cylindrical shells under θ-independent loads and has, therefore, the solutions

$$Q_\varphi \sqrt{\sin \varphi} = e^{\kappa\varphi} (B_1 \cos \kappa\varphi + B_2 \sin \kappa\varphi) + e^{-\kappa\varphi} (B_3 \cos \kappa\varphi + B_4 \sin \kappa\varphi), \tag{7.12b}$$

where we have absorbed the constant quantity $R/h^{1/2}$ in the arbitrary constants and we have included the contribution from the complex conjugate of Eq. 7.12a. To find β_φ from this expression, we use Eq. 7.1b, which, for the spherical shell of constant thickness, takes the form

$$\frac{d^2 Q_\varphi}{d\varphi^2} + \cot \varphi \frac{dQ_\varphi}{d\varphi} - \left(\frac{E_\theta}{E_\varphi} \cot^2 \varphi - \nu_{\varphi\theta}\right) Q_\varphi = -E_\theta h \beta_\varphi, \tag{7.12c}$$

where we have restricted our attention to the complementary solutions. Now let us change the variables according to the formula (see Eq. 7.8d):

$$z = y \exp\left(\tfrac{1}{2} \int \cot \varphi \, d\varphi\right), \tag{7.12d}$$

whereupon we obtain

$$Q_1 = Q_\varphi \sqrt{\sin \varphi}, \qquad \beta_1 = \beta_\varphi \sqrt{\sin \varphi} \tag{7.12e}$$

and, therefore,

$$\frac{d^2 Q_1}{d\varphi^2} - \left(\frac{E_\theta}{E_\varphi} \cot^2 \varphi - \nu_{\varphi\theta} + \frac{\cot^2 \varphi}{4} - \frac{\csc^2 \varphi}{2}\right) Q_1 = -E_\theta h \beta_1. \tag{7.12f}$$

Since we are restricting our attention to values of φ which are close to $\pi/2$, and since the second derivative of Q_1 with respect to φ will be κ^2 greater than Q_1, we can reduce Eq. 7.12f to

$$\frac{d^2 Q_1}{d\varphi^2} \cong -E_\theta h \beta_1, \tag{7.12g}$$

which, in conjunction with Eq. 7.12b, gives the result

$$\frac{E_\theta h \beta_\varphi \sqrt{\sin \varphi}}{2\kappa^2} = e^{\kappa\varphi} (B_1 \sin \kappa\varphi - B_2 \cos \kappa\varphi) + e^{-\kappa\varphi} (B_4 \cos \kappa\varphi - B_3 \sin \kappa\varphi). \tag{7.12h}$$

It is interesting that Eqs. 7.12b and 7.12h have, with the exception of the multiplicative factor $(\sin \varphi)^{1/2}$, the same form as Eqs. 7.5d and 7.5e of the Geckeler approximation.

As an illustration, we apply the foregoing solution to the clamped pressurized hemispherical shell which we have considered previously. Here we note that the decaying exponentials must again be suppressed by setting $B_3 = B_4 = 0$. The two remaining constants are then obtained from the application of the boundary conditions (Eqs. 7.6c) at the edge $\varphi = \pi/2$ to the functions 7.12b and 7.12h. We shall, however, omit the details of this procedure as it leads to expressions which are quite similar to Eqs. 7.6e. Numerical results which are obtained by the resulting formulas will be presented in Section 7.4 (see Table 7.1) along with the results of an exact analysis as obtained in Section 5.4*c* and the solution based upon Geckeler's approximation which was obtained in Section 7.2*a*.

7.3*b* Application to the Analysis of a Toroidal Shell

The method of asymptotic integration finds its greatest usefulness in the analysis of shells whose geometry does not permit a convenient exact analysis of the type described in Chapters 5 and 6 to be carried out. In this connection, we have in mind, for example, ellipsoidal, toroidal, and paraboloidal shells of revolution whose principal radii of curvature are complicated functions of meridional position.

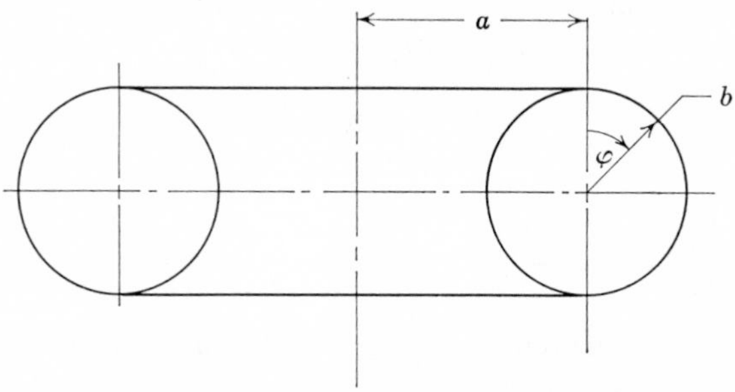

Figure 7.4 Geometry of a toroidal shell.

To illustrate the use of the method of asymptotic integration in the analysis of such shells, we shall, therefore, consider the analysis of a toroidal shell of revolution (as shown in Fig. 7.4) under loadings which are independent of polar position.[12] From Fig. 7.4, we note that the principal radii of

[12] Clark, R. A., "On the Theory of Thin Elastic Toroidal Shells," *J. Math. Phys.*, **29**, 146–178 (1950).

curvature of the toroidal shell are

$$r_\varphi = b, \qquad r_\theta = \frac{b(1 + \lambda \sin \varphi)}{\lambda \sin \varphi}, \qquad \lambda = b/a. \tag{7.13}$$

If we assume that the thickness of the shell is uniform, we find that the splitting function is

$$f = \frac{\nu_{\varphi\theta} h}{b}. \tag{7.13a}$$

Therefore, the splitting criterion is satisfied and we find that Eq. 7.9c takes the form

$$Y'' - \left\{\frac{\lambda^2 \cos^2 \varphi}{(1 + \lambda \sin \varphi)^2}\left(\frac{E_\theta}{E_\varphi} - \frac{1}{4}\right) - \left[\frac{\lambda}{2} + 2i\mu_T{}^2\left\{1 - \frac{\nu_{\varphi\theta}{}^2 E_\varphi h^2}{12b^2 E_\theta(1 - \nu_{\varphi\theta}\nu_{\theta\varphi})}\right\}^{1/2} \frac{\sin \varphi}{1 + \lambda \sin \varphi}\right]\right\} Y = 0 \tag{7.13b}$$

where

$$\mu_T{}^4 = 3(1 - \nu_{\varphi\theta}\nu_{\theta\varphi})\frac{E_\theta}{E_\varphi}\frac{b^4}{h^2 a^2}, \qquad Y = U(1 + \lambda \sin \varphi)^{1/2}. \tag{7.13c}$$

Since we are dealing with thin shells for which $h/b \ll 1$, we may replace the radical in Eq. 7.13b with unity. Then, since $\lambda < 1$, we may ignore $\lambda/2$ with respect to the large quantity $2i\mu_T{}^2$. As a result of these simplifications, the governing equation of the shell becomes,

$$Y'' + [2i\mu_T{}^2 \Psi^2(\varphi) + \Lambda(\varphi)]Y = 0, \tag{7.13d}$$

where

$$\Psi^2(\varphi) = \frac{\sin \varphi}{1 + \lambda \sin \varphi}, \tag{7.13e}$$

$$\Lambda(\varphi) = \left(\frac{1}{4} - \frac{E_\theta}{E_\varphi}\right)\frac{\lambda^2 \cos^2 \varphi}{(1 + \lambda \sin \varphi)^2}. \tag{7.13f}$$

Now we may observe, according to our description of the method of asymptotic integration, that $\Lambda(\varphi)$ has no poles because, in general, $\lambda < 1$. Thus, we find that (see Eqs. 7.10a) $A_1 = B_1 = 0$. Furthermore, if we recall that the sine function has the series representation

$$\sin \varphi = \varphi - \frac{\varphi^3}{3!} + \frac{\varphi^5}{5!} - \cdots, \tag{7.13g}$$

then we can write

$$\Psi^2 = \varphi \Psi_1{}^2, \tag{7.13h}$$

and, by Eqs. 7.10a, $\varphi_0 = 0$, $a = 1$. Thus, the asymptotic solution of Eq. 7.13d is (see Eqs. 7.10):

$$\begin{Bmatrix} Y_1 \\ Y_2 \end{Bmatrix} = \left(\frac{1 + \lambda \sin \varphi}{\sin \varphi}\right)^{1/4} \sigma^{1/2} \begin{Bmatrix} J_{1/3}(\sigma) \\ Y_{1/3}(\sigma) \end{Bmatrix}, \tag{7.13i}$$

where

$$\sigma = (2i\mu_T{}^2)^{1/2}\omega,$$
$$\omega = \int_0^{\varphi} \left(\frac{\sin \eta}{1 + \lambda \sin \eta}\right)^{1/2} d\eta. \tag{7.13j}$$

The integral in the definition of ω can be evaluated in various ways. For example, we can expand the integrand into a series of terms involving powers of $\sin \eta$ by employing the binomial expansion and then integrate term by term to obtain the series representation

$$\omega(\varphi, \lambda) = \frac{2}{3}(\sin \varphi)^{3/2}\left[1 - \frac{3\lambda}{10}\sin \varphi + \frac{3}{14}\left(1 + \frac{3\lambda^2}{4}\right)\sin^2 \varphi + \cdots\right]. \tag{7.13k}$$

This series has been evaluated for a wide range of the variables φ and λ by Clark.[12]

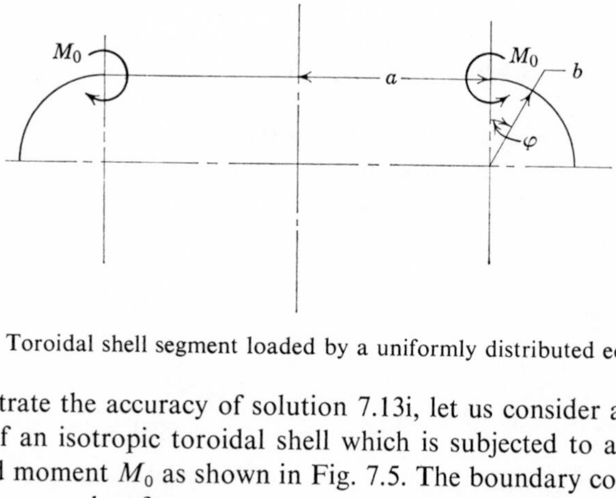

Figure 7.5 Toroidal shell segment loaded by a uniformly distributed edge moment.

To illustrate the accuracy of solution 7.13i, let us consider a 90 degree segment of an isotropic toroidal shell which is subjected to a uniformly distributed moment M_0 as shown in Fig. 7.5. The boundary conditions of the problem are, therefore,

$$\begin{aligned} M_\varphi &= M_0, \quad & N_\varphi &= 0 \quad \text{at} \quad \varphi = 0, \\ M_\varphi &= 0, \quad & Q_\varphi &= 0 \quad \text{at} \quad \varphi = \pi/2, \end{aligned} \tag{7.14a}$$

and the shell is assumed to be free of distributed loadings. An exact solution, based upon the power series method of Frobenius,[13] has been

[13] See, for example, Whittaker, E. T., and Watson, G. N., *Modern Analysis*, New York: Macmillan, Chapter X (1943).

obtained for this problem by Wissler[14] while the asymptotic solution of the problem is obtained by using the functions 7.13i. The results obtained by each method are given in Fig. 7.6,[12] where the meridional bending stress and the circumferential membrane stress (as defined by Eqs. 6.61d) for an isotropic shell with $\lambda = 0.1$, $b/h = 20$, and $\nu = 0.3$ are plotted. It is obvious, from Fig. 7.6, that the results obtained by asymptotic integration approximate very closely the exact results. Indeed, it is interesting that the agreement is so close because $2\mu_T^2 = 6.61$ for the problem under consideration, and this is certainly not a large value. It is also interesting to note that

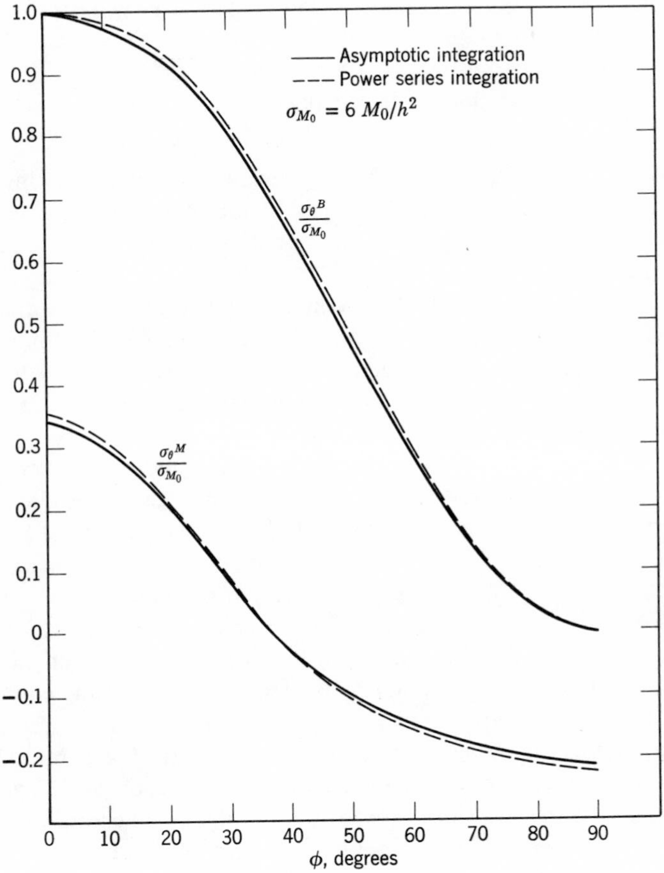

Figure 7.6 Stress distributions for the shell shown in Fig. 7.5.

[14] Wissler, H., "Festigkeitsberechnung von Ringflächenschalen," Dissertation. E. T. H. Zurich (1916).

the smallness of this value explains the fact that Fig. 7.6 does not show a pronounced edge effect of the type which we have observed in our previous calculations. For thinner shells, the edge effect will, of course, become more obvious and this fact can be used to introduce further simplification into the analysis. For example, if we wish to consider an edge effect near $\varphi = 0$, we can reduce the complexity of the analysis in a manner which is similar to the considerations of the Geckeler approximation. Near $\varphi = 0$, we notice that $\sin \varphi \approx \varphi$, $\cos \varphi \approx 1$, and Eq. 7.13d becomes

$$Y'' + 2i\mu_T{}^2\varphi Y = 0, \tag{7.15}$$

where we have ignored $\Lambda(\varphi)$ and neglected $\lambda\varphi$ in comparison to unity. The solution of this equation is left to the Exercises.

7.3c Further Applications of the Method of Asymptotic Integration

Although we have already given sufficient illustrations of the asymptotic integration of the equations which govern the behavior of thin elastic shells, it is well at this point to mention the wide applicability of the method in shell analysis by citing some additional studies in which it has been employed.

In the class of shells of revolution under θ-independent loads, the spherical and toroidal shells which we considered here had in common the feature that the splitting condition was satisfied because the shells were of uniform thickness and of constant meridional radius of curvature (r_φ) in each case. When ellipsoidal and paraboloidal shells of revolution of constant thickness are considered, the splitting condition is violated because their meridional radii of curvature are functions of meridional position. Thus, it would appear that, for such shells, the equations of the theory cannot be reduced to a single differential equation in the manner of Chapter 5 and that, therefore, the general asymptotic solution 7.10c which we have derived here would not be valid. However, studies of ellipsoidal shells[15] have shown that, if the solution of Eq. 7.9d is carried out for an ellipsoidal shell of constant thickness, ignoring the fact that the splitting condition is violated, the results turn out to be very close to results which are obtained by considering the same ellipsoidal shell but with a general thickness variation which causes the splitting criterion to be satisfied. Thus, it was concluded that the additional approximation that is inherent in the use of Eq. 7.9d as the governing differential equation of an ellipsoidal shell of uniform thickness is justified in spite of the fact that the splitting condition

[15] Naghdi, P. M., and DeSilva, C. N., "Deformation of Elastic Ellipsoidal Shells of Revolution," *Proc. 2nd U.S. National Congress of Applied Mechanics*, A.S.M.E., 333–343 (1955).

is violated. This additional approximation was then also made in a subsequent analysis of paraboloidal shells of revolution of uniform thickness by the asymptotic integration[16] of Eq. 7.9d.

The method of asymptotic integration is also applicable to shells of revolution under arbitrary loadings because, as we have shown in Chapter 6, these are also governed by second order differential equations. Such solutions have been carried out for arbitrarily loaded nonshallow spherical shells in order to avoid the use of the complex Legendre functions which appear in the exact solution and, thereby, to obtain solutions in terms of Bessel functions or exponential-trigonometric functions. In this connection, we may cite the work of Havers[17] and Leckie and Penny,[18, 19] who examined arbitrarily loaded nonshallow spherical shells. We may also mention in this connection the work of Schile[20] and Steele,[21] who employed the method of asymptotic integration in their analyses of shells of revolution with arbitrary meridians.

7.4 CLOSURE

In this chapter, we have derived and illustrated two approximate analytical procedures which have been commonly used in the analysis of shell structures. Although we established, in Section 7.3*b*, that the asymptotic solution approximates very closely the results of an exact analysis of a segment of a toroidal shell of revolution, we have not, as yet, discussed the accuracy of the Geckeler approximation, nor have we compared the results which are obtained by the two approximate methods for a given problem. Thus, it is now appropriate to bring together the results of the analyses of the clamped, pressurized, isotropic, hemispherical shell which we have carried out earlier. We have seen, in Section 5.4*c*, that the most significant results which were obtained in an exact analysis of this problem were M_φ and N_θ. At the same time, we found that N_φ does not vary appreciably from its value in the membrane state of stress over the shell and that M_θ

[16] DeSilva, C. N., "Deformation of Elastic Paraboloidal Shells of Revolution," *J. Appl. Mech.*, **24**, 397–404 (1957).

[17] Havers, A., "Asymptotische Biegetheorie der unbelasteten Kugelschale," *Ingr. Arch.*, **6**, 282–308 (1935).

[18] Leckie, F. A., "Localized Loads Applied to Spherical Shells," *J. Mech. Eng. Sci.*, **3**, 111–118 (1961).

[19] Leckie, F. A., and Penny, R. K., "A Critical Study of the Solutions for the Asymmetric Bending of Spherical Shells," *Weld. Res. Counc. Bull. No. 90* (1963).

[20] Schile, R. D., "Asymptotic Solution of Nonshallow Shells of Revolution Subjected to Nonsymmetric Loads," *J. Aerospace Sci.*, **29**, 1375–1379 (1962).

[21] Steele, C. R., "Nonsymmetric Deformation of Dome-shaped Shells of Revolution," *J. Appl. Mech.*, **29**, 353–361 (1962).

is roughly an order of magnitude smaller than M_φ. For purposes of comparison, therefore, we have listed in Table 7.1 the results which were

Table 7.1 Comparison of Results Obtained for Isotropic Clamped, Pressurized Hemispherical Shells by the Exact Solution, by Geckeler's Approximation, and by Asymptotic Integration

	$2N_\theta/pR$			M_φ/ph^2		
φ (deg)	Exact	Geckeler	Asymptotic	Exact	Geckeler	Asymptotic
			$R/h = 10$			
90	0.300	0.300	0.300	−1.066	−1.059	−1.059
85	0.371	0.369	0.373	−0.446	−0.437	−0.441
80	0.514	0.514	0.516	−0.061	−0.052	−0.059
75	0.669	0.672	0.670	+0.141	+0.148	+0.140
70	0.802	0.807	0.802	+0.219	+0.221	+0.217
65	0.903	0.908	0.901	+0.222	+0.218	+0.219
60	0.970	0.973	0.968	+0.186	+0.178	+0.183
55	1.009	1.010	1.007	+0.136	+0.127	+0.135
50	1.028	1.027	1.026	+0.089	+0.079	+0.088
45	1.033	1.030	1.031	+0.049	+0.041	+0.049
			$R/h = 100$			
90	0.300	0.300	0.300	−10.598	−10.591	−10.591
85	0.695	0.695	0.695	+1.611	+1.616	+1.609
80	0.988	0.988	0.988	+1.591	+1.583	+1.589
75	1.029	1.029	1.029	+0.281	+0.275	+0.281
70	1.010	1.009	1.009	−0.092	−0.091	−0.092
65	1.000	1.000	1.000	−0.057	−0.055	−0.057
60	0.999	0.999	0.999	−0.006	−0.006	−0.006

obtained for N_θ and M_φ in two shells by the exact analysis of Section 5.4*c*, by the Geckeler approximation of Section 7.2*a*, and by the asymptotic solution of Section 7.3*a*. It is clear, from the tabulation, that both methods improve in accuracy as the ratio of radius to thickness is increased. Both methods give excellent approximations of the exact results; however, the results which were obtained by asymptotic integration are closer to the exact results than those which are based upon the Geckeler approximation.[22] In view of the fact that the asymptotic solutions are applicable to a

[22] Such conclusions were also reached by M. Hetényi in his study of clamped pressurized spherical segments with a half angle of opening of 35 degrees and $R/h = 30$, see, "Spherical Shells Subjected to Axial Symmetric Bending," *Publications of the Internat. Assoc. of Bridge and Struct. Engrs.*, **5**, 173–185 (1938).

broader class of shell problems than the Geckeler approximation, and in view of the fact that an asymptotic solution gives a better approximation of the exact results for a problem to which both methods are applicable, the asymptotic method is preferred. Indeed, the Geckeler approximation appears to be useful mainly in the analysis of spherical shells.

In addition to the derivation of the approximate analytical solutions which we have discussed in this chapter, we have made the important observation that, when a shell is subjected to distributed loadings, the particular solutions that are required can in most cases be approximated very closely by the solution which corresponds to the loading under consideration in the membrane state of stress. This practice has been found to be reliable in the majority of analytical solutions be they exact or approximate in nature. However, in the case of the toroidal shell of revolution it has led to discrepancies[23] which are most readily resolved by using a numerical solution of the type which we shall consider in Chapter 10.

SUPPLEMENTARY REFERENCES

Clark, R. A., "Asymptotic Solutions of Toroidal Shell Problems," *Q. Appl. Math.*, **16**, 47–60 (1958).

Clark, R. A., Gilroy, T. I., and Reissner, E., "Stresses and Deformations of Toroidal Shells of Elliptical Cross Section," *J. Appl. Mech.*, **19**, 37–48 (1952).

DeSilva, C. N., and Naghdi, P. M., "Asymptotic Solutions of a Class of Elastic Shells of Revolution with Variable Thickness," *Q. Appl. Math.*, **15**, 169–182 (1957).

Dingle, R. B., "The Method of Comparison Equations in the Solution of Linear Second-Order Differential Equations," *Appl. Sci. Res.*, **5B**, 345–367 (1956).

Ferguson, H. B., Kudar, J., and Harvey, R. B., "The Stress Distribution in the Head of a Thin Walled Pressure Vessel," *Q. Journ. Mech. Appl. Math.*, **5**, 1–14 (1953).

Hoff, N. J., "The Effect of Meridian Curvature on the Influence Coefficients of Thin Spherical Shells," *Problems of Continuum Mechanics*, Philadelphia Pa.: The Society for Industrial and Applied Mathematics, pp. 178–197 (1961).

Horvay, G., Linkous, C., and Born, J. S., "Analysis of Short Thin Axisymmetrical Shells . . .," *J. Appl. Mech.*, **23**, 68–72 (1956).

Steele, C. R., "On the Asymptotic Solution of Nonhomogeneous Ordinary Differential Equations with a Large Parameter," *Q. Appl. Math.*, **23**, 193–201 (1965).

Steele, C. R., and Hartung, R. F., "Symmetric Loading of Orthotropic Shells of Revolution," *J. Appl. Mech.*, **32**, 337–345 (1965).

---

[23] Galletly, G. D., "On Particular Integrals for Toroidal Shells Subjected to Uniform Internal Pressure," *J. Appl. Mech.*, **25**, 412–413 (1958); Galletly, G. D., and Radok, J. R. M., "On the Accuracy of Some Shell Solutions," *J. Appl. Mech.*, **26**, 577–583 (1959).

EXERCISES

7.1 Analyze, by means of the Geckeler approximation, a complete isotropic spherical shell. Its bottom half is filled with a hot liquid whose temperature is sufficient to cause the wall of the lower half of the vessel to be at a uniform temperature which is T_0 degrees above the temperature of the upper half.

7.2 Analyze, by means of the Geckeler approximation, an orthotropic spherical shell segment which is free at its upper edge $\varphi = \varphi_0$ and subjected to a θ-independent distributed moment M_0 at its lower edge $\varphi = \varphi_1$.

7.3 Using the Geckeler approximation, find the general solution of a shell whose geometry is such that

$$\kappa = \frac{a}{b + \varphi}.$$

where a and b are constants.

7.4 Analyze the pressure vessel with a hemispherical head, which we considered in Section 5.5, by means of the Geckeler approximation.

7.5 Obtain the complementary solution for an ellipsoidal shell of revolution by means of asymptotic integration.

7.6 Solve equation 7.15.

7.7 Repeat Exercise 7.4 but employ the asymptotic solution for the hemispherical head.

7.8 In a formulation[24] of the problem of a nonshallow spherical shell under bending loads (which is an alternative to the formulation of our Section 6.4), it has been shown that the behavior of the shell is governed by the differential equation

$$\frac{d^2R_n}{d\varphi^2} + \cot\varphi\frac{dR_n}{d\varphi} + (1 + 2i\kappa^2 - n^2\csc^2\varphi)R_n = 0,$$

where κ is the usual large constant parameter. Obtain an asymptotic solution, in terms of Bessel functions, for this equation.

---

[24] Havers, loc. cit.

III

Dynamic Analysis of Shells

Natural frequencies of freely vibrating thin elastic shells are determined by exact and approximate analytical methods. Methods for calculating the response of a shell to transient loads of mechanical and thermal origin are described and illustrated.

Free Vibration of Shells

8.1 INTRODUCTION

Time-dependent vibratory motions are set up in a shell whenever it is disturbed from a position of stable equilibrium. If these motions occur in the absence of external loads, they are classified as "free" vibrations. If these motions are set up by time-dependent external loads, they are referred to as "forced" vibrations.

A shell, since it is an example of an elastic body, is composed of an infinite number of mass particles. As a consequence, when it is set into motion it possesses an infinite number of degrees of freedom. Its response to a disturbance may thus be analyzed into an infinite number of periodic motions which are referred to as its normal modes of free vibration. Each of these normal modes has an associated natural frequency of free vibration.

A knowledge of the free-vibration characteristics of thin elastic shells is important both to our general understanding of the fundamentals of the behavior of a shell and to the industrial application of shell structures. In connection with the latter, the natural frequencies of shell structures must be known in order to avoid the destructive effect of resonance with nearby rotating or oscillating equipment (such as jet and reciprocating aircraft engines, electrical machinery, marine turbines and screws, and the exhaust flames from rocket motors, to cite but a few).

Since free vibrations occur in the absence of *all* external loads, we are concerned in the free-vibration analysis of shells with the solution of a homogeneous system of partial differential equations with homogeneous boundary conditions. Thus, to begin the discussion of the free-vibration analysis, it is appropriate to set down the equations of motion of a thin elastic shell, in the absence of distributed loadings, as given in Chapter 2 (see Eqs. 2.71):

$$\begin{aligned}
&\frac{\partial N_1A_2}{\partial\alpha_1} + \frac{\partial N_{21}A_1}{\partial\alpha_2} + N_{12}\frac{\partial A_1}{\partial\alpha_2} - N_2\frac{\partial A_2}{\partial\alpha_1} + A_1A_2\frac{Q_1}{R_1} = A_1A_2\rho h\frac{\partial^2 u_1}{\partial t^2},\\
&\frac{\partial N_{12}A_2}{\partial\alpha_1} + \frac{\partial N_2A_1}{\partial\alpha_2} + N_{21}\frac{\partial A_2}{\partial\alpha_1} - N_1\frac{\partial A_1}{\partial\alpha_2} + A_1A_2\frac{Q_2}{R_2} = A_1A_2\rho h\frac{\partial^2 u_2}{\partial t^2},\\
&\frac{\partial Q_1A_2}{\partial\alpha_1} + \frac{\partial Q_2A_1}{\partial\alpha_2} - \left(\frac{N_1}{R_1} + \frac{N_2}{R_2}\right)A_1A_2 = A_1A_2\rho h\frac{\partial^2 w}{\partial t^2},\\
&\frac{\partial M_1A_2}{\partial\alpha_1} + \frac{\partial M_{21}A_1}{\partial\alpha_2} + M_{12}\frac{\partial A_1}{\partial\alpha_2} - M_2\frac{\partial A_2}{\partial\alpha_1} - Q_1A_1A_2 = 0,\\
&\frac{\partial M_{12}A_2}{\partial\alpha_1} + \frac{\partial M_2A_1}{\partial\alpha_2} + M_{21}\frac{\partial A_2}{\partial\alpha_1} - M_1\frac{\partial A_1}{\partial\alpha_2} - Q_2A_1A_2 = 0.
\end{aligned} \tag{8.1}$$

To simplify the discussion of these equations, we may rewrite them in the symbolic form

$$\begin{aligned}
\mathscr{L}_1\{u_1, u_2, w\} &= \rho h\frac{\partial^2 u_1}{\partial t^2},\\
\mathscr{L}_2\{u_1, u_2, w\} &= \rho h\frac{\partial^2 u_2}{\partial t^2},\\
\mathscr{L}_3\{u_1, u_2, w\} &= \rho h\frac{\partial^2 w}{\partial t^2},
\end{aligned} \tag{8.2}$$

where the $\mathscr{L}_i$ are differential operators which are obtained by eliminating the shearing forces from the first three of Eqs. 8.1, by using the last two of Eqs. 8.1, and then eliminating the stress resultants and stress couples from the resulting equations by using Eqs. 2.19 and 2.27. The explicit forms of the $\mathscr{L}_i$ will not be given here owing to their complexity for the general case. Their forms will, however, be given for the specific shells which will be discussed later.

Solutions of Eqs. 8.2 must also satisfy boundary conditions of the type (see Eqs. 2.90):

$$B_k\{u_1, u_2, w\} = 0, \qquad k = 1, 2, \ldots, N, \tag{8.3}$$

where the B_k are differential operators which take on the forms discussed, for example, in Section 2.7, and which generally are indicated to operate on all three displacements. N is the number of boundary conditions to be applied and depends on the theory being used and the type of problem being considered. For the theory which we have adopted here $N \leqslant 16$.

To determine the normal modes and natural frequencies of free vibration of a thin elastic shell, we observe, first, that each of the normal modes executes a simple harmonic motion with an associated natural frequency ω. We should also expect that the period and phase of the motion are the same for all points in the shell. With these considerations in mind, the time dependence of the shell variables can be removed by assuming that their spatial and temporal variations are separable and that they can be represented by expressions of the type

$$\begin{aligned} u_1(\alpha_1, \alpha_2, t) &= u(\alpha_1, \alpha_2) \cos \omega t, \\ u_2(\alpha_1, \alpha_2, t) &= v(\alpha_1, \alpha_2) \cos \omega t, \\ w(\alpha_1, \alpha_2, t) &= w(\alpha_1, \alpha_2) \cos \omega t, \end{aligned} \tag{8.4}$$

and so on. If these forms are substituted into the equations of motion and into the boundary conditions 8.2 and 8.3, we find that the modes of free vibration (u, v, and w) must satisfy the system

$$\begin{aligned} \mathscr{L}_1\{u, v, w\} + \rho h \omega^2 u &= 0, \\ \mathscr{L}_2\{u, v, w\} + \rho h \omega^2 v &= 0, \\ \mathscr{L}_3\{u, v, w\} + \rho h \omega^2 w &= 0, \end{aligned} \tag{8.5}$$

$$B_k\{u, v, w\} = 0, \qquad k = 1, 2, \ldots, N. \tag{8.6}$$

Equations 8.5 are sufficient to yield N independent solutions which are functions of α_1, α_2, and the, as yet unknown, frequency parameter ω, each multiplied by an arbitrary coefficient A_α for the purpose of satisfying the boundary conditions. When these solutions are substituted into the N boundary conditions (Eq. 8.6), there is obtained a system of N homogeneous linear equations in the N unknown constants A_α which can be written symbolically as

$$\sum_{\alpha=1}^{N} C_{\beta\alpha}(\omega) A_\alpha = 0, \qquad \beta = 1, 2, \ldots, N. \tag{8.7}$$

Here the $C_{\beta\alpha}$ are coefficients which are obtained from the application of the boundary conditions 8.6 to the general solutions of the system 8.5. As indicated above, these coefficients are functions of the unknown ω. To avoid the trivial solution $A_\alpha = 0$, the determinant of the system must be set to zero. Thus,

$$|C_{\beta\alpha}(\omega)| = 0, \qquad \alpha, \beta = 1, 2, \ldots, N. \tag{8.8}$$

This equation, which is known as the frequency equation, is generally transcendental and has an infinite number of roots ω, each corresponding to a natural frequency of free vibration.

Another consequence of the fact that the system (Eqs. 8.5 and 8.6) is homogeneous is that only $N - 1$ of the constants A_α will be independent and can, at best, be expressed as functions of the remaining arbitrary constant by use of any $N - 1$ of Eqs. 8.7. If, for example, $N = 3$, as would be the case for a shell with only one edge when it executes motions which are independent of θ, we would obtain, from the last two of Eqs. 8.7, the relationships

$$\begin{aligned} \frac{A_2}{A_1} &= \frac{C_{21}C_{33} - C_{31}C_{23}}{C_{32}C_{23} - C_{22}C_{33}}, \\ \frac{A_3}{A_1} &= \frac{C_{31}C_{22} - C_{21}C_{32}}{C_{32}C_{23} - C_{22}C_{33}}. \end{aligned} \tag{8.9}$$

There is a set of the foregoing ratios, which are called amplitude ratios, for every root ω of the frequency equation and, therefore, for every mode of free vibration. As will be seen later, the amplitude ratios are useful in the determination of the character of the motion which is associated with a given mode of free vibration.

It should be realized, at this point, that the general method which has been described is simply an example of the method of characteristic functions which is widely used in engineering and mathematical physics.[1] In the more general mathematical context, the natural frequencies are the characteristic numbers (or eigenvalues) of the boundary value problem which is posed by Eqs. 8.2 and 8.3, while the normal modes of free vibration are the characteristic functions (or eigenfunctions) of that problem. Furthermore, the complementary solutions, which we found in Part II, for shells subjected to static loadings at their edges are evidently a subclass, with $\omega = 0$, of the present category of solutions.

Except in the rare eventuality of a frequency equation which can be solved in closed form or in the event of a frequency equation whose roots have already been tabulated, the roots must be determined by a trial and error procedure such as the method of "false position" (regula falsi).[2] In such a method, one is concerned with the determination of ω such that

$$f(\omega) = 0. \tag{8.10a}$$

The process is initiated by evaluating $f(\omega)$ for successively incremented values of ω until two successive values, ω_0 and ω_1, are obtained, for which the corresponding functions f_0 and f_1 are opposite in sign (see Fig. 8.1). If we connect the two points $P_0(f_0, \omega_0)$ and $P_1(f_1, \omega_1)$ with a straight line, we

[1] See, for example, Churchill, R. V., *Fourier Series and Boundary Value Problems*, New York: McGraw-Hill, 2nd ed. (1963).

[2] Hildebrand, F. B., *Introduction to Numerical Analysis*, New York: McGraw-Hill, pp. 446–448 (1956).

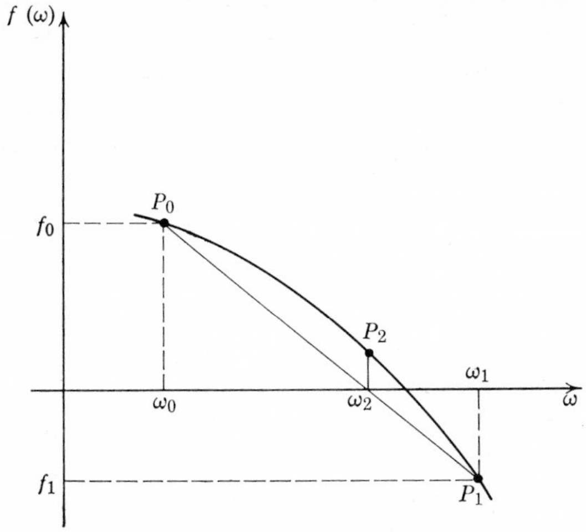

Figure 8.1

may determine the next estimate for ω by using the known slope of the line P_0P_1. Thus,

$$\omega_2 = \omega_1 - \frac{\omega_1 - \omega_0}{f_1 - f_0} f_1 = \frac{f_1\omega_0 - f_0\omega_1}{\omega_1 - \omega_0}, \tag{8.10b}$$

and this gives the point $P_2(\omega_2, f_2)$. The process is continued by means of the recursion relationship

$$\omega_k = \frac{f_{k-1}\omega_{k-2} - f_{k-2}\omega_{k-1}}{\omega_{k-1} - \omega_{k-2}}, \tag{8.10c}$$

until a root ω_k which has a desired accuracy is obtained; that is, the process is ended when, for example, the difference between ω_k and its previous value ω_{k-1} is less than a predetermined fraction of the original increment $\omega_1 - \omega_0$, or

$$\left| \frac{\omega_k - \omega_{k-1}}{\omega_1 - \omega_0} \right| \leqslant \epsilon, \tag{8.10d}$$

where ϵ is a small fraction. The method of false position is certain to converge, although it may do so slowly. Many refinements have, therefore, been proposed for the improvement of the process. For example, in one of these, the so-called second order method of false position, a parabola is fitted to the three points P_0, P_1, and P_2 which were obtained in the first step previously. The slope of the parabola at the point P_2 is then calculated and used to determine the location of the next estimate, ω_3. Then, $P_3(f_3, \omega_3)$ is determined and a parabola is fitted to the points P_3, P_2, and P_1 and the process is continued until, as before, a desired criterion on the accuracy of the estimate is met. At each step, the three most recent points are used in the estimation, whereas in the previous method only two points were used. Other higher order methods have been devised in which information from as many as five previous points is used in making the next estimate; however, they will not be described here. Interested readers are referred to the cited text by Hildebrand.[2]

The foregoing procedure must be followed in the search for as many roots as are desired of the frequency equation (Eq. 8.8). Once the first root has been found, the incrementing process is resumed until a second change of sign takes place in the frequency determinant and the associated root is obtained by another application of the false position procedure. Additional roots are obtained by repeating the cycle as many times as is desired.

Obviously, the solution of the frequency equation by methods of the foregoing type lends itself very well to digital computation if a computer is available. If one is not available, the laborious process of finding the natural frequencies by hand computation can be avoided by using one of the many variational methods that have been developed in the field of solid mechanics.[3] As an illustration of these methods, we shall next describe Rayleigh's method and Ritz's extension of it. It will be assumed, in the development which follows, that the reader has some prior familiarity with the variational approach for which the following description will, therefore, serve as a refresher.

The variational methods are based on the solution of the variational equation of the type which we have derived in Chapter 2. In particular, we refer to Eq. 2.70 of which a modified version will be applied here. The modification is achieved by the same procedure as was followed in the reduction of Eqs. 8.1 to Eqs. 8.2. Thus, for our present purposes, the variational equation takes the form

$$\int_{\alpha_1}\int_{\alpha_2} \{[\mathscr{L}_1\{u, v, w\} + \rho h\omega^2 u]\,\delta u + [\mathscr{L}_2\{u, v, w\} + \rho h\omega^2 v]\,\delta v + [\mathscr{L}_3\{u, v, w\} + \rho h\omega^2 w]\,\delta w\}A_1A_2\,d\alpha_1\,d\alpha_2 = 0, \quad (8.11)$$

from which the time dependence has been removed by substitution of Eqs. 8.4 and integration with respect to time over the interval t_0 to t_1 and, as before, the solutions must satisfy the boundary conditions (Eqs. 8.5). In the variational methods, approximate solution functions are constructed in such a manner that the boundary conditions are satisfied. The chosen solutions contain arbitrary coefficients which are then used to satisfy

[3] See, for example, Sokolnikoff, I. S., *Mathematical Theory of Elasticity*, New York: McGraw-Hill, 2nd ed., Chapter 7 (1956).

the variational equation (Eq. 8.11) and, thereby, to insure that the potential energy of the system will be a minimum. The various variational methods differ mainly in their construction of the approximate solutions. Of these, the simplest is Rayleigh's method in which a one term approximate solution which satisfies the boundary conditions is selected. Ritz's extension of the method involves the replacement of the one term approximation by one in the form of a series of functions, each of which satisfies the boundary conditions, and which may extend to as many terms as desired. The series method is generally referred to as the Rayleigh–Ritz method since it includes Rayleigh's method as a special case.

Let us then describe the solution of the free-vibration problem of a general shell by the Rayleigh–Ritz method. We assume a solution in the form

$$\begin{aligned} u &= \sum_{i=1}^{M} a_i f_i(\alpha_1, \alpha_2), \\ v &= \sum_{i=1}^{M} b_i g_i(\alpha_1, \alpha_2), \\ w &= \sum_{i=1}^{M} c_i h_i(\alpha_1, \alpha_2), \end{aligned} \tag{8.12a}$$

where the f_i, g_i, and h_i satisfy the boundary conditions of the problem to be solved, and the a_i, b_i, and c_i are arbitrary constants. The variations of the displacement functions are, therefore,

$$\begin{aligned} \delta u &= \sum_{i=1}^{M} (\delta a_i) f_i, \\ \delta v &= \sum_{i=1}^{M} (\delta b_i) g_i, \\ \delta w &= \sum_{i=1}^{M} (\delta c_i) h_i. \end{aligned} \tag{8.12b}$$

The solutions (8.12a) and their variations (8.12b) are now substituted into the variational equation (8.11) which gives, after the integrations have been carried out,

$$\begin{aligned} \Bigg\{ &\left[\sum_{i=1}^{M} (a_i F_{1i} + b_i G_{1i} + c_i H_{1i}) \right] \delta a_1 + \cdots \\ &+ \left[\sum_{i=1}^{M} (a_i F_{Mi} + b_i G_{Mi} + c_i H_{Mi}) \right] \delta a_M \\ &+ \left[\sum_{i=1}^{M} (a_i F_{1i}' + b_i G_{1i}' + c_i H_{1i}') \right] \delta b_1 + \cdots \end{aligned}$$

$$+ \left[\sum_{i=1}^{M} (a_i F_{Mi}' + b_i G_{Mi}' + c_i H_{Mi}')\right] \delta b_M$$

$$+ \left[\sum_{i=1}^{M} (a_i F_{1i}'' + b_i G_{1i}'' + c_i H_{1i}'')\right] \delta c_1 + \cdots$$

$$+ \left[\sum_{i=1}^{M} (a_i F_{Mi}'' + b_i G_{Mi}'' + c_i H_{Mi}'')\right] \delta c_M \Bigg\} = 0, \quad (8.12c)$$

where the capitalized coefficients represent the results of the double integration over the reference surface of the shell.

If the above equation is to be satisfied for an arbitrary set of variations, the square bracketed quantities must each vanish separately. This leads to $3M$ linear, homogeneous equations in $3M$ arbitrary constants. To avoid the trivial solution of the resulting system, the determinant of the coefficients is set to zero. This yields an equation of degree $3M$ in ω^2 from which $3M$ values of ω^2 can be found. The $3M$ arbitrary constants are not independent owing to the homogeneity of the system and, hence, we can only determine $3M - 1$ of them as a function of the remaining one from any $3M - 1$ equations of the system.

In the latter respects, the variational methods bear a strong resemblance to the exact analytical method which was described previously. For a finite M, however, the variational solution yields only M natural frequencies and modes of free vibration. Furthermore, the simplicity of the solution functions that are usually chosen leads to determinants whose roots can be determined analytically, as will be seen presently.

The natural frequencies obtained by the variational methods represent an upper bound on the true values. This is the usual result of the variational solution process and is attributed to the additional stiffness which is added to the system through the assumed deflection functions. This effective increase in stiffness leads to an increase in the natural frequencies of the system. By taking additional terms in the assumed solution, the accuracy of the upper bound can, however, be improved.

This ends our outline of the variational methods. For additional discussion of the Rayleigh–Ritz and other variational methods, the reader is referred to the cited text of Sokolnikoff.[3]

To illustrate the determination of the free-vibration characteristics and, at the same time, to bring out the behavior of freely vibrating thin elastic shells, we shall next apply the general procedures which we have described here to the analysis of cylindrical, shallow spherical, and nonshallow spherical shells. We shall also discuss the free-vibration analysis of composite shells and of shells vibrating freely in conjunction with a fluid medium.

8.2 FREE VIBRATION OF CYLINDRICAL SHELLS

We begin the free-vibration analysis of shells by taking up the problem of a freely vibrating circular cylindrical shell of finite length. As in the static case, we arbitrarily select, on the basis of their relative simplicity, the dynamic counterpart of the equations proposed for the analysis of cylinders by Donnell. We recall here that Donnell's formulation is based upon the assumptions that the expressions for the changes in curvature and twist of the cylinder are the same as those of a flat plate and that the effect of the transverse shearing-stress resultant Q_s on the equilibrium of forces in the circumferential direction is negligible. With these assumptions in mind, we may write the following dynamic counterparts of the equations of equilibrium of a thin circular cylindrical shell:

$$\frac{\partial^2 u_x}{\partial x^2} + \frac{1-\nu}{2a^2}\frac{\partial^2 u_x}{\partial \theta^2} + \frac{1+\nu}{2a}\frac{\partial^2 u_\theta}{\partial x\,\partial \theta} + \frac{\nu}{a}\frac{\partial w}{\partial x} - \frac{1-\nu^2}{E}\rho\frac{\partial^2 u_x}{\partial t^2} = 0, \quad (8.13a)$$

$$\frac{1+\nu}{2a}\frac{\partial^2 u_x}{\partial x\,\partial \theta} + \frac{1-\nu}{2}\frac{\partial^2 u_\theta}{\partial x^2} + \frac{1}{a^2}\frac{\partial^2 u_\theta}{\partial \theta^2} + \frac{1}{a^2}\frac{\partial w}{\partial \theta} - \frac{1-\nu^2}{E}\rho\frac{\partial^2 u_\theta}{\partial t^2} = 0, \quad (8.13b)$$

$$\frac{\nu}{a}\frac{\partial u_x}{\partial x} + \frac{1}{a^2}\frac{\partial u_\theta}{\partial \theta} + \frac{w}{a^2} + \frac{h^2}{12}\nabla^4 w + \frac{1-\nu^2}{E}\rho\frac{\partial^2 w}{\partial t^2} = 0. \quad (8.13c)$$

A cylinder, or any other shell undergoing free vibrations, may be deformed in a variety of ways, as shown in Fig. 8.2 where several configurations are given. Viewed from one end, the vibration of the cylinder may consist of any number of waves distributed around the circumference. Denoting the number of these waves by n, we see, in Fig. 8.2a, cases of n equal to 2, 3, and 4. When viewed from its side, the deformation of the cylinder consists of a number of waves distributed along the length of a generator. The appearance of the axial wave forms is, however, dependent upon the end conditions of the cylinder. For example, if the ends of the cylinder are completely free the motion of all points along the length of a given generator is the same. If the cylinder ends are simply supported, that is, maintained circular and free of axial moment, the axial wave forms are as shown in Fig. 8.2b. If we denote the number of axial half waves by m, then Fig. 8.2b depicts cases in which m equals 1, 2, and 3. On the other hand, if the ends of the cylindrical shell are clamped, the circumferential wave forms will again be as shown in Fig. 8.2a while the axial wave forms will be distorted as shown in Fig. 8.2c so as to conform to the end conditions. It is interesting, therefore, to realize, from a consideration of the axial wave forms, that for each type of end support the deformation of a generator of the shell resembles that of a beam which has the same end conditions as the shell. This fact will be shown to have analytical significance presently. As a pictorial

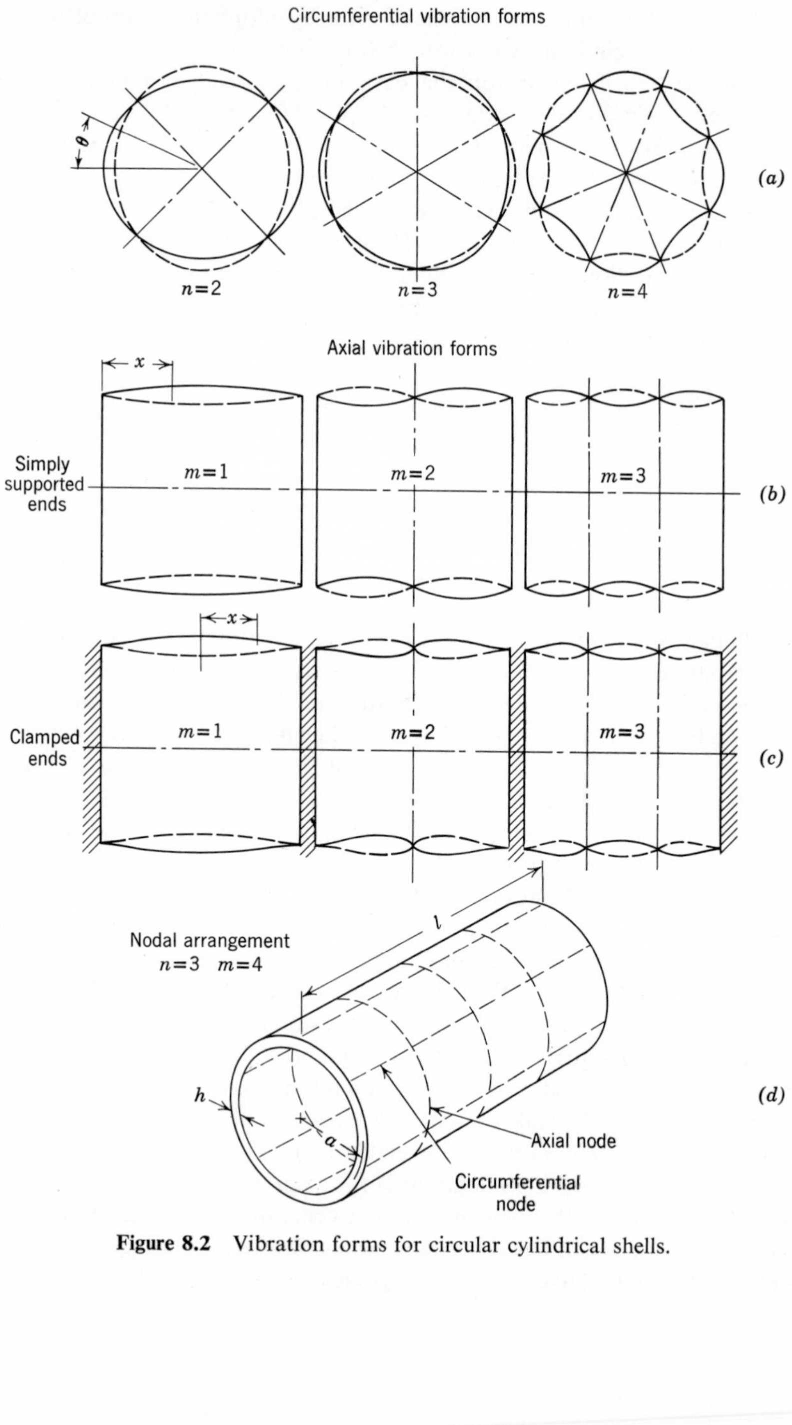

Figure 8.2 Vibration forms for circular cylindrical shells.

summary of the vibration forms of a cylindrical shell, we have shown, in Fig. 8.2d, the nodal pattern of a shell with $n = 3$ and $m = 4$, wherein the nodal lines and circles are the loci of points whose radial deflection is constant.

With this information at hand, we may now proceed to the analysis of a typical free-vibration problem of the circular cylindrical shell.

8.2*a* Variational Solution of Donnell's Equations of Motion

As our first approach to the solution of Eqs. 8.13, we select Rayleigh's method and apply it to the illustrative example of a cylindrical shell clamped at both ends. Thus, the solutions must satisfy the conditions

$$u_x = u_\theta = w = \frac{dw}{dx} = 0, \tag{8.14a}$$

at the ends $x = 0, l$ of the cylinder. In view of our previous remarks on the form of the vibration patterns taken on by a freely vibrating cylinder, we assume that the displacement functions which satisfy the above boundary conditions are given by

$$\begin{aligned} u_x &= A\left[-\sin\frac{\mu}{a}\left(\frac{l}{2} - x\right) + k\sinh\frac{\mu}{a}\left(\frac{l}{2} - x\right)\right]\cos n\theta\cos\omega t, \\ u_\theta &= B\left[\cos\frac{\mu}{a}\left(\frac{l}{2} - x\right) + k\cosh\frac{\mu}{a}\left(\frac{l}{2} - x\right)\right]\sin n\theta\cos\omega t, \\ w &= C\left[\cos\frac{\mu}{a}\left(\frac{l}{2} - x\right) + k\cosh\frac{\mu}{a}\left(\frac{l}{2} - x\right)\right]\cos n\theta\cos\omega t, \end{aligned} \tag{8.14b}$$

where A, B, and C are arbitrary coefficients and

$$k = \frac{\sin(\mu l/2a)}{\sinh(\mu l/2a)}. \tag{8.14c}$$

The quantity μ insures that the end conditions will be met and satisfies the equation

$$\tan\frac{\mu l}{2a} + \tanh\frac{\mu l}{2a} = 0, \tag{8.14d}$$

whose roots are

$$\frac{\mu l}{a} = 1.506\pi,\ 3.5\pi,\ 5.5\pi,\ 7.5\pi,\ \ldots \tag{8.14e}$$

These values correspond, respectively, to 1, 3, 5, 7, . . ., axial half waves. Notice that for an even number of half waves a different but similar form of solution would have to be assumed. The variational equation of the problem is:

$$\int_{t_0}^{t_1}\int_0^{2\pi}\int_0^{l}\left\{\left[\frac{\partial^2 u_x}{\partial x^2}+\frac{1-\nu}{2a^2}\frac{\partial^2 u_x}{\partial \theta^2}+\frac{1+\nu}{2a}\frac{\partial^2 u_\theta}{\partial x\,\partial\theta}+\frac{\nu}{a}\frac{\partial w}{\partial x}\right.\right.$$

$$\left.-\frac{1-\nu^2}{E}\rho\frac{\partial^2 u_x}{\partial t^2}\right]\delta u_x+\left[\frac{1+\nu}{2a}\frac{\partial^2 u_x}{\partial x\,\partial\theta}+\frac{1-\nu}{2}\frac{\partial^2 u_\theta}{\partial x^2}+\frac{1}{a^2}\frac{\partial^2 u_\theta}{\partial\theta^2}\right.$$

$$\left.+\frac{1}{a^2}\frac{\partial w}{\partial\theta}-\frac{1-\nu^2}{E}\rho\frac{\partial^2 u_\theta}{\partial t^2}\right]\delta u_\theta$$

$$+\left[\frac{\nu}{a}\frac{\partial u_x}{\partial x}+\frac{1}{a^2}\frac{\partial u_\theta}{\partial\theta}+\frac{w}{a^2}+\frac{h^2}{12}\nabla^4 w\right.$$

$$\left.\left.+\frac{1-\nu^2}{E}\rho\frac{\partial^2 w}{\partial t^2}\right]\delta w\right\}dx\,d\theta\,dt=0, \quad (8.14f)$$

and upon substitution of the assumed displacement functions and their variations followed by integration with respect to x and θ, we obtain the result

$$\{[\mu^2\theta_1+\tfrac{1}{2}(1-\nu^2)n^2\theta_2-\Delta\theta_2]A-\tfrac{1}{2}(1+\nu)\mu n\theta_2 B-\nu\mu\theta_2 C\}\,\delta A$$

$$+\left\{-\frac{1+\nu}{2}\mu n\theta_2 A+\left[n^2\theta_1+\frac{1-\nu}{2}\mu^2\theta_2-\Delta\theta_1\right]B+n\theta_1 C\right\}\delta B$$

$$+\left\{\nu\mu\theta_2 A-n\theta_1 B\right.$$

$$\left.-\left[\theta_1-\Delta\theta_1+\frac{1}{\xi}(\mu^4\theta_1+n^4\theta_1+2\mu^2n^2\theta_2)\right]C\right\}\delta C=0, \quad (8.14g)$$

where

$$\frac{1}{\xi}=\frac{h^2}{12a^2},$$

$$\Delta=\rho a^2(1-\nu^2)\frac{\omega^2}{E}, \quad (8.14h)$$

$$\theta_1=1+k^2, \qquad \theta_2=1-k^2+\frac{2a}{\mu l}\sin\frac{\mu l}{a}.$$

Since the variations δA, δB, and δC are arbitrary, the above equation can be satisfied only if the quantities in the braces which multiply these variations each vanish individually. If these quantities are set to zero, we obtain three homogeneous, linear equations in the three unknowns A, B, and C, the trivial solution of which is avoided by setting the determinant of the coefficients to zero. As a result, the following cubic equation for the natural frequencies is obtained:

$$\Delta^3-R_2\Delta^2+R_1\Delta-R_0=0, \quad (8.14i)$$

where

$$R_2 = \left(\frac{\theta_1}{\theta_2} + \frac{1-\nu}{2}\frac{\theta_2}{\theta_1}\right)\mu^2 + 1 + \frac{3-\nu}{2}n^2 + \frac{1}{\xi}\left(\mu^4 + n^4 + 2\mu^2 n^2 \frac{\theta_2}{\theta_1}\right),$$

$$\begin{aligned} R_1 = {} & \frac{1-\nu}{2}(\mu^4 + n^4) + \left(\frac{\theta_1}{\theta_2} - \frac{\nu\theta_2}{\theta_1}\right)\mu^2 n^2 + \frac{1-\nu}{2} n^2 \\ & + \mu^2\left[\frac{\theta_1}{\theta_2} + \frac{\theta_2}{\theta_1}\frac{(1-\nu-2\nu^2)}{2}\right] \\ & + \frac{1}{\xi}\left[\frac{1-\nu}{2}\left(n^2 + \mu^2\frac{\theta_2}{\theta_1}\right) + n^2 + \mu^2\frac{\theta_1}{\theta_2}\right] \\ & \times \left[\mu^4 + n^4 + 2\mu^2 n^2 \frac{\theta_2}{\theta_1}\right], \end{aligned} \tag{8.14j}$$

$$\begin{aligned} R_0 = {} & \frac{1-\nu}{2}\left[1 - \nu\left(\frac{\theta_2}{\theta_1}\right)^2\right]\mu^4 \\ & + \frac{1}{\xi}\left\{\mu^2 n^2\left[\frac{1+\nu}{2}\frac{\theta_2}{\theta_1} - \frac{\theta_1}{\theta_2} - \left(\frac{1-\nu}{2}\right)^2\frac{\theta_2}{\theta_1}\right]\right. \\ & \left. - \frac{(1-\nu)}{2}(\mu^4 + n^4)\right\}\left[\mu^4 + n^4 + 2\mu^2 n^2\frac{\theta_2}{\theta_1}\right]. \end{aligned}$$

In view of the requirement that the natural frequencies of free vibration must be real quantities, the foregoing equation will have three real, positive, unequal roots which, by using a variant, for real roots, of the scheme which we outlined in Section 6.4*a* (see Eqs. 6.57*l* to 6.57n) can be expressed as

$$\begin{aligned} \Delta_1 &= 2\alpha^{1/3}\cos\frac{\theta}{3} + \frac{R_2}{3}, \\ \Delta_2 &= 2\alpha^{1/3}\cos\frac{\theta + 2\pi}{3} + \frac{R_2}{3}, \\ \Delta_3 &= 2\alpha^{1/3}\cos\frac{\theta + 4\pi}{3} + \frac{R_2}{3}, \end{aligned} \tag{8.14k}$$

where

$$\begin{aligned} \alpha &= \left[-\frac{1}{27}\left(R_1 - \frac{R_2^{\,2}}{3}\right)^3\right]^{1/2}, \\ \theta &= \cos^{-1}\left\{\frac{1}{2\alpha}\left[R_0 - \frac{R_1 R_2}{3} + \frac{2R_2^{\,3}}{27}\right]\right\}. \end{aligned} \tag{8.14l}$$

Since the system 8.14g that relates *A*, *B*, and *C* is homogeneous, we can at best obtain two of these coefficients in terms of a third by solving any pair of the three equations relating A, B, and C. Thus, we find that

$$\frac{A}{C} = \frac{\nu\mu\left(n^2 + \frac{1-\nu}{2}\mu^2\frac{\theta_2}{\theta_1} - \Delta\frac{\theta_2}{\theta_1}\right) - \frac{1+\nu}{2}\mu n^2}{\left(\mu^2\frac{\theta_1}{\theta_2} - \frac{1-\nu}{2}n^2 - \Delta\right)\left(n^2 + \frac{1-\nu}{2}\mu^2\frac{\theta_2}{\theta_1} - \Delta\right)},$$

$$\frac{B}{C} = \frac{\nu\mu^2 n\frac{1+\nu}{2}\frac{\theta_2}{\theta_1} - n\left(\mu^2\frac{\theta_1}{\theta_2} + \frac{1-\nu}{2}n^2 - \Delta\right)}{\left(\mu^2\frac{\theta_1}{\theta_2} - \frac{1-\nu}{2}n^2 - \Delta\right)\left(n^2 + \frac{1-\nu}{2}\mu^2\frac{\theta_2}{\theta_1} - \Delta\right)}. \quad (8.14m)$$

These quantities are the amplitude ratios of the variational solution. For every combination of axial and circumferential waves, that is, for every pair of values of μ and n, the foregoing development will lead to three natural frequencies and, accordingly, three sets of amplitude ratios. Specific numerical results, as obtained by the solution which was developed here, will be given later after some additional methods of solution have been applied to the problem.

Before continuing, it is well to mention that an analysis of the type discussed here was first carried out by Arnold and Warburton[4] who also used the Rayleigh method and the deflection functions (Eqs. 8.14b). Their variational equations did not, however, embody the Donnell assumptions and, consequently, the frequency equation (Eq. 8.14i) has coefficients which are a special case of theirs. The differences in the coefficients involve small terms which lead to negligible differences in the natural frequencies obtained by Eq. 8.14i and the corresponding equation of Arnold and Warburton.

8.2*b* "Exact" Solution of Donnell's Equations of Motion

The exact solution of Eqs. 8.13 is facilitated, as it was in the static analysis, by rearranging them according to the following procedure that will lead to a dynamic counterpart of the Donnell equations (Eqs. 6.13):

First, operate on Eq. 8.13a successively with $\partial^2/\partial x^2$, $\partial^2/a^2\partial\theta^2$, and $\partial^2/\partial t^2$ and solve in each case for the term involving u_θ. Then substitute these expressions into the equation that is obtained by operating on Eq. 8.13b with $\partial^2/\partial x\,\partial\theta$ to give

$$\nabla^4 u_x + \frac{\nu}{a}\frac{\partial^3 w}{\partial x^3} - \frac{1}{a^3}\frac{\partial^3 w}{\partial x\,\partial\theta^2} = -\frac{2(1+\nu)}{E}\rho\frac{\partial^2}{\partial t^2}\left(\frac{1-\nu^2}{E}\rho\frac{\partial^2 u_x}{\partial t^2} - \frac{3-\nu}{2}\nabla^2 u_x - \frac{\nu}{a}\frac{\partial w}{\partial x}\right). \quad (8.15a)$$

[4] Arnold, R. N., and Warburton, G. B., "Flexural Vibrations of the Walls of Thin Cylindrical Shells Having Freely Supported Ends," *Proc. Royal Soc. Lond.*, **197A**, 238–256 (1949); and also "Flexural Vibrations of Thin Cylinders," *Proc. I. Mech. E.*, **167**, 62–74 (1953).

Now operate on Eq. 8.13b with $\partial^2/\partial x^2$, $\partial^2/\partial\theta^2$, and $\partial^2/\partial t^2$ and solve in each case for the term involving u_x. Substitute these expressions into the equation obtained by operating on Eq. 8.13a with $\partial^2/\partial x\,\partial\theta$ to give

$$\nabla^4 u_\theta + \frac{2+\nu}{a^2}\frac{\partial^3 w}{\partial x^2\,\partial\theta} + \frac{\partial^3 w}{a^4\,\partial\theta^3}$$
$$= -\frac{2(1+\nu)}{E}\rho\frac{\partial^2}{\partial t^2}\left(\frac{1-\nu^2}{E}\rho\frac{\partial^2 u_\theta}{\partial t^2} - \frac{3-\nu}{2}\nabla^2 u_\theta - \frac{1}{a^2}\frac{\partial w}{\partial\theta}\right). \qquad (8.15b)$$

A third equation is obtained by operating on Eqs. 8.15a and 8.15b with $\nu\,\partial/a\,\partial x$ and $\partial^2/a^2\,\partial\theta^2$, respectively, and adding the results. This gives

$$\nabla^4\left(\frac{\nu}{a}\frac{\partial u_x}{\partial x} + \frac{1}{a^2}\frac{\partial u_\theta}{\partial\theta}\right) + \frac{\nu^2}{a^2}\frac{\partial^4 w}{\partial x^4} + \frac{2}{a^4}\frac{\partial^4 w}{\partial x^2\,\partial\theta^2} + \frac{1}{a^6}\frac{\partial^4 w}{\partial\theta^4}$$
$$= -\frac{2(1+\nu)}{E}\rho\frac{\partial^2}{\partial t^2}\left[\frac{1-\nu^2}{E}\rho\frac{\partial^2}{\partial t^2}\left(\frac{\nu}{a}\frac{\partial u_x}{\partial x} + \frac{1}{a^2}\frac{\partial u_\theta}{\partial\theta}\right)\right.$$
$$\left. - \frac{3-\nu}{2}\nabla^2\left(\frac{\nu}{a}\frac{\partial u_x}{\partial x} + \frac{1}{a^2}\frac{\partial u_\theta}{\partial\theta}\right) - \frac{\nu^2}{a^2}\frac{\partial^2 w}{\partial x^2} - \frac{1}{a^4}\frac{\partial^2 w}{\partial\theta^2}\right]. \qquad (8.15c)$$

The quantity in parentheses which appears three times in the above can be expressed in terms of w from Eq. 8.13c. Upon substitution of that result into Eq. 8.15c, we obtain

$$\frac{h^2}{12}\nabla^8 w + \frac{1-\nu^2}{a^2}\frac{\partial^4 w}{\partial x^4} = -\frac{2(1+\nu)}{E}\rho\frac{\partial^2}{\partial t^2}\left[\left(\frac{1-\nu^2}{E}\rho\frac{\partial^2}{\partial t^2} - \frac{3-\nu}{2}\nabla^2\right)\right.$$
$$\times\left(\frac{1-\nu^2}{E}\rho\frac{\partial^2 w}{\partial t^2} + \frac{w}{a^2} + \frac{h^2}{12}\nabla^4 w\right)$$
$$\left. + \frac{1-\nu}{2}\nabla^4 w + \frac{\nu^2}{a^2}\frac{\partial^2 w}{\partial x^2} + \frac{1}{a^4}\frac{\partial^2 w}{\partial\theta^2}\right] \qquad (8.15d)$$

The solution of these equations follows closely the methods set forth in Chapter 6 for the static analysis of cylindrical shells. In the present case, we assume, therefore, that the solution is given by (see Eqs. 6.18a):

$$u_x = \sum_{i=1}^{8} A_i \exp(\lambda_i x/l)\cos n\theta\cos\omega t,$$
$$u_\theta = \sum_{i=1}^{8} B_i \exp(\lambda_i x/l)\sin n\theta\cos\omega t, \qquad (8.16a)$$
$$w = \sum_{i=1}^{8} C_i \exp(\lambda_i x/l)\cos n\theta\cos\omega t,$$

where A_i, B_i, and C_i are arbitrary constants and λ_i is to be determined such that the above forms will satisfy the equations of motion. If the assumed solutions are substituted into the dynamic Donnell equations, the result is

$$\frac{A_i}{C_i}\left[\frac{2}{1-\nu}\Delta^2 - \frac{3-\nu}{1-\nu}\Delta n^2\left(1-\frac{\lambda_i^2a^2}{n^2l^2}\right) + n^4\left(1-\frac{\lambda_i^2a^2}{n^2l^2}\right)^2\right] = -\frac{\lambda_i a}{l}\left[\frac{2\nu}{1-\nu}\Delta + n^2\left(1+\nu\frac{\lambda_i^2a^2}{n^2l^2}\right)\right], \quad (8.16b)$$

$$\frac{B_i}{C_i}\left[\frac{2\Delta^2}{1-\nu} - \frac{3-\nu}{1-\nu}\Delta n^2\left(1-\frac{\lambda_i^2a^2}{n^2l^2}\right) + n^4\left(1-\frac{\lambda_i^2a^2}{n^2l^2}\right)^2\right] = -n\left[-\frac{2}{1-\nu}\Delta + n^2\left\{1-(2+\nu)\frac{4\lambda_i^2a^2}{n^2l^2}\right\}\right], \quad (8.16c)$$

$$\begin{aligned}(1-\nu)(1-\nu^2)\left(\frac{\lambda_i a}{l}\right)^4 &= 2\Delta^3 - \Delta^2\left[2+(3-\nu)n^2\left(1-\frac{\lambda_i^2a^2}{n^2l^2}\right) + \frac{2n^4}{\xi}\left(1-\frac{\lambda_i^2a^2}{n^2l^2}\right)^2\right] \\ &\quad + \Delta\left[(3-\nu)n^2\left(1-\frac{\lambda_i^2a^2}{n^2l^2}\right) - 2n^2\left(1-\nu^2\frac{\lambda_i^2a^2}{n^2l^2}\right)\right. \\ &\quad \left. + (1-\nu)n^4\left(1-\frac{\lambda_i^2a^2}{n^2l^2}\right)^2 + (3-\nu)\frac{n^6}{\xi}\left(1-\frac{\lambda_i^2a^2}{n^2l^2}\right)^3\right] \\ &\quad - (1-\nu)\frac{n^8}{\xi}\left(1-\frac{\lambda_i^2a^2}{n^2l^2}\right)^4, \qquad i = 1, 2, \ldots, 8, \quad (8.16d)\end{aligned}$$

where ξ and Δ are given by Eqs. 8.14h. The assumed displacement functions (Eqs. 8.16a) must also satisfy the boundary conditions. Taking again the case of a cylinder clamped at both ends, the boundary conditions are given by Eq. 8.14a. Substitution of the assumed solutions into those boundary conditions results in eight homogeneous equations which relate A_i, B_i, and C_i. Since A_i and B_i are given as functions of C_i by Eqs. 8.16b and 8.16c, A_i and B_i may be eliminated from the boundary equations so that they become eight homogeneous equations in the eight unknown C_i. The trivial solution of these equations is avoided by setting the determinant of their coefficients to zero. This, then, is the frequency equation of the problem, wherein the frequency determinant is a function of both Δ and λ_i. The simultaneous solution of the frequency equation and Eq. 8.16d for Δ and λ_i involves an extremely laborious computation which can be tackled in several ways. In the most direct approach, we should take successively incremented values of Δ, solve the 8th degree Eq. 8.16d for eight values of λ_i, substitute the results into the frequency equation, and look for a change of sign and so on, as described in Section 8.1. When done by hand, this is exceedingly tedious, but, when a digital computer is available, the process becomes more reasonable. A second avenue of approach to the problem is to employ the Rayleigh method; we have shown in the preceding section that this can be carried out with little difficulty. There is, however, a third approach involving analytical simplifications which permit an "exact" solution to be carried out. The first of these simplifications was proposed by Yu[5] who restricted his attention to configurations for which

$$\frac{|\lambda_i^2|a^2}{n^2l^2} \ll 1, \tag{8.17a}$$

where the absolute value is necessary because the λ_i may be imaginary. The assumption limits the applicability of the resulting solution to long shells of small radius having a large number of circumferential waves and a small number of axial waves. With Eq. 8.17a, Eqs. 8.16b to 8.16d reduce to

$$\begin{aligned} A_i &= C_i\lambda_i \frac{a}{l} M, \\ B_i &= C_i N, \\ (1-\nu)(1-\nu^2)\left(\frac{\lambda_i a}{l}\right)^4 &= F, \qquad i = 1, 2, 3, 4, \end{aligned} \tag{8.17b}$$

where

$$\begin{aligned} M &= -\frac{2\nu\Delta + (1-\nu)n^2}{2\Delta^2 - (3-\nu)n^2\Delta + (1-\nu)n^4}, \\ N &= -\frac{-2n\Delta + (1-\nu)n^3}{2\Delta^2 - (3-\nu)n^2\Delta + (1-\nu)n^4}, \\ F &= 2\Delta^3 - \Delta^2\left[2 + (3-\nu)n^2 + \frac{2n^4}{\xi}\right] \\ &\quad + \Delta\left[(1-\nu)n^2(n^2+1) + (3-\nu)\frac{n^6}{\xi}\right] - (1-\nu)\frac{n^8}{\xi}. \end{aligned} \tag{8.17c}$$

In addition to a substantial simplification of the form of the equations, we find that the chief effect of assumption 8.17a is the reduction of the degree of the equation relating λ_i and Δ from eight to four. Therefore, for a given Δ there will be only four λ_i and only four sets of A_i, B_i, and C_i. The λ_i will be of the form

$$\begin{Bmatrix}\lambda_1\\ \lambda_2\end{Bmatrix} = \pm K, \qquad \begin{Bmatrix}\lambda_3\\ \lambda_4\end{Bmatrix} = \pm iK, \tag{8.17d}$$

where

$$K = [Fl^4/a^4(1-\nu)(1-\nu^2)]^{1/4}, \tag{8.17e}$$

[5] Yu, Y. Y., "Free Vibrations of Thin Cylindrical Shells Having Finite Lengths with Freely Supported and Clamped Edges," *J. Appl. Mech.*, **22**, 547–552 (1955).

is a real number. For the case of the cylinder with clamped ends, the boundary conditions 8.14a, when applied to Eqs. 8.16a, lead to the expressions

$$\sum_{i=1}^{4} C_i = 0, \qquad \sum_{i=1}^{4} C_i e^{\lambda_i} = 0,$$
$$\sum_{i=1}^{4} C_i\lambda_i = 0, \qquad \sum_{i=1}^{4} C_i\lambda_i e^{\lambda_i} = 0, \tag{8.17f}$$

where we have employed Eqs. 8.17b. The trivial solution of the above homogeneous linear system is avoided by setting the determinant of the coefficients equal to zero. In view of Eq. 8.17d, this determinant takes the form

$$\begin{vmatrix} 1 & 1 & 1 & 1 \\ e^K & e^{-K} & e^{iK} & e^{-iK} \\ K & -K & iK & -iK \\ K e^K & -K e^{-K} & iK e^{iK} & -iK e^{-iK} \end{vmatrix} = 8iK^2(\cos K \cosh K - 1) = 0. \tag{8.17g}$$

The first root of Eq. 8.17g is $K = 0$ and is discarded since it represents the case of zero displacement. The higher roots satisfy the equation

$$\cos K \cosh K - 1 = 0, \tag{8.17h}$$

and have been tabulated by Timoshenko and Young[6] who give the following values:

$$K = 1.506\pi, 2.500\pi, 3.500\pi, 4.500\pi, \ldots, \tag{8.17i}$$

corresponding to 1, 2, 3, 4, . . . axial half waves. Because Eqs. 8.17f are homogeneous, the four C_i are not independent and we can at best solve for three of them in terms of the fourth. Without giving the details of this calculation we may, therefore, write the final form of the displacement functions, valid for any number of axial half waves, as

$$\begin{aligned} w = 2C_1 &[(\sinh K - \sin K) - (\cosh K - \cos K)]^{-1} \\ &\times [(\sinh K - \sin K)(\cosh Kx - \cos Kx) \\ &- (\cosh K - \cos K)(\sinh Kx - \sin Kx)] \cos n\theta \cos \omega t, \end{aligned} \tag{8.17j}$$

$$u_x = Ma\frac{\partial w}{\partial x}, \qquad u_\theta = -\frac{N}{n}\frac{\partial w}{\partial \theta},$$

and the natural frequencies (three for each nodal configuration) are found from the third of Eqs. 8.17b after substitution of λ_i.

[6] Timoshenko, S., and Young, D. H., *Vibration Problems in Engineering*, 3rd ed., Princeton: D. Van Nostrand, pp. 336–341 (1955).

It is interesting to call attention to the fact that Eq. 8.17h also governs the natural frequencies of a beam clamped at its ends if K is replaced by kl, where l is the length of the beam and $k = \omega^2 A\rho/EI$ (here A and I are the area and moment of inertia of the beam, respectively). Indeed, Yu[5] found that, for each combination of boundary conditions, the governing equations for the roots K, from which the natural frequencies of a cylindrical shell are subsequently found, are identical to the frequency equations of beams with the same boundary conditions.

Numerical results based on the "exact" solution which was derived here will be presented in the next section.

8.2*c* Discussion of Results on Freely Vibrating Circular Cylindrical Shells

We now apply the foregoing methods to the free-vibration analysis of a specific cylindrical shell in order to bring out the behavior of freely vibrating cylinders and to evaluate the accuracy of these and other analytical approaches to the problem.

As we have seen previously in both the variational and the "exact" solutions of the problem of freely vibrating cylinders, the natural frequencies are obtained as the solutions of a cubic frequency equation. Thus, for a given configuration of axial and circumferential waves there exist three natural frequencies of free vibration. Characteristic of these natural frequencies is the fact that one is always much lower than the other two for any combination of axial and circumferential waves regardless of the method of solution. This is brought out clearly in Table 8.1 where the

Table 8.1 Natural Frequencies of Clamped Steel Cylinders (cycles/second) (a = 3 in., h = 0.01 in., l = 12 in.)

	$\frac{1}{2}$ Axial Wave ($m = 1$)			$1\frac{1}{2}$ Axial Waves ($m = 2$)		
n	f_1	f_2	f_3	f_1	f_2	f_3
3	1,176	27,071	36,866	4,350	30,578	46,524
4	783	32,418	47,318	3,139	36,021	54,848
5	597	38,118	58,107	2,342	41,551	64,210
6	552	44,071	69,055	1,823	47,242	74,170
7	611	50,194	80,092	1,503	53,096	84,489
8	736	56,436	91,184	1,338	59,088	95,038
9	902	62,763	102,313	1,302	65,192	105,742
10	1,100	69,151	113,467	1,369	71,386	116,555
11	1,321	75,586	124,639	1,512	77,651	127,449
12	1,568	82,056	135,825	1,710	83,973	138,402
13	1,837	88,554	147,022	1,950	90,340	149,401
14	2,128	95,074	158,228	2,224	96,746	160,437

natural frequencies of steel cylinders clamped at both ends, as calculated by Eqs. 8.14k of the variational solution, are given.

It is evident in Table 8.1 that the lowest frequencies f_1 are at least an order of magnitude smaller than are the f_2 and f_3 frequencies. It is also interesting to note that the f_2 and f_3 frequencies increase monotonically with an increase in the number of axial and circumferential waves. This is in keeping with results from the vibration of beams and plates where the natural frequencies increase as the shape of the displacement pattern becomes more complicated. In contrast to this, the lowest frequencies increase as the number of axial half waves is increased but decrease to a minimum before they increase as the number of circumferential waves is increased. This seemingly anomalous behavior was first observed by Arnold and Warburton,[4] who were able to explain it from a consideration of the strain energy associated with bending and stretching of the reference surface. Using a plot of the type given in Fig. 8.3, Arnold and Warburton demonstrated the relative contributions of the two forms of strain energy of the motion associated with the lowest natural frequency of the variational solution.[7] It is seen in Fig. 8.3 that at the low circumferential wave numbers the bending strain energy is low and the stretching strain energy is high while at the higher circumferential wave numbers the relative contributions from the two types of strain energy are reversed. Figure 8.3 shows also that the bending strain energy is insensitive to the number of axial waves while the stretching energy is strongly dependent on the number of such waves. The interchange in the relative contributions of the bending strain energy and the stretching strain energy as the number of circumferential waves is increased explains the decrease and subsequent increase in the lowest natural frequencies indicated in Table 8.1. The strong dependence of the stretching energy on the number of axial waves explains the fact that, in Table 8.1, the minimum in the lowest natural frequency occurs at a higher number of circumferential waves for $1\frac{1}{2}$ axial waves than it does for $\frac{1}{2}$ axial wave.

One would also expect, from the energy curves given in Fig. 8.3, that for large numbers of circumferential waves the motion associated with the lowest natural frequency could be predicted by a theory which considers bending only and neglects stretching. Indeed, such an analysis, the results

[7] The ordinate of Fig. 8.3 is a dimensionless factor which is defined from

$$\begin{Bmatrix} U_s \\ U_b \\ U_t \end{Bmatrix} = \frac{E\pi l C^2}{4(1-\nu^2)} \begin{Bmatrix} \eta_s \\ \eta_b \\ \eta_t \end{Bmatrix} \begin{matrix} \text{(stretching strain energy)} \\ \text{(bending strain energy)} \\ \text{(total strain energy)} \end{matrix} \tag{8.18}$$

Since $U_t = U_b + U_s$,

$$\eta_t = \eta_s + \eta_b.$$

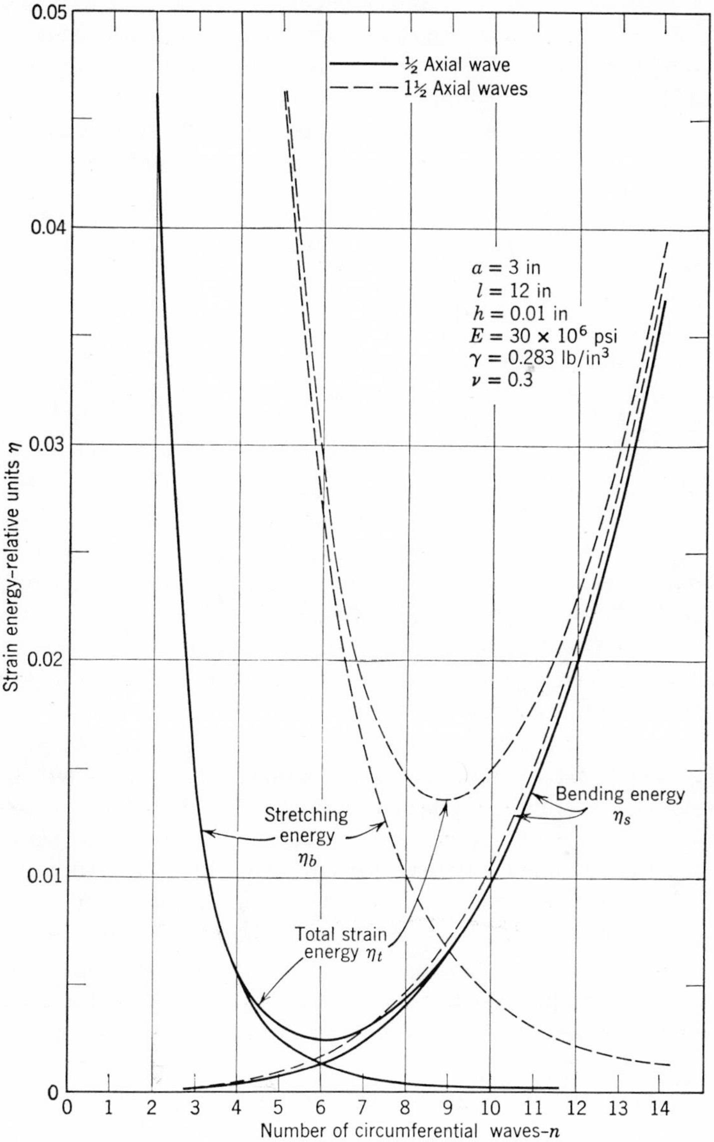

Figure 8.3 Strain energy contributions for a typical freely vibrating circular cylindrical shell.

of which we shall give later, was carried out by Rayleigh.[8] Notice, however, that since end conditions are associated with the number of axial waves and, therefore, the stretching energy, a theory which neglects stretching effects will give results which are independent of the end conditions, and for which the generators of the cylinder remain straight during vibration.

An interesting feature of the motions associated with the three frequencies corresponding to a given wave pattern is revealed by Table 8.2 where the

Table 8.2 Amplitude Ratios of Clamped Steel Cylinders ($n = 6$, $a = 3$ in., $h = 0.01$ in., $l = 12$ in.)

	$m = 1$		$m = 3$		$m = 5$		$m = 7$		$m = 9$	
	A/C	B/C	A/C	B/C	A/C	B/C	A/C	B/C	A/C	B/C
Δ_1	0.003	0.016	0.004	0.016	0.004	0.016	0.003	0.014	0.002	0.012
Δ_2	37.455	3.379	9.818	3.864	6.801	4.756	5.944	5.964	5.797	7.532
Δ_3	1.296	6.072	3.376	6.694	6.290	7.740	10.053	9.000	14.515	10.292

amplitude ratios, as calculated by Eqs. 8.14m of the variational solution, are given for several combinations of axial and circumferential waves.

The table shows that at the lowest frequency the predominant amplitude is C and the motion associated with that frequency is, therefore, mostly radial. We shall refer to such a mode of free vibration as a transverse mode. The motion of the next highest frequency (Δ_2) is mainly axial at low numbers of axial half waves but for higher numbers of axial half waves the axial and circumferential amplitudes are almost equal. At all numbers of axial half waves, the Δ_2 frequencies result in little radial motion and we refer to the modes of free vibration associated with these frequencies as longitudinal. The highest frequencies, Δ_3, involve motions which are predominantly circumferential at low numbers of axial waves and are equally axial and circumferential at the higher numbers of axial half waves. There is little radial motion associated with the Δ_3 frequencies at any number of axial half waves and their associated modes of free vibration are characterized as circumferential. As a result of these considerations, and because the highest two sets of frequencies are beyond the aural range and also difficult to observe experimentally, it is the lowest set of natural frequencies which is of greatest interest to analysts.

Now we shall present several additional analytical simplifications to the solution of the free-vibration problem of a cylinder. All of these will be

[8] Lord Rayleigh, *Theory of Sound*, London: Macmillan, 2nd ed. (1894).

based upon the knowledge that there is a lowest set of natural frequencies which are accompanied by predominantly transverse motion of the cylindrical shell.

By returning to Eqs. 8.17b and 8.17c of the "exact" solution, we may obtain a good approximation to the lowest natural frequency by neglecting the Δ_3 and Δ_2 terms in comparison to the remaining terms in the definition of F. This gives the following simple formula for the lowest natural frequency of a cylindrical shell clamped at its ends:

$$\Delta_1 = \frac{(n^8/\xi) + (1 - \nu^2)(Ka/l)^4}{n^2(n^2 + 1) + (3 - \nu)n^6/\xi(1 - \nu)}, \qquad (8.19)$$

where K is given by Eq. 8.17i. A similar solution could be derived from Eq. 8.14i of the variational solution but this will not be pursued here.

Another interesting simplification based on the radial character of the motion associated with the lowest natural frequencies was given by Koval and Cranch,[9] and later by Weingarten,[10] who neglected the longitudinal and circumferential inertia terms in the Donnell equations (8.13). With this simplification, Eq. 8.15d reduces to

$$\frac{h^2}{12}\nabla^8 w + \frac{1 - \nu^2}{a^2}\frac{\partial^4 w}{\partial x^4} + \rho\frac{(1 - \nu^2)}{E}\nabla^4\frac{\partial^2 w}{\partial t^2} = 0. \qquad (8.20a)$$

If we again assume that (see Eqs. 8.16a):

$$w = \sum_{i=1}^{8} C_i \exp(\lambda_i x/l)\cos n\theta \cos \omega t, \qquad (8.20b)$$

Equation 8.20a becomes

$$\frac{h^2}{12}\left(\frac{n}{a}\right)^8\left(1 - \frac{\lambda_i^2 a^2}{n^2 l^2}\right)^4 + \frac{1 - \nu^2}{a^2}\left(\frac{\lambda_i}{l}\right)^4 - \frac{\Delta}{a^2}\left(\frac{n}{a}\right)^4\left(1 - \frac{\lambda_i^2 a^2}{n^2 l^2}\right)^2. \qquad (8.20c)$$

This eighth degree equation relating λ_i and Δ is reduced to a fourth degree equation by using Yu's assumption (Eq. 8.17a) which restricts the solution to long cylinders with many circumferential waves. With this assumption, Eq. 8.20c is replaced by (see Eqs. 8.17b):

$$(1 - \nu^2)\left(\frac{\lambda_i a}{l}\right)^4 = \Delta n^4 - \frac{n^8}{\xi}, \qquad i = 1, 2, 3, 4, \qquad (8.20d)$$

and, as before, this equation can be shown to have roots that are of the

---

[9] Koval, L. R., and Cranch, E. T., "On the Free Vibrations of Thin Cylindrical Shells Subjected to an Initial Static Torque," *Proc. 4th U.S. Nat'l. Congr. Appl. Mech.*, 107–117 (1962).

[10] Weingarten, V. I., "Free Vibration of Thin Cylindrical Shells," *A.I.A.A. J.*, **2**, 717–722 (1964).

form 8.17d. The rest of the calculation proceeds in the same fashion as did the development in Section 8.2*b* and we shall not repeat the details here. The lowest natural frequency is found by rearrangement of Eq. 8.20d to be

$$\Delta_1 = \left[\frac{n^8}{\xi} + (1 - \nu^2)\left(\frac{Ka}{l}\right)^4\right]\frac{1}{n^4}. \tag{8.20e}$$

We note here the similarity between the above equation and Eq. 8.19 in which the longitudinal and circumferential inertia contributions are included. It is readily seen, since positive terms are involved, that the numerator of Eq. 8.20e is smaller than that of Eq. 8.19 and, therefore, the natural frequency with longitudinal and circumferential inertia effects neglected will be higher than when these effects are retained.

Finally, we add to the simplified solutions being considered here Rayleigh's original contribution to the free-vibration analysis of cylinders to which we have referred earlier.[8] Rayleigh postulated free vibrations in which the cylinder undergoes bending but no stretching and found that the natural frequencies of such a cylinder are given by

$$\Delta_1 = \frac{1}{\xi}\frac{n^2(n^2 - 1)^2}{n^2 + 1}, \tag{8.20f}$$

where n is the number of circumferential waves and all cross sections along the length of the cylinder perform the same motion; that is, there are no axial waves.

As a conclusion to this discussion, we now bring together, for comparison, results obtained for a particular cylinder by means of the various analytical methods which we have previously described. As a standard of reference, we shall use experimental data collected for the freely vibrating cylinder with clamped ends by Koval and Cranch[9] as part of a larger study. In Fig. 8.4, we have, therefore, plotted the lowest natural frequencies of a clamped cylindrical shell as a function of the number of circumferential and axial waves, as obtained experimentally by Koval and Cranch and by four analytical methods. The analytical solutions which were used in plotting Fig. 8.4 are the variational solution, from Eq. 8.14k, the "exact" solution from Eq. 8.19, the "exact" solution with longitudinal and circumferential inertia neglected from Eq. 8.20e, and Rayleigh's solution with stretching neglected from Eq. 8.20f. It is seen in Fig. 8.4 that, after the minimum point in the frequency is passed for each number of axial half waves, all of the analytical solutions agree very closely with each other and with the experimental data. Before the minimum is reached, the variational solution gives the closest agreement with the experimental data. The remaining analytical solutions, since they are based on the premise of a large number of circumferential waves, do not, understandably, agree as well

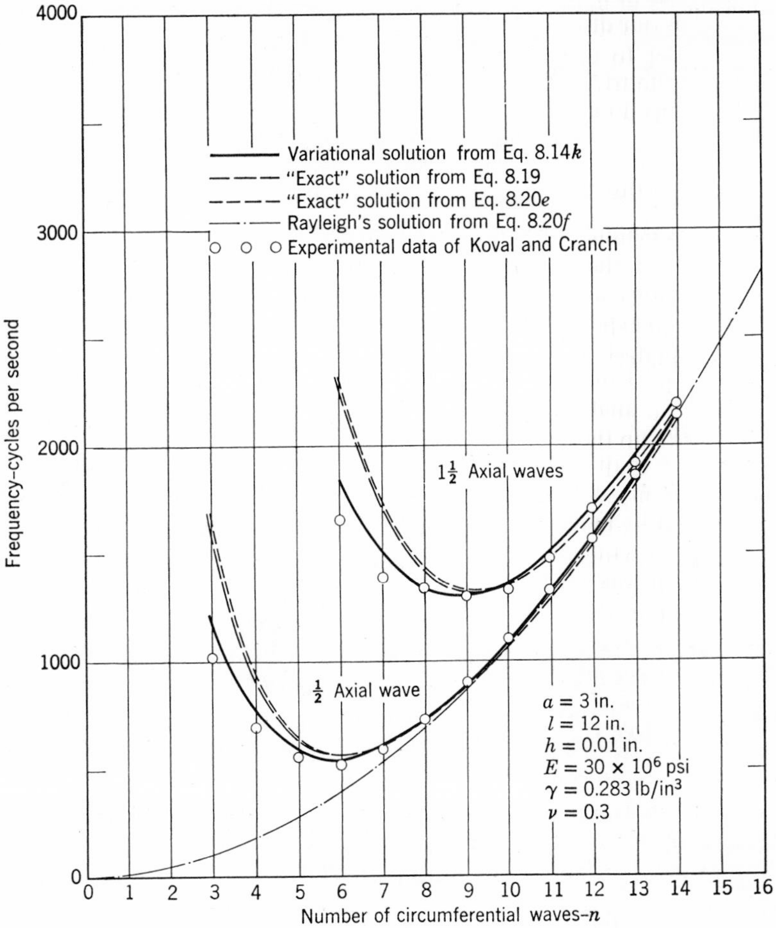

Figure 8.4 Natural frequencies for a freely vibrating circular cylindrical shell with clamped ends.

with the experimental data as does the variational solution. It is interesting to note, however, that the neglect of longitudinal and circumferential inertia does not affect the "exact" solutions appreciably although, as expected previously, the natural frequencies are higher when these inertia terms are neglected than when they are not. Finally, the Rayleigh solution in which stretching is neglected agrees as well with the experimental data as do any of the other analytical solutions at the highest circumferential wave numbers, regardless of the number of axial waves. Later on, in Chapter 11, we shall present some natural frequencies that were obtained by means of a numerical solution in which Donnell's assumptions and assumption 8.17a are not employed. These results will show an improvement in the agreement between analytical and experimental results at the lowest values of n.

This ends our discussion of freely vibrating cylindrical shells. We leave it to the reader to discover, through the Exercises, the behavior of freely vibrating cylindrical membrane shells as well as the behavior of cylindrical shells with bending resistance which undergo θ-independent free vibrations.

8.3 FREE VIBRATION OF SHALLOW SPHERICAL SHELLS

We have previously seen (in Chapter 6) that, when it is applicable, the assumption of shallowness leads to a considerable simplification of the basic equations and resulting static analysis of a spherical shell. It is reasonable to expect that a similar simplification will also occur in the free vibration analysis of a spherical shell if the assumption of shallowness is applicable. Consequently, we shall devote the present section to the free-vibration analysis of shallow spherical shells. In a following section, we shall take up the free-vibration analysis of nonshallow spherical shells in which we shall include the consideration of complete spherical shells.

At this point, we recall that in Chapter 6 we defined a spherical shell to be shallow if its base radius, a, is less than half of the radius of its middle surface, R, or, equivalently, if its angle of opening φ_0 is less than 30°. For such shells, it was assumed that the effect of the transverse shearing-stress resultants upon the equilibrium of forces in the circumferential direction was negligible and that the expressions for the changes in curvature of the reference surface are identical to those of a flat circular plate. For the purposes of the free-vibration analysis, we notice that the equations of motion are given by (see Eqs. 6.36a and 6.36e):

$$
\begin{aligned}
\frac{\partial(rN_r)}{\partial r} + \frac{\partial N_{r\theta}}{\partial \theta} - N_\theta &= \rho r h \frac{\partial^2 u_r}{\partial t^2}, \\
\frac{\partial(rN_{r\theta})}{\partial r} + \frac{\partial N_\theta}{\partial \theta} + N_{r\theta} &= \rho r h \frac{\partial^2 u_\theta}{\partial t^2}, \\
\frac{\partial(rQ_r)}{\partial r} + \frac{\partial Q_\theta}{\partial \theta} - \frac{r}{R}(N_r + N_\theta) &= \rho r h \frac{\partial^2 w}{\partial t^2}, \qquad (8.21) \\
\frac{\partial(rM_r)}{\partial r} + \frac{\partial M_{r\theta}}{\partial \theta} - M_\theta - rQ_r &= 0, \\
\frac{\partial(rM_{r\theta})}{\partial r} + \frac{\partial M_\theta}{\partial \theta} + M_{r\theta} - rQ_\theta &= 0,
\end{aligned}
$$

while the strain-displacement and change of curvature-displacement relationships are given by Eqs. 6.36b and 6.36f and the stress resultants and stress couples are related to the strains and changes of curvature by Eqs. 6.5.

In the static analysis of shallow spherical shells, we solved the governing equations of the arbitrarily loaded shell by introducing a stress function. Here we shall illustrate the free-vibration analysis by using two basic procedures. In the first, we shall assume that the vibrations are independent of the circumferential coordinate θ and we shall reduce Eqs. 8.21 to two simultaneous differential equations which relate the nonvanishing displacements u_r and w. In the second, we shall treat the arbitrary vibration of shallow spherical shells by introducing auxiliary functions which, as in the static analysis, simplify the analysis considerably.

8.3*a* Free, θ-independent Vibration of Shallow Spherical Shells

Under the assumption that the shallow spherical shell executes free vibrations which are independent of circumferential position, the equations of motion (Eqs. 8.21) reduce to the set

$$\begin{aligned} \frac{\partial}{\partial r}(rN_r) - N_\theta &= \rho r h \frac{\partial^2 u_r}{\partial t^2}, \\ \frac{\partial}{\partial r}(rQ_r) - \frac{r}{R}(N_r + N_\theta) &= \rho r h \frac{\partial^2 w}{\partial t^2}, \qquad (8.22a) \\ \frac{\partial}{\partial r}(rM_r) - M_\theta - rQ_r &= 0, \end{aligned}$$

where we have noted that all derivatives with respect to θ are zero and that $N_{r\theta} = M_{r\theta} = Q_\theta = u_\theta = 0$. Now, if the third of Eqs. 8.22a is used to eliminate Q_r from the other two equations of motion and if Eqs. 6.5, 6.36b and 6.36f are used to eliminate the stress resultants and couples from the resulting equations, we find that

$$\begin{aligned} K\left[L(ru) + \frac{1+\nu}{R} rw'\right] + h\rho\omega^2 ru &= 0, \\ D[L(rw')]' + K\left[(ru)' + 2r\frac{w}{R}\right]\frac{(1+\nu)}{R} - h\rho\omega^2 rw &= 0, \end{aligned} \qquad (8.22b)$$

where

$$\begin{aligned} L(\ldots) &= (\ldots)'' + \frac{1}{r}(\ldots)', \\ (\ldots)' &= \frac{d}{dr}(\ldots). \end{aligned} \qquad (8.22c)$$

In writing these equations, we have also assumed (see Eqs. 8.4) that the displacements of a freely vibrating shell can be expressed as

$$u_r(r, t) = u(r)\cos\omega t, \qquad w(r, t) = w(r)\cos\omega t. \tag{8.22d}$$

Elimination of (ru) or (rw') from the equilibrium-displacement equations then gives

$$DLLL\begin{Bmatrix} ru \\ rw' \end{Bmatrix} + D\frac{h\rho\omega^2}{K}LL\begin{Bmatrix} ru \\ rw' \end{Bmatrix} + \left[\frac{K}{R^2}(1-\nu^2) - h\rho\omega^2\right]L\begin{Bmatrix} ru \\ rw' \end{Bmatrix} + \left[\frac{2(1+\nu)K}{R^2} - h\rho\omega^2\right]\frac{h\rho\omega^2}{K}\begin{Bmatrix} ru \\ rw' \end{Bmatrix} = 0. \tag{8.22e}$$

The above sixth-order differential equation governs the solution of the θ-independent free vibration problem of a shallow spherical shell. In what follows, we shall consider the solution of that equation for two cases. In the first case, we shall neglect the effects of bending; that is, we shall let $M_r = M_\theta = Q_r = 0$ in Eqs. 8.22a or, equivalently, we shall set $D = 0$ in Eqs. 8.22b and 8.22e. In this manner, we arrive at the equations that are relevant to the θ-independent free-vibration problem of a shallow spherical membrane shell. In the second case, we shall consider the equations as they stand and solve the θ-independent free-vibration problem of a shallow spherical shell with bending resistance. The solutions will be found by both the exact and the variational methods.

Free, θ-independent Vibration of Shallow Spherical Membrane Shells. As indicated in the previous discussion, the equations which are relevant to the free vibration of shallow spherical membrane shells are obtained by setting $M_r = M_\theta = Q_r = D = 0$. If we restrict our attention to Eq. 8.22e, this then becomes

$$L\begin{Bmatrix} ru \\ rw' \end{Bmatrix} + \left(\frac{\mu}{a}\right)^2\begin{Bmatrix} ru \\ rw' \end{Bmatrix} = 0, \tag{8.23a}$$

where

$$\mu^2 = \frac{a^2\Omega^2}{R^2}(1+\nu)\frac{2-\Omega^2(1-\nu)}{1-\Omega^2}, \tag{8.23b}$$

$$\Omega^2 = \frac{\rho\omega^2 R^2}{E}. \tag{8.23c}$$

Since (ru) and (rw') satisfy the same equation, they will have the same general solution within a constant factor of proportionality which can be found by substituting the first of Eqs. 8.23a into the first of Eqs. 8.22b. The expression obtained thereby is

$$\frac{u}{w'} = \frac{R(1 + \nu)}{\mu^2 R^2/a^2 - \Omega^2(1 - \nu^2)}. \tag{8.23d}$$

To solve Eq. 8.23a, we first write it in its extended form for w', for example, as

$$\frac{d^2 w'}{dr^2} + \frac{1}{r}\frac{dw'}{dr} + \left(\frac{\mu^2}{a^2} - \frac{1}{r^2}\right) w' = 0, \tag{8.23e}$$

which we recognize to be Bessel's equation of order one. A general solution of this equation can be immediately written as[11]

$$w' = AJ_1\left(\frac{\mu r}{a}\right) + BY_1\left(\frac{\mu r}{a}\right), \tag{8.23f}$$

and, in view of Eq. 8.23d,

$$u = \frac{R(1 + \nu)}{\mu^2 R^2/a^2 - \Omega^2(1 - \nu^2)}\left[AJ_1\left(\frac{\mu r}{a}\right) + BY_1\left(\frac{\mu r}{a}\right)\right], \tag{8.23g}$$

where $J_1(\mu r/a)$ and $Y_1(\mu r/a)$ are, respectively, the Bessel functions of the first and second kind and order one. Integration of Eq. 8.23f now gives

$$w = -\frac{a}{\mu}\left[AJ_0\left(\frac{\mu r}{a}\right) + BY_0\left(\frac{\mu r}{a}\right)\right], \tag{8.23h}$$

where $J_0(\mu r/a)$ and $Y_0(\mu r/a)$ are, respectively, the Bessel functions of the first and second kind and order zero. In Eqs. 8.23g and 8.23h, A and B are arbitrary constants that are to be determined from the boundary conditions. Since, in the membrane theory, $M_r = Q_r \equiv 0$, we may only specify (see Eqs. 4.7) one of the pair u_r, N_r at an edge of constant r. Furthermore, if we restrict our attention to a shallow spherical cap which includes the origin $r = 0$, the solutions $Y_0(\mu r/a)$ and $Y_1(\mu r/a)$ which are singular at $r = 0$ must be suppressed by setting $B = 0$. Thus, for the shallow spherical membrane cap the solutions reduce to

$$\begin{aligned} w &= -A\left(\frac{a}{\mu}\right) J_0\left(\frac{\mu r}{a}\right), \\ u &= \frac{(1 + \nu)R}{\mu^2 R^2/a^2 - \Omega^2(1 - \nu^2)} AJ_1\left(\frac{\mu r}{a}\right), \end{aligned} \tag{8.23i}$$

and the boundary conditions at the edge $r = a$ of the cap are, according to the foregoing remarks,

$$u(a) = AJ_1(\mu) = 0,$$

[11] See, for example, Churchill, R. V., loc. cit., Chapter 8.

or,

$$N_r(a) = A\left\{J_0(\mu) - \frac{\mu R^2/a^2}{\mu^2 R^2/a^2 - \Omega^2(1-\nu^2)}[(\nu - 1)J_1(\mu) + \mu J_0(\mu)]\right\} = 0. \tag{8.23j}$$

Either of these conditions is satisfied by the trivial solution $A = 0$ which represents the case of no motion of the shell. The trivial solution is, therefore, avoided by setting

$$J_1(\mu) = 0,$$

or,

$$J_0(\mu) - \frac{\mu R^2/a^2}{\mu^2 R^2/a^2 - \Omega^2(1-\nu^2)}[(\nu - 1)J_1(\mu) + \mu J_0(\mu)] = 0. \tag{8.23k}$$

Each of the above transcendental equations has an infinite number of roots, each corresponding to a natural frequency of free vibration. The roots of the appropriate frequency equation are determined by the methods described in Section 8.1. Taking as an example the case of the spherical cap with zero tangential displacement prescribed at its edge, we require the roots of the first of Eqs. 8.23k. These have been tabulated widely and we find that the first five roots are[12]

$$\mu = 3.832, 7.016, 10.17, 13.32, 16.47, \ldots \tag{8.23l}$$

By use of the following formula, which is derived by inverting Eq. 8.23b, the natural frequencies which correspond to each of these roots can be derived:

$$2\Omega^2(1-\nu^2) = 2(1+\nu) + \left(\frac{\mu R}{a}\right)^2 \pm \left\{\left[2(1+\nu) + \left(\frac{\mu R}{a}\right)^2\right]^2 - 4(1-\nu^2)\left(\frac{\mu R}{a}\right)^2\right\}^{1/2}. \tag{8.23m}$$

This formula indicates that, for each of the roots 8.23*l*, there are two natural frequencies of θ-independent free vibration of the spherical membrane cap. Of these, the natural frequencies which correspond to the upper sign before the radical increase without bound as the roots μ increase, while those which correspond to the lower sign approach the limiting value $\Omega = 1$ as the roots μ increase. The existence of two families of frequencies which behave in this way was first postulated and discovered for spherical membranes by Lamb.[13]

---

[12] See, for example, Jahnke, E., and Emde, F., *Tables of Functions*, New York: Dover, 4th ed. (1945).

[13] Lamb, H., *Proc. London Math. Soc.*, **14**, 50–56 (1882).

It is of interest to also calculate the lowest natural frequency of the shell by using Rayleigh's method. For this purpose, let us assume the displacement function

$$u = A\frac{r}{a}\left(1 - \frac{r}{a}\right), \tag{8.24a}$$

which satisfies the boundary condition at $r = a$. Since no boundary conditions are available on w in this problem, we shall construct the w function from the u function by substituting the latter into the second of the equations of motion (Eqs. 8.22b), recalling that $D = 0$ for the membrane shell, and solving for w. This leads to the expression

$$w = \frac{AR}{\Omega^2(1 - \nu) - 2}\left(\frac{2}{a} - \frac{3r}{a^2}\right). \tag{8.24b}$$

The variational equation of the problem (see Eq. 8.11 and Eqs. 8.22b) with $D = 0$, is given by

$$\int_0^a \left\{\left[L(ru) + \frac{1 + \nu}{R}rw' + \frac{\Omega^2}{R^2}(1 - \nu^2)ru\right]\delta u \right.$$
$$\left. + \left[\frac{(1 + \nu)}{R}\left\{(ru)' + \frac{2rw}{R}\right\} - \Omega^2(1 - \nu^2)rw\right]\delta w\right\} dr = 0. \tag{8.24c}$$

If we substitute the assumed displacement functions and carry out the indicated integrations of Eq. 8.24c, taking note of the fact that the second square bracket is zero by virtue of our construction of w, we obtain the result

$$\left[\frac{a^2\Omega^2(1 - \nu^2)}{60R^2} - \frac{1}{4} - \frac{1 + \nu}{4\{\Omega^2(1 - \nu) - 2\}}\right] A\,\delta A = 0. \tag{8.24d}$$

Since the variation δA is arbitrary and since the constant A must be nonzero, the above equation is satisfied by the vanishing of the square bracketed terms. This leads to the following expression for the natural frequency:

$$2(1 - \nu^2)\Omega^2 = 2(1 + \nu) + \frac{15R^2}{a^2}$$
$$\pm \left\{\left[2(1 + \nu) + 15\frac{R^2}{a^2}\right]^2 - 60(1 - \nu^2)\frac{R^2}{a^2}\right\}^{1/2}. \tag{8.24e}$$

In order to compare the lowest natural frequency of the shallow spherical membrane with its edge restrained against tangential motion as obtained by the variational and the exact solutions of the problem, Eqs. 8.23m and 8.24e were applied to a shell with $R/a = 2$ and $\nu = 0.3$ with the following results:

$\Omega^2 = 0.97121$ Exact solution, Eq. 8.23m,

$\Omega^2 = 0.97165$ Variational solution, Eq. 8.24e.

We note that the variational solution is slightly higher than the exact result in accordance with the remarks that we made on this subject in Section 8.1.

Free, θ-independent Vibration of Shallow Spherical Shells with Bending Resistance. We now turn our attention to the full system (Eq. 8.22) which is appropriate to the analysis of shallow spherical shells with bending resistance which undergo θ-independent free vibrations. If we restrict our attention to Eq. 8.22e, we find that it can be rewritten, for convenience, in the form

$$a^6LLL\begin{Bmatrix} ru \\ rw' \end{Bmatrix} + A_2a^4LL\begin{Bmatrix} ru \\ rw' \end{Bmatrix} + A_1a^2L\begin{Bmatrix} ru \\ rw' \end{Bmatrix} + A_0\begin{Bmatrix} ru \\ rw' \end{Bmatrix} = 0, \quad (8.25\text{a})$$

where

$$\begin{aligned} A_2 &= (1 - \nu^2)\left(\frac{h}{a}\right)^2\left(\frac{\omega}{\omega_0}\right)^2, \\ A_1 &= -12(1 - \nu^2)\left[\left(\frac{\omega}{\omega_0}\right)^2 - 4\left(\frac{H}{h}\right)^2\right], \\ A_0 &= -12(1 - \nu^2)\left(\frac{h}{a}\right)^2\left(\frac{\omega}{\omega_0}\right)^2\left[(1 - \nu^2)\left(\frac{\omega}{\omega_0}\right)^2 - 8(1 + \nu)\left(\frac{H}{h}\right)^2\right], \\ \omega_0^2 &= Eh^2/\rho a^4. \end{aligned} \quad (8.25\text{b})$$

This equation may be factored as follows:

$$\left[L + \left(\frac{\mu_1}{a}\right)^2\right]\left[L + \left(\frac{\mu_2}{a}\right)^2\right]\left[L + \left(\frac{\mu_3}{a}\right)^2\right]\begin{Bmatrix} ru \\ rw' \end{Bmatrix} = 0, \quad (8.25\text{c})$$

and will have general solutions which are governed by equations of the type

$$L\begin{Bmatrix} ru \\ rw' \end{Bmatrix} - \left(\frac{\mu_\alpha}{a}\right)^2\begin{Bmatrix} ru \\ rw' \end{Bmatrix} = 0, \qquad \alpha = 1, 2, 3, \quad (8.25\text{d})$$

provided that the μ_α are the roots of the auxiliary equation

$$\mu_\alpha^6 - A_2\mu_\alpha^4 + A_1\mu_\alpha^2 - A_0 = 0. \quad (8.25\text{e})$$

Consequently, for each natural frequency of a given shell, there will be three roots μ_α^2 which can be obtained by using the formulas 6.57*l* to 6.57n.

Since (ru) and (rw') satisfy the same differential equation, their solutions will be the same within a factor of proportionality which can be shown, by substitution of the first of Eqs. 8.25d into the first of Eqs. 8.22b, to be

$$\frac{u_\alpha}{w_\alpha'} = \frac{1 + \nu}{a^2R}\left[\mu_\alpha^2 - (1 - \nu^2)\left(\frac{\omega}{\omega_0}\right)^2\left(\frac{h}{a}\right)^2\right]^{-1}. \quad (8.25\text{f})$$

It is now evident that the essential difference between the membrane and the bending solutions of the free vibration problem of a shallow spherical shell is the fact that the membrane problem was governed by one equation of the type of Eq. 8.23a and had two general solutions while the general problem with bending included is governed by three equations of the type of Eq. 8.25d and will have six general solutions. Indeed, since Eqs. 8.25d of the general problem are the same type of equation as is Eq. 8.23a of the membrane problem, we may immediately write the solution of the general problem (recalling Eqs. 8.23e to 8.23h) as

$$w = -\sum_{\alpha=1}^{3} \frac{a}{\mu_\alpha}\left[A_\alpha J_0\left(\frac{\mu_\alpha r}{a}\right) + B_\alpha Y_0\left(\frac{\mu_\alpha r}{a}\right)\right],$$

$$u = \frac{1+\nu}{a^2 R}\sum_{\alpha=1}^{3}\left[\mu_\alpha{}^2 + (1-\nu^2)\left(\frac{\omega}{\omega_0}\right)^2\left(\frac{h}{a}\right)^2\right]^{-1} \times \left[A_\alpha J_1\left(\frac{\mu_\alpha r}{a}\right) + B_\alpha Y_1\left(\frac{\mu_\alpha r}{a}\right)\right]. \tag{8.25g}$$

Here A_α and B_α are six arbitrary constants which are determined from six boundary conditions (three at each edge) which are to be applied in problems of shells of revolution whose motion is independent of the coordinate θ.

The solution for the shallow spherical shell includes, as a special case, the solution of a flat circular plate. Indeed, if we allow R to grow without bound, the displacement u vanishes and the vibrations associated with the above solution become purely transverse. This is to be expected since the longitudinal and transverse vibrations of flat circular plates are uncoupled. Coupling of these motions, which occurs as soon as a slight amount of curvature is introduced, is a basic characteristic of the vibration of shells.

Having found the normal modes of free vibration, we now turn to the determination of the natural frequencies. For this purpose, we take as an illustrative example the case of a shallow spherical shell which is closed at $r = 0$ and clamped at the edge $r = a$. Since the solutions $Y_0\,(\mu_\alpha r/a)$ and $Y_1(\mu_\alpha r/a)$ are singular at the origin, we remove these from the solution by setting $B_\alpha = 0$, $(\alpha = 1, 2, 3)$. Thus, the general solutions reduce to

$$u = \frac{1+\nu}{a^2 R}\sum_{\alpha=1}^{3}\left[\mu_\alpha{}^2 - (1-\nu^2)\left(\frac{\omega}{\omega_0}\right)^2\left(\frac{h}{a}\right)^2\right]^{-1} A_\alpha J_1\left(\frac{\mu_\alpha r}{a}\right),$$

$$w = -\sum_{\alpha=1}^{3}\frac{a}{\mu_\alpha} A_\alpha J_0\left(\frac{\mu_\alpha r}{a}\right). \tag{8.25h}$$

Now there are three arbitrary constants $A_\alpha(\alpha = 1, 2, 3)$ which are to be determined from three available boundary conditions at $r = a$. For the case of the clamped edge, these conditions are

$$w(a) = u_r(a) = w'(a) = 0. \tag{8.25i}$$

Upon substitution of the solutions 8.25h into these boundary conditions, we obtain the following homogeneous system of equations:

$$\begin{aligned}
&\frac{J_0(\mu_1)}{\mu_1}A_1 + \frac{J_0(\mu_2)}{\mu_2}A_2 + \frac{J_0(\mu_3)}{\mu_3}A_3 = 0,\\
&J_1(\mu_1)A_1 + J_1(\mu_2)A_2 + J_1(\mu_3)A_3 = 0,\\
&\frac{J_1(\mu_1)A_1}{\mu_1{}^2 - (1-\nu^2)(h/a)^2(\omega/\omega_0)^2} + \frac{J_1(\mu_2)A_2}{\mu_2{}^2 - (1-\nu^2)(h/a)^2(\omega/\omega_0)^2}\\
&\qquad + \frac{J_1(\mu_3)A_3}{\mu_3{}^2 - (1-\nu^2)(h/a)^2(\omega/\omega_0)^2} = 0.
\end{aligned} \tag{8.25j}$$

The trivial solution $A_1 = A_2 = A_3 = 0$ of the above system of equations is avoided by setting the determinant of the coefficients equal to zero. This yields the natural frequencies of the clamped shallow spherical cap. Since the system 8.25j is homogeneous, the three constants A_α are not independent and we can at best find two of them in terms of the third from the first two equations of 8.25j, for example, as follows:

$$\begin{aligned}
\frac{A_1}{A_3} &= \frac{\mu_1}{\mu_3}\,\frac{\mu_2 J_0(\mu_3)J_1(\mu_2) - \mu_3 J_0(\mu_2)J_1(\mu_3)}{\mu_2 J_0(\mu_1)J_1(\mu_2) - \mu_1 J_0(\mu_2)J_1(\mu_1)},\\
\frac{A_2}{A_3} &= \frac{\mu_2}{\mu_3}\,\frac{\mu_3 J_0(\mu_1)J_1(\mu_3) - \mu_1 J_0(\mu_3)J_1(\mu_1)}{\mu_2 J_0(\mu_1)J_1(\mu_2) - \mu_1 J_0(\mu_2)J_1(\mu_1)}.
\end{aligned} \tag{8.25k}$$

The foregoing represents the exact solution of the free-vibration problem of a clamped shallow spherical cap. For purposes of illustration and comparison, it is appropriate to also apply Rayleigh's method to the solution of the problem, and this will be done next. In the present case, the variational equation of the problem is (see Eqs. 8.11 and 8.22b):

$$\begin{aligned}
&\int_0^a \Big\{ K\left[L(ru) + \frac{1+\nu}{R}rw' + \frac{h\rho\omega^2}{K}ru\right]\delta u\\
&+ D\left[L(rw')' + \frac{1+\nu}{D}K\left((ru)' + \frac{2r}{R}w\right) - \frac{h\rho\omega^2}{D}rw\right]\delta w\Big\}\,dr = 0.
\end{aligned} \tag{8.26a}$$

Functions which satisfy the boundary conditions 8.25i at the clamped edge $r = a$ are assumed in the form

$$\begin{aligned}
u &= A\frac{r}{a}\left(1 - \frac{r}{a}\right), &\quad \delta u &= \delta A\frac{r}{a}\left(1 - \frac{r}{a}\right),\\
w &= B\left(1 - \frac{r^2}{a^2}\right)^2, &\quad \delta w &= \delta B\left(1 - \frac{r^2}{a^2}\right)^2,
\end{aligned} \tag{8.26b}$$

which, upon substitution into the variational equation and integration of the result, yield the expression

$$\left\{\left[\frac{1-\nu^2}{60}\left(\frac{\omega}{\omega_0}\right)^2\left(\frac{h}{a}\right)^2-\frac{1}{4}\right]A-\frac{22}{105}(1+\nu)\frac{H}{a}B\right\}\delta A$$

$$+\left\{\frac{264}{105}(1+\nu)\left(\frac{H}{h}\right)\left(\frac{a}{h}\right)A\right.$$

$$\left.-\left[12(1-\nu^2)\left(\frac{\omega}{\omega_0}\right)^2-96(1+\nu)\left(\frac{H}{h}\right)^2-\frac{32}{3}\right]B\right\}\delta B=0. \quad (8.26c)$$

Since the variations are arbitrary, the above equation can only be satisfied if their coefficients vanish; thus,

$$\left[\frac{1-\nu^2}{60}\left(\frac{\omega}{\omega_0}\right)^2\left(\frac{h}{a}\right)^2-\frac{1}{4}\right]A-\frac{22\,(1+\nu)}{105}\frac{H}{a}B=0,$$

$$\frac{264}{105}(1+\nu)\left(\frac{H}{h}\right)\left(\frac{a}{h}\right)A \quad (8.26d)$$

$$-\left[12(1-\nu^2)\left(\frac{\omega}{\omega_0}\right)^2-96(1+\nu)\left(\frac{H}{h}\right)^2-\frac{32}{3}\right]B=0.$$

For a nontrivial solution for A and B, the determinant of the above pair of equations must vanish, with the result that

$$(1-\nu^2)^2\left(\frac{\omega}{\omega_0}\right)^4-\left[\frac{80}{9}+8(1+\nu)\left(\frac{H}{h}\right)^2+15\frac{a^2}{h^2}\right](1-\nu^2)\left(\frac{\omega}{\omega_0}\right)^2$$

$$+\left(\frac{a}{h}\right)^2\left[\frac{400}{3}+120(1+\nu)\left(\frac{H}{h}\right)^2-96\left(\frac{11}{21}\right)^2(1+\nu)\left(\frac{H}{h}\right)^2\right]=0.$$

$$(8.26e)$$

Since for a thin shallow spherical shell we have $h/a \ll 1$ and $H/a \ll 1$, we find that the smaller of the two roots of Eq. 8.26e is given by

$$\frac{\omega}{\omega_0}=\frac{2.98}{(1-\nu^2)^{1/2}}\left\{1+[0.9+0.2(1+\nu)](1+\nu)\left(\frac{H}{h}\right)^2\right\}^{1/2}. \quad (8.26f)$$

Discussion of Results on θ-independent Free Vibration of Shallow Spherical Shells. At this point, it is well to bring together for discussion the results for the lowest natural frequency of a clamped shallow spherical cap as obtained above by the variational method, from the exact method involving the solution of the frequency determinant, and from several other approaches to the problem.

The solutions 8.25g and the frequency equations 8.25j were first derived by E. Reissner[14] who also derived the variational solution which appears as Eq. 8.26f. Later, Naghdi and Kalnins[15] rederived the solutions 8.25g and the frequency equations 8.25j and obtained the natural frequencies by determining the roots of the determinant of Eqs. 8.25j by a method of the type which we discussed in Section 8.1; their results will be given presently.

There are, however, two additional investigations which are of interest to the present discussion. In one of these, Federhofer[16] did not make the assumptions regarding the expressions for the changes of curvature and did not neglect the contribution of the transverse shearing force to the equilibrium of forces in the circumferential direction which we described in Section 6.3. By making only a geometrical definition of shallowness, that is, $(r/R)^2 \ll 1$, and by assuming displacement functions in the form

$$u = A\frac{r}{a}\left(1 - \frac{r^2}{a^2}\right), \qquad w = B\left(1 - \frac{r^2}{a^2}\right)^2, \tag{8.27a}$$

Federhofer obtained the following formula for the lowest natural frequency of a clamped shallow spherical cap:

$$\frac{\omega}{\omega_0} = \frac{2.98}{(1 - \nu^2)^{1/2}}\left\{1 + [0.9 + 0.19(1 + \nu)](1 + \nu)\left(\frac{H}{h}\right)^2\right\}^{1/2} \tag{8.27b}$$

by Rayleigh's method. This is virtually identical to our expression (Eq. 8.26f) which was obtained by Reissner.[14] Finally, Reissner[17] also proposed an additional simplifying assumption beyond those which have already been stated for a shallow spherical shell. He showed that, for a shallow shell, the contribution of the longitudinal inertia term $\rho h r \ddot{u}_r$ is negligible and was thereby able to reduce the equations of the dynamic theory of shallow spherical shells to those of his static theory (discussed in Chapter 6) except that the transverse load term in Eq. 6.38d was replaced by a transverse inertia term. Here we should recall that the neglect of longitudinal inertia was also found to be a useful method for determining the

[14] Reissner, E., "On Vibrations of Shallow Spherical Shells," *J. Appl. Phys.*, **17,** 1038–1042 (1946).
[15] Naghdi, P. M. and Kalnins, A., "Axisymmetric Vibrations of Shallow Elastic Spherical Shells," *J. Acoust. Soc. Am.* **32,** 342–347 (1960).
[16] Federhofer, K., "Zur Berechnung der Eigenschwingungen der Kugelschale," *Sitzber, Akad. Wiss. Wien, Mat. Naturwiss. Kl.* **146,** 57–69 (1937).
[17] Reissner, E., "On Transverse Vibrations of Thin Shallow Elastic Shells," *Q. Appl. Math.*, **13,** 169–176 (1955).

transverse modes of free vibration of a circular cylindrical shell.[18] Using this approach, Reissner[19] subsequently solved, among others, the problem of a clamped shallow spherical cap with the exact method of solution.

To compare the results of the various attacks on the free-vibration analysis of a shallow spherical shell, we present, in Table 8.3, the lowest natural frequency of a clamped shallow spherical cap as obtained by each method.

Table 8.3 Lowest Natural Frequency of a Clamped Shallow Spherical Cap ($H/h = 5$, $a/h = 20$)

Investigator	Basis	Method	(ω/ω_0)
Naghdi and Kalnins[15]	*a*, *b*	Exact	13.14
Reissner[19]	*a*, *b*, *c*	Exact	13.30
Reissner[14]	*a*, *b*	Rayleigh	14.65
Federhofer[16]	*a*	Rayleigh	14.75

Key: *a*, $(r/R)^2 \ll 1$; *b*, transverse shearing contributions and change of curvature effects neglected; and *c*, longitudinal inertia terms neglected.

The data of Table 8.3 indicate that the exact solution with longitudinal inertia neglected gives a slightly higher lowest natural frequency than does the exact solution with longitudinal inertia included. This result is consistent with the data which were found in a similar comparison of analyses of circular cylindrical shells (see our remarks in connection with Eq. 8.20e). The two variational solutions are seen, in Table 8.3, to give higher natural frequencies than the exact solutions. As we have already pointed out, this is typical since the assumed mode shapes introduce added stiffness into the system. To bring out more fully the accuracy of the variational method, we have plotted, in Fig. 8.5, the lowest natural frequencies of clamped shallow spherical caps over a range of H/h values as obtained from Reissner's[19] exact solution and his one term variational solution[14] (Eq. 8.26f). It is seen that for $H/h < 3$ the accuracy of the variational solution is quite good and that as H/h increases beyond three the accuracy falls off rapidly. For these higher values of H/h, the assumed forms for u and w should contain further terms in order to improve the approximation.

Finally, it is appropriate to recall here that the lowest natural frequency

[18] Koval and Cranch, loc. cit., and Weingarten, loc. cit.

[19] Reissner, E., "On Axisymmetrical Vibrations of Shallow Spherical Shells," *Q. Appl. Math.*, **13**, 279–290 (1955).

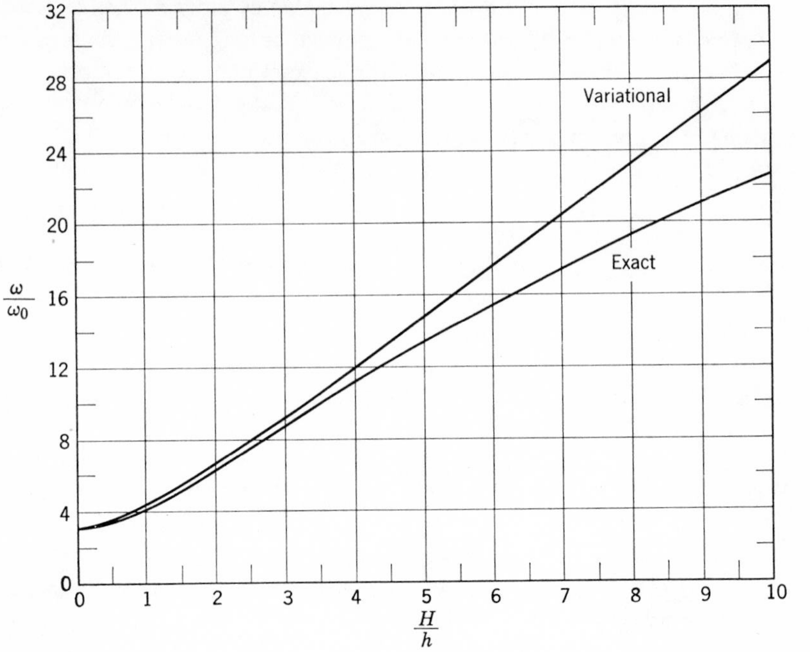

Figure 8.5 Lowest natural frequencies of shallow spherical shells with clamped edges.

which was obtained by the exact method of solution with bending resistance neglected was $\Omega^2 = 0.97121$. By using the definitions of Ω and ω_0, it can be shown that this is equivalent to the result $(\omega/\omega_0) = 9.857$ for $H/h = 5$ as used in Table 8.3. Since the bending stiffness is neglected in the membrane theory it is reasonable that this result should turn out to be much less than the results given in Table 8.3 for the same shell with bending resistance included. Thus it is seen, for this particular example, that the membrane analysis underestimates the lowest natural frequency of a shallow spherical cap appreciably.

The present results, it must be emphasized, are valid for shallow spherical shells which undergo free vibrations that are independent of the circumferential coordinate θ. In the next section, we shall discuss arbitrary free vibrations of such shells.

8.3*b* Free, Arbitrary Vibration of Shallow Spherical Shells

In the analysis of arbitrary free vibration of shallow spherical shells, we are concerned with the solution of Eqs. 8.21 in conjunction with Eqs. 6.36b and 6.36f and Eqs. 6.5. In this case, however, it is expedient to reduce the system to a form which is amenable to solution by expressing the displacements u_r and u_θ in terms of two auxiliary functions U and ψ as follows:[20]

$$u_r = \frac{\partial U}{\partial r} - r\psi,$$
$$u_\theta = \frac{1}{r}\frac{\partial U}{\partial \theta}. \tag{8.28a}$$

Substitution of these definitions into the expressions which relate the stress resultants to the displacements, followed by substitution of the latter into the first two equations of motion (Eqs. 8.21), gives

$$\frac{\partial}{\partial r}\left[\nabla^2 U - \frac{\lambda}{\omega^2}\frac{\partial^2 U}{\partial t^2} + \frac{1+\nu}{R}w\right] - r\frac{\partial^2 \psi}{\partial r^2} - 3\frac{\partial \psi}{\partial r} - \frac{1-\nu}{2}\frac{1}{r}\frac{\partial^2 \psi}{\partial \theta^2} + \frac{\lambda}{\omega^2}r\frac{\partial^2 \psi}{\partial t^2} = 0, \tag{8.28b}$$

$$\frac{\partial}{\partial \theta}\left[\nabla^2 U - \frac{\lambda}{\omega^2}\frac{\partial^2 U}{\partial t^2} + \frac{1+\nu}{R}w - \frac{1+\nu}{2}r\frac{\partial \psi}{\partial r} - 2\psi\right] = 0, \tag{8.28c}$$

where

$$\nabla^2(\ldots) = (\ldots)'' + \frac{1}{r}(\ldots)' + \frac{1}{r^2}\frac{\partial^2}{\partial \theta^2}(\ldots), \tag{8.28d}$$

$$\frac{\lambda}{\omega^2} = \frac{\rho(1-\nu^2)}{E}. \tag{8.28e}$$

These equations may be uncoupled by integrating Eq. 8.28c with respect to θ, then differentiating with respect to r and subtracting the result from Eq. 8.28b. This gives

$$\nabla^2 \psi = \frac{2}{1-\nu}\frac{\lambda}{\omega^2}\frac{\partial^2 \psi}{\partial t^2}, \tag{8.28f}$$

where the arbitrary function which arises in the integration with respect to θ has been set to zero without loss of generality. Now we substitute expressions 6.36f, that relate the changes of curvature and twist, into Eqs. 6.5, that relate the stress couples to the changes of curvature and twist, and find, upon substitution of the latter expressions into the last two of the equations of motion (Eqs. 8.21), that

$$Q_r = -D\frac{\partial}{\partial r}(\nabla^2 w),$$
$$Q_\theta = -D\frac{1}{r}\frac{\partial}{\partial \theta}(\nabla^2 w). \tag{8.28g}$$

[20] The substitution and subsequent derivation are due to Kalnins, A., "On Vibrations of Shallow Spherical Shells," *J. Acoust. Soc. Am.*, **33**, 1102–1107 (1961), where the effects of transverse shear and rotatory inertia are also considered.

Thus far, we have utilized the first two and the last two of the equations of motion (Eqs. 8.21). The third of these equations is now used, in conjunction with Eqs. 8.28a and 8.28g and the relationships between the stress resultants and the displacements, to derive the expression

$$\frac{h^2}{12}\nabla^2\nabla^2 w + \frac{1+\nu}{R}\nabla^2 U + \frac{2(1+\nu)}{R^2} w + \frac{\lambda}{\omega^2}\frac{\partial^2 w}{\partial t^2} - \frac{1+\nu}{R}\left(r\frac{\partial\psi}{\partial r} + 2\psi\right) = 0. \quad (8.28h)$$

The functions U and ψ are eliminated from this equation by using Eqs. 8.28c and 8.28f. As a result, we obtain the following equation for w:

$$\nabla^6 w + r_1\nabla^4 w + r_2\nabla^2 w + r_3 w = 0, \quad (8.28i)$$

where

$$r_1 = -\frac{\lambda}{\omega^2}\frac{\partial^2}{\partial t^2},$$
$$r_2 = \frac{12(1-\nu^2)}{h^2R^2} + \frac{12}{h^2}\frac{\lambda}{\omega^2}\frac{\partial^2}{\partial t^2}, \quad (8.28j)$$
$$r_3 = -\frac{12}{h^2}\frac{\lambda^2}{\omega^4}\frac{\partial^4}{\partial t^4} - \frac{24(1+\nu)}{h^2R^2}\frac{\lambda}{\omega^2}\frac{\partial^2}{\partial t^2}.$$

Equations 8.28f and 8.28i are the uncoupled differential equations which govern the arbitrary free vibration of shallow spherical shells. An expression for the function U can be derived by eliminating $\nabla^2 U$ from expressions 8.28c and 8.28h to give

$$\frac{\lambda}{\omega^2}\frac{\partial^2 U}{\partial t^2} = -\frac{h^2 R}{12(1+\nu)}\nabla^4 w - \left[\frac{1-\nu}{R} + \frac{R}{1+\nu}\frac{\lambda}{\omega^2}\frac{\partial^2}{\partial t^2}\right] w + \frac{1-\nu}{2} r\frac{\partial\psi}{\partial r}. \quad (8.28k)$$

Now all means are available for obtaining any desired variable of the free vibration problem of a shallow spherical shell. To solve Eq. 8.28i, we assume that the shallow spherical shell is closed with respect to θ and that, therefore, the radial, circumferential, and temporal variations of the deflection can be expressed in the form

$$w(r, \theta, t) = \left\{\sum_{\alpha=1}^{3} w_\alpha^*(r)\right\}\cos n\theta \cos \omega t. \quad (8.29a)$$

When this expression is substituted into Eq. 8.28i, we find, by methods which are analagous to those which led to the solution of Eq. 8.25a, that

$$w_\alpha^*(r) = A_\alpha J_n\left(\frac{\mu_\alpha r}{a}\right) + B_\alpha Y_n\left(\frac{\mu_\alpha r}{a}\right), \quad \alpha = 1, 2, 3 \quad (8.29b)$$

where J_n and Y_n are, respectively, the Bessel functions of the first and second kind and order n. The μ_α are the roots of the equation

$$\left(\frac{\mu_\alpha}{a}\right)^6 - r_1\left(\frac{\mu_\alpha}{a}\right)^4 + r_2\left(\frac{\mu_\alpha}{a}\right)^2 - r_3 = 0, \tag{8.29c}$$

in which the r_α are obtained from Eqs. 8.28j by replacing each second derivative with respect to time by the factor $(-\omega^2)$.

In a similar fashion, we express the auxiliary function ψ in the form

$$\psi(r, \theta, t) = \psi^*(r) \cos n\theta \cos \omega t, \tag{8.30a}$$

which, upon substitution into Eq. 8.28f, leads to the result

$$\psi^*(r) = A_4 J_n\left(\frac{\mu_4 r}{a}\right) + B_4 Y_n\left(\frac{\mu_4 r}{a}\right), \tag{8.30b}$$

where

$$\mu_4 = a[2\lambda/(1 - \nu)]^{1/2}. \tag{8.30c}$$

The remaining auxiliary function can now be obtained by first assuming that

$$U(r, \theta, t) = U^*(r) \cos n\theta \cos \omega t. \tag{8.31a}$$

Then, when this expression is substituted into Eq. 8.28k and Eqs. 8.29b and 8.30b are accounted for, we find that

$$U^*(r) = -\frac{1}{\lambda}\left\{\sum_{\alpha=1}^{3}\left[\frac{-h^2R}{12(1+\nu)}\left(\frac{\mu_\alpha}{a}\right)^4 - \frac{1-\nu}{R} + \frac{R\lambda}{1+\nu}\right] w_\alpha^*(r) + \frac{1-\nu}{2}\, r\, \frac{d\psi^*}{dr}\right\}. \tag{8.31b}$$

Any of the shell variables can now be obtained from Eqs. 8.29, 8.30, and 8.31 by use of Eqs. 8.28a and the equations of shell theory. For example, the displacements u_r and u_θ are given by

$$u_r = \frac{KR}{r}\left\{\sum_{\alpha=1}^{3} A_\alpha\, \delta_\alpha\left[\mu_\alpha \frac{r}{a} J_{n-1}\left(\frac{\mu_\alpha r}{a}\right) - nJ_n\left(\frac{\mu_\alpha r}{a}\right)\right] + A_4 n^2 J_n\left(\frac{\mu_4 r}{a}\right)\right\} \cos n\theta \cos \omega t, \tag{8.32a}$$

$$u_\theta = -\frac{KRn}{r}\left\{\sum_{\alpha=1}^{3} A_\alpha\, \delta_\alpha J_n\left(\frac{\mu_\alpha r}{a}\right) + A_4\left[\frac{\mu_4 r}{a} J_{n-1}\left(\frac{\mu_\alpha r}{a}\right) - nJ_n\left(\frac{\mu_4 r}{a}\right)\right]\right\} \sin n\theta \cos \omega t, \tag{8.32b}$$

where

$$\begin{aligned} \delta_\alpha &= \frac{1}{12}\left(\frac{h}{a}\right)^2 \mu_\alpha^4 + (1 - \nu^2)\left(\frac{a}{R}\right)^2 (1 - \Omega^2), \\ K &= [(1 + \nu)(1 - \nu^2)(R/a)^2\Omega^2]^{-1}, \end{aligned} \tag{8.32c}$$

and we have assumed that the shell is closed at $r = 0$. The rest of the analysis (that is, the determination of the natural frequencies) proceeds in the usual manner and we shall pursue its details no further, except to say that when $n = 0$, the development of the present section reduces to that of Section 8.3*a* in which we considered the θ-independent free vibration of a shallow spherical shell.

It is interesting, however, to discuss some results which were found by applying the present development to the analysis of arbitrary free vibra-

Table 8.4 Natural Frequencies, $\Omega' = \omega a(\rho/E)^{1/2}$, for Clamped Spherical Shells with $\nu = 0.3$, $a/h = 10$

	Mode	Type	$a/R = 0$	0.1	0.3	0.5	0.5^a
$n = 0$	1	T	0.3091	0.3386	0.5205	0.7515	0.7580
	2	T	1.204	1.205	1.247	1.331	1.339
	3	L	2.376	2.376	2.376	2.376	—
	4	T	2.696	2.698	2.711	2.737	2.749
	5	L	4.017	4.018	4.032	4.060	—
	6	L	4.351	4.351	4.351	4.351	—
	7	T	4.787	4.789	4.796	4.814	4.815
$n = 1$	1	T	0.6434	0.6520	0.7140	0.8195	0.8412
	2	T	1.841	1.841	1.844	1.852	1.913
	3	L	2.052	2.054	2.087	2.151	—
	4	L	3.332	3.332	3.332	3.334	—
	5	T	3.632	3.637	3.648	3.667	3.670
	6	L	5.250	5.251	5.253	5.255	—
	7	L	5.628	5.629	5.634	5.650	—
$n = 2$	1	T	1.056	1.060	1.099	1.168	1.182
	2	T	2.560	2.562	2.571	2.589	2.611
	3	L	3.195	3.196	3.208	3.230	—
	4	L	4.283	4.283	4.284	4.288	—
	5	T	4.655	4.657	4.664	4.683	4.683
$n = 3$	1	T	1.548	1.550	1.572	1.622	1.633
	2	T	3.360	3.361	3.369	3.383	3.399
	3	L	4.154	4.155	4.160	4.173	—
	4	L	5.266	5.267	5.269	5.273	—
	5	T	5.759	5.760	5.766	5.780	5.783

[a] Longitudinal inertia ignored.

tions of a clamped shallow spherical shell. These results,[21] which were obtained by evaluating the roots of the relevant frequency determinant with a procedure of the type discussed in Section 8.1, are summarized in Table 8.4 which gives a listing of natural frequencies for several values of n and a/R. The rows for which $n = 0$ correspond to shells which execute free vibrations that are independent of θ, and the column $a/R = 0$ gives results for the flat circular plate. Also included in the Table is a column of results obtained from an analysis in which the longitudinal inertia is ignored. The modes of free vibration are classified according to whether they are of transverse or longitudinal character by a T or an L, respectively.

This classification is accomplished by noting that a particular mode of the shallow shell becomes a transverse or a longitudinal mode of the uncoupled free vibration of a flat circular plate when the curvature in the present analysis goes to zero. Thus, the column for $a/R = 0$ is used as a reference for the classification of the modes of the shallow shell. As could be expected, the motion associated with the transverse modes in the shallow shell is predominantly transverse; that is, $w \gg u_r$, u_θ while the motion that is associated with the longitudinal modes is such that u_r, $u_\theta \gg w$.

To bring out the latter conclusion more fully, we have plotted, in Fig. 8.6, the displacements that are associated with the first six natural frequencies which are given for a shell with $a/R = 0.5$ and $n = 1$, in Table 8.4. The plots are given as a function of the variable r/a along the generator passing through $\theta = 0$. It is evident, from Fig. 8.6, that the motion associated with Ω_1', Ω_2', and Ω_5' is predominantly transverse while the motion associated with Ω_3', Ω_4' and Ω_6' is mainly longitudinal in nature. This is consistent with the classification of these modes in Table 8.4.

In conclusion, it is interesting to note, from Table 8.4, that the neglect of longitudinal inertia has two main effects. Of these, the first involves the fact that the natural frequencies with longitudinal inertia neglected are slightly higher than those which are obtained when longitudinal inertia is included. The second effect of ignoring longitudinal inertia is that the so-called longitudinal modes cannot be obtained from the resulting analysis.

This concludes, for the time being, our discussion of shallow spherical shells. In the next section on nonshallow spherical shells, we shall clarify the range of validity of the shallow shell approximation in free-vibration analyses. Then, in Chapter 9, we shall make some final comments on the validity of ignoring longitudinal inertia when we consider the analysis of shells under transient loadings.

---

[21] Kalnins, A., "Free Nonsymmetrical Vibrations of Shallow Spherical Shells," *Proc. 4th U.S. National Cong. Appl. Mech.*, 225–233 (1962).

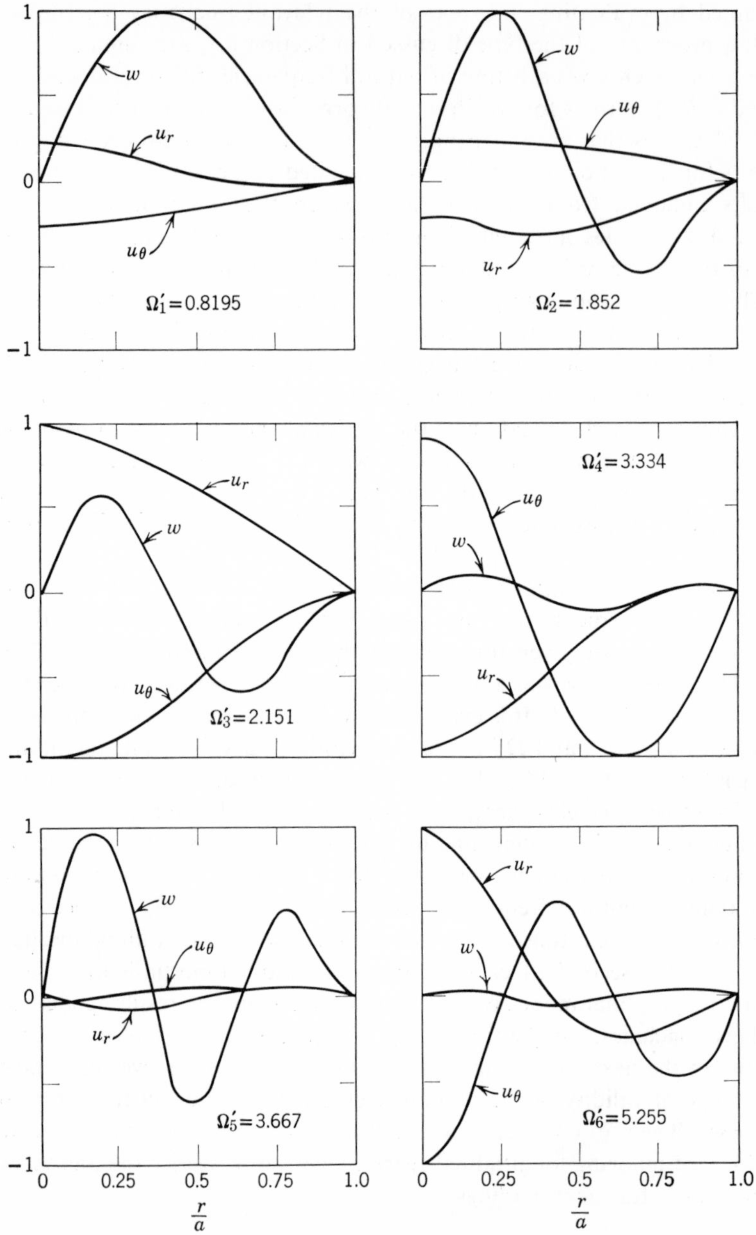

Figure 8.6 Displacement patterns for a clamped shallow spherical shell ($a/R=0.5$, $n=1$).

8.4 FREE VIBRATION OF NONSHALLOW SPHERICAL SHELLS

As a final detailed example, we consider the free vibration analysis of non-shallow spherical shells, in which we shall consider as special cases the shallow shell considered in the preceding section and the complete spherical shell. If, at first, we restrict our attention to θ-independent free vibrations, the equations of motion are given by

$$\begin{aligned} \frac{\partial N_\varphi}{\partial \varphi} + (N_\varphi - N_\theta)\cot\varphi + Q_\varphi &= R\rho h\,\frac{\partial^2 u_\varphi}{\partial t^2}, \\ \frac{\partial Q_\varphi}{\partial \varphi} + Q_\varphi \cot\varphi - (N_\varphi + N_\theta) &= R\rho h\,\frac{\partial^2 w}{\partial t^2}, \\ \frac{\partial M_\varphi}{\partial \varphi} + (M_\varphi - M_\theta)\cot\varphi - RQ_\varphi &= 0, \end{aligned} \tag{8.33a}$$

and the stress resultants and couples are related to the displacements of the reference surface by expressions which can be derived from Eqs. 6.5.

If we assume that the temporal and spatial dependence of the modes of free vibration are separable (see Eqs. 8.4):

$$\begin{aligned} u_\varphi(\varphi, t) &= u(\varphi)\cos\omega t, \\ w(\varphi, t) &= w(\varphi)\cos\omega t, \end{aligned} \tag{8.33b}$$

and if we substitute these forms along with the expressions for the stress resultants and couples and the third equation of motion into the first two equations of motion, we obtain the following equations:

$$\begin{aligned} &\frac{d^3w}{d\varphi^3} + \cot\varphi\,\frac{d^2w}{d\varphi^2} - (\nu + \cot^2\varphi)\frac{dw}{d\varphi} - \xi\left[\frac{d^2u}{d\varphi^2} + \cot\varphi\,\frac{du}{d\varphi}\right. \\ &\qquad \left. - (\nu + \cot^2\varphi)u\right] - \xi(1+\nu)\frac{dw}{d\varphi} - \xi\Omega^2(1-\nu^2)u = 0, \end{aligned} \tag{8.33c}$$

$$\begin{aligned} &\frac{d^4w}{d\varphi^4} + 2\cot\varphi\,\frac{d^3w}{d\varphi^3} - (1 + \nu + \cot^2\varphi)\frac{d^2w}{d\varphi^2} + (2 - \nu + \cot^2\varphi)\cot\varphi\,\frac{dw}{d\varphi} \\ &\qquad - \frac{d^3u}{d\varphi^3} - 2\cot\varphi\,\frac{d^2u}{d\varphi^2} + (1 + \nu + \cot^2\varphi)\frac{du}{d\varphi} \\ &\qquad - u(2 - \nu + \cot^2\varphi)\cot\varphi \\ &\qquad + \xi(1+\nu)\left(\frac{du}{d\varphi} + u\cot\varphi + 2w\right) - \xi\Omega^2(1-\nu^2)w = 0, \end{aligned} \tag{8.33d}$$

where

$$\Omega^2 = \frac{\rho R^2\omega^2}{E}, \qquad \xi = \frac{12R^2}{h^2}, \tag{8.33e}$$

as before. Here, as in Section 6.4, we shall neglect unity in comparison to the large parameter ξ wherever it is appropriate to do so.

Now we define

$$u = \frac{dU}{d\varphi}, \tag{8.33f}$$

and with this, Eq. 8.33c becomes

$$\frac{d}{d\varphi}\left[-H(w) + \xi H(U) - \xi(1+\nu)(U-w) + \xi\Omega^2(1-\nu^2)U\right] = 0, \tag{8.33g}$$

where

$$H(\ldots) = \frac{d^2(\ldots)}{d\varphi^2} + \cot\varphi\,\frac{d(\ldots)}{d\varphi} + 2(\ldots). \tag{8.33h}$$

Equation 8.33g indicates that the quantity in the square brackets is a constant that, on account of Eq. 8.33f, contributes nothing to u and may thus be taken as zero. This, and the introduction of the operator $H(\ldots)$ into Eq. 8.33d, leads to the equations

$$H(w) - \xi H(U) - \xi(1+\nu)(w-U) - \xi\Omega^2(1-\nu^2)U = 0, \tag{8.33i}$$

$$\begin{aligned} HH(U-w) + (3+\nu)H(w) - \xi(1+\nu)H(U) \\ - \xi[2(1+\nu) - \Omega^2(1-\nu^2)]w + 2\xi(1+\nu)U = 0. \end{aligned} \tag{8.33j}$$

Either of the variables may now be eliminated to reduce the free-vibration problem to the solution of one equation. Since the same equation is obtained in either case, we may write

$$HHH\begin{Bmatrix} w \\ U \end{Bmatrix} + C_2 HH\begin{Bmatrix} w \\ U \end{Bmatrix} + C_1 H\begin{Bmatrix} w \\ U \end{Bmatrix} + C_0\begin{Bmatrix} w \\ U \end{Bmatrix} = 0, \tag{8.33k}$$

where

$$\begin{aligned} C_2 &= \Omega^2(1-\nu^2) - 2, \\ C_1 &= \xi(1-\nu^2)(1-\Omega^2), \\ C_0 &= \xi\Omega^2(1-\nu^2)[3(1+\nu) - \Omega^2(1-\nu^2)]. \end{aligned} \tag{8.33l}$$

This sixth-order differential equation governs the free vibration of symmetrically loaded spherical shells. We shall consider its solution for two cases (as was done for the shallow spherical shell in the previous section). First we shall consider nonshallow spherical membrane shells for which $M_\varphi = M_\theta = Q_\varphi = 0$, or equivalently $1/\xi = 0$, and then we shall consider nonshallow spherical shells with resistance to bending included. As a special case, we shall take up the free vibration of a complete spherical shell with and without bending resistance.

8.4*a* Free θ-independent Vibration of Nonshallow Spherical Membrane Shells

The equations that govern the free vibration of the nonshallow spherical membrane shell are obtained by setting $M_\varphi = M_\theta = Q_\varphi = 1/\xi = 0$. If we restrict our attention to Eq. 8.33k, we find that with $1/\xi = 0$ it reduces to

$$H\begin{Bmatrix} w \\ U \end{Bmatrix} + r\begin{Bmatrix} w \\ U \end{Bmatrix} = 0, \tag{8.34a}$$

where

$$r = \frac{(1 + \nu)\Omega^2[3 - \Omega^2(1 - \nu)]}{1 - \Omega^2}. \tag{8.34b}$$

Since w and U satisfy the same differential equation, they will have the same solution and will be proportional to each other. Substitution of Eq. 8.34a into Eq. 8.33i along with $1/\xi = 0$ shows that the ratio of the two solutions is

$$\frac{w}{U} = \frac{1 + (1 + \nu)\Omega^2}{1 - \Omega^2}. \tag{8.34c}$$

Equation 8.34a, in its extended form, is given by

$$\frac{d^2w}{d\varphi^2} + \cot\varphi\,\frac{dw}{d\varphi} + (2 + r)\,w = 0, \tag{8.34d}$$

and is seen to be a case of Legendre's differential equation. Therefore, the general solution of Eq. 8.34d is

$$w = CP_\lambda(\cos\varphi) + DQ_\lambda(\cos\varphi), \tag{8.34e}$$

provided that

$$\lambda(\lambda + 1) = 2 + r, \tag{8.34f}$$

or,

$$\lambda = -\tfrac{1}{2} + \sqrt{\tfrac{9}{4} + r}. \tag{8.34g}$$

Here $P_\lambda(\cos\varphi)$ and $Q_\lambda(\cos\varphi)$ are the Legendre functions[22] of the first and second kind and order λ. We leave it to the exercises to show that no new information is obtained upon consideration of the negative square root in Eq. 8.34g. With the ratio 8.34c and the definition 8.33f, the solution for the meridional displacement becomes

$$u = \frac{1 - \Omega^2}{1 + (1 + \nu)\Omega^2}\,[CP_\lambda'(\cos\varphi) + DQ_\lambda'(\cos\varphi)]. \tag{8.34h}$$

---

[22] See, for example, Magnus, W., and Oberhettinger, F., *Formulas and Theorems for the Functions of Mathematical Physics*, New York: Chelsea, pp. 49–73 (1954).

where the prime denotes a derivative with respect to φ. The solutions 8.34e and 8.34h are valid for a spherical membrane with two concentric edges at each of which either u_φ or N_φ may be prescribed. Since the Legendre function $Q_\lambda(\cos\varphi)$ is singular at the origin, we must, when considering a spherical membrane which is closed at $\varphi = 0$, suppress such a solution by setting $D = 0$. Thus, for nonshallow spherical caps, to which we shall restrict our subsequent attention, the solutions from the membrane theory reduce to

$$\begin{aligned} w &= CP_\lambda(\cos\varphi), \\ u &= \frac{1 - \Omega^2}{1 + (1 + \nu)\Omega^2} CP_\lambda'(\cos\varphi). \end{aligned} \tag{8.34i}$$

In terms of the foregoing solutions, the boundary conditions of zero meridional displacement or zero meridional stress resultant at the edge $\varphi = \varphi_0$ of a nonshallow spherical membrane cap are given, respectively, as

$$\begin{gathered} CP_\lambda'(\cos\varphi_0) = 0, \\ C\{\cot\varphi_0 P_\lambda'(\cos\varphi_0) + [1 + (1 + \nu)\Omega^2]P_\lambda(\cos\varphi_0)\} = 0. \end{gathered} \tag{8.34j}$$

The trivial solution $C = 0$ is avoided by setting the braces equal to zero. From this, the natural frequencies can be found.

Results based on the second condition of 8.34j, that is, the case of a force free edge,[23] are given in Fig. 8.7. In that Figure, the natural frequencies of spherical membranes with free edges as obtained by the exact method of solution are plotted as a function of φ_0, the angle of opening. It is seen that the natural frequencies arrange themselves into two groupings which are referred to as the upper branch and the lower branch. The lower branch is made up of an infinite number of natural frequencies which lie in the shaded area bounded by the line $\Omega = 1$ and the lower curve. The upper branch, of which the first three natural frequencies for each angle of opening are plotted, has an infinite range of frequencies. As could be expected, the results obtained with the membrane theory are independent of thickness.

Closed Spherical Membrane Shell. To apply the results on nonshallow spherical membrane shells to closed spherical membrane shells, that is, shells for which $0 \leqslant \varphi \leqslant \pi$, the solutions 8.34i must be modified. The reason for this is that the Legendre functions of the first kind, $P_\lambda(\cos\varphi)$, are singular at $\varphi = \pi$ unless λ is an integer. In this case, the Legendre functions $P_\lambda(\cos\varphi)$ reduce to the more familiar Legendre polynomials[22]

[23] Kalnins, A., "Effect of Bending on Vibration of Spherical Shells," *J. Acoust. Soc. Am.*, **36**, 74–81 (1964).

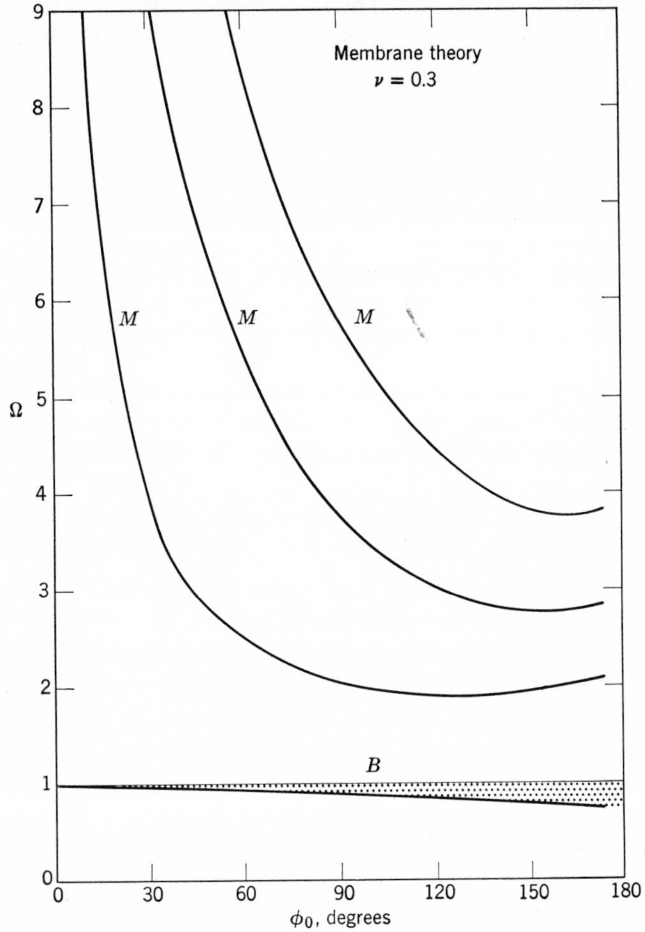

Figure 8.7 Natural frequencies of spherical membrane shells with free edges.

$P_n(\cos\varphi)$ and the solutions for the complete spherical membrane shell are given by

$$w = CP_n(\cos\varphi),$$
$$u = \frac{1 - \Omega^2}{1 + (1 + \nu)\Omega^2} CP_n'(\cos\varphi). \tag{8.35a}$$

We observe now that the removal of the singularity at $\varphi = 0$ has replaced the application of a boundary condition at that point. Since we have shown that the quantity λ must be replaced by the integers n, the formula for the natural frequencies of a closed spherical membrane shell follows immediately from Eq. 8.34b which, upon substitution of Eq. 8.34f, becomes

$$2(1 - \nu^2)\Omega^2 = 1 + 3\nu + n(n + 1) \pm \{[1 + 3\nu + n(n + 1)]^2 - 4(1 - \nu^2)[n(n + 1) - 2]\}^{1/2}, \quad n = 0, 1, 2, \ldots \quad (8.35b)$$

The foregoing formula was first derived by Lamb[13] and again by Federhofer[16] and Baker.[24] As could be expected, it is similar in form to

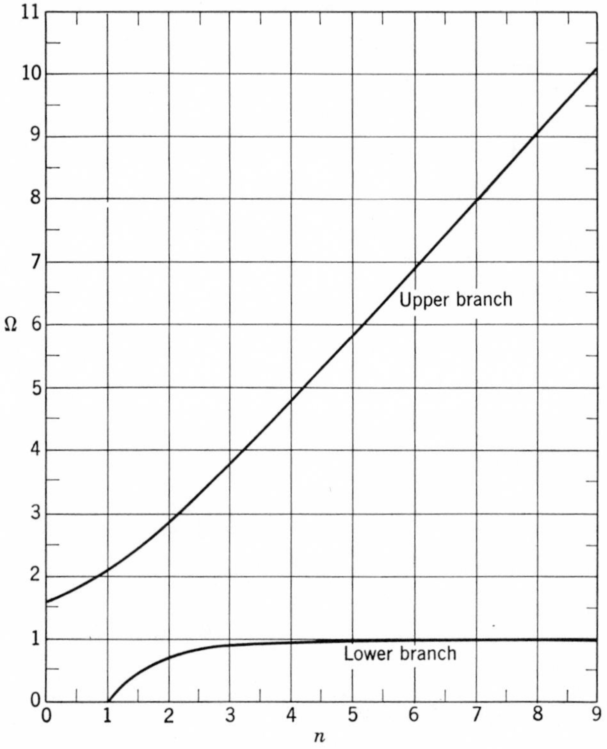

Figure 8.8 Natural frequencies of complete spherical membrane shells.

Eq. 8.23m that we derived earlier for the shallow spherical membrane shell. In Fig. 8.8, where we have plotted the foregoing equation for the case $\nu = 0.3$, the character of the natural frequencies of the complete spherical membrane shell is immediately evident. As in Fig. 8.7, we again have an upper branch and a lower branch which in this case arise, respectively,

[24] Baker, W. E., "Axisymmetric Modes of Vibration of Thin Spherical Shells," *J. Acoust. Soc. Am.*, **33**, 1749–1758 (1961).

from the positive and the negative square roots in Eq. 8.35b. It should be noticed that, for the $n = 0$ mode, the frequency corresponding to the lower branch is imaginary and has, therefore, been discarded as a spurious mode. The upper branch for the $n = 0$ mode gives the natural frequency

$$\Omega_0 = [2/(1 - \nu)]^{1/2}. \tag{8.35c}$$

Although this lowest frequency of the upper branch is higher than all of the frequencies of the lower branch, it is referred to as the fundamental frequency because it involves purely radial motion and because it is the frequency of the single mode which occurs in the symmetrical free vibration ($u_\varphi = 0,\ w \neq 0$) of a closed spherical membrane shell.

8.4*b* Free, θ-independent Vibration of Nonshallow Spherical Shells with Bending Resistance

Let us now consider the solution of the full version of Eq. 8.33k that is appropriate to the free-vibration analysis of spherical shells with bending resistance, and which we repeat here for convenience:

$$HHH\begin{Bmatrix} w \\ U \end{Bmatrix} + C_2HH\begin{Bmatrix} w \\ U \end{Bmatrix} + C_1H\begin{Bmatrix} w \\ U \end{Bmatrix} + C_0\begin{Bmatrix} w \\ U \end{Bmatrix} = 0. \tag{8.36a}$$

This equation may be rewritten in the form

$$[H + r_\alpha][H + r_\alpha][H + r_\alpha]\begin{Bmatrix} w \\ U \end{Bmatrix} = 0, \tag{8.36b}$$

and will have solutions governed by equations of the type

$$H\begin{Bmatrix} w \\ U \end{Bmatrix} + r_\alpha\begin{Bmatrix} w \\ U \end{Bmatrix} = 0, \qquad \alpha = 1, 2, 3, \tag{8.36c}$$

provided that the r_α are the roots of the equation

$$r_\alpha^3 - C_2r_\alpha^2 + C_1r_\alpha - C_0 = 0. \tag{8.36d}$$

The roots of Eq. 8.36d can be found by using the formulas 6.57*l* to 6.57n and the solution for U can be determined by substituting Eq. 8.36c into Eq. 8.33i with the result

$$\left(\frac{U}{w}\right)_\alpha = \frac{(1 + \nu) + r_\alpha/\xi}{r_\alpha + (1 + \nu) - \Omega^2(1 - \nu^2)}. \tag{8.36e}$$

Now, if we recall the form of the solution of the free-vibration problem of a nonshallow spherical membrane shell which we obtained in Section

8.4*a*, we may write the solution of the corresponding problem with bending resistance included as:

$$w = \sum_{\alpha=1}^{3} [C_\alpha P_{\lambda_\alpha}(\cos\varphi) + D_\alpha Q_{\lambda_\alpha}(\cos\varphi)],$$

$$u = \sum_{\alpha=1}^{3} \frac{\xi(1+\nu) + r_\alpha}{\xi(r_\alpha + 1 + \nu) - \xi\Omega^2(1-\nu^2)} \times [C_\alpha P_{\lambda_\alpha}'(\cos\varphi) + D_\alpha Q_{\lambda_\alpha}'(\cos\varphi)], \tag{8.36f}$$

where

$$\lambda_\alpha(\lambda_\alpha + 1) = 2 + r_\alpha, \tag{8.36g}$$

or,

$$\lambda_\alpha = -\tfrac{1}{2} + \sqrt{\tfrac{9}{4} + r_\alpha}. \tag{8.36h}$$

If we again restrict our attention to shells that are closed at $\varphi = 0$, the solutions $Q_{\lambda_\alpha}(\cos\varphi)$, which are singular at $\varphi = 0$, must be suppressed by setting $D_\alpha = 0$. Therefore, the solution for this case reduces to

$$w = \sum_{\alpha=1}^{3} C_\alpha P_{\lambda_\alpha}(\cos\varphi),$$

$$u = \sum_{\alpha=1}^{3} C_\alpha P_{\lambda_\alpha}'(\cos\varphi) \frac{\xi(1+\nu) + r_\alpha}{\xi(r_\alpha + 1 + \nu) - \xi\Omega^2(1-\nu^2)}. \tag{8.36i}$$

It remains now to determine the natural frequencies of the free-vibration problem of the nonshallow spherical shell from an application of the boundary conditions.

Complete Spherical Shell with Bending Resistance. As a first example of spherical shells with bending resistance, let us consider the special case of a complete shell. Here we encounter the same requirement as we met in the analysis of a complete spherical membrane shell; that is, in order for the solution 8.36i to be valid at $\varphi = \pi$, the Legendre functions, which are singular at that point, must be replaced by Legendre polynomials. Thus, λ must be an integer n, for example, and the solution becomes

$$w = C_n P_n(\cos\varphi),$$

$$u = \frac{\xi(1+\nu) + r_n}{\xi(r_n + 1 + \nu) - \xi\Omega^2}(1-\nu^2) C_n P_n'(\cos\varphi), \tag{8.37a}$$

and, from Eq. 8.36g,

$$r_n = n(n+1) - 2, \qquad n = 0, 1, 2, \ldots. \tag{8.37b}$$

The following formula for the natural frequencies of a closed spherical shell with bending resistance may now be obtained by rearrangement of Eq. 8.36d:

$$2\Omega^2(1 - \nu^2) = 3(1 + \nu) + r_n + \frac{1}{\xi}(r_n + 3)(r_n + 1 + \nu)$$
$$\pm \left\{\left[3(1 + \nu) + r_n + \frac{1}{\xi}(r_n + 3)(r_n + 1 + \nu)\right]^2 - 4r_n\left[(1 - \nu^2) + \frac{1}{\xi}(r_n^2 + 2r_n + 1 - \nu^2)\right]\right\}^{1/2}. \quad (8.37c)$$

As in our previous analyses, the foregoing formula indicates that the natural frequencies of the complete spherical shell with bending resistance arrange themselves into two branches. Indeed, upon setting the stiffness parameter $1/\xi$ to zero, the formula 8.37c reduces to formula 8.35b for the complete spherical membrane shell.

8.4c Discussion of Results on Free, θ-independent Vibration of Nonshallow Spherical Shells

The derivations which we have given in the foregoing free-vibration analysis of spherical shells with bending resistance were first presented by Federhofer.[16] Later, Naghdi and Kalnins[25] presented the derivation by a different procedure and, more recently, Kalnins[23] carried out a comprehensive study of freely vibrating spherical shells with and without bending resistance in which the motions are independent of θ. Some of the results of that study are reproduced here in Figs. 8.9 to 8.12. In Figs. 8.9 and 8.10, we have plotted the natural frequencies as a function of the thickness to radius ratio h/R for spherical shells with free edges which have half angles of opening, φ_0, of 60 deg. and 90 deg., respectively. At a free edge, we recall that the boundary conditions in the θ-independent state of deformation are

$$Q_\varphi(\varphi_0) = M_\varphi(\varphi_0) = N_\varphi(\varphi_0) = 0. \quad (8.38a)$$

Consequently, the elements of the frequency determinant (Eq. 8.8) take the form

$$C_{1\alpha} = \left[1 + \left(\frac{U}{W}\right)_\alpha\right](\nu + 1 - r_\alpha)P_{\lambda_\alpha}'(\cos\varphi_0),$$
$$C_{2\alpha} = \frac{1 - \nu}{1 + \nu}\left(\frac{U}{W}\right)_\alpha \cot\varphi_0 P_{\lambda_\alpha}'(\cos\varphi_0) + \left[1 + \left(\frac{U}{W}\right)_\alpha \frac{2 - r_\alpha}{1 + \nu}\right]P_{\lambda_\alpha}(\cos\varphi_0), \quad (8.38b)$$
$$C_{3\alpha} = \left[1 + \left(\frac{U}{W}\right)_\alpha\right](2 - r_\alpha)P_{\lambda_\alpha}(\cos\varphi_0) + (1 - \nu)\cot\varphi_0 P_{\lambda_\alpha}'(\cos\varphi_0), \qquad \alpha = 1, 2, 3.$$

[25] Naghdi, P. M., and Kalnins, A., "On Vibrations of Elastic Spherical Shells," *J. Appl. Mech.*, **29**, 65–72 (1962).

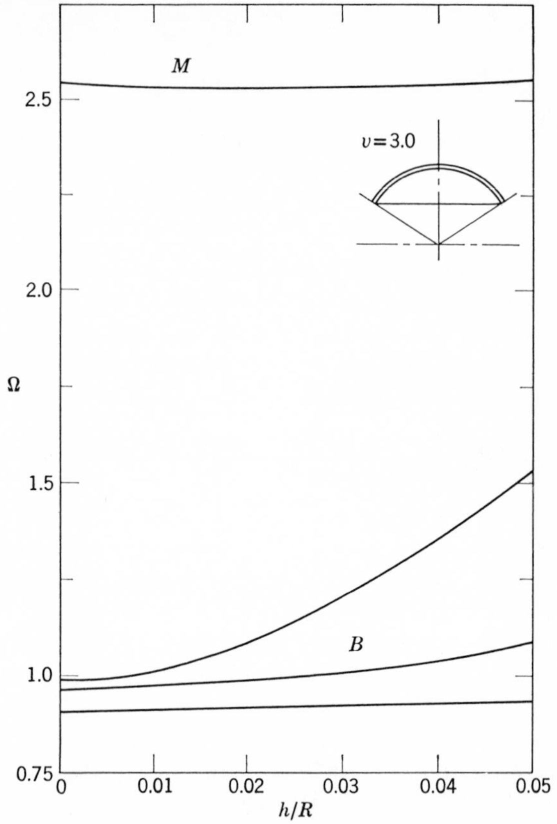

Figure 8.9 Natural frequencies of spherical shells with free edges ($\varphi_0=60°$).

The natural frequencies which are shown in Figs. 8.9 and 8.10 were obtained by the exact method,[23] while the frequencies shown in Fig. 8.11 were obtained from formula 8.37c for a closed spherical shell. The classifications "*M*" and "*B*" which are indicated on the plots identify the character of the modes of free vibration. Thus, *M* refers to those modes which involve motions that are primarily longitudinal and are called membrane modes while *B* refers to those modes which involve motions that are transverse and are called bending modes. The results of Figs. 8.9 to 8.11 indicate that the membrane modes are imperceptibly affected by variations of thickness and have natural frequencies that are much higher than those of the bending modes. The bending modes are appreciably affected by the thickness of the shell, the variation being greatest for the closed shell and more pronounced for the shallower of the two open shells.

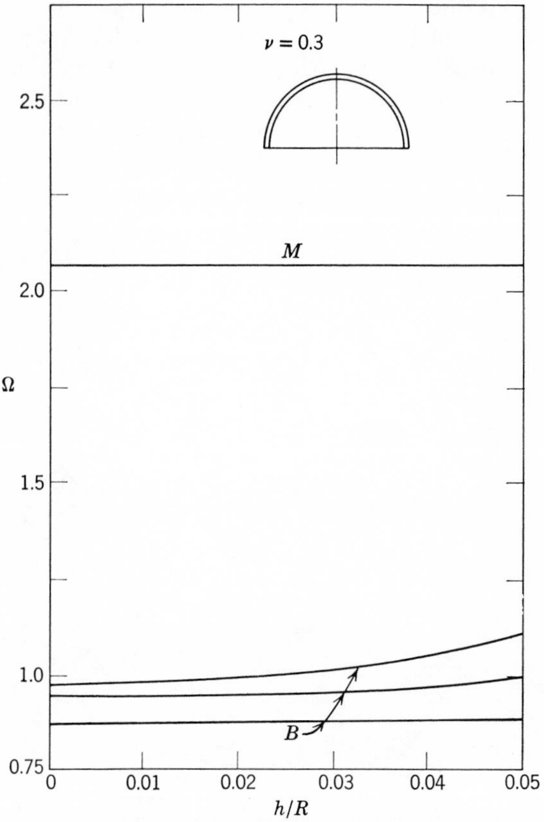

Figure 8.9 Same as Fig. 8.9. for $\varphi_0 = 90°$.

For comparison of these results to results obtained for membrane shells, we recall Fig. 8.7. It is interesting to note that, for $h = 0$, the results for the lowest bending mode in each of Figs. 8.9 to 8.11 are identical to those of the lower set in Fig. 8.7 and all fall below the limiting value $\Omega = 1$ for the lower set of Fig. 8.7. As soon as the shell is allowed to have some thickness, however small, the range of the natural frequencies of the bending modes is no longer limited, as shown in Figs. 8.9 to 8.11. Based on these data it can be concluded[23] that the lower set of modes predicted by the membrane theory and shown in Fig. 8.7 is a degenerate set of bending modes that is valid only for $h = 0$. Hence, the lower set in Fig. 8.7 is labelled with a B. If, for $h = 0$, the frequencies of the membrane modes of Figs. 8.9 to 8.11 are compared with the upper set of modes in Fig. 8.7, it is seen that the agreement is quite close. Hence, the upper set of modes in Fig. 8.7 is labelled with an M. From this, it may be further concluded that the membrane theory predicts the membrane (longitudinal) modes of a spherical shell with bending resistance very well. On the other hand, since it neglects bending, the membrane theory cannot predict the bending (transverse) modes of a spherical shell with bending resistance except for $h = 0$.

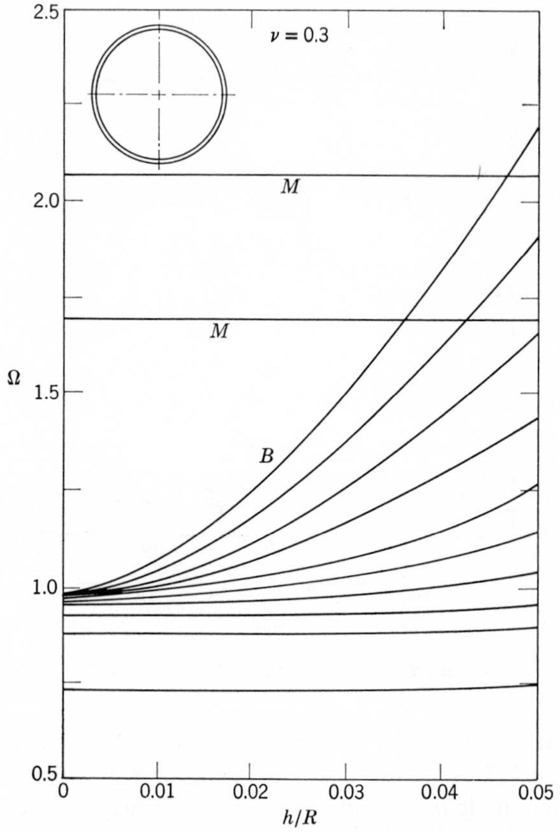

Figure 8.11 Natural frequencies of complete spherical shells with bending resistance.

It is also instructive to use the results of the present analysis of freely vibrating nonshallow spherical shells to obtain a bound on the range of validity of the shallow shell analysis which was presented in Section 8.3. For this purpose, the lowest natural frequency obtained from the shallow and the nonshallow free vibration analyses of a clamped spherical shell segment[23] with bending resistance is plotted as a function of a/R in Fig. 8.12. It has previously been stated that the shallow shell theory gives reliable results in static analyses for $a/R \leqslant 0.5$. Figure 8.12 shows that, for this limiting value, the lowest natural frequency obtained with the shallow shell theory is 2.5% above the result obtained by the nonshallow

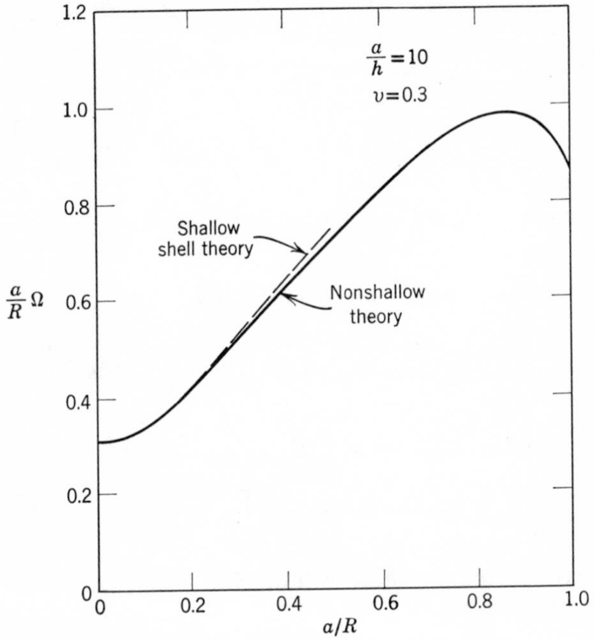

Figure 8.12 Lowest natural frequencies of clamped spherical shell segments.

shell theory. Thus, the previously cited limit of validity of the shallow shell theory appears to be applicable to the free-vibration analysis as well.

8.4*d* Free, Arbitrary Vibration of Nonshallow Spherical Shells with Transverse Shearing Stress and Rotatory Inertia Effects Included

It is now appropriate to outline the analysis of arbitrary free vibrations of nonshallow spherical shells. Since the procedure which will be followed is very similar to that followed in the analysis of arbitrary vibrations of nonshallow shells let us, therefore, make the present development more general by including rotatory inertia and transverse shearing effects. This will permit us to see how such considerations affect the analysis and will give us a means to discuss their effect on the behavior of the shell. To this end we repeat here, for spherical shells, the equations of motion which were derived in Section 3.3*b*:

$$\frac{\partial N_\varphi}{\partial \varphi} + \frac{\partial N_{\varphi\theta}}{\partial \theta} \csc \varphi + (N_\varphi - N_\theta) \cot \varphi + Q_\varphi = R\rho h \left[k_1 \frac{\partial^2 u_\varphi}{\partial t^2} + Rk_2 \frac{\partial^2 \beta_\varphi}{\partial t^2}\right],$$

$$\frac{\partial N_{\varphi\theta}}{\partial \varphi} + \frac{\partial N_\theta}{\partial \theta} \csc \varphi + 2N_{\varphi\theta} \cot \varphi + Q_\theta = R\rho h \left[k_1 \frac{\partial^2 u_\theta}{\partial t^2} + Rk_2 \frac{\partial^2 \beta_\theta}{\partial t^2}\right],$$

$$\frac{\partial Q_\varphi}{\partial \varphi} + \frac{\partial Q_\theta}{\partial \theta} \csc \varphi + Q_\varphi \cot \varphi - (N_\varphi + N_\theta) = R\rho h k_1 \frac{\partial^2 w}{\partial t^2}, \tag{8.39a}$$

$$\frac{\partial M_\varphi}{\partial \varphi} + \frac{\partial M_{\varphi\theta}}{\partial \theta} \csc \varphi + (M_\varphi - M_\theta) \cot \varphi - RQ_\varphi = \tfrac{1}{12} R\rho h^3 \left[(c_r/a) \frac{\partial^2 u_\varphi}{\partial t^2} + k_r \frac{\partial^2 \beta_\varphi}{\partial t^2}\right],$$

$$\frac{\partial M_{\varphi\theta}}{\partial \varphi} + \frac{\partial M_\theta}{\partial \theta} \csc \varphi + 2M_{\varphi\theta} \cot \varphi - RQ_\theta = \tfrac{1}{12} R\rho h^3 \left[(c_r/a) \frac{\partial^2 u_\theta}{\partial t^2} + k_r \frac{\partial^2 \beta_\theta}{\partial t^2}\right],$$

where we have ignored the effect of transverse normal stress and we have employed the tracers

$$k_1 = 1 + \frac{h^2}{12R^2}, \qquad k_r = 1 + \frac{3h^2}{20R^2}, \qquad k_2 = \frac{h^2}{6R^2}, \qquad c_r = 2, \tag{8.39b}$$

to identify the transverse shearing stress and rotatory inertia effects. If, instead, $k_r = k_2 = c_r = 0$ and $k_1 = 1$, the equations reduce to Eqs. 8.1 for the case of a spherical shell. In addition to the usual equations which relate the stress resultants and stress couples to the strains and changes in curvature and, therefore, to the displacements, we must add the following expressions for the transverse shearing stress resultants:

$$Q_\varphi = \frac{Ehk_s}{2(1+\nu)} \left[\beta_\varphi - \frac{1}{R}\left(u_\varphi - \frac{\partial w}{\partial_\varphi}\right)\right],$$

$$Q_\theta = \frac{Ehk_s}{2(1+\nu)} \left[\beta_\theta - \frac{1}{R}\left(u_\theta - \frac{\partial w}{\partial \theta} \csc \varphi\right)\right], \tag{8.39c}$$

where k_s is another tracer which identifies the transverse shearing stress contribution. If $k_s = \frac{5}{6}$, the effect of transverse shearing stress is included and, if $k_s = 0$, it is not.

The equations of the nonshallow spherical shell are uncoupled by introducing auxiliary functions according to the following definitions:[26, 27]

$$u_\varphi = \frac{\partial U}{\partial \varphi} - \psi \sin \varphi, \qquad Q_\varphi = \frac{\partial V}{\partial \varphi} - \Lambda \sin \varphi,$$
$$u_\theta = \frac{\partial U}{\partial \theta} \csc \varphi, \qquad Q_\theta = \frac{\partial V}{\partial \theta} \csc \varphi. \tag{8.40}$$

Here U and ψ are analogous to U and ψ which were used for the shallow spherical shell (see Eqs. 8.28a) while V and Λ are functions which are required in the consideration of transverse shearing stress and rotatory inertia effects. When Eqs. 8.40 are substituted into the expressions which relate the stress resultants and stress couples to the displacements and rotations, equations are obtained which relate these quantities to the auxiliary functions and w.

By a procedure that is similar to the one with which we uncoupled the equations of the shallow spherical shell and whose details we shall not repeat here, the equations of the nonshallow spherical shell can be reduced to the following set of uncoupled differential equations:[26]

$$\nabla^6 w + c_1 \nabla^4 w + c_2 \nabla^2 w + [2(1 + \nu) - k_1 \Omega^2 (1 - \nu^2)]w = 0,$$
$$k_s \nabla^4 \psi - (b_3 + b_4 - 2k_s b_5)\nabla^2 \psi - 2c_3 \psi/(1 - \nu) = 0, \tag{8.41a}$$

where we have assumed that the time dependence of the shell variables during the free vibration of the shell is sinusoidal. The other auxiliary functions are governed by the equations

$$\Lambda = -Eh(\nabla^2 \psi + 2b_5 \psi)/2R(1 + \nu),$$
$$U = [d_1 \nabla^4 w/(1 + \nu) + d_2 \nabla^2 w + d_3 w + d_1 F_1 + (d_1 + e_1) b_4 F_2]/c_3(d_1 + e_1), \tag{8.41b}$$
$$V = -[e_1 \nabla^4 w/(1 - \nu) + e_2 \nabla^2 w + e_3 w + (1 + \nu)\, e_1 F_1/(1 - \nu) + (d_1 + e_1) b_5 F_2] Eh/R(1 + \nu) c_3 (d_1 + e_1),$$

where $\nabla^2(\ldots)$ is defined by Eq. 6.54e. For the sake of clarity, we shall not give the definitions of the subscripted variables here.[26]

Solutions of Eqs. 8.41a are of the form

$$w = \sum_{n=0}^{\infty} \sum_{\alpha=1}^{3} w_\alpha{}^n \cos n\theta \cos \omega t,$$
$$\psi = \sum_{n=1}^{\infty} \sum_{\beta=1}^{\delta} \psi_0{}^n \cos n\theta \cos \omega t, \tag{8.41c}$$

---

26 Wilkinson, J. P., and Kalnins, A., "On Nonsymmetric Dynamic Problems of Elastic Spherical Shells," *J. Appl. Mech.*, **32**, 525–532 (1965).

27 Prasad, C., "On Vibrations of Spherical Shells," *J. Acoust. Soc. Am.*, **36**, 489–494 (1964).

and so on where

$$
\begin{aligned}
w_\alpha{}^n &= A_\alpha{}^n P_{\mu_\alpha}{}^n(\cos\varphi) + B_\alpha{}^n Q_{\mu_\alpha}{}^n(\cos\varphi),\\
\psi_\beta{}^n &= C_\beta{}^n P_{\eta_\beta}{}^n(\cos\varphi) + D_\beta{}^n Q_{\eta_\beta}{}^n(\cos\varphi).
\end{aligned}
\tag{8.41d}
$$

If transverse shearing stress and rotatory inertia effects are considered, $\delta = 2$ and β takes on the values 1 and 2; however, if these effects are ignored $\delta = 1$ and, hence, $\beta = 1$. The quantities $A_\alpha{}^n$, $B_\alpha{}^n$, $C_\beta{}^n$, $D_\beta{}^n$ are arbitrary constants and it is readily seen that, for each value of n, there will be ten arbitrary constants in the solution when the higher-order effects are considered and eight arbitrary constants when these effects are ignored. This is consistent with the number of boundary conditions that must be satisfied in the two treatments (see Eqs. 2.80 and the first five of Eqs. 3.43). The functions $P_\alpha{}^n(\cos\varphi)$ and $Q_\alpha{}^n(\cos\varphi)$ are the associated Legendre functions which we have previously encountered. Their indexes satisfy the relationships

$$
\begin{aligned}
\mu_\alpha &= -\tfrac{1}{2} + (\tfrac{1}{4} + r_\alpha)^{1/2},\\
\eta_\beta &= -\tfrac{1}{2} + (\tfrac{1}{4} + m_\beta)^{1/2},
\end{aligned}
\tag{8.41e}
$$

where r_α and m_β are the roots of the equations

$$
\begin{gathered}
r_\alpha{}^3 - c_1 r_\alpha{}^2 + c_2 r_\alpha - [2(1+\nu) - \Omega^2(1-\nu^2)k_1]c_3 = 0,\\
k_s m_\beta{}^2 + (b_3 + b_4 - 2k_s b_5)m_\beta - 2c_3/(1-\nu) = 0,\\
\alpha = 1, 2, 3, \quad \beta = 1, 2,
\end{gathered}
\tag{8.41f}
$$

which are based on the knowledge that the Legendre functions satisfy the equations

$$
\nabla^2 \begin{Bmatrix} \begin{bmatrix} P_\mu{}^n(\cos\varphi) \\ Q_\mu{}^n(\cos\varphi) \end{bmatrix} \\ \begin{bmatrix} P_\eta{}^n(\cos\varphi) \\ Q_\eta{}^n(\cos\varphi) \end{bmatrix} \end{Bmatrix} + \begin{Bmatrix} r \begin{bmatrix} P_\mu{}^n(\cos\varphi) \\ Q_\mu{}^n(\cos\varphi) \end{bmatrix} \\ m \begin{bmatrix} P_\eta{}^n(\cos\varphi) \\ Q_\eta{}^n(\cos\varphi) \end{bmatrix} \end{Bmatrix} = 0.
\tag{8.41g}
$$

This completes the outline of the formal solution of the problem. It is interesting to notice that, if Ω is set to zero, and if the higher-order effects are eliminated by setting $k_s = k_r = c_r = k_2 = 0$, $k_1 = 1$, the development reduces to a form which is identical, after differences in notation are accounted for, to the static solution which we carried out in greater detail in Section 6.4.

To bring out the effect of transverse shear and rotatory inertia on the natural frequencies of freely vibrating spherical shells, the analysis that we have just described was applied to the calculation of the natural frequencies of two simply supported hemispherical shells undergoing θ-independent motions.[28] The resulting data, which are summarized in Table 8.5 for shells with $R/h = 50$ and 10, were calculated by using $n = 0$ in the preceding development. Results that pertain to the theory of Chapter 2, which is based on Love's postulates, were obtained by setting $k_s = k_r = k_2 = c_r = 0$,

Table 8.5 Natural Frequencies of Simply Supported Steel Hemispherical Shells

	$R/h = 50$				$R/h = 10$		
Type	Ω_L	Ω_{RN}	Percent difference	Type	Ω_L	Ω_{RN}	Percent difference
T	0.7548	0.7547	0.01	*T*	0.8060	0.8034	0.32
T	0.9432	0.9428	0.04	*T*	1.2054	1.1804	2.12
T	1.0152	1.0142	0.10	*F*	1.6179	1.5913	1.67
T	1.1082	1.1056	0.24	*T*	1.9051	1.8044	5.60
T	1.2523	1.2464	0.48	*T*	2.7205	2.4771	9.83
T	1.4576	1.4461	0.80	*L*	2.9301	2.8337	3.40
F	1.6558	1.6502	0.34	*T*	4.0274	3.3967	18.57
T	1.7636	1.7457	1.03	*T*	5.5142	4.3643	26.35
T	2.0886	2.0523	1.77	*L*	4.8182	4.7966	0.45
T	2.4870	2.4304	2.33	*T*	7.2524	5.4368	33.39
L	2.8307	2.8119	0.67	*T*	9.2348	6.5295	41.43
T	2.9677	2.8980	2.41	*L*	6.8741	6.8543	0.29
T	3.4731	3.3514	3.63	*T*	11.4464	7.6829	48.98
T	4.0427	3.8742	4.35	*T*	13.8975	8.8224	57.53
T	4.6607	4.4382	5.01	*L*	8.9568	8.9428	0.16
L	4.8199	4.8109	0.19		.	.	.
T	5.3453	5.0497	5.85		.	.	.
T	6.0704	5.6879	6.72		.	.	.
T	6.8310	6.3627	7.36	*T*		18.4727	
L	6.8934	6.8724	0.31	*L*	19.3948	19.2890	0.55
T	7.6757	7.0760	8.48	*T*		19.6874	
T	8.5507	7.8127	9.47	*R*		19.7316	
T	9.4792	8.5803	10.48	*R*		20.0843	
L	8.9579	8.9554	0.03	*R*		20.6980	
T	10.4531	9.3793	11.45	*T*		20.8849	
				L	21.5738	21.3684	0.96

[28] Kalnins, A., and Kraus, H., "Effect of Transverse Shear and Rotatory Inertia on Vibration of Spherical Shells," *Proc. 5th U.S. National Congress of Applied Mechanics*, A.S.M.E., 134 (1966).

$k_1 = 1$ in that development. Results that pertain to the Reissner–Naghdi theory in which transverse shear and rotatory inertia effects, but not transverse normal stress effects,[29] are considered were then obtained by using the values given for the various tracers by Eqs. 8.39b.

In the table, the dimensionless natural frequencies Ω_L and Ω_{RN} (see Eq. 8.33e) as obtained by the theory of Chapter 2 and the Reissner–Naghdi theory, respectively, are listed along with an indication of the percentage difference between the results using the Reissner–Naghdi theory as a basis.

Also given in the table is an indication of the type of motion that is predominant in each mode. Thus, a T refers to predominantly transverse motion (bending modes), an L refers to predominantly longitudinal motion (membrane modes), and an R refers to predominantly rotatory motion (thickness shear modes). Of these, the thickness shear modes have not been encountered previously because they are incompatible with the neglect, in any theory that is based upon Love's postulates, of transverse shearing strains. When such strains are permitted, as in the Reissner–Naghdi theory, the so-called thickness shear modes arise in the solution. The modes labelled F are the so-called fundamental modes which involve purely radial motion and whose frequencies are approximated by formula 8.35c of the closed spherical membrane shell.

It is interesting to observe, from the tabulations, that for those modes which can be classified as membrane modes (L), the natural frequencies obtained by the theory based upon Love's postulates approximate very closely the results of the theory with transverse shear and rotatory inertia effects included over the entire frequency spectrum shown in Table 8.5. This is to be expected since transverse shear and rotatory inertia effects are absent in the membrane state of stress. On the other hand, the bending modes are predicted with decreasing accuracy by the theory based upon Love's postulates as the frequencies increase. This is also to be expected since bending effects are linked to the transverse shearing stresses and rotations. For this reason, the bending modes of the theory based upon Love's postulates are not even listed at the higher frequency levels for the thicker shell in Table 8.5.

The thickness-shear modes begin to appear at the highest frequencies predicted by the higher-order theory for the thicker of the two shells. It is interesting to observe that, for the first thickness shear mode, the dimensionless natural frequency is $\Omega = 19.7316$ for $R/h = 10$. This approximates very closely the dimensionless natural frequency of the lowest antisymmetric thickness shear mode as obtained from an exact

[29] See footnotes 11 and 12 in Chapter 3.

analysis, within the framework of the theory of elasticity, for an infinite flat plate;[30] that is,

$$\Omega_s = \left(\frac{\rho \omega_s^2 R^2}{E}\right)^{1/2} = \frac{\pi R}{h}[2(1+\nu)]^{-1/2} = 19.4. \qquad (8.42)$$

In the calculations for shells with $R/h = 50$, the lowest thickness shear mode (not shown) has a natural frequency of 98.08, a value which approximates very closely the result $\Omega = 97$ that is obtained from Eq. 8.42 for $R/h = 50$. It appears, therefore, that the lowest thickness shear modes are independent of the curvature of the shell.

To summarize our assessment of the theory based upon Love's postulates as it pertains to the dynamic analysis of shells, we may thus say that it predicts very closely the natural frequencies of the membrane modes at all frequency levels. As far as the bending modes are concerned, the theory based upon Love's postulates predicts their natural frequencies within an error of 10% in the frequency range $0 < \Omega < 0.1\Omega_s$, where Ω_s is the frequency of the first thickness shear mode. Thus, the higher-order theory should be used to calculate the natural frequencies in the range $0.1\Omega_s < \Omega < \Omega_s$. If, as is usually the case in design, we are only interested in the lowest natural frequency of free vibration, then the theory based on Love's postulates gives a reliable result.

8.5 FREE VIBRATIONS OF MISCELLANEOUS SHELLS

In the preceding development, we have described the common methods that are employed in the free-vibration analysis of shells and we have applied these in detail to the analysis of freely vibrating cylinders, shallow spherical shells, and nonshallow spherical shells.[31]

Before closing this chapter, however, it is interesting to touch briefly

[30] Mindlin, R. D., "An Introduction to the Mathematical Theory of Vibrations of Elastic Plates," U.S. Army Signal Corps Engineering Laboratories Monograph, Fort Monmouth, N. J. (1955) ASTIA No. 88471.

[31] Conical shells are treated by the same methods in these investigations: Federhofer, K., "Eigenschwingungen der Kegelschale," *Ingr. Arch.*, **9**, 288–309 (1938); Goldberg, J. E., "Axisymmetric Oscillations of Conical Shells," *Proc. IXth Internat. Cong. Appl. Mech.*, 333–343 (1957); Hermann, G., and Mirsky, I., "On Vibrations of Conical Shells," *J. Aerospace Sci.*, **25**, 451–458 (1958); Saunders, H., Wisniewski, E. J., and Paslay, P. R., "Vibrations of Conical Shells," *J. Acoust. Soc. Am.*, **32**, 765–772 (1960); and Lindholm, U. S., and Hu, W. C. L., "Nonsymmetric Transverse Vibrations of Truncated Conical Shells," Tech. Report No. 3, Contract NASr-94(06), Southwest Research Institute, March 1965. Of these, all but the exact investigation of Goldberg are handled by variational procedures which are similar to the treatment of cylindrical shells which we have given in Section 8.2.

upon the analysis of several additional problems. In particular, we shall discuss the free vibration of composite shells and shells interacting with a liquid. In each case, our aim will be to point out the salient features of the analysis without giving the details.

8.5*a* Free Vibration of Composite Shells

In technical applications, it is highly likely that a shell structure will be built up as a combination of simpler shell segments, particularly when we are dealing with shells of revolution such as pressure vessels and missiles. In this section we shall, therefore, outline the solution of the free vibration problem of composite shell structures by the exact and the variational methods.

Given an assembly of two shells of revolution, designated as Shell *A* and Shell *B*, for example, the solution of the free-vibration problem proceeds as follows (see Section 5.5):

Assuming that the natural frequency of the whole assembly is denoted by ω, the mode shapes of the two component shells during free vibration of the assembly are governed by the equations (see Eqs. 8.5):

$$\begin{aligned} \mathscr{L}_{1a}\{u_{1a}, u_{2a}, w_a\} + \rho_a h_a \omega^2 u_{1a} &= 0, \\ \mathscr{L}_{2a}\{u_{1a}, u_{2a}, w_a\} + \rho_a h_a \omega^2 u_{2a} &= 0, \\ \mathscr{L}_{3a}\{u_{1a}, u_{2a}, w_a\} + \rho_a h_a \omega^2 w_a &= 0, \end{aligned} \tag{8.43a}$$

for Shell *A*, and

$$\begin{aligned} \mathscr{L}_{1b}\{u_{1b}, u_{2b}, w_b\} + \rho_b h_b \omega^2 u_{1b} &= 0, \\ \mathscr{L}_{2b}\{u_{1b}, u_{2b}, w_b\} + \rho_b h_b \omega^2 u_{2b} &= 0, \\ \mathscr{L}_{3b}\{u_{1b}, u_{2b}, w_b\} + \rho_b h_b \omega^2 w_b &= 0, \end{aligned} \tag{8.43b}$$

for Shell *B*, where the subscripts *a* and *b* refer to Shell *A* and Shell *B*, respectively. Solutions of the above equations must satisfy the boundary conditions (see Eqs. 8.6):

$$B_{ka}\{u_{1a}, u_{2a}, w_a\}_e = 0, \qquad k = 1, 2, \ldots, N/2. \tag{8.43c}$$

at the end of Shell *A* that is remote from the junction, and

$$B_{kb}\{u_{1b}, u_{2b}, w_b\}_e = 0, \qquad k = 1, 2, \ldots, N/2, \tag{8.43d}$$

at the end of Shell *B* that is remote from the junction. The shells are connected by applying the following conditions to the end of each shell at their junction in order to insure the continuity of all forces, moments, deflections, and rotations across the junction:

$$B_{ka}\{u_{1a}, u_{2a}, w_a\}_j = B_{kb}\{u_{1b}, u_{2b}, w_b\}_j, \qquad k = 1, 2, \ldots, N, \tag{8.43e}$$

Here the subscripts e and j are used to denote the ends and the junction of the shells respectively. Equations 8.43a and 8.43b are sufficient to yield $2N$ independent solutions, each multiplied by an unknown constant A_α. When these solutions are substituted into the boundary conditions 8.43c and 8.43d and continuity conditions 8.43e, there is obtained a set of $2N$ linear homogeneous equations of the type

$$\sum_{\alpha=1}^{2N} C_{\beta\alpha}(\omega)A_\alpha = 0, \qquad \beta = 1, 2, \ldots, 2N, \tag{8.43f}$$

where the $C_{\beta\alpha}$ are coefficients which are obtained from the application of the boundary and continuity conditions to the solutions of the governing equations. To avoid the trivial solution $A_\alpha = 0$, the determinant of the system must be set to zero; thus:

$$|C_{\beta\alpha}(\omega)| = 0, \qquad \alpha, \beta = 1, 2, \ldots, 2N. \tag{8.43g}$$

The rest of the procedure is as described previously for the single shell. The main effect of joining two shells is thus an increase in the size and complexity of the frequency determinant. Indeed, it is obvious that if n segments are joined, the size of the frequency determinant becomes nN by nN. Obviously, the digital computer is needed for the solution of such frequency equations.

It is also possible to apply the variational method to problems of freely vibrating composite shells, as follows, taking again the assembly of two shells of revolution, A and B.

The variational equation 8.11 is modified by the addition of integrals, one for each additional shell so that, for example, the variational equation of our two shell composite would be given by

$$\begin{aligned}
&\iint_{S_a} \{[\mathscr{L}_{1a}\{u_{1a}, u_{2a}, w_a\} + \rho_a h_a \omega^2 u_{1a}]\,\delta u_{1a} \\
&\qquad + [\mathscr{L}_{2a}\{u_{1a}, u_{2a}, w_a\} + \rho_a h_a \omega^2 u_{2a}]\,\delta u_{2a} \\
&\qquad + [\mathscr{L}_{3a}\{u_{1a}, u_{2a}, w_a\} + \rho_a h_a \omega^2 w_a]\,\delta w_a\}\, d\alpha_{1a}\, d\alpha_{2a} \\
&+ \iint_{S_b} \{[\mathscr{L}_{1b}\{u_{1b}, u_{2b}, w_b\} + \rho_b h_b \omega^2 u_{1b}]\,\delta u_{1b} \\
&\qquad + [\mathscr{L}_{2b}\{u_{1b}, u_{2b}, w_b\} + \rho_b h_b \omega^2 u_{2b}]\,\delta u_{2b} \\
&\qquad + [\mathscr{L}_{3b}\{u_{1b}, u_{2b}, w_b\} + \rho_b h_b \omega^2 w_b]\,\delta w_b\}\, d\alpha_{1b}\, d\alpha_{2b} = 0,
\end{aligned} \tag{8.44a}$$

where S_a, S_b, α_{1a}, α_{1b}, α_{2a}, α_{2b} refer to the reference surfaces and curvilinear coordinates of the two component shells A and B. In the variational methods, approximate solution functions are constructed such that the boundary conditions (Eqs. 8.43c and 8.43d) are satisfied by solutions of the type

$$\begin{aligned} u_{1a} &= \sum_{i=1}^{M} a_{ia} f_{ia}(\alpha_{1a}, \alpha_{2a}), \\ u_{2a} &= \sum_{i=1}^{M} b_{ia} g_{ia}(\alpha_{1a}, \alpha_{2a}), \\ w_a &= \sum_{i=1}^{M} c_{ia} h_{ia}(\alpha_{1a}, \alpha_{2a}), \end{aligned} \tag{8.44b}$$

for Shell A, and

$$\begin{aligned} u_{1b} &= \sum_{i=1}^{M} a_{ib} f_{ib}(\alpha_{1b}, \alpha_{2b}), \\ u_{2b} &= \sum_{i=1}^{M} b_{ib} g_{ib}(\alpha_{1b}, \alpha_{2b}), \\ w_b &= \sum_{i=1}^{M} c_{ib} h_{ib}(\alpha_{1b}, \alpha_{2b}), \end{aligned} \tag{8.44c}$$

for Shell B. The two shells are connected as before by means of the continuity conditions 8.43e which yield a set of relationships between the coefficients in the solutions 8.44b and 8.44c. The remainder of the procedure consists of substituting the assumed solutions and their variations into the variational equation 8.44a and carrying out the solution just as was indicated in Section 8.1 for the single shell. The generalization of this procedure to an arbitrary number of connected shells is straightforward; however, it should be mentioned that as a result of taking M terms in the assumed solutions, we always obtain M natural frequencies of the composite shell.

As an example of the application of the variational method to the free-vibration analysis of a composite shell, we may cite the investigation of Saunders and Paslay,[32] who considered the analysis of a spherical cap mounted on a truncated conical shell in simulation of a missile nose cone. They investigated the nonsymmetrical vibration of such a composite using Rayleigh's method and the further assumption that the middle surfaces of the component shells remain unextended during the motion. Numerical results from this analysis agreed within 5 per cent with experimental results which were also collected during the study.

[32] Saunders, H., and Paslay, P. R., "Inextensional Vibrations of a Sphere-Cone Shell Combination," *J. Acoust. Soc. Am.*, **31**, 579–583 (1959).

8.5*b* Free Vibration of a Shell Interacting with a Liquid

Another interesting problem of shell vibrations is motivated by the use of tanks containing a liquid in aerospace applications. When these tanks, which are generally shells of revolution, become only partially full, coupled oscillations of the liquid and the walls of the tank may be induced by various dynamic effects such as sudden changes in the direction or magnitude of the thrust applied to the vehicle.

The determination of the modes and natural frequencies of a tank partially filled with liquid follows closely the methods outlined in the previous section on composite shells. However, in the present case we are interested, so to speak, in the free vibration of composite media. The present description thus represents both an illustration and an extension of methods described in the previous section.

As an approximation of the problem, Beal, Coale, and Nagano[33] considered a cylindrical shell with a rigid bottom partially filled to a height H with an incompressible inviscid liquid. In what follows, we shall outline briefly the solution of the above problem as carried out in the cited investigation.

The partially filled cylindrical shell is analyzed by dividing the system into two elements; that is, a cylindrical shell and a cylinder of liquid. These elements are described, under the assumption that their behavior is symmetric about the axis of the tank, as follows.

The motion of the cylinder of liquid can be expressed in terms of a velocity potential $\varphi(r, z, t)$ which satisfies Laplace's equation[34]

$$\nabla^2\varphi = \frac{\partial^2\varphi}{\partial r^2} + \frac{1}{r}\frac{\partial\varphi}{\partial r} + \frac{\partial^2\varphi}{\partial z^2} = 0. \tag{8.45a}$$

The boundary conditions that are to be satisfied by the velocity potential are

$$\left.\frac{\partial\varphi}{\partial r}\right|_{r=0} = \left.\frac{\partial^2\varphi}{\partial t^2} + g\frac{\partial\varphi}{\partial z}\right|_{z=H} = \left.\frac{\partial\varphi}{\partial z}\right|_{z=0} = 0. \tag{8.45b}$$

Of these conditions, the first insures that the solution will be finite at the axis, the second is the free surface condition at the top of the cylinder of liquid, and the third states that there should be no flow through the bottom of the tank. In addition, the velocity distribution **u** of the fluid is determined from

$$\mathbf{u} = \boldsymbol{\nabla}\varphi, \tag{8.45c}$$

[33] Beal, T. R., Coale, C. W., and Nagano, M., "Influence of Shell Inertia and Bending Stiffness on the Axisymmetric Modes of a Partially Filled Cylindrical Tank," AIAA Preprint 65–412, 2nd Annual Meeting, San Francisco, California, July 1965.

[34] Lamb, H., *Hydrodynamics*, New York: Dover (1956).

and the pressure distribution is given by

$$p = -\rho_f \frac{\partial \varphi}{\partial t}. \tag{8.45d}$$

Here g is the acceleration of gravity and ρ_f is the density of the fluid.

The θ-independent behavior of the cylinder is governed by (see Section 8.2):

$$\begin{aligned} \frac{\partial^4 w}{\partial z^4} + \frac{12E}{ha^2 D} w &= -\frac{12\rho_s}{hD}\frac{\partial^2 w}{\partial t^2} + \frac{12 p_r}{h^2 D}, \qquad 0 \leqslant z \leqslant H, \\ &= -\frac{12\rho_s}{hD}\frac{\partial^2 w}{\partial t^2}, \qquad H \leqslant z \leqslant l, \end{aligned} \tag{8.45e}$$

where ρ_s is the density of the shell, l is the height of the tank, and p_r is the pressure acting on it. Notice that the pressure only acts over the interval $0 \leqslant z \leqslant H$. If we assume, for the sake of argument, that the top and bottom edges of the tank are clamped, the boundary conditions are given by

$$w|_{z=0} = w|_{z=l} = \left.\frac{\partial w}{\partial z}\right|_{z=0} = \left.\frac{\partial w}{\partial z}\right|_{z=l} = 0. \tag{8.45f}$$

The separate elements of the system have thus been individually described. To connect the two elements, we shall require that the pressure and normal velocity must be constant across their interface, or

$$\left.\begin{aligned} p_r &= -\rho_f \left.\frac{\partial \varphi}{\partial t}\right|_{r=a}, \\ \left.\frac{\partial \varphi}{\partial r}\right|_{r=a} &= \frac{\partial w}{\partial t}, \end{aligned}\right\} \quad 0 \leqslant z \leqslant H. \tag{8.45g}$$

The problem statement is now complete. We shall not pursue the solution since it follows the general procedure of the exact method which we have described previously, and has been given in the cited reference. The solution is, however, complicated by the fact that the system of equations described here is three dimensional; that is, the behavior is a function of r, z, and t. Thus, describing it in the sense of the method of characteristic functions (see Section 8.1) the problem will have two sets of interdependent characteristic values (eigenvalues), whereas all of our previous analyses have only involved one set of characteristic values.

An interesting outcome of the analysis is the fact that the bending resistance of the tank has a negligible effect on the tank-liquid system. The assumption of a rigid bottom has, however, been found to be unjustifiably restrictive, and in a later analysis the tank was, therefore, replaced by a hemispherical membrane shell.[35]

8.6 CLOSURE

In this chapter, we have presented the results of free-vibration analyses of a variety of shell configurations for which we have used the exact and the variational methods of solution as well as some additional approximate analytical procedures. While we have indicated that the variational solutions give very good predictions of the lowest natural frequency of a shell, it is evident, from the outline given in Section 8.1, that the determination of a significant number of additional natural frequencies of free vibration involves manipulations which rival the complexity of the exact analytical solutions.

We found that in a shell the various motions are coupled to each other by virtue of its curvature. For shells with a slight amount of curvature, that is, for shallow shells, the coupling of the motions was found to be slight and the modes could be classified as transverse or longitudinal by comparing them to those of a flat plate. As a consequence, a class of approximate analyses, in which only the transverse inertia term is retained, was developed for shallow spherical shells and for the Donnell theory of cylindrical shells. Analyses of this type were found to be able to predict only the transverse modes of free vibration and gave very close approximations of the natural frequencies of such modes. The longitudinal modes were, however, lost in such an analysis which, therefore, cannot be used to predict the complete frequency spectrum of a shell.

Another approximation which we considered at length was the so-called membrane analysis in which the bending resistance of the shell was neglected. Such analyses yielded a frequency spectrum with two branches. Of these, one consisted of an infinite number of modes spaced within a finite frequency interval at the lower end of the spectrum and the other consisted of an infinite set of modes above those of the first set. In an analysis of spherical shells, it was found that the upper set consists of the "membrane" modes which are predominantly extensional in nature while the lower set is a degenerate set of "bending" modes. When the bending resistance is restored the membrane modes are unaffected, but the bending modes are completely rearranged and no longer occur within a finite frequency interval. While it was found that the membrane analysis could predict the membrane modes successfully, it led to considerable error in its

---

[35] Coale, C. W., and Nagano, M., "Axisymmetric Modes of an Elastic Cylindrical-Hemispherical Tank Partially Filled with Liquid," AIAA Structural Dynamics Conference, Boston, September 1965.

prediction of the bending modes. We demonstrated, however, that the functional form of the differential equation which governs the membrane solution is identical to that of the differential equation which governs the bending solution. The only difference in the case of spherical shells, for example, is that the order of the governing equation of the membrane analysis is one third of the order of the governing equation of the bending analysis. Thus, it is felt that the additional work which is involved in the more complete bending solution is not prohibitive and should, in general, be carried out.

At this point, it is appropriate to comment on the validity of the theory of thin elastic shells in free-vibration analysis.

As far as the dynamic theory of shells is concerned, we may recall here that the basic assumptions upon which the theory of Chapter 2 is based concern the preservation of the normal element and the neglect of transverse shear and rotatory inertia effects. Consequently, all motions which are dependent on the thickness coordinate ζ are suppressed and only transverse and longitudinal motions are predicted. In an exact solution based upon the theory of elasticity, the motions which depend on ζ are not suppressed and, in addition to the transverse and longitudinal motions, so-called thickness shear and thickness stretch motions are predicted.[30, 36, 37] The first three modes of each of these motions as obtained from an exact analysis within the framework of the theory of elasticity are shown in Fig. 8.13 for the illustrative case of a freely vibrating infinite elastic plate.[30] Similar motions occur in elastic shells.[37]

Obviously, the motions shown in Fig. 8.13 are incompatible with Love's postulates. However, in a higher-order theory in which transverse shear and rotatory inertia effects, but not transverse normal strain effects, are included, the thickness stretch modes would still be suppressed while thickness shear modes would be predicted. This occurs because the normal element is no longer assumed to remain normal to the reference surface, although it is still assumed to remain straight, during deformation. As a result, motions which resemble the lowest antisymmetric thickness shear mode can occur. However, the higher thickness shear modes of the exact behavior, as illustrated in Fig. 8.13 for the flat plate, are still lost because their shape is incompatible with the assumptions of the higher-order theory to which we have referred.

---

[36] Mindlin, R. D., "Waves and Vibrations in Isotropic Elastic Plates," *Proc. 1st Symp. on Naval Structural Mechanics*, Goodier, J. N., and Hoff, N. J., eds., New York: Pergamon Press, 199–232 (1960).

[37] Gazis, D. C., "Three-Dimensional Investigation of the Propagation of Waves in Hollow Circular Cylinders. I. Analytical Foundation, II. Numerical Results," *J. Acoust. Soc. Am.*, **31**, 568–573, 573–578 (1959).

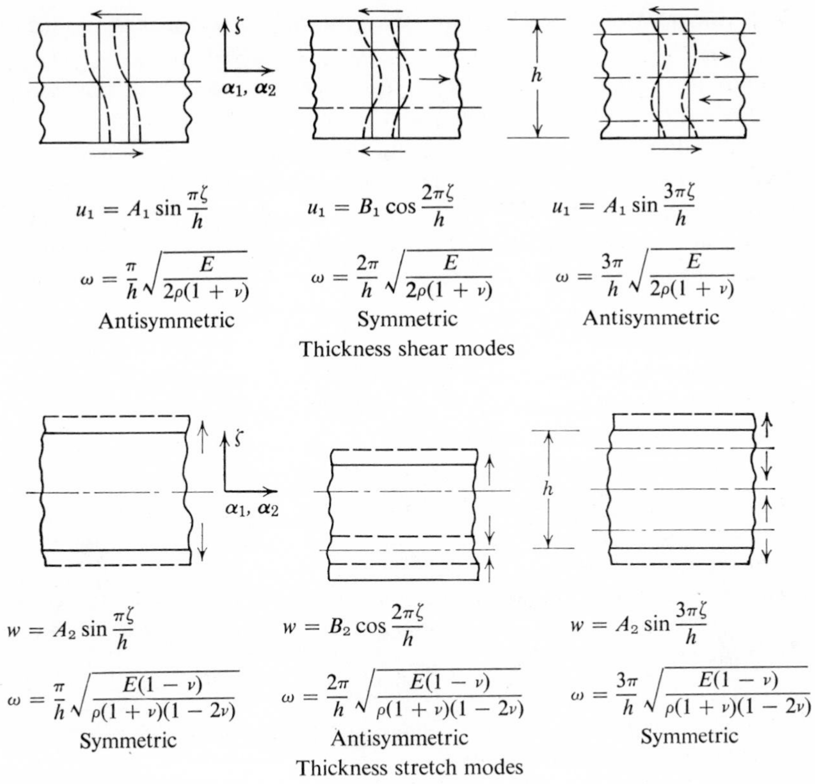

Figure 8.13 Thickness modes of free vibration for an infinite elastic plate.

In Section 8.4*d*, we showed that the frequency of the first thickness shear mode lies well above that of the lowest bending mode in a spherical shell. Using the flat plate as an example once more, we can show that the first thickness stretch mode occurs well above the first thickness shear mode. Indeed, we note from Fig. 8.13 that the ratio of the frequencies of the first thickness stretch mode to the frequency of the first thickness shear mode is $[2(1-\nu)/(1-2\nu)]^{1/2}$. For steel, this factor takes the value 1.875.

We may, therefore, conclude that the ranges of applicability that were suggested for the various shell theories at the end of Section 8.4*d* should suffice in practical applications. That is, a theory based upon Love's postulates will give reliable results in the range $0 \leqslant \Omega < 0.1\Omega_s$ and a theory in which transverse shear and rotatory inertia effects are taken into account will give reliable results in the range $0 \leqslant \Omega < \Omega_s$. The frequency Ω_s of the lowest thickness shear mode can be estimated from the flat plate formula (Eq. 8.42). For frequencies beyond Ω_s, it would be necessary to also take transverse normal stress effects into account. Such a theory was derived in Section 3.3*b*.

All of the analyses which we have described here concern relatively simple geometrical shell configurations which involve no variations in thickness, material properties, or geometry along the generators of the shell. When considerations such as the latter are introduced, the free-vibration analysis becomes so difficult that a numerical integration of the relevant differential equations on a digital computer presents the only hope of a meaningful solution. Such analyses of the free-vibration problem will be described in Chapter 11.

As a final remark, we notice that, with $\omega = 0$, the solutions which we have derived here reduce to the complementary solutions of the corresponding static analyses which we considered in Part II.

SUPPLEMENTARY REFERENCES

Gros, C. G., and Forsberg, K., "Vibrations of Thin Shells: A Partially Annotated Bibliography," Lockheed Missiles and Space Company, Sunnyvale, Calif., SB-63-43, April 1963.

Hu, W. C. L., "A Survey of the Literature on the Vibrations of Thin Shells," Southwest Research Institute, San Antonio, Texas, Tech. Report No. 1, Contract NASr-94(06), June 1964.

Kalnins, A., "Dynamic Problems of Thin Elastic Shells," *Appl. Mech. Revs.*, **18**, 867–872 (1965).

Federhofer, K., "Zur Berechnung der Eigenschwingungen der Kugelschale," *Sitzb. Akad. Wiss. Wien, Math.-naturwiss. Kl.*, **146**, 505–514 (1937).

Hermann, G., and Mirsky, I., "Three-Dimensional and Shell Theory Analysis of Axially Symmetric Motion of Cylinders," *J. Appl. Mech.*, **23**, 563–568 (1956).

Hu, W. C. L., "Free Vibrations of Conical Shells," NASA TN D-2666 (1965).

Hu, W. C. L., Gormley, J. F., and Lindholm, U. S., "Flexural Vibrations of Conical Shells with Free Edges," NASA CR-384 (1966).

Johnson, M. W., and Reissner, E., "On Transverse Vibration of Shallow Spherical Shells," *J. Math. Phys.*, **15**, 367–380 (1958).

Naghdi, P. M., and Berry, J. G., "On the Equations of Motion of Cylindrical Shells," *J. Appl. Mech.*, **21**, 160–166 (1954).

Yu, Yi-Yuan, "Vibrations of Thin Cylindrical Shells Analyzed by Means of Donnell's Equations," *J. Aerosp. Sci.*, **25**, 699–715 (1958).

Garnet, H., Goldberg, M. A., and Salerno, V. L., "Torsional Vibrations of a Shell of Revolution," *J. Appl. Mech.*, **28**, 571–573 (1961).

Garnet, H., and Kempner, J., "Axisymmetric Free Vibrations of Conical Shells," *J. Appl. Mech.*, **31**, 458–466 (1964).

EXERCISES

8.1 Show that the root $K = 0$ of Eq. 8.17g leads to zero displacement.

8.2 Repeat the analyses of Sections 8.2*a* and 8.2*b* for the case of a simply supported cylindrical shell.

8.3 Derive expressions for the quantities η_s and η_b appearing in footnote 7 for a cylinder with simply supported ends.

8.4 Find the lowest natural frequency of an annular shallow spherical membrane shell at whose edges the tangential displacement is prescribed to be zero. Use the exact method of solution and then a variational solution for a comparison of results.

8.5 Improve the accuracy of the free-vibration analysis of the clamped spherical cap by taking an additional term in each of the assumed mode shapes given by Eqs. 8.26b and applying the Rayleigh–Ritz method. Compare the results to those given in Fig. 8.5.

8.6 Show that consideration of a negative square root in Eqs. 8.34g and 8.36h would lead to no new information.

8.7 Show that Ω approaches unity as n approaches infinity when the negative sign is taken before the radical in Eq. 8.35b.

8.8 Reduce Eq. 8.33k by making the geometrical definition of shallowness and compare the resulting equation to Eq. 8.25a which we derived for the free vibration of shallow spherical shells with bending resistance. Discuss any differences.

8.9 Analyze the free vibrations of a cylindrical shell which is constrained to execute radial motions only ($u_x = u_s = 0$, $w \neq 0$).

8.10 Analyze the free vibration of a spherical shell segment which is constrained to execute radial motions only ($u_\varphi = u_\theta = 0$, $w \neq 0$).

8.11 Analyze the free vibration of a conical shell segment which is constrained to execute radial motions only ($u_s = u_\theta = 0$, $w \neq 0$).

8.12 Set up the θ-independent frequency determinant of a composite shell which is made up of a hemispherical shell attached to a cylindrical shell.

8.13 Analyze the free, θ-independent vibration of a cylindrical shell with bending resistance.

8.14 Analyze the arbitrary free vibration of a cylindrical membrane shell.

8.15 Show that in the free θ-independent vibration of a shell of revolution with bending resistance u_θ type motions (called torsional modes) can arise and are uncoupled from the other motions of the shell.

9

Forced Vibration of Shells

9.1 INTRODUCTION

In this chapter, we shall be concerned with the determination of the response of thin elastic shells to external time-dependent forces such as blast and impact loads and to transient thermal environments (thermal shock).[1] Problems of this type involve the analysis of shells under prescribed time-dependent surface and/or edge loads and are concerned, therefore, with the solution of the inhomogeneous partial differential equations of shell theory under inhomogeneous boundary and initial conditions.

As a basis of the solution of the problem of forced vibration of thin elastic shells, we shall employ the classical method of spectral representation wherein the dependent variables of the theory of shells are expanded in infinite series of the normal modes of free vibration. These normal modes are presumed to be known for the shell under consideration from an analysis of the type described in the previous chapter. In these expansions, each normal mode is multiplied by an unknown time-dependent coefficient whose determination represents the central aim of the forced vibration analysis. The expansion procedure is equivalent to the physical argument that, in general, an external disturbance excites all of the normal modes of free vibration of a body and that, therefore, the response of that body to the disturbance can be determined as the sum of suitably weighted contributions from each of its modes of free vibration.

As in the case of the free-vibration analysis of thin elastic shells, the forced-vibration analysis is merely an extension of the principles which we assume the reader has previously encountered in the vibration analysis of

[1] The chapter is based on results reported in Kraus, H., and Kalnins, A., "On Transient Vibration of Thin Elastic Shells," *J. Acoust. Soc. Am.*, **38**, 992–1002 (1965).

bars, beams, and plates. As a matter of fact, formally speaking, the determination of the response of a shell will be shown to lead to certain expressions that are equally valid for the determination of the transient response of beams, plates, and so on.

The present chapter begins with a description of the method of spectral representation in which we include a derivation of the orthogonality condition of the theory of thin elastic shells, without the existence of which it would be impossible to apply the method. This is followed by a general solution for the transient response of a shell whose free vibration characteristics are known, first, to a transient surface load and then to a transient edge load. The solutions are illustrated by applying them to the forced-vibration analysis of a spherical shell subjected in one case to a step change of internal pressure and in a second case to a step change of heat flux.

Before taking up these matters, it should be mentioned that we do not intend to include here the consideration of buckling due to dynamic loads or the response of shells to random loads.

9.2 SPECTRAL REPRESENTATION; ORTHOGONALITY OF MODES OF FREE VIBRATION

In the determination of the response of a thin elastic shell to some transient disturbance, we seek the solution of the full system (see Eqs. 2.71) of inhomogeneous differential equations of the theory of thin elastic shells. We repeat here the equations of equilibrium from which the shear forces Q_1 and Q_2 have been eliminated:

$$\frac{\partial A_2N_1}{\partial \alpha_1} + \frac{\partial A_1N_{21}}{\partial \alpha_2} + N_{12}\frac{\partial A_1}{\partial \alpha_2} - N_2\frac{\partial A_2}{\partial \alpha_1} + \frac{1}{R_1}\left[\frac{\partial A_2M_1}{\partial \alpha_1} + \frac{\partial A_1M_{21}}{\partial \alpha_2} + M_{12}\frac{\partial A_1}{\partial \alpha_2} - M_2\frac{\partial A_2}{\partial \alpha_1}\right] = -A_1A_2\left(p_1 - ku_1 - \lambda\frac{\partial u_1}{\partial t} - \rho h\frac{\partial^2 u_1}{\partial t^2}\right), \tag{9.1a}$$

$$\frac{\partial A_2N_{12}}{\partial \alpha_1} + \frac{\partial A_1N_2}{\partial \alpha_2} + N_{21}\frac{\partial A_2}{\partial \alpha_1} - N_1\frac{\partial A_1}{\partial \alpha_2} + \frac{1}{R_2}\left[\frac{\partial A_2M_{12}}{\partial \alpha_1} + \frac{\partial A_1M_2}{\partial \alpha_2} + M_{21}\frac{\partial A_2}{\partial \alpha_1} - M_1\frac{\partial A_1}{\partial \alpha_2}\right] = -A_1A_2\left(p_2 - ku_2 - \lambda\frac{\partial u_2}{\partial t} - \rho h\frac{\partial^2 u_2}{\partial t^2}\right), \tag{9.1b}$$

$$\frac{\partial}{\partial \alpha_1}\frac{1}{A_1}\left\{\frac{\partial A_2 M_1}{\partial \alpha_1} + \frac{\partial A_1 M_{21}}{\partial \alpha_2} + M_{12}\frac{\partial A_1}{\partial \alpha_2} - M_2\frac{\partial A_2}{\partial \alpha_1}\right\}$$
$$+ \frac{\partial}{\partial \alpha_2}\frac{1}{A_2}\left\{\frac{\partial A_2 M_{12}}{\partial \alpha_1} + \frac{\partial A_1 M_2}{\partial \alpha_2} + M_{21}\frac{\partial A_2}{\partial \alpha_1} - M_1\frac{\partial A_1}{\partial \alpha_2}\right\}$$
$$- A_1 A_2\left(\frac{N_1}{R_1} + \frac{N_2}{R_2}\right)$$
$$= -A_1 A_2\left(-p - kw - \lambda\frac{\partial w}{\partial t} - \rho h\frac{\partial^2 w}{\partial t^2}\right). \tag{9.1c}$$

where the loads q_1, q_2, and q_n that appear in Eqs. 2.71 have been replaced by Eqs. 2.35a.

For convenience, we have assumed that the foundation parameters k and λ are the same for the three coordinate directions (see Section 2.6*a*). These equations, together with the force displacement relationships (Eqs. 2.27) and suitable boundary and initial conditions, represent the mathematical formulation of the problem of forced-vibration analysis of thin elastic shells. To keep the development as general as possible, we have retained the coordinates (α_1, α_2) of the general formulation.

To derive a complete solution of the forced vibration problem, we employ the method of spectral representation. If we designate by a y any of the dependent variables of the theory of thin elastic shells, then we may express the spectral representation of that variable by the expansion

$$y(\alpha_1, \alpha_2, t) = \sum_{n=1}^{\infty} q_n(t)\, Y_n(\alpha_1, \alpha_2), \tag{9.2}$$

where $q_n(t)$ are known as the generalized coordinates and represent the time-dependent aspect of the solution. The Y_n are the dependent variables associated with the nth mode of free vibration having a natural frequency ω_n, and satisfy the equations of the theory if, as in the previous chapter, we set $p = p_1 = p_2 = k = \lambda = 0$ and let

$$y(\alpha_1, \alpha_2, t) = Y_n(\alpha_1, \alpha_2)\cos \omega_n t. \tag{9.3}$$

The employment of an expansion of the type given by Eq. 9.2 is based on the premise that the normal modes of free vibration of a thin elastic shell are orthogonal. Thus, before we carry out the general forced-vibration solution, we must derive the orthogonality condition for the modes of free vibration of a thin elastic shell. This proceeds as follows:[2]

We recall here that the mathematical statement of Hamilton's Principle is (see Eq. 2.40):

$$\delta\int_{t_0}^{t_1} (\Pi - K)\, dt = 0. \tag{9.4a}$$

[2] The derivation is by A. Clebsch. See Love, A. E. H., *A Treatise on the Mathematical Theory of Elasticity*, 4th ed., New York: Dover Publications, p. 180 (1944).

For the application of this principle to the modes of free vibration of thin elastic shells, we observe that

$$\delta \Pi = \int_{\alpha_1}\int_{\alpha_2}\int_{\zeta} \sigma_{ij}\,\delta\epsilon_{ij} A_1 A_2 (1 + \zeta/R_1)(1 + \zeta/R_2)\, d\alpha_1\, d\alpha_2\, d\zeta, \quad (9.4b)$$

$$\delta K = -\int_{\alpha_1}\int_{\alpha_2} \rho h(\ddot{u}_1\,\delta u_1 + \ddot{u}_2\,\delta u_2 + \ddot{w}\,\delta w) A_1 A_2\, d\alpha_1\, d\alpha_2. \quad (9.4c)$$

In writing these expressions, we have used Eqs. 2.58 and 2.67b and we have ignored all external loads because of our interest in free vibrations. Now, in accordance with Eq. 9.3, let the displacements corresponding to the nth mode of free vibration be given by

$$\begin{aligned} u_1(\alpha_1, \alpha_2, t) &= u_{1n}(\alpha_1, \alpha_2)\cos\omega_n t,\\ u_2(\alpha_1, \alpha_2, t) &= u_{2n}(\alpha_1, \alpha_2)\cos\omega_n t,\\ w(\alpha_1, \alpha_2, t) &= w_n(\alpha_1, \alpha_2)\cos\omega_n t, \end{aligned} \quad (9.4d)$$

and let the displacement variations take the form

$$\begin{aligned} \delta u_1(\alpha_1, \alpha_2, t) &= u_{1m}(\alpha_1, \alpha_2)\cos\omega_m t,\\ \delta u_2(\alpha_1, \alpha_2, t) &= u_{2m}(\alpha_1, \alpha_2)\cos\omega_m t,\\ \delta w(\alpha_1, \alpha_2, t) &= w_m(\alpha_1, \alpha_2)\cos\omega_m t. \end{aligned} \quad (9.4e)$$

Substitution of Eqs. 9.4d and 9.4e into Eqs. 9.4b and 9.4c, followed by substitution of the resulting expressions into Eq. 9.4a, gives

$$\int_{\alpha_1}\int_{\alpha_2}\int_{\zeta} \sigma_{ij}^{(n)}\epsilon_{ij}^{(m)} A_1 A_2 (1 + \zeta/R_1)(1 + \zeta/R_2)\, d\alpha_1\, d\alpha_2\, d\zeta$$

$$= \omega_n^2 \int_{\alpha_1}\int_{\alpha_2} \rho h(u_{1n}u_{1m} + u_{2n}u_{2m} + w_n w_m) A_1 A_2\, d\alpha_1\, d\alpha_2, \quad (9.4f)$$

and, with m and n interchanged in Eqs, 9.4d and 9.4e,

$$\int_{\alpha_1}\int_{\alpha_2}\int_{\zeta} \sigma_{ij}^{(m)}\epsilon_{ij}^{(n)} A_1 A_2 (1 + \zeta/R_1)(1 + \zeta/R_2)\, d\alpha_1\, d\alpha_2\, d\zeta$$

$$= \omega_m^2 \int_{\alpha_1}\int_{\alpha_2} \rho h(u_{1n}u_{1m} + u_{2n}u_{2m} + w_n w_m) A_1 A_2\, d\alpha_1\, d\alpha_2, \quad (9.4g)$$

where the stresses $\sigma_{ij}^{(n)}$ correspond to the displacements given by Eqs. 9.4d and the strains $\epsilon_{ij}^{(m)}$ correspond to the displacement variations as given by Eqs. 9.4e. In view of the fact that the stresses are related to the strains, it follows that the integrands involving these quantities are symmetric with respect to m and n. Therefore, upon subtraction of Eq. 9.4g from Eq. 9.4f, we obtain the result

$$(\omega_m^2 - \omega_n^2)\int_{\alpha_1}\int_{\alpha_2} (u_{1m}u_{1n} + u_{2m}u_{2n} + w_m w_n) A_1 A_2\, d\alpha_1\, d\alpha_2 = 0. \quad (9.5a)$$

The foregoing equation can only be satisfied in two ways. If we are dealing with two solution states (normal modes) having the same natural frequency, then Eq. 9.5a is an identity because $\omega_m^2 - \omega_n^2 \equiv 0$. On the other hand, if we are dealing with two solution states having different natural frequencies, then Eq. 9.5a can be satisfied only if the integral vanishes, or

$$\iint_S (u_{1m}u_{1n} + u_{2m}u_{2n} + w_m w_n) A_1 A_2 \, d\alpha_1 \, d\alpha_2 = 0. \tag{9.5b}$$

The two situations can be summarized by the expression

$$\iint_S (u_{1m}u_{1n} + u_{2m}u_{2n} + w_m w_n) A_1 A_2 \, d\alpha_1 \, d\alpha_2 = \delta_{mn} N_n, \tag{9.5c}$$

where δ_{mn} is the Kronecker symbol and

$$N_n = \iint_S (u_{1n}^2 + u_{2n}^2 + w_n^2) A_1 A_2 \, d\alpha_1 \, d\alpha_2. \tag{9.5d}$$

Equation 9.5b represents the orthogonality condition of the modes of free vibration of a thin elastic shell and allows us to proceed with the general solution of the forced-vibration problem of a thin elastic shell.

9.3 RESPONSE OF A SHELL TO TRANSIENT SURFACE LOADS OF MECHANICAL ORIGIN

We now resume the analysis of the forced-vibration problem by substituting the assumed solution 9.2 into Eqs. 9.1 and observing the equations which the modes of free vibration must satisfy. The latter are obtained by substituting equations of the type of Eq. 9.3 into Eqs. 9.1. The end result of the procedure is the set of equations

$$\sum_{n=1}^{\infty} \left\{ \rho h \frac{d^2 q_n}{dt^2} + \lambda \frac{dq_n}{dt} + (k + \rho h \omega_n^2) q_n \right\} \begin{Bmatrix} u_{1n} \\ u_{2n} \\ w_n \end{Bmatrix} = \begin{Bmatrix} p_1 \\ p_2 \\ -p \end{Bmatrix}. \tag{9.6a}$$

Multiplication of each of Eqs. 9.6a by u_{1m}, u_{2m}, and w_m, respectively, addition of the three resulting equations, and integration over the reference surface of the shell then gives

$$\begin{aligned} \iint_S \sum_{n=1}^{\infty} \left\{ \rho h \frac{d^2 q_n}{dt^2} + \lambda \frac{dq_n}{dt} + (k + \rho h \omega_n^2) q_n \right\} \\ \times \{u_{1n}u_{1m} + u_{2n}u_{2m} + w_n w_m\} A_1 A_2 \, d\alpha_1 \, d\alpha_2 \\ = \iint_S (p_1 u_{1m} + p_2 u_{2m} - p w_m) A_1 A_2 \, d\alpha_1 \, d\alpha_2. \end{aligned} \tag{9.6b}$$

Since, by the orthogonality condition, the integral of the products of the displacement components will vanish unless $m = n$, the sum on the left-hand side of the above expression reduces to one term, or

$$\frac{d^2q_n}{dt^2} + \frac{\lambda}{\rho h}\frac{dq_n}{dt} + \left(\omega_n{}^2 + \frac{k}{\rho h}\right) q_n = \frac{1}{\rho h} G_n(t), \tag{9.6c}$$

where

$$G_n(t) = \frac{1}{N_n} \iint_S (p_1 u_{1n} + p_2 u_{2n} - p w_n) A_1 A_2 \, d\alpha_1 \, d\alpha_2. \tag{9.6d}$$

To solve the foregoing differential equation, we must also account for the initial conditions which, in terms of the assumed solution 9.2, take the form

$$\begin{Bmatrix} u_{10} \\ u_{20} \\ w_0 \end{Bmatrix} = \sum_{n=1}^{\infty} q_n(0) \begin{Bmatrix} u_{1n} \\ u_{2n} \\ w_n \end{Bmatrix}, \tag{9.7a}$$

$$\begin{Bmatrix} \dot{u}_{10} \\ \dot{u}_{20} \\ \dot{w}_0 \end{Bmatrix} = \sum_{n=1}^{\infty} \dot{q}_n(0) \begin{Bmatrix} u_{1n} \\ u_{2n} \\ w_n \end{Bmatrix}, \tag{9.7b}$$

where a dot refers to a derivative with respect to time, and the subscript zero denotes the initial values of the displacements and velocities of the shell. Multiplication of each of Eqs. 9.7a and 9.7b by u_{1m}, u_{2m}, and w_m, respectively, addition of the three resulting equations of each set, and integration over the reference surface of the shell leads, with the orthogonality condition, to the following pair of initial conditions:

$$\begin{aligned} q_n(0) &= \frac{1}{N_n} \iint_S (u_{10} u_{1n} + u_{20} u_{2n} + w_0 w_n) A_1 A_2 \, d\alpha_1 \, d\alpha_2, \\ \dot{q}_n(0) &= \frac{1}{N_n} \iint_S (\dot{u}_{10} u_{1n} + \dot{u}_{20} u_{2n} + \dot{w}_0 w_n) A_1 A_2 \, d\alpha_1 \, d\alpha_2. \end{aligned} \tag{9.7c}$$

The differential equation 9.6c has constant coefficients. Its complementary solution may, therefore, be obtained by assuming that

$$q_n = e^{rt}. \tag{9.8a}$$

Substitution of this solution into the homogeneous portion of Eq. 9.6c gives the auxiliary equation

$$r^2 + \frac{\lambda}{\rho h} r + \left(\frac{k}{\rho h} + \omega_n{}^2\right) = 0, \tag{9.8b}$$

which has the roots

$$\begin{Bmatrix} r_1 \\ r_2 \end{Bmatrix} = -\frac{\lambda}{2\rho h} \pm \left[\left(\frac{\lambda}{2\rho h}\right)^2 - \left(\frac{k}{\rho h} + \omega_n^2\right)\right]^{1/2}. \tag{9.8c}$$

According to whether the quantity under the radical in Eq. 9.8c is positive, zero, or negative, there will be three categories of roots obtained from Eq. 9.8c which we now consider, one at a time.

Case (a): $(\lambda/2\rho h)^2 < (k/\rho h + \omega_n^2)$

This represents the so-called "underdamped" foundation for which Eq. 9.8c yields the two complex conjugate roots

$$\begin{Bmatrix} r_1 \\ r_2 \end{Bmatrix} = -\frac{\lambda}{2\rho h} \pm i\gamma_n, \tag{9.9a}$$

where

$$i = \sqrt{-1}, \qquad \gamma_n^2 = \frac{k}{\rho h} + \omega_n^2 - \left(\frac{\lambda}{2\rho h}\right)^2. \tag{9.9b}$$

The complementary solution of Eq. 9.6c is then, according to Eq. 9.8a:

$$X_a = A_n\, e^{-[(\lambda/2\rho h)+i\gamma_n]t} + B_n\, e^{-[(\lambda/2\rho h)-i\gamma_n]t}, \tag{9.9c}$$

and has the more convenient, equivalent, form

$$X_1 = e^{-(\lambda/2\rho h)t}\,(C_n \cos \gamma_n t + D_n \sin \gamma_n t), \tag{9.9d}$$

where C_n and D_n are arbitrary constants. The particular solution of Eq. 9.6c can be shown by standard methods, such as variation of parameters, to be

$$X_2 = \frac{1}{\rho h \gamma_n} \int_0^t G_n(\tau)\, e^{-\lambda(t-\tau)/2\rho h} \sin \gamma_n(t - \tau)\, d\tau. \tag{9.9e}$$

Equations 9.9d and 9.9e are now combined to give the following general solution:

$$q_n(t) = e^{-\lambda t/2\rho h}\,(C_n \cos \gamma_n t + D_n \sin \gamma_n t) + \frac{1}{\rho h \gamma_n} \int_0^t G_n(\tau)\, e^{-\lambda(t-\tau)/2\rho h} \sin \gamma_n(t - \tau)\, d\tau. \tag{9.9f}$$

Upon application of the initial conditions 9.7c to the above, the arbitrary constants C_n and D_n can be shown to be

$$\begin{aligned} C_n &= \frac{1}{N_n} \iint_S (u_{10}u_{1n} + u_{20}u_{2n} + w_0 w_n) A_1 A_2\, d\alpha_1\, d\alpha_2 \\ D_n &= \frac{\lambda}{2\rho h \gamma_n} C_n + \frac{1}{\gamma_n N_n} \iint_S (\dot{u}_{10}u_{1n} + \dot{u}_{20}u_{2n} + \dot{w}_0 w_n) A_1 A_2\, d\alpha_1\, d\alpha_2. \end{aligned} \tag{9.9g}$$

The solution 9.9f indicates that a shell resting on an underdamped foundation will oscillate with ever decreasing amplitude until a steady state, constant value is reached.

Case (b): $(\lambda/2\rho h)^2 > (k/\rho h + \omega_n^2)$

This represents the so-called "overdamped" foundation for which Eq. 9.8c gives two real, negative roots. The complementary solution of Eq. 9.6c is, according to Eq. 9.8a,

$$X_1 = e^{-\lambda t/2\rho h}\,(E_n\, e^{\gamma_n t} + F_n\, e^{-\gamma_n t}). \tag{9.10a}$$

The particular solution is, again by variation of parameters,

$$X_2 = \frac{1}{\rho h \gamma_n}\int_0^t G_n(\tau)\, e^{-\lambda(t-\tau)/2\rho h}\sinh \gamma_n(t-\tau)\, d\tau, \tag{9.10b}$$

with which the general solution for this case is

$$q_n(t) = e^{-\lambda t/2\rho h}\,(E_n\, e^{\gamma_n t} + F_n\, e^{-\gamma_n t}) + \frac{1}{\rho h \gamma_n}\int_0^t G_n(\tau)\, e^{-\lambda(t-\tau)/2\rho h}\sinh \gamma_n(t-\tau)\, d\tau. \tag{9.10c}$$

If the initial conditions 9.7c are applied to the above solution, the following expressions for the arbitrary constants E_n and F_n are obtained:

$$\begin{Bmatrix} E_n \\ F_n \end{Bmatrix} = \frac{1}{2N_n}\left(1 \pm \frac{\lambda}{2\rho h \gamma_n}\right)\iint_S (u_{10}u_{1n} + u_{20}u_{2n} + w_0 w_n)A_1A_2\, d\alpha_1\, d\alpha_2 \pm \frac{1}{2N_n\gamma_n}\iint_S (\dot{u}_{10}u_{1n} + \dot{u}_{20}u_{2n} + \dot{w}_0 w_n)A_1A_2\, d\alpha_1\, d\alpha_2. \tag{9.10d}$$

From the solution 9.10c, it is seen that, for the overdamped foundation, no oscillations will occur and that once displaced the shell will creep to an equilibrium position.

Case (c): $(\lambda/2\rho h)^2 = (k/\rho h + \omega_n^2)$

This is the case of the "critically damped" foundation which represents the transition point between the underdamped oscillatory solution of Case (*a*) and the overdamped nonoscillatory solution of Case (*b*). In this case, the roots of Eq. 9.8b are real, negative, and equal, and the complementary solution of Eq. 9.6c is

$$X_1 = (C_{1n} + C_{2n}t)\, e^{-\lambda t/2\rho h}. \tag{9.11a}$$

The particular solution of Eq. 9.6c is, by variation of parameters,

$$X_2 = \int_0^t \frac{G_n(\tau)}{\rho h} (t - \tau)\, e^{-\lambda(t-\tau)/2\rho h}\, d\tau, \tag{9.11b}$$

whereupon the complete general solution of Eq. 9.6c is

$$q_n(t) = (C_{1n} + C_{2n}t)\, e^{-\lambda t/2\rho h} + \frac{1}{\rho h}\int_0^t G_n(\tau)(t - \tau)\, e^{-\lambda(t-\tau)/2\rho h}\, d\tau. \tag{9.11c}$$

The arbitrary constants, upon application of the initial conditions 9.7c, can be shown to be

$$\begin{aligned} C_{1n} &= \frac{1}{N_n}\iint_S (u_{10}u_{1n} + u_{20}u_{2n} + w_0 w_n)A_1A_2\, d\alpha_1\, d\alpha_2, \\ C_{2n} &= \frac{\lambda}{2\rho h} C_{1n} + \frac{1}{N_n}\iint_S (\dot{u}_{10}u_{1n} + \dot{u}_{20}u_{2n} + \dot{w}_0 w_n)A_1A_2\, d\alpha_1\, d\alpha_2. \end{aligned} \tag{9.11d}$$

Case (*d*): $\lambda = k = 0$

As a special case of the underdamped foundation, we have the case of no foundation at all. Since the foundation parameters $k = \lambda = 0$ of this case meet the definition of Case (*a*), we may immediately write the solution

$$q_n(t) = C_n \cos \omega_n t + D_n \sin \omega_n t + \frac{1}{\rho h \omega_n}\int_0^t G_n(\tau) \sin \omega_n(t - \tau)\, d\tau, \tag{9.12a}$$

and

$$\begin{aligned} C_n &= \frac{1}{N_n}\iint_S (u_{10}u_{1n} + u_{20}u_{2n} + w_0 w_n)A_1A_2\, d\alpha_1\, d\alpha_2, \\ D_n &= \frac{1}{\omega_n N_n}\iint_S (\dot{u}_{10}u_{1n} + \dot{u}_{20}u_{2n} + \dot{w}_0 w_n)A_1A_2\, d\alpha_1\, d\alpha_2, \end{aligned} \tag{9.12b}$$

which follow from Eqs. 9.9f and 9.9g upon setting $k = \lambda = 0$ and, therefore, $\gamma_n = \omega_n$. It is evident, from Eq. 9.12a, that under the influence of any time-dependent load the shell will continue to oscillate indefinitely.

Having thus derived the q_n for the various combinations of the foundation parameters, we have arrived at the complete solution of the problem of forced vibration of a thin elastic shell under an arbitrary system of time-dependent surface loads. The deflections of the shell, for instance, can now be written, according to Eq. 9.2, as

$$\begin{Bmatrix} u_1 \\ u_2 \\ w \end{Bmatrix} = \sum_{n=1}^{\infty} q_n(t) \begin{Bmatrix} u_{1n}(\alpha_1, \alpha_2) \\ u_{2n}(\alpha_1, \alpha_2) \\ w_n(\alpha_1, \alpha_2) \end{Bmatrix}. \tag{9.13}$$

where, as we have stated previously, u_{1n}, u_{2n}, and w_n are obtained from a free-vibration analysis of the shell under consideration. Formally speaking, the solutions obtained here actually apply simultaneously to the forced-vibration analysis of any elastic body once the appropriate free-vibration characteristics, foundation parameters, and initial conditions are known.

Inherent in the foregoing general solution is the assumption that the foundation parameters k and λ are equal in the three coordinate directions of a shell. If this were not the case, that is, if $k \neq k_1 \neq k_2$ and $\lambda \neq \lambda_1 \neq \lambda_2$, then we could not pass from Eqs. 9.6a to Eq. 9.6c in spite of the orthogonality of the undamped modes of free vibration which we have used. To account for foundations with unequal elastic and viscous parameters, we should have to utilize the damped modes of free vibration of the shell. These are generally not available in the present state of development of results on the free vibration of shells. Until more of such results are forthcoming, the present forced-vibration solutions are not felt to be seriously limited.

9.4 RESPONSE OF A SHELL TO TRANSIENT EDGE LOADS

It may be necessary in forced-vibration analysis to consider a shell under the influence of a time-dependent force, moment, displacement, or rotation at a given edge. In the particular case of dynamic thermal stress analysis, the definitions (Eqs. 2.27) of the stress resultants and couples contain contributions from the time-dependent thermal force and moment which result in a time-dependent boundary condition even when the net force or moment at a given edge are required to vanish.

In the case of time-dependent edge loads, we are, therefore, confronted with new complications which are associated with the fact that the boundary conditions are themselves inhomogeneous. However, methods have been proposed by means of which these time-dependent inhomogeneities can be accommodated.[3] These methods rely upon the principle that homogeneous differential equations with inhomogeneous boundary conditions are essentially equivalent to inhomogeneous differential equations with homogeneous boundary conditions.[4] In what follows, we shall outline the method by means of which the conversion referred to in this principle may be accomplished. Of course, if, as will be the case here, the differential

[3] See, Mindlin, R. D., and Goodman, L. E., "Beam Vibrations with Time Dependent Boundary Conditions," *J. Appl. Mech., Trans. A.S.M.E.*, **72**, 377–380 (1950) and also Berry, J. G., and Naghdi, P. M., "On the Vibration of Elastic Bodies Having Time Dependent Boundary Conditions," *Quart. Appl. Math.* **14**, 43–50 (1956).

[4] Courant, R., and Hilbert, D., *Methods of Mathematical Physics*, volume I, New York: Interscience Publishers, 1953, p. 277.

equations are themselves inhomogeneous by virtue of the presence of surface loads (such as were considered in the previous section) then the accommodation of the inhomogeneous boundary conditions will simply lead to additional inhomogeneities in the differential equations.

Let us then write Eqs. 9.1 in operator form in order to simplify our subsequent discussions, as follows (see Eqs. 8.2):

$$\begin{aligned}
\mathscr{L}_1\{u_1, u_2, w\} &= -A_1A_2\left[p_1 - ku_1 - \lambda\frac{\partial u_1}{\partial t} - \rho h\frac{\partial^2 u_1}{\partial t^2}\right. \\
&\qquad \left. - \frac{1}{A_1(1-\nu)}\left(\frac{\partial N_T}{\partial \alpha_1} + \frac{1}{R_1}\frac{\partial M_T}{\partial \alpha_1}\right)\right], \\
\mathscr{L}_2\{u_1, u_2, w\} &= -A_1A_2\left[p_2 - ku_2 - \lambda\frac{\partial u_2}{\partial t} - \rho h\frac{\partial^2 u_2}{\partial t^2}\right. \\
&\qquad \left. - \frac{1}{A_2(1-\nu)}\left(\frac{\partial N_T}{\partial \alpha_2} + \frac{1}{R_2}\frac{\partial M_T}{\partial \alpha_2}\right)\right], \\
\mathscr{L}_3\{u_1, u_2, w\} &= -A_1A_2\left\{-p - kw - \lambda\frac{\partial w}{\partial t} - \rho h\frac{\partial^2 w}{\partial t^2}\right. \\
&\qquad + \frac{N_T}{1-\nu}\left(\frac{1}{R_1} + \frac{1}{R_2}\right) \\
&\qquad \left. - \frac{1}{A_1A_2(1-\nu)}\left[\frac{\partial}{\partial \alpha_1}\left(\frac{A_2}{A_1}\frac{\partial M_T}{\partial \alpha_1}\right) + \frac{\partial}{\partial \alpha_2}\left(\frac{A_1}{A_2}\frac{\partial M_T}{\partial \alpha_2}\right)\right]\right\},
\end{aligned} \tag{9.14}$$

where, without giving their definitions explicitly, we note simply that $\mathscr{L}_1$, $\mathscr{L}_2$, $\mathscr{L}_3$ are differential operators which are obtained upon substitution of the stress resultants and couples given by Eqs. 2.27 and the strain-displacement relationships 2.19 into Eqs. 9.1.

Since there can be, at most, four edges in a shell with four boundary conditions to be prescribed at each edge, the resulting total of sixteen boundary conditions can be written as follows, assuming that the spatial and temporal variations of any inhomogeneous boundary conditions are separable:

$$B_k\{u_1, u_2, w\} = g_k(\alpha_i, \alpha_j{}^m) f_l(t)\, \delta_{lk}. \qquad \begin{matrix} i, j = 1, 2. \\ i \neq j \end{matrix} \tag{9.15}$$

This particular form indicates that α_1 is variable on edges of constant $\alpha_j = \alpha_j{}^m$ (see Section 2.3) and vice versa where $m = 0, 1$. The index k ranges from 1 to 16 in correspondence with the total number of boundary conditions that can, in the most general case, be applied. The index l may take on any or all values between 1 and 16 in order to identify which boundary conditions are actually inhomogeneous. The Kronecker symbol is introduced to include those boundary conditions that are homogeneous in the representation. We notice that the B_k are differential operators which need not involve all three components u_1, u_2, and w; these are included only for generality. The functions $g_k(\alpha_1, \alpha_2)$ and $f_l(t)$ represent the spatial and temporal variations of any inhomogeneous boundary condition. The time dependence of the boundary conditions can now be accommodated by assuming that the displacement components take the following form:

$$\begin{Bmatrix} u_1 \\ u_2 \\ w \end{Bmatrix} = \sum_{n=1}^{\infty} q_n^*(t) \begin{Bmatrix} u_{1n}(\alpha_1, \alpha_2) \\ u_{2n}(\alpha_1, \alpha_2) \\ w_n(\alpha_1, \alpha_2) \end{Bmatrix} + \sum_l f_l(t) \begin{Bmatrix} u_1^l(\alpha_1, \alpha_2) \\ u_2^l(\alpha_1, \alpha_2) \\ w^l(\alpha_1, \alpha_2) \end{Bmatrix}, \tag{9.16}$$

where u_{1n}, u_{2n}, and w_n are, as before, the modes of free vibration which satisfy the homogeneous portions of the differential equations and boundary conditions. $q_n^*(t)$ are the generalized coordinates of the forced-vibration problem associated with time-dependent boundary conditions (compare to q_n used for time-dependent surface loads). The second summation is over all relevant values of l, each corresponding to one inhomogeneous boundary condition, and the functions u_1^l, u_2^l, w^l are corrections by means of which the time-dependent boundary conditions are accommodated. Thus, in the case of time-dependent edge conditions, the forced-vibration analysis involves the determination of the generalized coordinates $q_n^*(t)$ as well as the correction functions u_i^l. If we now substitute the assumed representations 9.16 into the equilibrium equations 9.14, and take into account the equilibrium equations which the undamped modes of free vibration must satisfy, the result is

$$\sum_{n=1}^{\infty} \left\{ \rho h \frac{d^2 q_n^*}{dt^2} + \lambda \frac{dq_n^*}{dt} + (k + \rho h \omega_n^2) q_n^* \right\} \begin{Bmatrix} u_{1n} \\ u_{2n} \\ w_n \end{Bmatrix} = \begin{Bmatrix} p_1^* \\ p_2^* \\ p^* \end{Bmatrix}, \tag{9.17a}$$

where

$$p_i^* = p_i - \frac{1}{A_i(1-\nu)} \left(\frac{\partial N_T}{\partial \alpha_i} + \frac{1}{R_i} \frac{\partial M_T}{\partial \alpha_i} \right) - \sum_l (k f_l + \lambda \dot{f}_l + \rho h \ddot{f}_l) u_i^l$$
$$+ \sum_l \frac{f_l}{A_1 A_2} \mathscr{L}_i\{u_i^l\}, \qquad i = 1, 2 \tag{9.17b}$$

$$p^* = -p - \frac{1}{A_1 A_2 (1-\nu)} \left[\frac{\partial}{\partial \alpha_1} \left(\frac{A_2}{A_1} \frac{\partial M_T}{\partial \alpha_1} \right) + \frac{\partial}{\partial \alpha_2} \left(\frac{A_1}{A_2} \frac{\partial M_T}{\partial \alpha_2} \right) \right]$$
$$+ \frac{N_T}{1-\nu} \left(\frac{1}{R_1} + \frac{1}{R_2} \right) - \sum_l (k f_l + \lambda \dot{f}_l + \rho h \ddot{f}_l) w^l$$
$$+ \sum_l \frac{f_l}{A_1 A_2} \mathscr{L}_3\{w^l\}. \tag{9.17c}$$

Now multiply each of Eqs. 9.17a by u_{1m}, u_{2m}, and w_m, respectively. Addition of the three resulting equations followed by integration over the reference surface of the shell then gives, in view of the orthogonality condition,

$$\frac{d^2q_n^*}{dt^2} + \frac{\lambda}{\rho h}\frac{dq_n^*}{dt} + \left(\frac{k}{\rho h} + \omega_n^2\right) q_n^* = \frac{1}{\rho h} G_n^*(t), \qquad (9.17d)$$

where

$$\begin{aligned} G_n^*(t) = \frac{1}{N_n}\iint\Bigg\{&\left[p_1 - \frac{1}{A_1(1-\nu)}\left(\frac{\partial N_T}{\partial \alpha_1} + \frac{1}{R_1}\frac{\partial M_T}{\partial \alpha_1}\right)\right] u_{1n} \\ &+ \left[p_2 - \frac{1}{A_2(1-\nu)}\left(\frac{\partial N_T}{\partial \alpha_2} + \frac{1}{R_2}\frac{\partial M_T}{\partial \alpha_2}\right)\right] u_{2n} \\ &+ \left[-p + \frac{N_T}{1-\nu}\left(\frac{1}{R_1} + \frac{1}{R_2}\right) - \frac{1}{A_1A_2(1-\nu)}\right. \\ &\times \left.\left\{\frac{\partial}{\partial \alpha_1}\left(\frac{A_2}{A_1}\frac{\partial M_T}{\partial \alpha_1}\right) + \frac{\partial}{\partial \alpha_2}\left(\frac{A_1}{A_2}\frac{\partial M_T}{\partial \alpha_2}\right)\right\}\right] w_n \\ &- \sum_l (\rho h \ddot{f}_l + \lambda \dot{f}_l + k f_l)(u_1^l u_{1n} + u_2^l u_{2n} + w^l w_n) \\ &+ \frac{1}{A_1A_2}\sum_l f_l\,[u_{1n}\mathscr{L}_1\{u_1^l\} + u_{2n}\mathscr{L}_2\{u_2^l\} \\ &+ w_n\mathscr{L}_3\{w^l\}]\Bigg\} A_1A_2\, d\alpha_1\, d\alpha_2. \end{aligned} \qquad (9.17e)$$

We may note that, in the event that there are no thermal effects and no time-dependent edge conditions, Eqs. 9.17 reduce to Eqs. 9.6.

To determine the corrections u_i^l, we substitute the assumed representations 9.16 into the boundary conditions 9.15, whereupon the latter take the form

$$\sum_{n=1}^{\infty} q_n^* B_k\{u_{1n}, u_{2n}, w_n\} = g_k(\alpha_i, \alpha_j^m) f_l(t)\, \delta_{lk} - \sum_l f_l B_k\{u_1^l, u_2^l, w^l\}. \qquad (9.18a)$$

Thus, if we insure that

$$B_k\{u_1^l, u_2^l, w^l\} = g_k(\alpha_i, \alpha_j^m)\, \delta_{lk}, \qquad (9.18b)$$

Equation 9.18a will reduce to

$$\sum_{n=1}^{\infty} q_n^* B_k\{u_{1n}, u_{2n}, w_n\} = 0, \qquad (9.18c)$$

and this is satisfied term by term by those modes of free vibration which are appropriate to a problem having the homogeneous counterpart of the present boundary conditions. Equations 9.18b are the governing equations for the determination of the u_1^l, u_2^l, and w^l. Notice that the representation 9.18b stands, in general, for sixteen equations of which all but the lth ones are homogeneous, and that, in general, there may be as many as sixteen equations of the type of Eq. 9.18c. The determination of $u_1{}^l$, $u_2{}^l$, w^l will not be outlined, but an example in which functions of this type must be constructed is given in Section 9.6. In this connection, however, the reader is invited to consult the references cited in footnote 3. To complete the solution, we must again account for the initial conditions which, in terms of the assumed solution 9.16, take the form

$$\begin{Bmatrix} u_{10} \\ u_{20} \\ w_0 \end{Bmatrix} = \sum_{n=1}^{\infty} q_n{}^*(0) \begin{Bmatrix} u_{1n} \\ u_{2n} \\ w_n \end{Bmatrix} + \sum_l f_l(0) \begin{Bmatrix} u_1{}^l \\ u_2{}^l \\ w^l \end{Bmatrix}, \tag{9.19a}$$

$$\begin{Bmatrix} \dot{u}_{10} \\ \dot{u}_{20} \\ \dot{w}_0 \end{Bmatrix} = \sum_{n=1}^{\infty} \dot{q}_n{}^*(0) \begin{Bmatrix} u_{1n} \\ u_{2n} \\ w_n \end{Bmatrix} + \sum_l \dot{f}_l(0) \begin{Bmatrix} u_1{}^l \\ u_2{}^l \\ w^l \end{Bmatrix}. \tag{9.19b}$$

Multiplication of each of Eqs. 9.19a and then Eqs. 9.19b by u_{1m}, u_{2m}, and w_m, respectively, addition of the three resulting equations of each set, and integration over the reference surface of the shell leads, in view of the orthogonality property, to the following pair of initial conditions:

$$\begin{aligned} q_n{}^*(0) &= \frac{1}{N_n} \iint_S \Big\{ \Big[u_{10} - \sum_l u_1{}^l f_l(0) \Big] u_{1n} + \Big[u_{20} - \sum_l u_2{}^l f_l(0) \Big] u_{2n} \\ &\quad + \Big[w_0 - \sum_l f_l(0) w^l \Big] w_n \Big\} A_1 A_2 \, d\alpha_1 \, d\alpha_2, \\ \dot{q}_n{}^*(0) &= \frac{1}{N_n} \iint_S \Big\{ \Big[\dot{u}_{10} - \sum_l u_1{}^l \dot{f}_l(0) \Big] u_{1n} + \Big[\dot{u}_{20} - \sum_l u_2{}^l \dot{f}_l(0) \Big] u_{2n} \\ &\quad + \Big[\dot{w}_0 - \sum_l w^l \dot{f}_l(0) \Big] w_n \Big\} A_1 A_2 \, d\alpha_1 \, d\alpha_2. \end{aligned} \tag{9.19c}$$

The generalized coordinate $q_n{}^*$ of the inhomogeneous differential equations with inhomogeneous boundary conditions can now be determined by proceeding in precisely the same way as we did in the case of the generalized coordinate q_n of the inhomogeneous differential equations with homogeneous boundary conditions. Indeed, it is readily seen that Eqs. 9.6c and 9.6d and 9.7c which involve q_n are special cases of Eqs. 9.17d and 9.17e and 9.19c for $q_n{}^*$. Thus, it is unnecessary for us to repeat for $q_n{}^*$ the solution process which we gave in Section 9.3 for q_n.

9.5 PARTICIPATION OF NORMAL MODES IN THE FORCED VIBRATION SOLUTION

In the previous chapter, we made some remarks on the extent of the participation of the modes of free vibration in the analysis of shallow and nonshallow shells. It is in the present consideration of the forced-vibration analysis of thin elastic shells that the question of mode participation can be resolved. Therefore, let us explore the contribution which is made by the individual modes of free vibration to the transient solution given in Section 9.3. For this purpose, it is convenient to write all variables and parameters in a nondimensional form. After the introduction of a general reference length L and a reference pressure p_0 for each shell, as well as a reference length l_n for the nth mode of free vibration, we define the following nondimensional quantities:

$$\begin{aligned} \{U_1, U_2, W\} &= (D/L^4 p_0)\{u_1, u_2, w\}, \\ \tau &= (D/L^4 \rho h)^{1/2} t, \\ K &= (L^4/D)k, \\ \Lambda &= (L^4/\rho h D)^{1/2}\lambda/2, \\ \Omega_n &= (\rho/E)^{1/2}\omega_n. \end{aligned} \tag{9.20a}$$

Assuming that the surface loads are separable in the form

$$\begin{aligned} p_1(\alpha_1, \alpha_2, t) &= f_1(t)P_1^*(\alpha_1, \alpha_2), \\ p_2(\alpha_1, \alpha_2, t) &= f_2(t)P_2^*(\alpha_1, \alpha_2), \\ -p(\alpha_1, \alpha_2, t) &= f(t)P^*(\alpha_1, \alpha_2), \end{aligned} \tag{9.20b}$$

we can introduce the "mode participation factors"[5] of the nth mode of free vibration by means of the definitions

$$\begin{Bmatrix} m_{1n} \\ m_{2n} \\ m_n \end{Bmatrix} = (l_n/p_0 N_n) \iint_S \begin{Bmatrix} P_1^* u_{1n} \\ P_2^* u_{2n} \\ P^* w_n \end{Bmatrix} A_1 A_2 \, d\alpha_1 \, d\alpha_2, \tag{9.20c}$$

and then denote the time-dependent parameters of the forced-vibration solution of a shell resting on an underdamped foundation for example, by (see Eq. 9.9f):

$$\begin{Bmatrix} F_{1n}(\tau) \\ F_{2n}(\tau) \\ F_n(\tau) \end{Bmatrix} = \int_0^\tau \begin{Bmatrix} f_{1n}(\eta) \\ f_{2n}(\eta) \\ f_n(\eta) \end{Bmatrix} e^{-\Lambda(\tau-\eta)} \sin \Gamma_n(\tau - \eta) \, d\eta. \tag{9.20d}$$

With this notation, the generalized coordinates of the forced-vibration solution can be written as

$$\begin{aligned} q_n(\tau) = e^{-\tau\Lambda} (C_n \cos \Gamma_n \tau + D_n \sin \Gamma_n \tau) \\ + (L^4 p_0 / D l_n \Gamma_n)(m_{1n} F_{1n} + m_{2n} F_{2n} + m_n F_n), \end{aligned} \tag{9.20e}$$

[5] Thomson, W. T., and Barton, M. V., "The Response of Mechanical Systems to Random Excitation," *J. Appl. Mech.* **24**, 248–251 (1957).

where

$$\Gamma_n = [K + 12(1 - \nu^2)\Omega_n^2(L/h)^2 - \Lambda^2]^{1/2}, \qquad (9.20f)$$

and similar expressions can be derived for shells resting on critically damped and overdamped foundations as well as for the case of no foundation at all. It follows, from Eqs. 9.2 and 9.20e, that, for large values of τ, the dependent variables in the transient response of a shell resting on an underdamped foundation are given by

$$(D/l^4 p_0)y(\alpha_1, \alpha_2, t) = \sum_{n=1}^{\infty} \frac{Y_n(\alpha_1, \alpha_2)}{l_n \Gamma_n} (m_{1n}F_{1n} + m_{2n}F_{2n} + m_n F_n). \quad (9.21)$$

In order to assess the participation of the modes of free vibration, we can consider the response of the shell produced by the three components of the surface load p_1, p_2, p acting separately (one at a time), since the total response can then be obtained by superposition. For example, consider the case when $p_1 = p_2 = 0$. Then for large values of τ, the nth term in the series given by Eq. 9.21 is dependent on m_n. Clearly, if a mode of free vibration has w_n much smaller than the other displacements, then the m_n calculated from Eqs. 9.20c will be much smaller than the m_n of some of the other modes, and the participation of this mode in the solution produced by p will be small. By a similar argument, those modes which have a small u_{1n} (or u_{2n}) will not affect appreciably the response produced by p_1 (or p_2).

These conclusions are of importance in the theory of transient vibration of shallow shells for which, as we indicated in the previous chapter, it has been proposed by Reissner[6] that the analysis can be simplified by neglecting the longitudinal inertia terms and considering only the transverse vibration. In the previous chapter, it was shown[7] that if the longitudinal inertia terms for a shallow spherical shell are neglected, then the transverse modes are almost the same as those predicted by the exact equations and the longitudinal modes are lost. Moreover, the complete analysis of the modes of free vibration of shallow spherical shells with longitudinal inertia included[7] shows that the absolute values of the displacement components obey the following rule: for the transverse modes $w > u_1, u_2$ and for the longitudinal modes $u_1, u_2 > w$. From Eq. 9.21 it follows, therefore, that in the presence of a normal load p, the longitudinal modes will have a small participation in the response if the ratio of the m_n of the longitudinal modes to the m_n of the transverse modes is a small number. If this is true, then, in the

[6] Reissner, E., "On Transverse Vibrations of Thin Shallow Elastic Shells," *Q. Appl. Math.*, **13**, 169–176 (1955) and also "On Axisymmetric Vibrations of Shallow Spherical Shells," Ibid., pp. 279–290.

[7] Kalnins, A., "Free Nonsymmetric Vibrations of Shallow Spherical Shells," *Proc. 4th U.S. Nat'l Congr. Appl. Mech.*, pp. 225–233 (1962).

transient response produced by p, the longitudinal modes can indeed be neglected and only the frequency spectrum predicted by the shallow shell analysis[6] with longitudinal inertia neglected need be employed, as will be demonstrated presently. Similarly, if, in the response produced by p_1 (or p_2), the factors m_{1n} (or m_{2n}) of the transverse modes are much smaller than those of the longitudinal modes, then it should be possible to use only the longitudinal modes as predicted by the membrane theory and to omit the transverse (bending) modes.

However, it is possible that the latter may not be true and, therefore, in the calculation of the response of a shallow shell to a time-dependent load p_1 (or p_2), the complete frequency spectrum made up of both the longitudinal and the transverse modes may have to be employed. This point could bear further investigation, although it is likely that, in applications, we shall be more concerned with the effect of a normal surface load, p, than with the effect of a tangential surface load, p_1 or p_2.

A quantitative discussion of the role of longitudinal inertia in the response of a shell to a normal load will be made in Section 9.6 after the results of a numerical example are presented.

9.6 EXAMPLES: TRANSIENT PRESSURE AND THERMAL LOADS ON SPHERICAL SHELLS

We now illustrate the foregoing discussion by considering the forced-vibration analysis of a simply supported spherical shell segment first to a step change in normal pressure and then to a step change in heat flux, each of which are applied uniformly to the surface of the sphere. For such a shell the relevant parameters are given by $\alpha_1 = \varphi$, $\alpha_2 = \theta$, $A_1 = R$, and $A_2 = R \sin \varphi$ where we have taken R to be the radius of the middle surface of the sphere. The components of the displacement vector are $u_1 = u_\varphi(\varphi, t)$, $u_2 = u_\theta = 0$, and $w = w(\varphi, t)$. Before taking up the two loading conditions to be considered, it is convenient to set down those governing equations which are common to both situations. In doing so, we notice that, for a shell of revolution under the action of θ-independent loads, the three equations of motion (Eqs. 9.14) reduce to two and, for the case of a spherical shell, take on the form

$$\frac{\partial}{\partial \varphi}\{H(w) + \xi H(U) - \xi(1 + \nu)(w + U)\}$$

$$= -\frac{R^4}{D}\left(p_\varphi - ku_\varphi - \lambda \frac{\partial u_\varphi}{\partial t} - \rho h \frac{\partial^2 u_\varphi}{\partial t^2}\right)$$

$$+ \frac{R^3}{D(1 - \nu)} \frac{\partial}{\partial \varphi}\left(N_T + \frac{M_T}{R}\right),$$

$$
\begin{aligned}
HH(U+w) &- (3+\nu)H(w) - \xi(1+\nu)H(U) + 2\xi(1+\nu)(U+w) \\
&= \frac{-R^4}{D}\left(p + kw + \lambda\frac{\partial w}{\partial t} + \rho h\frac{\partial^2 w}{\partial t^2}\right) \\
&\quad - \frac{R^3}{D(1-\nu)}\left[2N_T + \frac{1}{R}\left(\frac{\partial^2 M_T}{\partial \varphi^2} + \cot\varphi\frac{\partial M_T}{\partial \varphi}\right)\right], \qquad (9.22)
\end{aligned}
$$

of which the homogeneous portions were previously given in Chapter 8 where the operator H and the variable U were also introduced. Here w is, however, considered positive inward. In each of the examples to be discussed, we shall assume that the shell is closed at its apex ($\varphi = 0$) and simply supported at its edge ($\varphi = \varphi_0$). The latter condition is expressed as

$$
\begin{aligned}
u_\varphi(\varphi_0, t) &= 0, \\
w(\varphi_0, t) &= 0, \\
M_\varphi(\varphi_0, t) &= -\frac{D}{R^2}\left[\frac{\partial u_\varphi}{\partial \varphi} + \nu u_\varphi \cot\varphi_0 \right. \qquad (9.23) \\
&\qquad \left. + \frac{\partial^2 w}{\partial \varphi^2} + \nu\frac{\partial w}{\partial \varphi}\cot\varphi_0\right] - \frac{M_T}{1-\nu} = 0.
\end{aligned}
$$

Notice that the moment condition will be inhomogeneous when we consider the suddenly heated shell. Finally, we shall assume that the shells to be considered are initially at rest, or,

$$u_0 = w_0 = \dot{u}_0 = \dot{w}_0 = 0. \qquad (9.24)$$

9.6*a* Transient Pressure Load on a Spherical Shell

We first consider the transient response of the spherical shell (that is described by the foregoing system of differential equations) to a sudden change of normal pressure applied uniformly to its surface. For this example,

$$N_T = M_T = 0, \qquad (9.25a)$$

and the applied loads take on the values

$$p_\varphi = 0, \qquad p = f(t)P. \qquad (9.25b)$$

It is convenient here to adopt the dimensionless variables defined in Section 9.5 and to choose the reference parameters $L = R$, $l_n = w_n(0)$, $p_0 = 1$. If we assume that the shell is initially at rest on an underdamped foundation (see Case (*a*) of Section 9.3), it follows, from Eq. 9.9g, that $C_n = D_n = 0$. The prescribed pressure at the middle surface of the shell is

$$
\begin{aligned}
P &= \text{constant}, \\
f(t) &= 0, \qquad t < 0, \qquad (9.25c) \\
&= 1, \qquad t \geqslant 0,
\end{aligned}
$$

and, therefore, from Eq. 9.20d, we obtain the results

$$F_{1n}(\tau) = F_{2n}(\tau) = 0,$$
$$F_n(\tau) = \Gamma_n \frac{1 - e^{-\Lambda\tau}(\Lambda \sin \Gamma_n\tau + \Gamma_n \cos \Gamma_n\tau)/\Gamma_n}{K + 12(1 - \nu^2)\Omega_n^2(R/h)^2}. \tag{9.25d}$$

The formal solution for the displacements can thus be written in the form

$$W(\varphi, \tau) = \sum_{n=1}^{\infty} \frac{w_n(\varphi)}{w_n(0)} \frac{m_n F_n(\tau)}{\Gamma_n},$$
$$U_\varphi(\varphi, \tau) = \sum_{n=1}^{\infty} \frac{u_{\varphi n}(\varphi)}{w_n(0)} \frac{m_n F_n(\tau)}{\Gamma_n}. \tag{9.25e}$$

For a large value of τ the normal displacement at the apex ($\varphi = 0$) of the shell approaches the value

$$W_{st} = \sum_{n=1}^{\infty} \frac{m_n}{K + 12(1 - \nu^2)\Omega_n^2(R/h)^2}, \tag{9.25f}$$

which should converge to the solution of the corresponding static problem. By knowing the static solution, we can obtain some indication of the number of modes that is necessary in the transient solution.

The foregoing analysis was applied to spherical shells with half angles of opening of 15° and 90° resting on a variety of foundations.[1] The natural frequencies and the individual modes of free vibration required for the mode participation factors were obtained from a free-vibration analysis of nonshallow spherical shells.[8] In the course of these calculations, the integrals appearing in the definitions of the mode participation factors were numerically evaluated by means of Simpson's Rule,[9] a procedure which was necessitated by the lack of analytical results on the integration of complex Legendre functions which are, as shown in Chapter 8, the basis of the modes of free vibration of a nonshallow spherical shell.

For the calculation of the free-vibration characteristics, whose results are given in Tables 9.1 and 9.2 and Figs. 9.1 to 9.3, the simply supported shells were assumed to have the following properties: $R = 20$, $h = 1$, $\nu = 0.3$, $E = 3 \times 10^7$, $P = 1$. We note that, although the Tables give data for both the 15° and 90° shells, the Figures give information only for the case of 90°. The results for the case of 15° are not sufficiently interesting or different to warrant their presentation.

---

[8] Kalnins, A., "Effect of Bending on Vibration of Spherical Shells," *J. Acoust. Soc. Am.*, **36**, 74–81 (1964).

[9] See, for example, Hildebrand, F. B., *Introduction to Numerical Analysis*, New York: McGraw-Hill, 1956, p. 73.

Table 9.1 Results for a Typical Simply Supported Shallow Spherical Shell[a] ($\varphi_0 = 15°$, $R/h = 20$, $\nu = 0.3$, $k = 0$)

n	m_n	$m_{\varphi n}$	Ω_n	q_n	W_{st}
1	0.15924 E 01	−0.85479 E −01	1.863	0.10536 E −03	0.10536 E −03
2	−0.10444 E 01	−0.19336 E 00	6.618	−0.54763 E −05	0.99889 E −04
3	0.63996 E −01	0.93213 E 00	15.35	0.62351 E −07	0.99951 E −04
4	0.76549 E 00	−0.65718 E 00	16.43	0.65117 E −06	0.10060 E −03
5	−0.13295 E −01	−0.10480 E 00	28.15	−0.38542 E −08	0.10059 E −03
6	−0.69489 E 00	0.30452 E −01	30.56	−0.17090 E −06	0.10042 E −03
7	0.15599 E −02	0.13750 E 00	40.84	0.21479 E −09	0.10042 E −03
8	0.61725 E 00	−0.13740 E −01	49.01	0.59038 E −07	0.10048 E −03
9	0.10651 E −01	−0.94045 E −01	53.56	0.85282 E −09	0.10048 E −03
10	−0.10017 E −01	−0.69344 E −01	65.98	−0.52845 E −09	0.10048 E −03
11	−0.55460 E 00	0.17924 E 00	72.06	−0.24530 E −07	0.10046 E −03
12	−0.72507 E −02	−0.26795 E −01	78.73	−0.26872 E −09	0.10046 E −03
			Result from static analysis[10]:		0.10048 E −03

[a] The notation $AE \pm N$ stands for $A(10^{\pm N})$.

Table 9.2 Results for a Typical Simply Supported Nonshallow Spherical Shell[a] ($\varphi_0 = 90°$, $R/h = 20$, $\nu = 0.3$, $k = 0$)

n	m_n	$m_{\varphi n}$	Ω_n	q_n	W_{st}
1	0.48079 E −01	−0.10020 E 01	0.773	0.18454 E −04	0.18454 E −04
2	−0.10486 E 00	0.23184 E 00	1.010	−0.23610 E −04	−0.51561 E −05
3	0.35821 E 00	−0.43871 E 00	1.242	0.53323 E −04	0.48166 E −04
4	−0.15912 E 01	0.25153 E 00	1.578	−0.14652 E −03	−0.98362 E −04
5	0.27978 E 01	0.88919 E −01	1.720	0.21689 E −03	0.11852 E −03
6	−0.87944 E 00	−0.55614 E 00	2.192	−0.41994 E −04	0.76534 E −04
7	0.37398 E 00	0.26197 E 01	2.793	0.10999 E −04	0.87534 E −04
8	0.26195 E 00	−0.14683 E 01	2.941	0.69521 E −05	0.94486 E −04
9	−0.48004 E 00	0.13182 E 00	3.733	−0.79110 E −05	0.86575 E −04
10	0.35957 E 00	0.18832 E 00	4.682	0.37684 E −05	0.90344 E −04
11	0.47701 E −01	−0.30506 E 00	4.843	0.46709 E −06	0.90811 E −04
12	−0.37829 E 00	−0.52766 E −01	5.804	−0.25789 E −05	0.88232 E −04
13	0.55733 E −01	0.67072 E 00	6.876	0.27078 E −06	0.88503 E −04
14	0.30631 E 00	−0.45152 E 00	7.047	0.14172 E −05	0.89920 E −04
15	−0.34113 E 00	−0.21393 E −01	8.366	−0.11158 E −05	0.88804 E −04
				Result from static analysis[10]:	0.89751 E −04

[a] The notation $AE \pm N$ stands for $A(10^{\pm N})$.

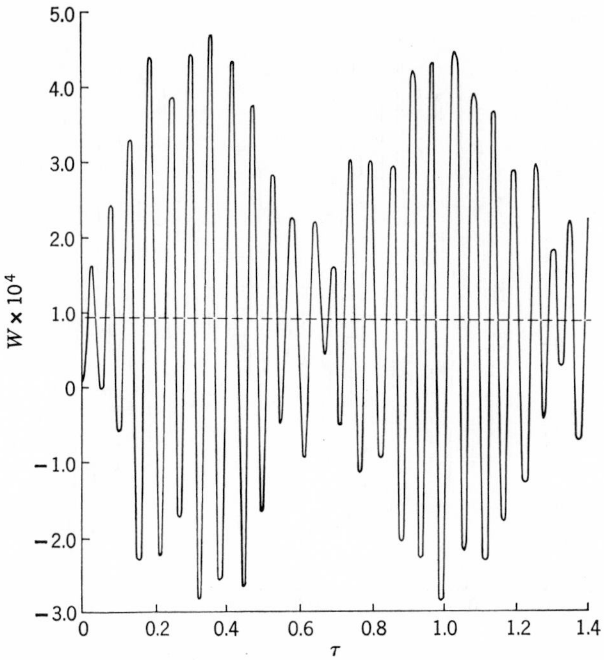

Figure 9.1 Response at apex of a hemispherical shell to a sudden application of pressure ($\Lambda = K = 0$).

In Figs. 9.1 to 9.3, we have plotted the normal deflection history at the apex of a hemispherical shell resting on foundations described by the following parameter combinations: $\Lambda = K = 0$; $\Lambda = 0$, $K = 3000$; and $\Lambda = 20$, $K = 0$, 3000, respectively. In the Figures, we have also indicated, with horizontal lines, the appropriate static deflection for each case as obtained from Eq. 9.25f (see also Tables 9.1 and 9.2). For the two cases where $K = 0$, the static deflections agree with the results obtained by means of a computer program for the static analysis of general shells of revolution.[10] No direct check of the static deflection for those cases where $K = 3000$ is available.

It is seen, from Figs. 9.1 and 9.2, that the response of a shell resting on a purely elastic foundation consists of an oscillation about the appropriate static deflection and that this oscillation continues for all values of time. For the case of a shell resting on a viscoelastic foundation, Fig. 9.3 shows that the period of the oscillation is greatly increased while its amplitude decays and the deflection approaches the appropriate static result as time goes on.

[10] This will be discussed further in Chapter 10.

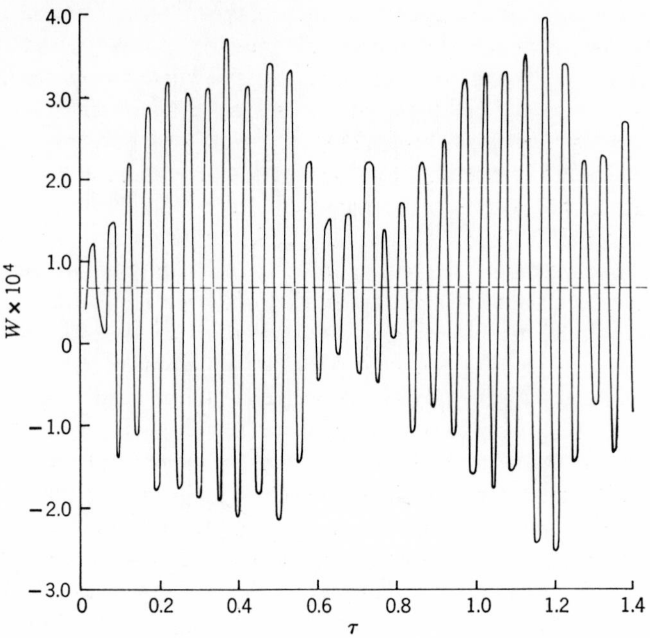

Figure 9.2 Same as Fig. 9.1 for $\Lambda = 0$, $K = 3000$.

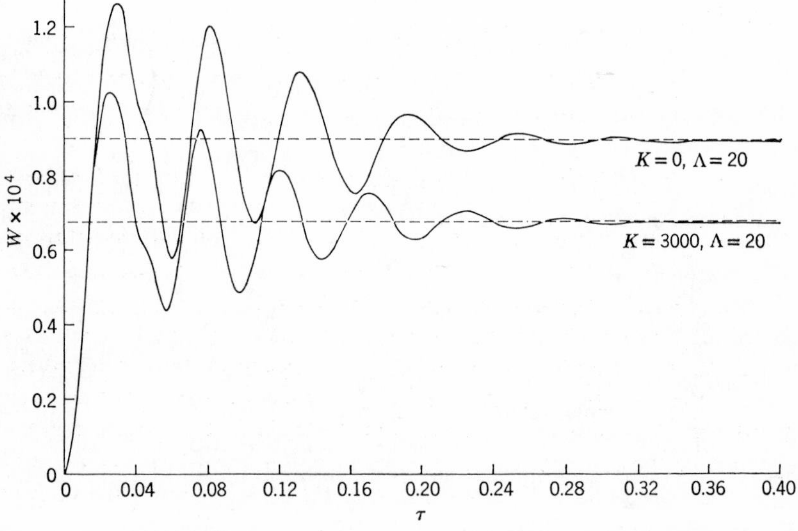

Figure 9.3 Same as Fig. 9.1 for $\Lambda = 20$ $K = 0$ and 3000.

Figures 9.1 and 9.2 suggest that the phenomenon of beating is taking place between two of the more predominant modes in the transient response at the apex of the hemispherical shell under consideration (the 15° shell considered here does not respond in this manner). To investigate this possibility, Tables 9.1 and 9.2 can be searched to find two consecutive modes which are predominant in the solution and which have roughly the same frequency and order of magnitude. Table 9.1 reveals no such cases for the 15° shell. Table 9.2 indicates several cases where consecutive modes have almost the same frequency, but only in the case of the 4th and 5th modes are the modes predominant in the solution and also of roughly the same amplitude, q_n. The conclusion is clinched by recalling that, when beating occurs, the frequency of the beats is equal to the difference in the frequencies of the modes involved. In the present situation, this means that the frequency of beating should be $\Omega_5 - \Omega_4 = 0.142$ and the period of one beat should be $2\pi/(\Gamma_5 - \Gamma_4) = 0.668$. It is seen, in Figs. 9.1 and 9.2, that the period of the envelope surrounding the response is just this value, within the accuracy of the plot. Furthermore, the period of the more rapid vibrations should be, according to the present reasoning, $2\pi/\Gamma_5 = 0.056$; this is also confirmed by Figs. 9.1 and 9.2. Undoubtedly, beating is also taking place between other modes in the response. However, in the other possible cases, such as modes 10 and 11 in Table 9.2, the amplitudes of the two modes differ by an order of magnitude and are small in comparison to the overall response. As a result, the effect of these beats is not as pronounced in Figs. 9.1 and 9.2 as is the beating between modes 4 and 5.

As could be expected from Eqs. 9.25d and 9.25e, Figs. 9.1 to 9.3 indicate that one of the main effects of the elasticity of the foundation on which the shell rests is an alteration of its static deflection. The period and amplitude of its response are also affected.

To obtain information on the convergence of the method of spectral representation, we may study the convergence toward the static solution. It is seen, in the last column of each of Tables 9.1 and 9.2, that the convergence of the static solution is fairly rapid, especially in the case of the 15° shell where it appears that the first mode alone gives virtually the correct result. The solution for the 90° shell converges less rapidly; a situation which is attributed to the close spacing of the natural frequencies of that shell (notice that the first five natural frequencies of the 90° shell occur before the first natural frequency of the 15° shell). It is reasonable to assume that the convergence of the static solution toward the known result as demonstrated above is representative of the convergence of the solution at any other value of time.

Finally, it is appropriate to make an assessment of the role of longitudinal inertia in the transient response of a shell to a normal load. To facilitate this discussion, we have presented, in Tables 9.1 and 9.2, the mode participation factors m_n and $m_{\varphi n}$ for the two spherical shells which have been studied. As can be seen from Eqs. 9.25e, only the m_n are used in the determination of the response to a normal pressure and, therefore, the magnitude of m_n for a given mode of free vibration will give an indication of the participation of that mode in the response to p. For a shallow shell, as exemplified by the 15° case, it can be seen from Table 9.1 that those modes which have m_n less than $m_{\varphi n}$ have very little participation in the response to a normal load. These modes are the longitudinal modes,[7] whose contribution can, therefore, be safely ignored in the calculation of the response of a normally loaded shallow shell.

For a nonshallow configuration, as exemplified by a hemispherical shell, Table 9.2 indicates that for many modes, where m_n is less than $m_{\varphi n}$, the two values are nevertheless of the same order of magnitude, and consequently the contributions of none of these modes can be neglected. A striking example is that of the first mode in Table 9.2 where m_1 is much less than $m_{\varphi 1}$, and yet the contribution of that mode to the final result is significant. Thus, it is seen that, for the hemispherical shell, the participation of all the modes is important and none can be omitted in the determination of the response to a normal load.

We may conclude, therefore, that in the determination of the response of a shell to a dynamic normal pressure, the longitudinal modes must be considered if the shell is nonshallow but can be neglected if the shell is shallow.

9.6*b* Transient Thermal Load on a Spherical Shell[11]

As a second example, let us consider the transient response of a simply supported spherical shell to a heat flux which is suddenly applied to it over its entire outer surface. This example is of interest for two reasons: first, it is a case in which the assumption of a simply supported edge yields one time-dependent boundary condition and affords us an opportunity to illustrate the method which we outlined in Section 9.4. Second, it is of interest to determine the role of inertia in the dynamic thermal stress analysis of shells. In conventional dynamic thermal stress analyses of heated structures, the inertia of the body is ignored and time comes in as a parameter from the transient temperature distribution. The analysis is thus referred to as a quasistatic one. The assumption of negligible inertia was first proposed by Duhamel[12] and has successfully formed the basis of

[11] Kraus, H., "Thermally Induced Vibrations of Thin Nonshallow Spherical Shells," *AIAA J.*, **4**, 500–505 (1966).

[12] Duhamel, J. M. C., "Seconde Memoire sur les Phenomenes Thermomechaniques," *J. Ecole Polytech.*, **15**, 1–57 (1837).

the bulk of dynamic thermal stress analyses. However, recent developments in the areas of nuclear power generation and the reentry of missiles into the earth's atmosphere have involved the consideration of extremely rapid rates of heating. Consequently, it has become interesting to reassess the role of inertia in dynamically heated structures, as exemplified by a shell subjected to a transient thermal load.

To begin the determination of the response of the shell to the sudden application of a heat flux, the temperature distribution in the shell must be found. Since the thermal conditions are assumed to be constant over the surfaces of the shell the temperature is obtained from the following equation of heat conduction (see the Appendix to Chapter 2):

$$\frac{\partial^2 \tilde{T}}{\partial \eta^2} = \frac{\partial \tilde{T}}{\partial \tau}. \tag{9.27a}$$

To this equation, we add the boundary and initial conditions

$$\frac{\partial \tilde{T}}{\partial \eta} = 0, \qquad \eta = -\tfrac{1}{2}, \qquad \tau > 0, \tag{9.27b}$$

$$\begin{aligned} \frac{\partial \tilde{T}}{\partial \eta} &= 1, \qquad \eta = \tfrac{1}{2}, \qquad \tau > 0, \\ \tilde{T} &= 0, \qquad \text{all } \eta, \qquad \tau = 0, \end{aligned} \tag{9.27c}$$

which express the fact that the shell is initially at a uniform temperature and that, subsequently, its outer surface is subjected to a constant heat flux while its inner surface is insulated.

In the above formulation of the thermal aspect of the problem, we have defined the dimensionless variables

$$\tau = \kappa t/h^2, \qquad \eta = \zeta/h, \qquad \tilde{T} = kT/Q_0 h, \tag{9.27d}$$

where Q_0 is the applied heat flux and k is the thermal conductivity. The solution of the thermal problem can be found by standard methods to be[13]

$$\tilde{T} = \tau + \frac{1}{2}\left(\eta + \frac{1}{2}\right)^2 - \frac{1}{6} - \frac{2}{\pi^2}\sum_{j=1}^{\infty}\frac{(-1)^j}{j^2}\, e^{-j^2\pi^2\tau}\cos j\pi\left(\eta + \frac{1}{2}\right). \tag{9.27e}$$

The above temperature distribution leads through Eqs. 2.28 to the following expressions for the dimensionless thermal force and moment:

$$\begin{aligned} \tilde{N}_T &= \frac{kK(1-\nu)}{E\alpha Q_0 h^2} N_T = \int_{-1/2}^{1/2} \tilde{T}\, d\eta = \tau, \\ \tilde{M}_T &= \frac{kD(1-\nu)}{E\alpha Q_0 h^3 R} M_T = \int_{-1/2}^{1/2} \tilde{T}\eta\, d\eta = \frac{1}{2} - \frac{48}{\pi^4}\sum_{j,\,\text{odd}}^{\infty}\frac{e^{-j^2\pi^2\tau}}{j^4}. \end{aligned} \tag{(9.27f)}$$

[13] See, for example, Carslaw, H. S., and Jaeger, J. C., *Conduction of Heat in Solids*, London, England: Oxford University Press, 2nd ed. (1959), Chapter 1.

In the determination of the response of the shell to the prescribed thermal conditions, we assume that there are no additional surface loads and that there is no foundation involved; that is, $p = p_\varphi = k = \lambda = 0$. Furthermore, the nondimensional variables which were used in Sections 9.5 and 9.6*a* are not appropriate because the applied load is of different origin. Hence, we define the following new dimensionless variables for use in the determination of the response of a spherical shell to a suddenly applied heat flux:

$$\begin{aligned}
\{\tilde{w}, \tilde{u}\} &= \frac{\{w, u\}k}{Q_0\alpha R^2(1+\nu)}, \\
\tau &= \frac{\kappa t}{h^2}, \\
\bar{\omega}_n{}^2 &= \frac{\rho h R^4 \omega_n{}^2}{D}, \\
\tilde{u} &= \frac{\partial \tilde{U}}{\partial \varphi}.
\end{aligned} \tag{9.28a}$$

Upon introduction of these definitions into the equilibrium displacement equations (Eqs. 9.22), they take on the form

$$\begin{aligned}
\mathscr{L}_U\{\tilde{w}, \tilde{U}\} &= \frac{1}{B^4}\frac{\partial^2}{\partial \tau^2}\left(\frac{\partial \tilde{U}}{\partial \varphi}\right), \\
\mathscr{L}_w\{\tilde{w}, \tilde{U}\} &= -\frac{1}{B^4}\frac{\partial^2 \tilde{w}}{\partial \tau^2} - 24\left(\frac{R}{h}\right)\tilde{N}_T,
\end{aligned} \tag{9.28b}$$

where the quantity

$$B^4 = \frac{D}{\rho h R^4}\frac{h^4}{\kappa^2}, \tag{9.28c}$$

is known as the inertia parameter, and

$$\begin{aligned}
\mathscr{L}_U\{\tilde{w}, \tilde{U}\} &= \frac{\partial}{\partial \varphi}\{H(\tilde{w}) + \xi H(\tilde{U}) - \xi(1+\nu)(\tilde{w} + \tilde{U})\}, \\
\mathscr{L}_w\{\tilde{w}, \tilde{U}\} &= HH(\tilde{U} + \tilde{w}) - (3+\nu)H(\tilde{w}) - \xi(1+\nu)H(U) \\
&\quad + 2\xi(1+\nu)(\tilde{U} + \tilde{w}).
\end{aligned} \tag{9.28d}$$

Furthermore, the boundary conditions in terms of the dimensionless variables become

$$\begin{aligned}
&\frac{\partial^2 \tilde{U}}{\partial \varphi^2} + \nu \frac{\partial \tilde{U}}{\partial \varphi}\cot\varphi + \frac{\partial^2 \tilde{w}}{\partial \varphi^2} + \nu\frac{\partial \tilde{w}}{\partial \varphi}\cot\varphi = -\tilde{M}_T, \\
&\frac{\partial \tilde{U}}{\partial \varphi} = \tilde{w} = 0, \qquad \text{at} \quad \varphi = \varphi_0, \quad \tau > 0.
\end{aligned} \tag{9.28e}$$

Thus, we see that there is one inhomogeneous boundary condition to be accommodated and that, therefore, the solutions of Eqs. 9.28b should be written according to Eqs. 9.16 as

$$\tilde{U} = \sum_{n=1}^{\infty} \tilde{U}_n q_n^*(\tau) + \tilde{U}^1 f_1(\tau),$$
$$\tilde{w} = \sum_{n=1}^{\infty} \tilde{w}_n q_n^*(\tau) + \tilde{w}^1 f_1(\tau). \tag{9.28f}$$

Here $\tilde{U}^1$ and $\tilde{w}^1$ are to be found from Eqs. 9.18b which, for the problem at hand, take the form

$$B_k\{\tilde{U}^1, \tilde{w}^1\} = g_k(\varphi_0)\, \delta_{k1}, \qquad \varphi = \varphi_0, \qquad k = 1, 2, 3,$$
$$B_k\{\tilde{U}^1, \tilde{w}^1\} = 0, \qquad \varphi = 0, \quad k = 4, 5, 6, \tag{9.28g}$$
$$g_1 = 1, \qquad f_1(\tau) = -\tilde{M}_T.$$

In the above, the expressions corresponding to $k = 1, 2, 3$ represent the condition of simple support at the edge $\varphi = \varphi_0$ and the expressions corresponding to $k = 4, 5, 6$ represent symmetry conditions which the correction functions $\tilde{U}^1$ and $\tilde{w}^1$ must satisfy at the apex $\varphi = 0$. In extended form, Eqs. 9.28g are given by

$$\left[\frac{d^2}{d\varphi^2} + \nu \cot \varphi \frac{d}{d\varphi}\right](\tilde{w}^1 + \tilde{U}^1) = 1,$$
$$\frac{d\tilde{U}^1}{d\varphi} = \tilde{w}^1 = 0, \qquad \varphi = \varphi_0, \tag{9.28h}$$

$$\frac{d^2\tilde{w}^1}{d\varphi^2} = \frac{d\tilde{U}^1}{d\varphi} = \frac{d^2\tilde{U}^1}{d\varphi^2} = 0, \qquad \varphi = 0. \tag{9.28i}$$

In the solution of problems concerning the free vibration of shells, it was shown in Chapter 8 that the solutions are related to complex Legendre functions. Since Mindlin and Goodman[3] used ordinary polynomials in the construction of solutions that accommodate time-dependent boundary conditions in the forced-vibration analysis of beams, it seems reasonable to try to accomplish the same for the forced-vibration analysis of a spherical shell by using Legendre polynomials. Because Legendre polynomials can be expressed as functions of powers of cos φ, we may carry the reasoning one step further by assuming that the correction functions are of the form

$$\tilde{w}^1 = a_1 + b_1 \cos \varphi + c_1 \cos^2 \varphi,$$
$$\tilde{U}^1 = \bar{a}_1 + \bar{b}_1 \cos \varphi + \bar{c}_1 \cos^2 \varphi. \tag{9.29a}$$

We notice that the forms 9.29a will also insure that the transverse shearing-stress resultant Q^1, which is associated with the correction functions, will vanish as φ approaches zero as is required by the symmetry of the problem.

Upon substitution of Eqs. 9.29a into conditions 9.28h and 9.28i, the arbitrary constants a_1, b_1, c_1, $\bar{a}_1$, $\bar{b}_1$, $\bar{c}_1$ can be shown to be such that the correction functions take the final form

$$\tilde{U}^1 \equiv 0, \qquad \tilde{w}^1 = \frac{\cos^2\varphi - \cos\varphi\cos\varphi_0}{2\sin^2\varphi_0 - (1+\nu)\cos^2\varphi_0}. \tag{9.29b}$$

The $q_n{}^*$ can now be determined by use of the method outlined in Section 9.4. By using the present definitions of the dimensionless variables and by noting that there is no foundation involved here, Eq. 9.17d becomes

$$\frac{d^2q_n{}^*}{d\tau^2} + \bar{\omega}_n{}^2B^4q_n{}^* = \frac{B^4}{N_n}\int_0^{\varphi_0}(F_w\tilde{w}_n - F_U\tilde{u}_{\varphi n})\sin\varphi\,d\varphi, \tag{9.29c}$$

where

$$F_w = -24(R/h)\tilde{N}_T + \frac{B^{-4}\ddot{\tilde{M}}_T(\cos^2\varphi - \cos\varphi\cos\varphi_0) + 2\tilde{M}_T[6\cos^2\varphi - 2\sin^2\varphi - (3+\nu)(1-2\cos^2\varphi) + \xi(1+\nu)(\cos^2\varphi - \cos\varphi\cos\varphi_0)]}{2\sin^2\varphi_0 - (1+\nu)\cos^2\varphi_0}, \tag{9.29d}$$

$$F_U = \frac{\tilde{M}_T\sin\varphi[8\cos\varphi - \xi(1+\nu)(\cos\varphi_0 - 2\cos\varphi)]}{2\sin^2\varphi_0 - (1+\nu)\cos^2\varphi_0}.$$

Associated with the above differential equation are two initial conditions which, from Eqs. 9.19c expressed in terms of the present variables, are

$$q_n{}^*(0) = 0,$$

$$\dot{q}_n{}^*(0) = \frac{6}{N_n}\int_0^{\varphi_0}\frac{\cos\varphi(\cos\varphi - \cos\varphi_0)}{2\sin^2\varphi_0 - (1+\nu)\cos^2\varphi_0}\tilde{w}_n\sin\varphi\,d\varphi. \tag{9.29e}$$

Here the following identities

$$\sum_{j,\,\mathrm{odd}}^{\infty}\frac{1}{j^4} = \frac{\pi^4}{96}, \qquad \sum_{j,\,\mathrm{odd}}^{\infty}\frac{1}{j^2} = \frac{\pi^2}{8}, \tag{9.29f}$$

have been used to establish the results

$$\tilde{M}_T(0) = 0, \qquad \dot{\tilde{M}}_T(0) = 6. \tag{9.29g}$$

Equation 9.29d is an example of Case (*d*) of Section 9.3. Thus, the solution 9.12a under the initial conditions 9.29e takes the following form in terms of the variables which have been defined here:

$$q_n{}^*(\tau) = \frac{6\sin\bar{\omega}_nB^2\tau}{\bar{\omega}_nB^2N_n}\int_0^{\varphi_0}\frac{\cos\varphi(\cos\varphi - \cos\varphi_0)}{2\sin^2\varphi_0 - (1+\nu)\cos^2\varphi_0}\tilde{w}_n\sin\varphi\,d\varphi + \frac{B^2}{\bar{\omega}_nN_n}\int_0^{\varphi_0}\int_0^{\tau}(F_w\tilde{w}_n - F_U\tilde{u}_{\varphi n})\sin\varphi\sin\bar{\omega}_nB^2(\tau - \bar{\tau})\,d\varphi\,d\bar{\tau}, \tag{9.29h}$$

and this completes the formal solution of the response of the spherical shell to the prescribed thermal environment.

It is interesting at this point to also obtain q_n^* for two limiting values of B as follows. We have previously indicated that, in a conventional quasi-static solution of the problem we are considering here, the inertia terms would be ignored. Such a solution can be obtained from the present one by allowing B to grow without bound in Eq. 9.29c, whereupon the generalized coordinates are immediately obtained as

$$q_{ns}^*(\tau) = \frac{1}{\bar{\omega}_n{}^2 N_n} \int_0^{\varphi_0} (F_{ws}\tilde{w}_n - F_U\tilde{u}_{\varphi n}) \sin\varphi \, d\varphi, \tag{9.30a}$$

where

$$F_{ws} = \frac{\begin{aligned}-24(R/h)\tilde{N}_T \\ + 2\tilde{M}_T[6\cos^2\varphi - 2\sin^2\varphi - (3+\nu)(1 - 2\cos^2\varphi) \\ + \xi(1+\nu)\cos\varphi(\cos\varphi - \cos\varphi_0)]\end{aligned}}{2\sin^2\varphi_0 - (1+\nu)\cos^2\varphi_0}. \tag{9.30b}$$

At the other extreme lies the case of infinite inertia for which the solution can be found by letting B go to zero. This procedure yields

$$q_{n0}^*(\tau) = \frac{\tilde{M}_T}{N_n} \int_0^{\varphi_0} \frac{\cos^2\varphi - \cos\varphi\cos\varphi_0}{2\sin^2\varphi_0 - (1+\nu)\cos^2\varphi_0} \tilde{w}_n \sin\varphi \, d\varphi, \tag{9.30c}$$

which, with the orthogonality relationship, can be shown to represent a case of zero deflections at any finite time (See the Exercises).

As in the case of the shell loaded by a step change in pressure, the integrals over φ must be carried out numerically owing to the scarcity of results on the integration of complex Legendre functions. The integrals with respect to time can, however, be carried out analytically.

The foregoing analysis was used in the determination of the dynamic behavior of spherical shells subjected to a step change in heat flux.[11] In Figs. 9.4 and 9.5, the effect of the inertia parameter on the response of the shell is shown, respectively, for a typical nonshallow shell with $\varphi_0 = 60°$ and a typical shallow shell with $\varphi_0 = 30°$. It is immediately evident from these plots that the dynamic solutions oscillate about the corresponding quasi-static result. The period of these oscillations is that of the lowest mode of free vibration in each solution and can be found from Eq. 9.29h to be

$$P = 2\pi/\bar{\omega}_1 B^2. \tag{9.31}$$

In Tables 9.1 and 9.2 it was indicated that, for two shells which differ only in their angle of opening, the natural frequencies of the shallow shell are higher than the corresponding frequencies of the nonshallow shell. This explains the fact that, in Fig. 9.5, the peak amplitudes of the shallow

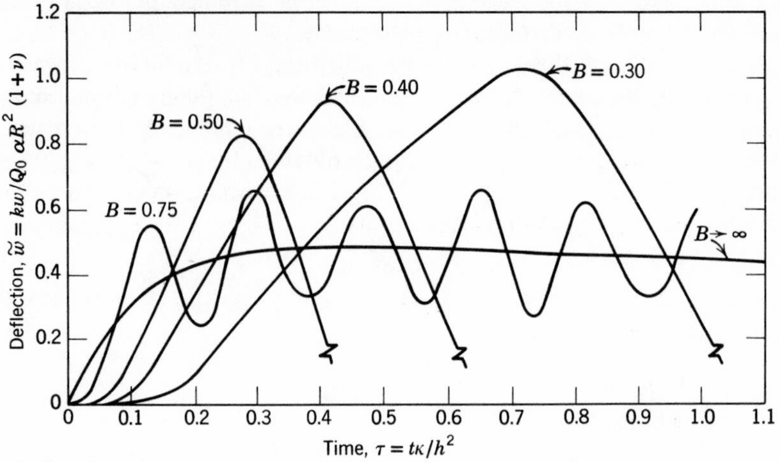

Figure 9.4 Response at apex of a spherical shell to a sudden application of heat ($\varphi_0 = 60°$).

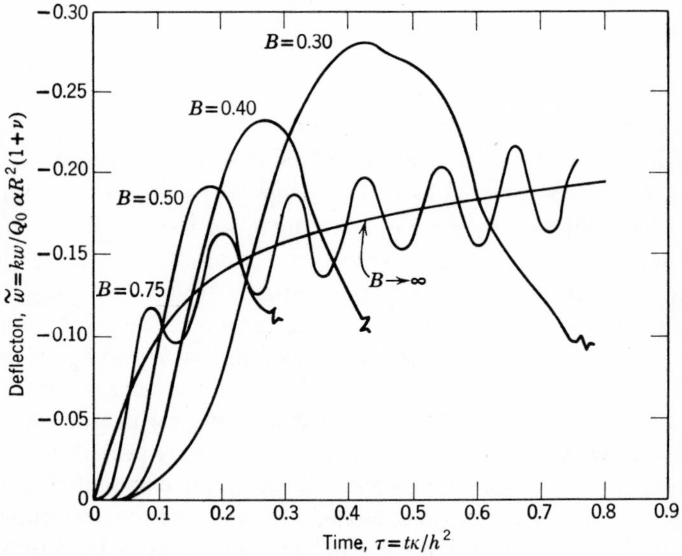

Figure 9.5 Same as Fig. 9.4 for $\varphi_0 = 30°$.

shell occur earlier than do the corresponding peaks of the nonshallow shell shown in Fig. 9.4. The Figures and Eq. 9.31 also show that as the inertia parameter decreases the period of vibration of a given mode increases, and in the limit as B approaches zero, it takes an infinite time for the oscillation to occur. In conjunction with this, recall the remarks made in connection with Eq. 9.30c where it was stated that for vanishing B there is no deflection at any finite time interval. On the other hand, as the inertia parameter increases, the period of oscillation decreases and eventually the quasistatic solution is obtained in which no oscillations are experienced.

To obtain a practical evaluation of the importance of the thermally induced vibrations calculated in the foregoing, we may consider the following example of an aluminum shell which has $\nu = 0.33$, $\kappa = 0.1333$ in²/sec., $\sqrt{E/\rho} = 2 \times 10^5$ in/sec. Assuming, as in Figs. 9.4 and 9.5, that the shell has $R/h = 20$, the definition of the inertia parameter can be used to establish the following table:

B	h
0.30	7.87×10^{-5}
0.40	1.40×10^{-4}
0.50	2.19×10^{-4}
0.75	4.92×10^{-4}
1.00	8.75×10^{-4}

Thus, it is seen that the significant oscillations about the quasistatic result shown in Figs. 9.4 and 9.5 for the lower values of the inertia parameter occur (in the present example of $R/h = 20$) only for shells which could be of no interest in a practical application.

Results of a similar nature were obtained in a study of suddenly heated conical shells which was carried out by Lu and Sun[14] and in a study of shells of arbitrary profile which was performed by Heer.[15]

9.7 CLOSURE

We have derived and illustrated a procedure, based on the method of spectral representation, by means of which the response of thin elastic shells to transient loads can be determined. As we have shown in Tables 9.1 and 9.2, the convergence of the series representation is fairly rapid and, therefore, the approach presents no computational difficulties. Similar solution procedures can also be derived for the higher-order theories but it must be borne in mind while doing this that the higher-order theories will require an extended orthogonality condition. The method is applicable to

---

[14] Lu, S. Y., and Sun, C. L., "Vibrations of Thin Conical Shells Subjected to Sudden Heating," Preprint 65–788, AIAA/RAeS/JSASS, Aircraft Design and Technology Meeting, November 15–18, 1965, Los Angeles, California.

[15] Heer, E., "Response of Shells to Steady and Nonsteady Temperature Fields," *AIAA J.* (to appear).

any shell for which a free-vibration solution is available. Consequently, it is the availability of free-vibration results which acts as the main limitation upon the success that one can expect in applying the method to various shells.

EXERCISES

9.1 Verify the particular solutions 9.9e, 9.10b, and 9.11b for the three types of foundations considered in Section 9.3.

9.2 How would the analysis of Section 9.3 have to be modified to account for $k \neq k_1 \neq k_2$ and $\lambda_1 \neq \lambda_2 = \lambda$?

9.3 Show that the solution 9.30c leads to no deflection of the shell at any finite time.

9.4 Derive correction functions u^l and w^l for a spherical shell closed at its apex and subjected to a prescribed normal deflection $w(\varphi_0, t) = f(t)$ at its edge $\varphi = \varphi_0$. The shell is free of surface and edge loads.

9.5 Derive correction functions u^l and w^l for a spherical shell closed at its apex which is subjected to some thermal condition that leads to known N_T and M_T functions and is (a) clamped, (b) free, (c) simply supported but free to move in meridional direction, at the edge $\varphi = \varphi_0$.

9.6 Derive a general dynamic solution for a conical cap which is simply supported at its edge and subjected to a step change in internal pressure.

9.7 Repeat 9.6 for a step change of temperature at the outside surface and a constant zero temperature at the inside surface of the shell.

9.8 Derive the orthogonality condition for a theory in which transverse shear and rotatory inertia effects are accounted for.

IV

Numerical Analysis of Shells

The use of digital computers for the solution of problems in the theory of thin elastic shells is described. Various numerical procedures are applied to the static and dynamic analysis of shell structures. Solutions obtained by computer programs which are currently in use are given and compared to the earlier analytical solutions and to experimental data.

10

Numerical Analysis of Shells under Static Loadings

10.1 INTRODUCTION

In our previous work on statically loaded shells, we were able to obtain exact analytical solutions by means of the classical procedures of mathematical physics. While this served amply the purpose of bringing out the behavior of thin elastic shells, it could only be accomplished by restricting the development to single shells of uniform thickness and elastic properties and, in the case of arbitrarily loaded shells, to isotropic materials. Furthermore, we found that convenient exact solutions could be obtained only for those shells which had in common the property of constant meridional curvature, r_φ^{-1}. Such shells admitted solutions in terms of the classical functions of mathematical physics such as Bessel functions, Kelvin functions, and Legendre functions. We were also able to extend the class of shells for which some sort of analytical solution is available with the method of asymptotic integration, by means of which we found that accurate solutions could be obtained for toroidal, ellipsoidal, and paraboloidal shells of arbitrary thickness, under θ-independent loads, in terms of Bessel functions.

The solutions which we developed have demonstrated the behavior of thin elastic shells under static loads to the extent that we should not expect any drastic deviation from the pattern which has developed when shells of variable geometric and elastic properties are considered. Thus, if the description of typical behavior were our only goal, we should not need to go on because that goal has been accomplished.

But now let us suppose that we are interested in the analysis of an assembly of arbitrary shells under an arbitrary system of static loadings which does not fall into any of the categories which we considered in Part II. Such problems are the rule rather than the exception in modern technology and, until about ten years ago, before the advent of the digital computer, could not be handled except in a very grossly approximate manner. Indeed, even the nonshallow spherical shell solutions of Chapter 6 were avoided until the computer made the tabulation of the complex Legendre functions feasible.

As a consequence of the availability and widespread use of the computer, we are now in a position to consider a second goal; that is, the development of a procedure for the solution of the most general problems which could arise within the framework of the theory of thin elastic shells. This goal can be achieved by means of digital computer programs which are based upon the application of available techniques of numerical analysis to the equations of the theory. For this purpose, therefore, we shall now discuss several numerical procedures[1] which have been found to be useful in the analysis of shells. We shall also demonstrate the capabilities of the numerical approach by presenting results which have been obtained by digital computer programs which are based on each method.[2]

Since our remarks on the solution of arbitrary problems in the theory of shells are no less true for the dynamic analysis of shells than they are for the static analysis of shells, we shall also discuss the numerical analysis of shells under dynamic loadings in Chapter 11.

10.2 APPLICATION OF NUMERICAL TECHNIQUES TO THE STATIC ANALYSIS OF SHELLS

The basic step in the application of any numerical technique to the analysis of shells of revolution involves the approximation of the interval subtended by the generator of the shell by a finite number of subintervals. This is true

[1] Our treatment of the individual procedures of numerical analysis must, of necessity, be brief and it is, therefore, recommended that the reader consult additional references to deepen his understanding of these methods. In this connection we may cite the following texts:

Hildebrand, F. B., *Introduction to Numerical Analysis*, New York: McGraw-Hill (1956).

Todd, J., ed., *Survey of Numerical Analysis*, New York: McGraw-Hill (1962).

Forsythe, G. E., and Wasow, W. R., *Finite Difference Methods for Partial Differential Equations*, New York: John Wiley (1960).

[2] The chapter is based upon results which have been reported in Kraus, H., "A Review and Evaluation of Computer Programs for the Analysis of Stresses in Pressure Vessels," *Welding Research Council Bulletin No. 108*, 11–28 (1965).

for both arbitrary and θ-independent loads because, as we have seen earlier, any dependence on θ can be removed by suitable Fourier expansions. The designation of the subintervals requires judgment which is best obtained by experience. In general, however, regions over which bending effects are significant should be divided into smaller intervals than those regions over which bending effects are negligible. This, as will be seen presently, may not always be convenient and in such an event a uniform spacing which is small enough to accommodate the region over which bending effects predominate should be used for the entire interval. If discontinuities in the thickness, radii of curvature, material properties, load, or temperature exist, the intervals must, for the sake of simplicity as well as accuracy, be arranged so that each such discontinuity coincides with the end of a subinterval.

It is in the treatment of the resulting ensemble of intervals that the various numerical procedures differ and, for this reason, we have chosen to consider, within the context of the static theory of shells, three commonly used numerical methods: the method of finite differences, the finite element method, and the stepwise integration method.

10.2*a* The Method of Finite Differences

In the method of finite differences, the governing differential equations of the theory are approximated by using the following formulas for the first and second derivatives of the general variable Y with respect to φ at a general point φ_i of the mesh into which the generator of the shell has been subdivided:

$$\left(\frac{dY}{d\varphi}\right)_i = \frac{Y_{i+1} - Y_{i-1}}{2\Delta},$$

$$\left(\frac{d^2 Y}{d\varphi^2}\right)_i = \frac{Y_{i+1} - 2Y_i + Y_{i-1}}{\Delta^2}, \tag{10.1a}$$

where

$$Y_i = Y(\varphi_i), \qquad \Delta = \varphi_{i+1} - \varphi_i.$$

The mesh spacing Δ is generally a constant for convenience in the derivation. However, if greater flexibility is required in the setting up of the mesh, we can divide the generator into several regions over each of which a different, but uniform, mesh spacing can be defined. Special care must then be exercised when writing the derivatives at the transition points between these regions (see Exercise 10.1).

To illustrate the application of this technique to the static analysis of shells, let us use as an example the solution of the equations of an isotropic shell of revolution[3-8] which we derived in Chapter 5 and which are repeated here in compact form:

$$A\frac{d^2U}{d\varphi^2} + B\frac{dU}{d\varphi} + CU + Ehr_\varphi\beta_\varphi = G,$$
$$A\frac{d^2\beta_\varphi}{d\varphi^2} + H\frac{d\beta_\varphi}{d\varphi} + I\beta_\varphi - \frac{Ur_\varphi}{D_\varphi} = J, \tag{10.1b}$$

where

$$U = r_\theta Q_\varphi, \qquad A = r_\theta/r_\varphi,$$
$$B = \frac{r_\theta}{r_\varphi}\cot\varphi + \frac{d}{d\varphi}\left(\frac{r_\theta}{r_\varphi}\right) - \frac{r_\theta}{r_\varphi}(m+n),$$
$$-C = \frac{r_\varphi}{r_\theta}\cot^2\varphi - \nu - \nu\cot\varphi(m+n),$$
$$H = \frac{r_\theta}{r_\varphi}\cot\varphi + \frac{d}{d\varphi}\left(\frac{r_\theta}{r_\varphi}\right) + \frac{r_\theta}{r_\varphi}(n+3m),$$
$$-I = \frac{r_\varphi}{r_\theta}\cot^2\varphi + \nu - \nu\cot\varphi(n+3m),$$
$$J = r_\theta\alpha_t(1+\nu)\frac{dT_1}{d\varphi},$$
$$\begin{aligned} G = &-\frac{d}{d\varphi}\left[r_\theta F_1\left(\nu + \frac{r_\theta}{r_\varphi}\right) - qr_\theta^2\right] \\ &+ \left[r_\theta F_1\left(\nu + \frac{r_\theta}{r_\varphi}\right) - qr_\theta^2\right](m+n) \\ &- \cot\varphi\left[(r_\varphi + \nu r_\theta)F_1 + (r_\theta + \nu r_\varphi)\left(F_1\frac{r_\theta}{r_\varphi} - qr_\theta\right)\right] \\ &- Eh\left[\frac{d}{d\varphi}(\alpha_t r_\theta T_0) - \alpha_t T_0(r_\varphi - r_\theta)\cot\varphi\right], \end{aligned} \tag{10.1c}$$

[3] Kraus, H., Bilodeau, G. G., and Langer, B. F., "Stresses in Thin-walled Pressure Vessels with Ellipsoidal Heads," *Trans. A.S.M.E.*, **82B**, 29–42 (1961).
[4] Galletly, G. D., Kyner, W. T., and Moller, C. E., "Numerical Methods and the Bending of Ellipsoidal Shells," *J.S.I.A.M.*, **9** 489–513 (1961).
[5] Penny, R. K., "Symmetric Bending of the General Shell of Revolution by Finite Difference Methods," *J. Mech. Eng. Sci.*, **3**, 369–377 (1961).
[6] Hubka, R. E., "A Generalized Finite Difference Solution of Axisymmetric Stress States in Thin Shells of Revolution," Report EM-11-19, Space Technology Laboratories, Los Angeles, Calif. (1961).
[7] Sepetoski, W. K., Pearson, C. E., Dingwell, I. W., and Adkins, A. W., "A Digital Computer Program for the General Axially Symmetric Thin Shell Problem," *J. Appl. Mech.*, **29**, 655–661 (1962).
[8] Radkowski, P. P., Davis, R. M., and Bolduc, M. R., "Numerical Analysis of Equations of Thin Shells of Revolution," *A.R.S.J.*, **32**, 36–41 (1962).

$$F_1 = \frac{1}{r_\theta \sin^2 \varphi}\left[C_1 + \int_{\varphi_0}^{\varphi} r_\theta r_\varphi \sin \eta (q \cos \eta + q_\varphi \sin \eta)\, d\eta\right],$$

$$m = \frac{1}{h}\frac{dh}{d\varphi}, \qquad n = \frac{1}{E}\frac{dE}{d\varphi}.$$

It should be emphasized that Eqs. 10.1b with coefficients 10.1c are valid for the analysis of isotropic, homogeneous shells of revolution in which the thickness, principal radii of curvature, loadings, and temperature are arbitrary functions of meridional position but independent of circumferential position. Poisson's ratio is, however, assumed to be constant. The extension of the finite difference method to orthotropic layered shells under θ-independent as well as arbitrary loadings is, of course, possible and has been accomplished.[9,10] Such solutions will not be pursued here because we wish to keep this first exposure to numerical solutions as straightforward as possible and because such shells can be treated in a more straightforward manner by the stepwise integration method which will be discussed in Section 10.2*c*.

The first step in the application of the finite difference method is to rewrite Eqs. 10.1b by using the approximate expressions of Eqs. 10.1a for the first and second derivatives. Thus, after dividing the generator into N finite subintervals (see Fig. 10.1), we obtain the following, so-called, difference equations at the ith point along the generator of the shell:

$$\begin{aligned} A_i \left(\frac{U_{i+1} - 2U_i + U_{i-1}}{\Delta^2}\right) + B_i \left(\frac{U_{i+1} - U_{i-1}}{2\Delta}\right) \qquad & \\ + C_i U_i + (Ehr_\varphi \beta_\varphi)_i &= G_i, \\ A_i \left(\frac{\beta_{\varphi,i+1} - 2\beta_{\varphi i} + \beta_{\varphi,i-1}}{\Delta^2}\right) + H_i \left(\frac{\beta_{\varphi,i+1} - \beta_{\varphi,i-1}}{2\Delta}\right) \qquad & \\ + I_i \beta_{\varphi i} - \left(\frac{Ur_\varphi}{D}\right)_i &= J_i. \end{aligned} \tag{10.1d}$$

Now, if we collect terms these equations can be written in the form

$$\begin{aligned} \bar{a}_i U_{i+1} + b_i U_i + \bar{c}_i U_{i-1} + 2\Delta^2 r_{\varphi i} \theta_i &= 2\Delta^2 G_i, \\ d_i \theta_{i+1} + e_i \theta_i + f_i \theta_{i-1} - 24\Delta^2 r_{\varphi i}(1 - \nu^2) U_i / h_i^2 &= 2\Delta^2 J_i (Eh)_i. \end{aligned} \tag{10.1e}$$

---

[9] Radkowski, P. P., "Stress Analysis of Orthotropic Thin Multilayer Shells of Revolution," Preprint 2889-63, AIAA Launch and Space Vehicle Shell Structures Conference, Palm Springs, Calif., April 1963.

[10] Budiansky, B., and Radkowski, P. P., "Numerical Analysis of Unsymmetrical Bending of Shells of Revolution," *AIAA J.*, **1**, 1833–1842 (1963).

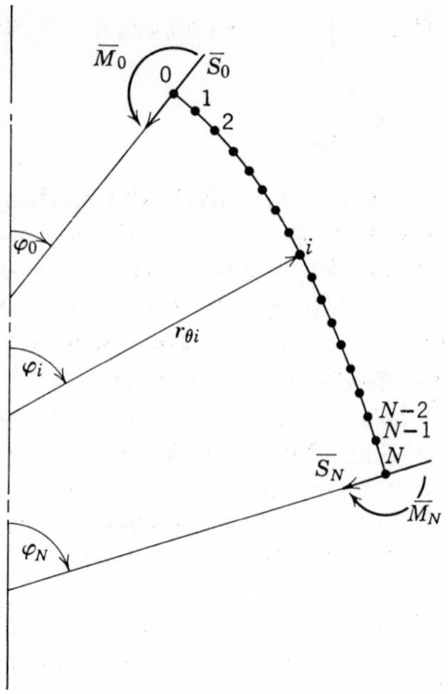

Figure 10.1

where

$$
\begin{aligned}
&\theta_i = (Eh\beta_\varphi)_i, \\
\bar{a}_i &= 2A_i + \Delta B_i, \qquad d_i = \frac{(Eh)_i}{(Eh)_{i+1}}(2A_i + \Delta H_i), \\
b_i &= 2\Delta^2 C_i - 4A_i, \qquad e_i = 2\Delta^2 I_i - 4A_i, \\
\bar{c}_i &= 2A_i - \Delta B_i, \qquad f_i = \frac{(Eh)_i}{(Eh)_{i-1}}(2A_i - \Delta H_i).
\end{aligned}
\tag{10.1f}
$$

To simplify these equations further, we define

$$
U_i = (r_\theta Q_\varphi)_i, \qquad S_i = 2\lambda_i^2 Q_{\varphi i}, \qquad \lambda_i^2 = [3(1-\nu^2)]^{1/2}(r_\theta/h)_i,
\tag{10.1g}
$$

and multiply the first of Eqs. 10.1e by $2[3(1-\nu^2)]^{1/2}$ to give

$$
\begin{aligned}
a_i S_{i+1} + b_i S_i + c_i S_{i-1} + g_i \theta_i &= \gamma_{1i}, \\
d_i \theta_{i+1} + e_i \theta_i + f_i \theta_{i-1} - g_i S_i &= \gamma_{2i},
\end{aligned}
\tag{10.1h}
$$

where

$$
\begin{aligned}
a_i = \bar{a}_i h_{i+1}/h_i, \qquad c_i = \bar{c}_i h_{i-1}/h_i, \qquad g_i = 4\Delta^2\lambda_i^2(r_\varphi/r_\theta)_i, \\
\gamma_{1i} = g_i G_i / r_{\varphi i}, \qquad \gamma_{2i} = 2\Delta^2 J_i (Eh)_i.
\end{aligned}
\tag{10.1i}
$$

Equations 10.1h govern the solution at the interior points along the generator of the shell; that is, at all φ_i for $1 \leqslant i \leqslant N - 1$. At the end points, $i = 0, N$, the relevant equations are obtained from the boundary conditions. The latter can be handled in a variety of ways; to keep matters as simple as possible, let us restrict our attention to situations involving shells which are subjected to a known shearing force S and a known axial moment M_φ at each edge. Such an arrangement is useful when we wish to calculate influence coefficients such as we discussed in Section 5.5 or, equivalently, if we wish to analyze an assembly of shells. Thus, we shall consider boundary conditions of the type

$$\begin{aligned} S_0 &= \bar{S}_0 \\ M_{\varphi 0} &= \bar{M}_0 \end{aligned} \quad \text{at} \quad \varphi = \varphi_0, \qquad \begin{aligned} S_N &= \bar{S}_N \\ M_{\varphi N} &= \bar{M}_N, \end{aligned} \quad \text{at} \quad \varphi = \varphi_N \tag{10.1j}$$

if the shell has two edges. If the shell were to be closed at $\varphi_0 = 0$, we should substitute the condition

$$S_0 = \theta_0 = 0 \qquad \text{at} \quad \varphi = \varphi_0 = 0. \tag{10.1k}$$

If we restrict our attention to shells with two edges we notice, for application of the boundary conditions, that with Eqs. 10.1a the expression for the axial moment at the ith point is

$$\begin{aligned} M_{\varphi i} &= \frac{r_{\theta i}{}^2}{8 r_{\varphi i} \Delta \lambda_i{}^4} [\theta_{i+1} + i_i \theta_i - \theta_{i-1} - E_i h_i \alpha_{ti} r_{\varphi i} T_{1i}(1 + \nu)], \\ i_i &= \nu \frac{r_{\varphi i}}{r_{\theta i}} \cot \varphi_i - (m + n)_i. \end{aligned} \tag{10.1l}$$

By rearrangement of the foregoing, we then obtain

$$\begin{aligned} \theta_{i+1} + i_i \theta_i - \theta_{i-1} &= -j_i N_i, \\ N_i &= \frac{M_{\varphi i}}{r_{\varphi i}} + \left(\frac{E h \alpha_t r_\varphi (1 + \nu) T_1}{j} \right)_i, \\ -j_i &= \frac{8 \Delta \lambda_i{}^4 r_{\varphi i}{}^2}{r_{\theta i}{}^2}. \end{aligned} \tag{10.1m}$$

When Eq. 10.1m is written at the end points $i = 0, N$, it is found that fictitious values θ_{-1} and θ_{N+1} at points outside of the interval under consideration become involved. This situation can, however, be accommodated by requiring that the difference equations 10.1h be satisfied at the end points $i = 0, N$ as well as at the interior points of the interval.[11] Then,

[11] Galletly, et al., loc. cit., have found that this procedure is more accurate than the usual procedure in which one-sided difference expressions are used at the end points of the interval.

the boundary conditions

$$\begin{aligned} \theta_{-1} &= j_0 N_0 + \theta_1 + i_0 \theta_0, \\ \theta_{N+1} &= -j_N N_N + \theta_{N-1} - i_N \theta_N, \end{aligned} \tag{10.1n}$$

which are obtained by writing Eq. 10.1m at $i = 0$, N can be used to define θ_{-1} and θ_{N+1} for use in the difference equations 10.1h at the end points of the generator.

We have thus replaced the two differential equations 10.1b by $2(N + 1)$ simultaneous linear equations which, when solved, yield the values of θ_i and S_i at every point in the mesh. The solution of these equations can be carried out in many ways and it is in this regard that individual analyses which are based upon the finite difference method vary. One direct approach to the solution proceeds as follows.

First, we write Eqs. 10.1h in extended form so as to reveal their basic features. Thus, the first of Eqs. 10.1h represents the set of expressions

$$\begin{aligned}
&\underline{i = 0}: a_0 S_1 + c_0 S_{-1} + g_0 \theta_0 = \gamma_{10} - b_0 \bar{S}_0, \\
&\underline{i = 1}: a_1 S_2 + b_1 S_1 + g_1 \theta_1 = \gamma_{11} - c_1 \bar{S}_0, \\
&\underline{i = 2}: a_2 S_3 + b_2 S_2 + c_2 S_1 + g_2 \theta_2 = \gamma_{12}, \\
&\quad \cdots \\
&\underline{i = N - 2}: a_{N-2} S_{N-1} + b_{N-2} S_{N-2} \\
&\qquad\qquad + c_{N-2} S_{N-3} + g_{N-2} \theta_{N-2} = \gamma_{1,N-2}, \\
&\underline{i = N - 1}: b_{N-1} S_{N-1} + c_{N-1} S_{N-2} + g_{N-1} \theta_{N-1} \\
&\qquad\qquad = \gamma_{1,N-1} - a_{N-1} \bar{S}_N, \\
&\underline{i = N}: a_N S_{N+1} + c_N S_{N-1} + g_N \theta_N = \gamma_{1N} - b_N \bar{S}_N,
\end{aligned} \tag{10.1o}$$

where we have used the end conditions (Eqs. 10.1j) for S_0 and S_N. The second of Eqs. 10.1h represents the set of expressions

$$\begin{aligned}
&\underline{i = 0}: x_0 \theta_1 + w_0 \theta_0 = \gamma_{20} + g_0 \bar{S}_0 - f_0 j_0 N_0, \\
&\underline{i = 1}: d_1 \theta_2 + e_1 \theta_1 + f_1 \theta_0 - g_1 S_1 = \gamma_{21}, \\
&\quad \cdots \\
&\underline{i = N - 1}: d_{N-1} \theta_N + e_{N-1} \theta_{N-1} \\
&\qquad\qquad + f_{N-1} \theta_{N-2} - g_{N-1} S_{N-1} = \gamma_{2,N-1}, \\
&\underline{i = N}: y_N \theta_{N-1} + z_N \theta_N = \gamma_{2N} + g_N \bar{S}_N + d_N j_N N_N,
\end{aligned} \tag{10.1p}$$

where we have used Eqs. 10.1n to eliminate θ_{-1} and θ_{N+1} and where we have defined

$$\begin{aligned} w_0 &= e_0 + f_0 i_0, \qquad & y_N &= d_N + f_N, \\ x_0 &= d_0 + f_0, \qquad & z_N &= e_N - i_N d_N. \end{aligned} \tag{10.1q}$$

The system of Eqs. 10.1o and 10.1p can now be written in the following partitioned matrix form:

$$\left[\begin{array}{c|c} X_1 & Y_1 \\ \hline Y_2 & X_2 \end{array}\right]\left[\begin{array}{c} S \\ \hline \theta \end{array}\right] = \left[\begin{array}{c} F_1 \\ \hline F_2 \end{array}\right] \tag{10.1r}$$

where $[X_1]$ and $[X_2]$ are the tridiagonal $(N + 1)$ by $(N + 1)$ square matrices:

$$[X_1] = \begin{bmatrix} c_0 & a_0 & & & & & & & \\ & b_1 & a_1 & & & & & & \\ & c_2 & b_2 & a_2 & & & & & \\ & & \ddots & \ddots & \ddots & & & & \\ & & & c_i & b_i & a_i & & & \\ & & & & \ddots & \ddots & \ddots & & \\ & & & & & c_{N-2} & b_{N-2} & a_{N-2} & \\ & & & & & & c_{N-1} & b_{N-1} & \\ & & & & & & & c_N & a_N \end{bmatrix} \tag{10.1s}$$

$$[X_2] = \begin{bmatrix} w_0 & x_0 & & & & & \\ f_1 & e_1 & d_1 & & & & \\ & \ddots & \ddots & \ddots & & & \\ & & f_i & e_i & d_i & & \\ & & & \ddots & \ddots & \ddots & \\ & & & & f_{N-1} & e_{N-1} & d_{N-1} \\ & & & & & y_N & z_N \end{bmatrix} \tag{10.1t}$$

$[Y_1]$ and $[Y_2]$ are the diagonal $(N + 1)$ by $(N + 1)$ square matrices:

$$[Y_2] = \begin{bmatrix} 0 & & & & & & & & \\ & -g_1 & & & & & & & \\ & & -g_2 & & & & & & \\ & & & \ddots & & & & & \\ & & & & -g_i & & & & \\ & & & & & \ddots & & & \\ & & & & & & -g_{N-2} & & \\ & & & & & & & -g_{N-1} & \\ & & & & & & & & 0 \end{bmatrix} \tag{10.1u}$$

$$[Y_1] = \begin{bmatrix} g_0 & & & & & & \\ & g_1 & & & & & \\ & & \ddots & & & & \\ & & & g_i & & & \\ & & & & \ddots & & \\ & & & & & g_{N-1} & \\ & & & & & & g_N \end{bmatrix} \tag{10.1v}$$

and $[S]$, $[\theta]$, $[F_1]$, and $[F_2]$ are the $(N + 1)$ element column matrices (vectors):

$$[S] = \begin{bmatrix} S_{-1} \\ S_1 \\ S_2 \\ \vdots \\ S_{N-2} \\ S_{N-1} \\ S_N \end{bmatrix} \qquad [\theta] = \begin{bmatrix} \theta_0 \\ \theta_1 \\ \theta_2 \\ \vdots \\ \theta_{N-2} \\ \theta_{N-1} \\ \theta_N \end{bmatrix} \tag{10.1w}$$

$$[F_1] = \begin{bmatrix} \gamma_{10} - b_0\bar{S}_0 \\ \gamma_{11} - c_1\bar{S}_0 \\ \gamma_{12} \\ \vdots \\ \gamma_{1i} \\ \vdots \\ \gamma_{1,N-2} \\ \gamma_{1,N-1} - a_{N-1}\bar{S}_N \\ \gamma_{1N} - b_N\bar{S}_N \end{bmatrix} \qquad [F_2] = \begin{bmatrix} \gamma_{20} + g_0\bar{S}_0 - f_0 j_0 N_0 \\ \gamma_{21} \\ \vdots \\ \gamma_{2i} \\ \vdots \\ \gamma_{2,N-1} \\ \gamma_{2N} + g_N\bar{S}_N + d_N j_N N_N \end{bmatrix} \tag{10.1x}$$

In the foregoing, the elements of the matrices $[X_1]$, $[X_2]$, $[Y_1]$, $[Y_2]$, $[F_1]$, and $[F_2]$ are known while the elements of the matrices $[S]$ and $[\theta]$ are to be determined. In terms of matrix manipulations, the system of Eqs. 10.1r can be solved for $[S]$ and $[\theta]$ as follows:

First, carry out the matrix multiplication that is indicated for the partitioned matrices in Eq. 10.1r to obtain the two matrix equations

$$\begin{aligned} [X_1][S] + [Y_1][\theta] &= [F_1], \\ [Y_2][S] + [X_2][\theta] &= [F_2]. \end{aligned} \tag{10.1y}$$

The first of these, when premultiplied by $[X_1]^{-1}$, yields the expression

$$[S] = [X_1]^{-1}\{[F_1] - [Y_1][\theta]\}, \tag{10.1z}$$

and this expression, when substituted into the second of Eqs. 10.1y, gives

$$\{[X_2] - [Y_2][X_1]^{-1}[Y_1]\}[\theta] = \{[F_2] - [Y_2][X_1]^{-1}[F_1]\}. \tag{10.1aa}$$

Then, upon premultiplication by $\{[X_2] - [Y_2][X_1]^{-1}[Y_1]\}^{-1}$, the following solution is obtained for $[\theta]$:

$$[\theta] = \{[X_2] - [Y_2][X_1]^{-1}[Y_1]\}^{-1}\{[F_2] - [Y_2][X_1]^{-1}[F_1]\}. \tag{10.1bb}$$

$[S]$ can then be obtained from Eq. 10.1z. It is seen, therefore, that the basic step in the solution of the difference equations is the inversion of the matrices $[X_1]$ and $\{[X_2] - [Y_2][X_1]^{-1}[Y_1]\}$. Such matters are standard problems in numerical analysis and, since they have no connection with the theory of shells, we leave them to the previously cited references.[12] Once the matrices $[S]$ and $[\theta]$ have been obtained, the values of S_i and θ_i at every point of the mesh are known and we can calculate any desired quantity in the shell by means of finite difference equivalents which can be written for any of the shell variables (see Exercise 10.2).

The accuracy of the finite difference approach is governed by the number of subintervals into which the generator of the shell is divided. If the mesh is too coarse, the so-called truncation errors in the finite difference approximations to the derivatives are large, but round-off errors, which occur when differences between very large, nearly equal numbers are taken in the calculation, are small. If, on the other hand, the mesh is too fine, the truncation errors in the derivatives are small but the round-off errors are large. Also, fine meshes naturally require a large storage capacity on the part of the computer and add significantly to the running time. With these two opposing effects at work there is obviously an optimum mesh. However, this is difficult to predict and must be sought by experimentation.

As an example of this, consider the data of Table 10.1 where we have

Table 10.1[13]

Mesh (in.)	Exact	$\frac{1}{2}$	$\frac{1}{4}$	$\frac{1}{8}$	$\frac{1}{16}$	$\frac{1}{32}$	$\frac{1}{64}$
$\lvert A\rvert$	71.49874	71.8555	71.5847	71.520	71.5039	71.4982	71.4944
$\lvert B\rvert$	8.062878	8.5270	8.1787	8.0917	8.0698	8.0638	8.0609
$\lvert C\rvert$	16.18223	16.2091	16.1891	16.1840	16.1828	16.1829	16.1841

listed the edge influence coefficients for an isotropic cylindrical shell as obtained with various uniformly spaced meshes as well as an exact solution of the type considered in Section 5.2*a*.[14] The shell is loaded by a uniformly distributed shearing force Q_0 and an axial moment M_0 at each end and its dimensions are $a = 10$ in., $h = 1$ in., $l = 3$ in., and $\nu = 0.3$.

The results of Table 10.1 indicate that, in this particular case, when the mesh becomes finer and finer the results decrease monotonically toward the exact solution up to and including the $\frac{1}{32}$ in. mesh. This means that the

[12] See footnote 1.

[13] The notation of Table 10.1 is

$$Ew(0) = Ew(l) = AQ_0 + BM_0,$$
$$E\beta_x(0) = E\beta_x(l) = BQ_0 + CM_0.$$

[14] Timoshenko, S., and Woinowsky–Krieger, S., "Theory of Plates and Shells," New York: McGraw-Hill, 2nd ed., pp. 478–479 (1959).

truncation errors are decreasing faster than the round-off errors are increasing. However, in passing to the $\frac{1}{64}$ in. mesh, $|A|$ and $|B|$ continue to decrease but $|C|$ suddenly increases slightly. This is attributed to the fact that the round-off errors have become predominant and, eventually, $|A|$ and $|B|$ will be similarly affected. It would have been desirable to try additional, still finer, meshes but this could not be done because the storage capacity of the computer program[15] that was used in the preparation of Table 10.1 would have been exceeded. This, however, illustrates one of the practical limitations which are often met with in numerical analysis, even though it is not customary in typical computations to use such fine meshes. Indeed, the $\frac{1}{8}$ in. mesh appears satisfactory for engineering purposes in this particular example.

Further discussion of results obtained with the finite difference method will be presented in Section 10.3.

10.2*b* The Finite Element Method

The finite element method can be viewed as an extension to very many short segments of the method which we presented for the analysis of composite shells in Section 5.5. Indeed, in this method each of the finite subintervals into which an arbitrary shell is divided for numerical analysis is approximated by a short shell whose behavior is known. The most common practice is to represent each interval by a short conical shell whose behavior has been analyzed at length in Section 5.3.

For purposes of illustration, let us, therefore, assume that a given shell of revolution which is under the influence of a θ-independent system of loads and temperatures has been replaced, for analysis, by an ensemble of short conical shells whose lengths are not necessarily equal. Each of these segments has constant material properties and thickness that are the average of the properties and thickness of that region of the shell which the segment represents. Thus, variations in properties and thickness over the generator of the shell can be accommodated. Once these conical segments have been defined, the problem becomes one of analyzing a shell that is an assembly of many short conical shells and its solution proceeds according to the following generalization of the method that we described in Section 5.5:[16]

The ith and $(i + 1)$st segments of the assembly of conical shells which approximates the original shell are shown in Fig. 10.2 where the conventions for describing the geometry of each segment as well as the forces and

[15] Penny, R. K., loc. cit.

[16] Meyer, R. R., and Harmon, M. B., "Conical Segment Method for Analyzing Open Crown Shells of Revolution for Edge Loading," *AIAA J.*, **1**, 886–891 (1963).

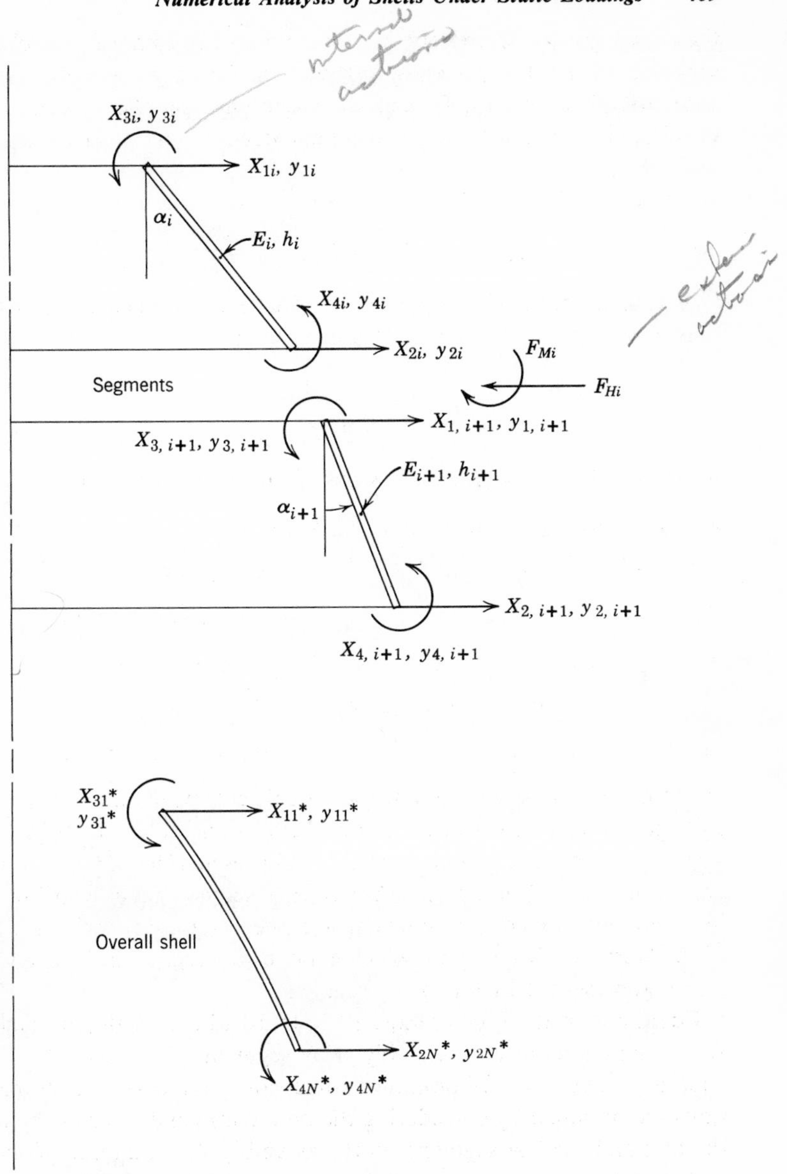

Figure 10.2

moments which act upon it are defined. We notice, from Fig. 10.2, that the X_{1i}, X_{2i}, X_{3i}, X_{4i} represent the internal discontinuity forces and moments which act between the segments, that the F_{Mi}, F_{Hi} represent the externally applied moment and horizontal force (if any) applied at each joint, and that the $y_{1i}, y_{2i}, y_{3i}, y_{4i}$ represent the displacement and rotation at each end of a segment. To join the ith segment to the $(i + 1)$st segment, for example, we note, first, that the sum of the forces and moments at their junction must be equal to any external force and moment which might be applied at the joint. Thus,

$$X_{2i} + X_{1,i+1} = F_{Hi},$$
$$X_{4i} + X_{3,i+1} = F_{Mi}. \tag{10.2a}$$

Furthermore, for continuity of the structure, the displacement and rotation must be continuous across each joint. Therefore,

$$y_{2i} = y_{1,i+1},$$
$$y_{4i} = y_{3,i+1}, \tag{10.2b}$$

which, in terms of the forces and the moments, can be expressed as

$$X_{1i}\,\delta_{21i} + X_{2i}\,\delta_{22i} + X_{3i}\,\delta_{23i} + X_{4i}\,\delta_{24i} + \delta_{2i}{}^{L}$$
$$= X_{1,i+1}\,\delta_{11,i+1} + X_{2,i+1}\,\delta_{12,i+1} + X_{3,i+1}\,\delta_{13,i+1}$$
$$+ X_{4,i+1}\,\delta_{14,i+1} + \delta^{L}_{1,i+1}, \tag{10.2c}$$

$$X_{1i}\,\delta_{41i} + X_{2i}\,\delta_{42i} + X_{3i}\,\delta_{43i} + X_{4i}\,\delta_{44i} + \delta_{4i}{}^{L}$$
$$= X_{1,i+1}\,\delta_{31,i+1} + X_{2,i+1}\,\delta_{32,i+1} + X_{3,i+1}\,\delta_{33,i+1}$$
$$+ X_{4,i+1}\,\delta_{34,i+1} + \delta^{L}_{3,i+1}, \tag{10.2d}$$

where the δ_{abc} are the edge influence coefficients which denote (see Section 5.5) the contributions to the edge deflections and rotations from the edge shearing forces and moments and $\delta_{ab}{}^{L}$ represents the contribution to the deflection and rotation at each end of each segment from distributed loadings and temperature. For convenience, the latter are taken as the average of the load and temperature which act over the region in the original shell that is represented by any given segment.

Equations of the type of Eqs. 10.2a to 10.2d are written at each of the $N - 1$ junctions in the assembly of N segments. This leads to $4(N - 1)$ equations involving $4N$ unknown forces and moments. Additional equations are obtained by considering the boundary conditions at the edges of the first and the last segments in the assembly. For example, if the forces and moments are prescribed at the two ends of the assembly we can write (see Fig. 10.2):

$$X_{11} = X_{11}{}^{*}, \qquad X_{31} = X_{31}{}^{*} \tag{10.2e}$$

at the upper end of the first segment and

$$X_{2N} = X_{2N}{}^{*}, \qquad X_{4N} = X_{4N}{}^{*} \tag{10.2f}$$

at the lower end of the Nth segment. This reduces the problem to one involving $4N$ simultaneous equations which can be solved for the $4N$ unknown discontinuity forces and moments. If, on the other hand, the displacements and rotations at the upper and lower ends of the assembly are prescribed, then we should have

$$\begin{aligned} y_{11}^* &= X_{11}\,\delta_{111} + X_{21}\,\delta_{121} + X_{31}\,\delta_{131} + X_{41}\,\delta_{141} + \delta_{11}{}^L, \\ y_{31}^* &= X_{11}\,\delta_{311} + X_{21}\,\delta_{321} + X_{31}\,\delta_{331} + X_{41}\,\delta_{341} + \delta_{31}{}^L, \end{aligned} \tag{10.2g}$$

at the upper end of the first segment, and

$$\begin{aligned} y_{2N}^* &= X_{1N}\,\delta_{21N} + X_{2N}\,\delta_{22N} + X_{3N}\,\delta_{23N} + X_{4N}\,\delta_{24N} + \delta_{2N}{}^L, \\ y_{4N}^* &= X_{1N}\,\delta_{41N} + X_{2N}\,\delta_{42N} + X_{3N}\,\delta_{43N} + X_{4N}\,\delta_{44N} + \delta_{4N}{}^L, \end{aligned} \tag{10.2h}$$

at the lower end of the Nth segment. Equations 10.2g and 10.2h provide four expressions which, together with the junction conditions, yield a set of $4N$ equations in $4N$ unknowns. If the end conditions are mixed, that is, if a deflection and a moment or a rotation and a force are prescribed, an intermediate situation arises which can be handled in a similar fashion.

To illustrate the solution, let us assume that the forces and moments at the ends of the assembly are prescribed (see Eqs. 10.2e and 10.2f) and that we are, therefore, concerned with the solution of $4(N-1)$ junction conditions in $4(N-1)$ discontinuity forces and moments. First, we notice from the force and moment equilibrium conditions (Eqs. 10.2a) that

$$\begin{aligned} X_{1i} &= F_{H,i-1} - X_{2,i-1}, \\ X_{3i} &= F_{M,i-1} - X_{4,i-1}. \end{aligned} \tag{10.2i}$$

Therefore, the continuity conditions (Eqs. 10.2c and 10.2d) take the form

$$\begin{aligned} -X_{2,i-1}\,\delta_{21i} &+ X_{2i}(\delta_{22i} + \delta_{11,i+1}) - X_{2,i+1}\,\delta_{12,i+1} \\ &\qquad - X_{4,i-1}\,\delta_{23i} + X_{4i}(\delta_{24i} + \delta_{13,i+1}) - X_{4,i+1}\,\delta_{14,i+1} \\ &= \delta^L_{1,i+1} - \delta_{2i}{}^L - F_{H,i-1}\,\delta_{21i} - F_{M,i-1}\,\delta_{23i} \\ &\qquad + F_{Hi}\,\delta_{11,i+1} + F_{Mi},\,\delta_{13,i+1}, \end{aligned} \tag{10.2j}$$

$$\begin{aligned} -X_{2,i-1}\,\delta_{41i} &+ X_{2i}(\delta_{42i} + \delta_{31,i+1}) - X_{2,i+1}\,\delta_{32,i+1} \\ - X_{4,i-1}\,\delta_{43i} &+ X_{4i}(\delta_{44i} + \delta_{33,i+1}) - X_{4,i+1}\,\delta_{34,i+1} \\ &= \delta^L_{3,i+1} - \delta_{4i}{}^L - F_{H,i-1}\,\delta_{41i} - F_{M,i-1}\,\delta_{43i} \\ &\qquad + F_{Hi}\,\delta_{31,i+1} + F_{Mi}\,\delta_{33,i+1}. \end{aligned} \tag{10.2k}$$

These equations can be written in the following matrix form:

$$\begin{bmatrix} A_1 & B_1 \\ B_2 & A_2 \end{bmatrix} \begin{bmatrix} F_2 \\ F_4 \end{bmatrix} = \begin{bmatrix} \Delta_2 \\ \Delta_4 \end{bmatrix} \tag{10.2l}$$

where $[A_1]$, $[A_2]$, $[B_1]$, and $[B_2]$ are the known tridiagonal $(N-1)$ by $(N-1)$ square matrices:

$$[A_1] = \begin{bmatrix} (\delta_{221}+\delta_{112}) & -\delta_{122} & & & & \\ -\delta_{212} & (\delta_{222}+\delta_{113}) & -\delta_{123} & & & \\ \ddots & \ddots & \ddots & & & \\ & -\delta_{21i} & (\delta_{22i}+\delta_{11,i+1}) & -\delta_{12,i+1} & & \\ & & \ddots & \ddots & \ddots & \\ & & & -\delta_{21,N-2} & (\delta_{22,N-2}+\delta_{11,N-1}) & -\delta_{12,N-1} \\ & & & & -\delta_{21,N-1} & (\delta_{22,N-1}+\delta_{11N}) \end{bmatrix} \tag{10.2m}$$

$$[B_1] = \begin{bmatrix} (\delta_{241}+\delta_{132}) & -\delta_{142} & & & & \\ -\delta_{232} & (\delta_{242}+\delta_{133}) & -\delta_{143} & & & \\ \ddots & \ddots & \ddots & & & \\ & -\delta_{23i} & (\delta_{24i}+\delta_{13,i+1}) & -\delta_{14,i+1} & & \\ & & \ddots & \ddots & \ddots & \\ & & & -\delta_{23,N-2} & (\delta_{24,N-2}+\delta_{13,N-1}) & -\delta_{14,N-1} \\ & & & & -\delta_{23,N-1} & (\delta_{24,N-1}+\delta_{13N}) \end{bmatrix} \tag{10.2n}$$

$$[A_2] = \begin{bmatrix} (\delta_{441}+\delta_{332}) & -\delta_{342} & & & & \\ -\delta_{432} & (\delta_{442}+\delta_{333}) & -\delta_{343} & & & \\ \ddots & \ddots & \ddots & & & \\ & -\delta_{43i} & (\delta_{44i}+\delta_{33,i+1}) & -\delta_{34,i+1} & & \\ & & \ddots & \ddots & \ddots & \\ & & & -\delta_{43,N-2} & (\delta_{44,N-2}+\delta_{33,N-1}) & -\delta_{34,N-1} \\ & & & & -\delta_{43,N-1} & (\delta_{44,N-1}+\delta_{33N}) \end{bmatrix} \tag{10.2o}$$

$$[B_2] = \begin{bmatrix} (\delta_{421}+\delta_{312}) & -\delta_{322} & & & & & \\ -\delta_{412} & (\delta_{422}+\delta_{313}) & -\delta_{323} & & & & \\ & \ddots & \ddots & \ddots & & & \\ & & -\delta_{41i} & (\delta_{42i}+\delta_{31,i+1}) & -\delta_{32,i+1} & & \\ & & & \ddots & \ddots & \ddots & \\ & & & & -\delta_{41,N-2} & (\delta_{42,N-2}+\delta_{31,N-1}) & -\delta_{32,N-1} \\ & & & & & -\delta_{41,N-1} & (\delta_{42,N-1}+\delta_{31N}) \end{bmatrix} \tag{10.2p}$$

and $[F_2]$, $[F_4]$, $[\Delta_2]$, and $[\Delta_4]$ are the $(N-1)$ element column matrices (vectors):

$$[F_2] = \begin{bmatrix} X_{21} \\ X_{22} \\ \vdots \\ X_{2i} \\ \vdots \\ X_{2,N-2} \\ X_{2,N-1} \end{bmatrix} \qquad [F_4] = \begin{bmatrix} X_{41} \\ X_{42} \\ \vdots \\ X_{4i} \\ \vdots \\ X_{4,N-2} \\ X_{4,N-1} \end{bmatrix} \tag{10.2q}$$

$$[\Delta_2] = \begin{bmatrix} \delta_{12}{}^L - \delta_{21}{}^L - X_{11}{}^* \delta_{211} - X_{31}{}^* \delta_{231} \\ + F_{H1}\,\delta_{112} + F_{M1}\,\delta_{132} \\ \delta_{13}{}^L - \delta_{22}{}^L - F_{H1}\,\delta_{212} - F_{M1}\,\delta_{232} + F_{H2}\,\delta_{113} + F_{M2}\,\delta_{133} \\ \cdots \\ \delta_{1,i+1}^L - \delta_{2i}{}^L - F_{H,i-1}\,\delta_{21i} - F_{M,i-1}\,\delta_{23i} \\ + F_{Hi}\,\delta_{11,i+1} + F_{Mi}\,\delta_{13,i+1} \\ \cdots \\ \delta_{1,N-1}^L - \delta_{2,N-2}^L - F_{H,N-3}\,\delta_{21,N-2} - F_{M,N-3}\,\delta_{23,N-2} \\ + F_{H,N-2}\,\delta_{11,N-1} + F_{M,N-2}\,\delta_{13,N-1} \\ \delta_{1N}{}^L - \delta_{2,N-1}^L - F_{H,N-2}\,\delta_{21,N-1} - F_{M,N-2}\,\delta_{23,N-1} \\ + F_{H,N-1}\,\delta_{11N} + F_{M,N-1}\,\delta_{13N} + X_{2N}{}^*\,\delta_{12N} + X_{4N}{}^*\,\delta_{14N} \end{bmatrix} \tag{10.2r}$$

$$[\Delta_4] = \begin{bmatrix} \delta_{32}{}^L - \delta_{41}{}^L - X_{11}{}^* \delta_{411} - X_{31}{}^* \delta_{431} \\ + F_{H1}\,\delta_{312} + F_{M1}\,\delta_{332} \\ \delta_{33}{}^L - \delta_{42}{}^L - F_{H1}\,\delta_{412} - F_{M1}\,\delta_{432} + F_{H2}\,\delta_{313} + F_{M2}\,\delta_{333} \\ \cdots \\ \delta_{3,i+1}^L - \delta_{4i}{}^L - F_{H,i-1}\,\delta_{41i} - F_{M,i-1}\,\delta_{43i} \\ + F_{Hi}\,\delta_{31,i+1} + F_{Mi}\,\delta_{33,i+1} \\ \cdots \\ \delta_{3,N-1}^L - \delta_{4,N-2}^L + F_{H,N-3}\,\delta_{41,N-2} - F_{M,N-3}\,\delta_{43,N-2} \\ + F_{H,N-2}\,\delta_{31,N-1} + F_{M,N-2}\,\delta_{33,N-1} \\ \delta_{3N}{}^L - \delta_{4,N-1}^L - F_{H,N-2}\,\delta_{41,N-1} - F_{M,N-2}\,\delta_{43,N-1} \\ + F_{H,N-1},\delta_{31N} + F_{M,N-1}\,\delta_{33N} + X_{2N}{}^*\,\delta_{32N} + X_{4N}{}^*\,\delta_{34N} \end{bmatrix} \tag{10.2s}$$

The matrix equation 10.2l can be solved by the procedure which was described in Section 10.2a (see Eqs. 10.1r, 10.1y, 10.1z, 10.1aa, and 10.1bb), with the following result:

$$[F_4] = \{[A_2] - [B_2][A_1]^{-1}[B_1]\}^{-1}\{[\Delta_4] - [B_2][A_1]^{-1}[\Delta_2]\},$$
$$[F_2] = [A_1]^{-1}\{[\Delta_2] - [B_1][F_4]\}. \tag{10.2t}$$

Thus, it is seen that the basic steps here involve the inversion of the matrices $[A_1]$ and $\{[A_2] - [B_2][A_1]^{-1}[B_1]\}$. The formulas 10.2t then yield X_{2i} and X_{4i} at every junction and the equilibrium conditions (Eqs. 10.2i), in turn, give X_{1i} and X_{3i}. Any desired shell variable in any of the N segments can then be determined from any analysis of the type given in Section 5.3 for conical shell segments under prescribed edge and surface loadings.

The foregoing analysis concerned an arbitrary shell with two edges at which known forces and moments were applied. The extension to shells with two edges at which the displacements are prescribed is straightforward and is left to the Exercises. If the shell extends to its axis, the segment at the axis can be taken to be either a small conical cap if the slope of the generator does not vanish or a small circular plate if the slope of the generator vanishes at the axis.

If (once the discontinuity forces and moments have been determined by the foregoing procedure) we wish to calculate the edge influence coefficients for the entire original shell, the procedure to be followed would be, in the absence of all external loadings and temperature, as follows.

Evaluate the matrices $[F_2]$ and $[F_4]$ by setting each of the loads at the first and last edges of the assembly in turn equal to unity while keeping the remaining three loads in each case equal to zero. Thus

$$\begin{aligned}
&\textit{Case I: } X_{11} = 1, && X_{31} = X_{2N} = X_{4N} = 0,\\
&\textit{Case II: } X_{2N} = 1, && X_{11} = X_{31} = X_{4N} = 0,\\
&\textit{Case III: } X_{31} = 1, && X_{11} = X_{2N} = X_{4N} = 0,\\
&\textit{Case IV: } X_{4N} = 1, && X_{11} = X_{2N} = X_{31} = 0.
\end{aligned} \tag{10.2u}$$

The $[F_2]$ matrix can then be written in the form

$$[F_2] = \begin{bmatrix} X_{21}{}^{\mathrm{I}} & X_{21}{}^{\mathrm{II}} & X_{21}{}^{\mathrm{III}} & X_{21}{}^{\mathrm{IV}} \\ X_{22}{}^{\mathrm{I}} & X_{22}{}^{\mathrm{II}} & X_{22}{}^{\mathrm{III}} & X_{22}{}^{\mathrm{IV}} \\ \vdots & \vdots & \vdots & \vdots \\ X^{\mathrm{I}}_{2,N-2} & X^{\mathrm{II}}_{2,N-2} & X^{\mathrm{III}}_{2,N-2} & X^{\mathrm{IV}}_{2,N-2} \\ X^{\mathrm{I}}_{2,N-1} & X^{\mathrm{II}}_{2,N-1} & X^{\mathrm{III}}_{2,N-1} & X^{\mathrm{IV}}_{2,N-1} \end{bmatrix} \tag{10.2v}$$

and similarly for $[F_4]$ where the Roman superscripts identify the contribution from each of the cases of Eqs. 10.2u.

Next, we observe that the edge deflections and rotations are given in terms of the edge forces and moments which act on the overall shell by the following set of equations:

$$\begin{bmatrix} y_{11} \\ y_{2N} \\ y_{31} \\ y_{4N} \end{bmatrix} = \begin{bmatrix} \delta_{11} & \delta_{12} & \delta_{13} & \delta_{14} \\ \delta_{21} & \delta_{22} & \delta_{23} & \delta_{24} \\ \delta_{31} & \delta_{32} & \delta_{33} & \delta_{34} \\ \delta_{41} & \delta_{42} & \delta_{43} & \delta_{44} \end{bmatrix} \begin{bmatrix} X_{11} \\ X_{2N} \\ X_{31} \\ X_{4N} \end{bmatrix} \tag{10.2w}$$

where the δ_{ij} are the edge influence coefficients of the original shell. Now we recall that (see Eqs. 10.2g and 10.2h) the above deflections and rotations are also given by

$$\begin{bmatrix} y_{11} \\ y_{2N} \\ y_{31} \\ y_{4N} \end{bmatrix} = \begin{bmatrix} \delta_{111} & \delta_{121} & \delta_{131} & \delta_{141} & 0 & 0 & 0 & 0 \\ 0 & 0 & 0 & 0 & \delta_{21N} & \delta_{22N} & \delta_{23N} & \delta_{24N} \\ \delta_{311} & \delta_{321} & \delta_{331} & \delta_{341} & 0 & 0 & 0 & 0 \\ 0 & 0 & 0 & 0 & \delta_{41N} & \delta_{42N} & \delta_{43N} & \delta_{44N} \end{bmatrix} \begin{bmatrix} X_{11} \\ X_{21} \\ X_{31} \\ X_{41} \\ X_{1N} \\ X_{2N} \\ X_{3N} \\ X_{4N} \end{bmatrix} \tag{10.2x}$$

In view of the fact that the quantities X_{21}, X_{41}, X_{1N}, and X_{3N} in the column matrix of Eq. 10.2x are functions of X_{11}, X_{31}, X_{2N}, and X_{4N}, and in view of the definition of the four unit load cases (Eqs. 10.2u), we may conclude that the matrix of edge influence coefficients for the original shell can be obtained from the expression

$$[\delta] = [\bar{D}][\bar{E}], \tag{10.2y}$$

where $[\delta]$ is the square matrix in Eq. 10.2w, $[\bar{D}]$ is the eight by four matrix in Eq. 10.2x, and,

$$[\bar{E}] = \begin{bmatrix} 1 & 0 & 0 & 0 \\ X_{21}{}^{\mathrm{I}} & X_{21}{}^{\mathrm{II}} & X_{21}{}^{\mathrm{III}} & X_{21}{}^{\mathrm{IV}} \\ 0 & 0 & 1 & 0 \\ X_{41}{}^{\mathrm{I}} & X_{41}{}^{\mathrm{II}} & X_{41}{}^{\mathrm{III}} & X_{41}{}^{\mathrm{IV}} \\ X_{1N}{}^{\mathrm{I}} & X_{1N}{}^{\mathrm{II}} & X_{1N}{}^{\mathrm{III}} & X_{1N}{}^{\mathrm{IV}} \\ 0 & 1 & 0 & 0 \\ X_{3N}{}^{\mathrm{I}} & X_{3N}{}^{\mathrm{II}} & X_{3N}{}^{\mathrm{III}} & X_{3N}{}^{\mathrm{IV}} \\ 0 & 0 & 0 & 1 \end{bmatrix} \tag{10.2z}$$

The accuracy of the finite element approximation is governed by the number of segments into which the shell that is to be analyzed is subdivided. Therefore, for the purpose of demonstrating the influence of the number of approximating conical segments we have plotted, in Figs. 10.3

and 10.4, the results of some studies of edge influence coefficients and stresses which were performed on toroidal and ellipsoidal shells with the finite element method.[17] Figure 10.3 shows the variation with the number of approximating cones of four edge influence coefficients for a toroidal shell segment. The results, which are normalized to the case of twenty approximating cones, show that, even with as few as four approximating cones, the error, using the twenty cone solution as a standard, is very small. Similar results for the circumferential stress resultant caused by a unit

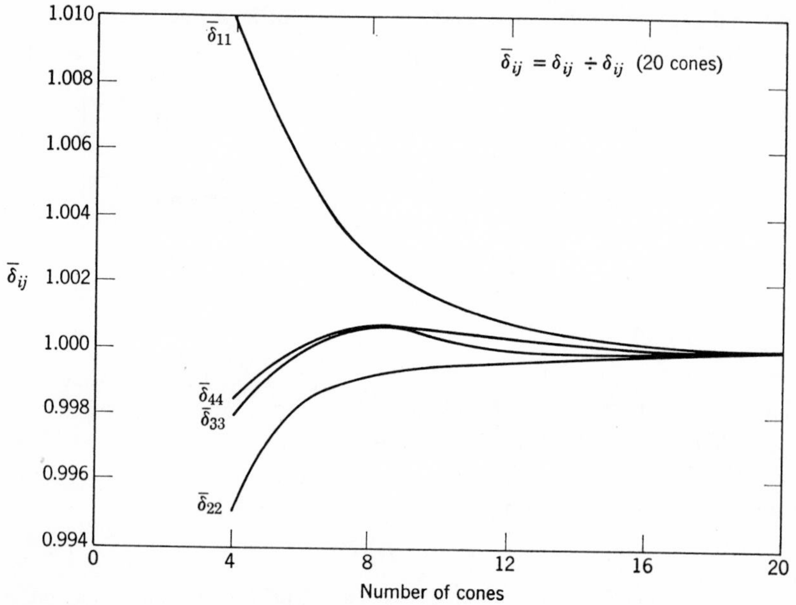

Figure 10.3 Effect of the number of approximating cones for a toroidal shell segment.

moment acting, as shown, at the edge of an ellipsoidal shell segment are given in Fig. 10.4. It is again seen that an accurate result can be obtained with a fairly small number of approximating cones. Both figures also show that for the cases cited no significant change in the results is obtained by using more than ten cones to approximate the original shell.

Further results, as obtained by the finite element method, will be cited in Section 10.3 when the various numerical approaches are compared. In the meantime, it is well to mention some additional capabilities of the method, as follows.

Our development of the finite element method is applicable in its present

[17] Meyer, R. R., and Harmon, M. B., loc. cit.

form to orthotropic materials as well as to isotropic materials; all that is required in either case is an appropriate analysis of a conical shell segment as given in Section 5.3. Although the development was carried out for an arbitrary shell of revolution under θ-independent loads and temperatures, it is possible to extend it to arbitrary loads and temperatures. This relies, as in our previous work on arbitrarily loaded shells of revolution, upon

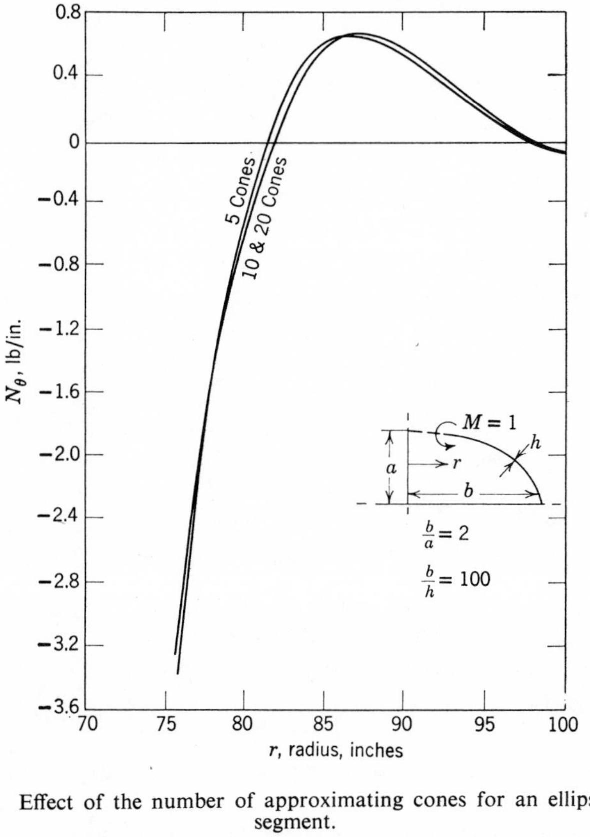

Figure 10.4 Effect of the number of approximating cones for an ellipsoidal shell segment.

Fourier expansions of all of the shell variables with respect to the coordinate θ. Then the derivation is carried out for the nth component of these expansions in much the same manner as we have done here. One must remember, however, that for nonzero values of the index n, additional equilibrium and continuity conditions must be written at each junction to take into account the circumferential displacement and rotation u_θ and β_θ and the shearing force and twisting moment $T_{\varphi\theta}$ and $M_{\varphi\theta}$ which accompany an arbitrary load system.

It is also well to mention here that there exists a variant of the finite element method which is referred to as the direct stiffness method. In that method, the shell is again broken down into an assembly of finite elements. For each of these elements, relationships can be derived using its elastic properties and reasonable approximations of its interior deformation, which give the forces at the ends of the element in terms of the displacements at the ends of the element. These equations are written in matrix form as

$$[F] = [k][U], \tag{10.3a}$$

where $[F]$ and $[U]$ are column matrices of forces and displacements of the ends of the segment and $[k]$ is the so-called stiffness matrix of the segment in analogy to the stiffness of a spring. A similar relationship for the entire assembly is obtained by superposition and is given by

$$[F] = [K][U], \tag{10.3b}$$

where $[K]$ is the stiffness matrix of the entire assembly. The foregoing can be partitioned so that

$$\left[\begin{array}{c} P \\ \hline R \end{array}\right] = \left[\begin{array}{c|c} K_{11} & K_{12} \\ \hline K_{21} & K_{22} \end{array}\right]\left[\begin{array}{c} y \\ \hline C \end{array}\right] \tag{10.3c}$$

where $[P]$ represents the loads which are applied to the shell, $[R]$ represents the unknown reactions at points where the displacements are specified, $[y]$ represents the unknown displacements and $[C]$ represents the specified displacements (if any). Equations 10.3c can be solved to give the following expressions for the unknown displacements and reactions:

$$\begin{aligned} [y] &= [K_{11}]^{-1}\{[P] - [K_{12}][C]\}, \\ [R] &= [K_{21}][y] + [K_{22}][C]. \end{aligned} \tag{10.3d}$$

The stresses in the assembly can then be found from the displacements by relationships of the type

$$[\sigma] = [S][y], \tag{10.3e}$$

where $[S]$ is the matrix of stress influence coefficients and $[\sigma]$ is the matrix of stresses.

It is seen that the fundamental quantities that are to be determined in the direct stiffness method are the stiffness and the stress matrices of the assembly. These are generally obtained from the principle of virtual work.[18, 19]

---

[18] Grafton, P. E., and Strome, D. R., "Analysis of Axisymmetrical Shells by the Direct Stiffness Method," *AIAA J.*, **1**, 2342–2347 (1963).

[19] Friedrich, C. M., "SEAL SHELL -2, A Computer Program for the Stress Analysis of a Thick Shell of Revolution with Axisymmetric Pressures, Temperatures, and Distributed Loads," WAPD-TM-398, Westinghouse Bettis Atomic Power Laboratory, Pittsburgh, Pa. (1963).

10.2c Method of Stepwise Integration

In the method of stepwise integration, the governing equations of a given two point boundary value problem are reduced to first order equations and various schemes are used to integrate the resulting equations in a step-by-step fashion across the given interval, starting from prescribed values at the initial point. A solution which also satisfies the conditions that are prescribed at the final point, as would be the case in a shell, is found by performing additional manipulations which will be described. Some choice is available in the selection of a stepwise integration method. Therefore, we shall outline two methods which have been found useful in shell analysis; that is, the fourth order Runge–Kutta method[20–23] and Adams' method.[24–25]

All of the stepwise integration methods rely, by means of a change of variable or other rearrangement, on the reduction of the governing equations of a problem to first order differential equations of the type

$$\frac{dy}{dx} = f(x, y). \tag{10.4a}$$

In the fourth order Runge–Kutta method,[26] the length of the generator of the shell is divided, as before, into a number of subintervals. The integration of equations of the type of Eqs. 10.4a then proceeds from point to point by repeated use of the following algorithm:

$$y_{i+1} = y_i + \tfrac{1}{6}(k_0 + 2k_1 + 2k_2 + k_3), \tag{10.4b}$$

where

$$\begin{aligned} k_0 &= \Delta f(x_i, y_i), \\ k_1 &= \Delta f\left(x_i + \frac{\Delta}{2}, y_i + \frac{k_0}{2}\right), \\ k_2 &= \Delta f\left(x_i + \frac{\Delta}{2}, y_i + \frac{k_1}{2}\right), \end{aligned} \tag{10.4c}$$

---

[20] Galletly, G. D., "Influence Coefficients for Open Crown Hemispheres," *Trans. A.S.M.E.*, **82A**, 73–81 (1960).

[21] Galletly, G. D., "Edge Influence Coefficients for Toroidal Shells," *Trans. A.S.M.E.*, **82B**, 60–64, 65–68 (1960).

[22] Galletly, G. D., "Bending of Open Crown Ellipsoidal Shells," *Welding Research Council Bulletin No. 54* (1959).

[23] Galletly, G. D., Kyner, W. T., and Moller, C. E., loc. cit.

[24] Mirabal, J. A., and Dight, D. G., "SOR-II, A Program to Perform Stress Analysis of Shells of Revolution," KAPL-M-EC-19, Knolls Atomic Power Laboratory, Schenectady, N.Y. (1962).

[25] Kalnins, A., "Analysis of Shells of Revolution Subjected to Symmetrical and Non-symmetrical Loads," *J. Appl. Mech.*, **31**, 467–476 (1964).

[26] Hildebrand, F. B., loc. cit., 233–243.

$$k_3 = \Delta f(x_i + \Delta, y_i + k_2),$$
$$\Delta = x_{i+1} - x_i.$$

It is apparent, from the definition of the fourth order Runge–Kutta process, that the use of a nonuniform step length leads to no particular complications. In Adams' method,[27] the integration of Eq. 10.4a is carried out in a stepwise fashion by repeated use of the algorithm:

$$Y_{i+1} = y_i + \frac{\Delta}{24}(55y_i' - 59y_{i-1}' - 37y_{i-2}' - 9y_{i-3}'), \tag{10.4d}$$

$$Y_{i+1}' = f(x_{i+1}, Y_{i+1}), \tag{10.4e}$$

$$y_{i+1} = y_i + \frac{\Delta}{24}(9Y_{i+1}' + 19y_i' - 5y_{i-1}' + y_{i-2}'), \tag{10.4f}$$

where

$$y_i' = f(x_i, y_i). \tag{10.4g}$$

Methods of this type are referred to as "predictor-corrector" methods since predicted values of the function and its derivative are calculated with formulas 10.4d and 10.4e and then a corrected value of the function is calculated with formula 10.4f. For additional accuracy, the result from formula 10.4f may be substituted back into formula 10.4e and the process may be continued until two successive values of y_{i+1} agree within a certain small predetermined tolerance. It is interesting to note, from Eqs. 10.4d to 10.4f, that the predictor-corrector methods use information from previous points in the integration process. This means that the algorithm is not self-starting and that a variable step size can be accommodated only with additional complication.[28] The former deficiency can, however, be overcome by using the Runge–Kutta method, which is self starting, for the first few steps. The choice between the Runge–Kutta and the Adams methods is arbitrary. The former is simpler to use and allows variable step sizes while the latter is slightly more complicated to use, but at the same time it is more accurate.

Having described two typical methods of stepwise integration, let us now discuss the application of such methods to the static analysis of shells. For this purpose, we must convert the equations of the theory to a set of first order differential equations of the type Eqs. 10.4a. We do this by observing from the natural boundary conditions of the theory of Chapter 2 (see Eqs. 2.80a and 2.80b) that there are, in effect, eight fundamental variables

[27] Hildebrand, F. B., loc. cit., pp. 188–201.

[28] See, for example, Glauz, R. D., Computing Services Report No. 13, Aerojet-General Corporation, Sacramento, Calif., May 12, 1960; and also Hildebrand, F. B., loc. cit., pp. 188–201.

when that theory is applied to the analysis of arbitrarily loaded shells of revolution. These are the generalized displacements w, u_φ, u_θ, and β_φ and the generalized stress resultants V, N_φ, T, and M_φ where (see Eqs. 2.78):

$$T = T_{\varphi\theta} = N_{\varphi\theta} + \frac{1}{r_\theta} M_{\varphi\,\theta}, \qquad (10.5a)$$

$$V = V_\varphi = Q_\varphi + \frac{1}{r} \frac{\partial M_{\varphi\theta}}{\partial \theta},$$

for a shell of revolution. It is thus reasonable to seek a set of eight first order differential equations which involve only these variables. In the derivation of these equations, we shall utilize, as the independent variable, the arc length s which is related to the meridional coordinate φ by the expression

$$\frac{\partial}{\partial s} = \frac{1}{r_\varphi} \frac{\partial}{\partial \varphi}. \qquad (10.5b)$$

Furthermore, we shall permit the consideration of orthotropic non-homogeneous materials by adopting the following form of the relationships between the stress resultants, stress couples, and the strains and changes of curvature of the reference surface (see Eqs. 2.24 and 2.25):

$$N_{\varphi m} = C_{11}\epsilon_{\varphi m}{}^0 + C_{12}\epsilon_{\theta m}{}^0 + K_{11}\kappa_{\varphi m} + K_{12}\kappa_{\theta m} - N^*_{T\varphi m},$$

$$N_{\theta m} = C_{12}\epsilon_{\varphi m}{}^0 + C_{22}\epsilon_{\theta m}{}^0 + K_{12}\kappa_{\varphi m} + K_{22}\kappa_{\theta m} - N^*_{T\theta m},$$

$$M_{\varphi m} = D_{11}\kappa_{\varphi m} + D_{12}\kappa_{\theta m} + K_{11}\epsilon_{\varphi m}{}^0 + K_{12}\epsilon_{\theta m}{}^0 - M^*_{T\varphi m},$$

$$M_{\theta m} = D_{12}\kappa_{\varphi m} + D_{22}\kappa_{\theta m} + K_{12}\epsilon_{\varphi m}{}^0 + K_{22}\epsilon_{\theta m}{}^0 - M^*_{T\theta m},$$

$$T_m = \left(C_{66} + \frac{1}{r_\theta} K_{66}\right)\left(\epsilon_m + \frac{du_{\theta m}}{ds}\right) + \left(K_{66} + \frac{1}{r_\theta} D_{66}\right)\left(\kappa_m + \frac{1}{r_\theta}\frac{du_{\theta m}}{ds}\right), \qquad (10.6a)$$

$$M_{\varphi\theta m} = K_{66}\left(\epsilon_m + \frac{du_{\theta m}}{ds}\right) + D_{66}\left(\kappa_m + \frac{1}{r_\theta}\frac{du_{\theta m}}{ds}\right),$$

where

$$\epsilon_m = \gamma^0_{\varphi\theta m} - \frac{du_{\theta m}}{ds}, \qquad \kappa_m = \tau_m - \frac{1}{r_\theta}\frac{du_{\theta m}}{ds},$$

$$C_{11} = \int_\zeta E_\varphi{}^*\, d\zeta, \qquad C_{12} = \int_\zeta E_\theta{}^* \nu_{\theta\varphi}\, d\zeta, \qquad C_{22} = \int_\zeta E_\theta{}^*\, d\zeta,$$

$$K_{11} = \int_\zeta E_\varphi{}^* \zeta\, d\zeta, \qquad K_{12} = \int_\zeta E_\theta{}^* \nu_{\theta\varphi}\, \zeta\, d\zeta, \qquad K_{22} = \int_\zeta E_\theta{}^* \zeta\, d\zeta, \qquad (10.6b)$$

$$D_{11} = \int_\zeta E_\varphi{}^* \zeta^2 \, d\zeta, \qquad D_{12} = \int_\zeta E_\theta{}^* \nu_{\theta\varphi} \zeta^2 \, d\zeta, \qquad D_{22} = \int_\zeta E_\theta{}^* \zeta^2 \, d\zeta,$$

$$C_{66} = \int_\zeta G_{\varphi\theta} \, d\zeta, \qquad K_{66} = \int_\zeta G_{\varphi\theta} \zeta \, d\zeta, \qquad D_{66} = \int_\zeta G_{\varphi\theta} \zeta^2 \, d\zeta, \tag{10.6c}$$

and we have eliminated the dependence of all of the shell variables upon the coordinate θ by means of expansions of the type Eqs. 6.57f.

The eight first order differential equations which involve the eight fundamental variables can now be presented as follows:[29]

8 PDE

$$\begin{aligned}
\frac{du_{\theta m}}{ds} &= \frac{1}{A_2}\left[T_m - \left(C_{66} + \frac{1}{r_\theta} K_{66}\right)\epsilon_m - \left(K_{66} + \frac{1}{r_\theta} D_{66}\right)\kappa_m\right], \\
\frac{dw_m}{ds} &= \frac{1}{r_\varphi} u_{\varphi m} - \beta_{\varphi m}, \\
\frac{du_{\varphi m}}{ds} &= \epsilon_{\varphi m}{}^0 - \frac{w_m}{r_\varphi}, \\
\frac{d\beta_{\varphi m}}{ds} &= \kappa_{\varphi m},
\end{aligned} \tag{10.6d}$$

$$\begin{aligned}
\frac{dN_{\varphi m}}{ds} &= -\frac{m}{r} T_m + m\left(\frac{1}{r_\varphi} + \frac{1}{r_\theta}\right)\frac{M_{\varphi\theta m}}{r} + \frac{\cos\varphi}{r} N_{\theta m} \\
&\quad - N_{\varphi m}\frac{\cos\varphi}{r} - \frac{1}{r_\varphi} V_m - q_{\varphi m}, \\
\frac{dM_{\varphi m}}{ds} &= M_{\theta m}\frac{\cos\varphi}{r} - \frac{2m}{r} M_{\varphi\theta m} - M_{\varphi m}\frac{\cos\varphi}{r} + V_m, \\
\frac{dV_m}{ds} &= -\frac{2m\cos\varphi}{r^2} M_{\varphi\theta m} - T_m\frac{\cos\varphi}{r} + \frac{N_{\theta m}}{r_\theta} + \frac{N_{\varphi m}}{r_\varphi} \\
&\quad + \frac{m^2}{r^2} M_{\theta m} + q_m, \\
\frac{dT_m}{ds} &= \left(\frac{1}{r_\varphi} - \frac{1}{r_\theta}\right)\frac{\cos\varphi}{r} M_{\varphi\theta m} - \frac{2\cos\varphi}{r} T_m + \frac{m}{r} N_{\theta m} \\
&\quad + \frac{m \sin\varphi}{r^2} M_{\theta m} - q_{\theta m},
\end{aligned} \tag{10.6e}$$

[29] The equations of shell theory were first cast into such a form in a study of conical shells by Goldberg, J. E., and Bogdanoff, J. L., "Static and Dynamic Analysis of Nonuniform Conical Shells under Symmetrical and Unsymmetrical Conditions," *Proc. Sixth Symp. on Ballistic Missile and Aerospace Technology*, New York: Academic Press, Volume 1, 219–238 (1961). The method was applied to arbitrary isotropic shells of revolution by Bogdanoff, J. L., Goldberg, J. E., Ohira, H., and Alspaugh, D. W., "Stress and Deformation in Unsymmetrically Loaded Shells of Revolution," Midwest Applied Science Corp. Report 61-1, (1961) and by Kalnins, loc. cit. Kalnins also applied it to orthotropic layered shells of revolution in the paper "On Free and Forced Vibration of Rotationally Symmetric Layered Shells," *J. Appl. Mech.*, **32**, 941–943 (1965).

where

$$A_2 = C_{66} + \frac{2}{r_\theta} K_{66} + \left(\frac{1}{r_\theta}\right)^2 D_{66}. \tag{10.6f}$$

Of these equations, the first four were obtained by simple rearrangement of the fifth of Eqs. 10.6a, the first of Eqs. 6.4, the first of Eqs. 6.2, and the first of Eqs. 6.3, respectively. The next two equations were obtained by simple rearrangement of the first and fourth of the equilibrium equations 6.1, respectively. The seventh equation was obtained by elimination of $Q_{\theta m}$ from the third and fifth of Eqs. 6.1, while the eighth equation was obtained by elimination of $Q_{\theta m}$ from the second and fifth of Eqs. 6.1.

To express the foregoing equations solely in terms of the eight fundamental variables, we shall have need for the following additional relationships:

$$\begin{aligned}
\epsilon_{\theta m}{}^0 &= \frac{1}{r}(mu_{\theta m} + u_{\varphi m}\cos\varphi + w_m \sin\varphi),\\
\beta_{\theta m} &= \frac{1}{r}(mw_m + u_{\theta m}\sin\varphi),\\
\kappa_{\theta m} &= \frac{1}{r}(m\beta_{\theta m} + \beta_{\varphi m}\cos\varphi),\\
\epsilon_m &= \frac{-1}{r}(mu_{\varphi m} + u_{\theta m}\cos\varphi),\\
\kappa_m &= \frac{1}{r}\left[-\frac{2m\cos\varphi}{r} w_m + \frac{m}{r_\varphi} u_{\varphi m}\right.\\
&\qquad\left. + \cos\varphi\left(\frac{1}{r_\varphi} - \frac{2}{r_\theta}\right) u_{\theta m} - 2m\beta_{\varphi m}\right],\\
\epsilon_{\varphi m}{}^0 &= \frac{1}{A_1}[(N_{\varphi m} + N^*_{T\varphi m} - C_{12}\epsilon_{\theta m}{}^0 - K_{12}\kappa_{\theta m})D_{11}\\
&\qquad - (M_{\varphi m} + M^*_{T\varphi m} - K_{12}\epsilon_{\theta m}{}^0 - D_{12}\kappa_{\theta m})K_{11}],\\
\kappa_{\varphi m} &= \frac{1}{A_1}[(M_{\varphi m} + M^*_{T\varphi m} - K_{12}\epsilon_{\theta m}{}^0 - D_{12}\kappa_{\theta m})C_{11}\\
&\qquad - (N_{\varphi m} + N^*_{T\varphi m} - C_{12}\epsilon_{\theta m}{}^0 - K_{12}\kappa_{\theta m})K_{11}],\\
A_1 &= C_{11}D_{11} - K_{11}{}^2,\\
N_{\theta m} &= C_{12}\epsilon_{\varphi m}{}^0 + C_{22}\epsilon_{\theta m}{}^0 + K_{12}\kappa_{\varphi m} + K_{22}\kappa_{\theta m} - N^*_{T\theta m},\\
M_{\theta m} &= D_{12}\kappa_{\varphi m} + D_{22}\kappa_{\theta m} + K_{12}\epsilon_{\varphi m}{}^0 + K_{22}\epsilon_{\theta m}{}^0 - M^*_{T\theta m},\\
M_{\theta\varphi m} &= K_{66}\left(\epsilon_m + \frac{du_{\theta m}}{ds}\right) + D_{66}\left(\kappa_m + \frac{1}{r_\theta}\frac{du_{\theta m}}{ds}\right).
\end{aligned} \tag{10.6g}$$

Of these equations the first three were obtained directly from the second of Eqs. 6.2, the second of Eqs. 6.4, and the second of Eqs. 6.3, respectively. The fourth and fifth were obtained from the definitions 10.6b along with the third of Eqs. 6.2 and the third of Eqs. 6.3, respectively. The sixth, seventh, and eighth were obtained from a solution of the pair of simultaneous equations formed by the first and fourth of Eqs. 10.6a and the ninth, tenth, and eleventh are simply the second, fourth, and sixth of Eqs. 10.6a. Thus, we have formulated the theory of shells in terms of eight first order differential equations in the eight fundamental variables which are involved in the boundary conditions at the edges of a shell of revolution. The form of the eight equations is such that the stepwise integration processes with which we are concerned here are directly applicable to their solution. Moreover, the equations are free of all derivatives with respect to s of the thickness, radii of curvature, load, temperature, and material properties. This makes it necessary to deal only with point values of these quantities in the numerical solution and avoids the errors which attend the numerical approximation of derivatives of these quantities when other formulations are used. Furthermore, no additional manipulation must be carried out after the solution is completed since the eight variables of the preceding formulation are the variables which are generally of interest in analyses of shells.

Equations 10.6d and 10.6e can be written symbolically in the form

$$\frac{d}{ds}[y(s)] = [A(s)][y(s)] + [B(s)], \tag{10.7a}$$

where $[y(s)]$ is, in the case of arbitrary loadings, a column matrix which involves the eight fundamental variables, $[A(s)]$ represents an eight by eight matrix of coefficients, and $[B(s)]$ is an eight element column matrix which is formed by the inhomogeneous loading and temperature functions. The system 10.7a is to be solved in the interval $a \leqslant s \leqslant b$ at the ends of which the solutions must satisfy the general set of boundary conditions

$$[F_a][y(a)] + [F_b][y(b)] = [G], \tag{10.7b}$$

where $[F_a]$ and $[F_b]$ are eight by eight matrices and $[G]$ is an eight element column matrix which are obtained from the boundary conditions in a given problem.

Now let the complete solution of the system 10.7a be formally written as

$$[y(s)] = [Y(s)][C] + [Z(s)], \tag{10.7c}$$

where $[Y(s)]$ and $[Z(s)]$ are, respectively, an eight by eight matrix of complementary solutions and an eight element column matrix of particular solutions which satisfy the equations

$$\frac{d}{ds}[Y(s)] = [A(s)][Y(s)],$$
$$\frac{d}{ds}[Z(s)] = [A(s)][Z(s)] + [B(s)]. \tag{10.7d}$$

while $[C]$ is an eight element column matrix of arbitrary constants. Since the methods which are now under discussion are begun with known values at the initial point of an interval and proceed in a stepwise fashion to the end point of the interval, some special measures must be taken when the solution must, as in the case of shells, also satisfy prescribed values at the final point. To accomplish this, we take as initial conditions for the determination of $[Y(s)]$ and $[Z(s)]$ the values

$$[Y(a)] = [I],$$
$$[Z(a)] = 0, \tag{10.7e}$$

where $[I]$ is the unit matrix. Evaluation of the general solution 10.7c at $s = a$ then leads, in view of Eqs. 10.7e, to the result

$$[C] = [y(a)], \tag{10.7f}$$

and with this the general solution, when evaluated at $s = b$, takes the form

$$[y(b)] = [Y(b)][y(a)] + [Z(b)]. \tag{10.7g}$$

The combination of Eq. 10.7g and the boundary conditions 10.7b now provides a system of sixteen linear equations from which the sixteen unknown elements of $[y(a)]$ and $[y(b)]$ can be determined. Thus, the two point boundary value problem (Eqs. 10.7a and 10.7b) has been replaced by a set of initial value problems (Eqs. 10.7d and 10.7e) to which the stepwise integration methods can be applied.

It has been found,[30] however that, in the solution of the equations of shell theory with the stepwise integration methods, all accuracy is lost when the generator of the shell exceeds a critical length that is roughly equal to the decay length which we discussed in Chapter 5. The loss of accuracy is not caused by cumulative errors in the integration process; rather, it is caused by the subtraction of almost equal, very large numbers. In particular, the difficulty can be explained, as far as the analysis of shells is concerned, by first recalling that in our exact complementary solutions we always found two types of solution functions. Of these, one type decayed exponentially while the other grew exponentially with the meridional

[30] Sepetoski, W. K., et al., and Galletly, G. D., et al., loc. cit.

coordinate. With this in mind, let us consider Eq. 10.7g which connects the solutions at the end points of the interval (a, b). If we apply unit loads, say, to one end of a shell, that is, if the elements of $[y(a)]$ are of the order of unity, then we may recall from our previous work that, on account of the localized nature of bending effects in shells, the solution $[y(b)]$ which corresponds to the edge values $[y(a)]$ becomes smaller and smaller as the length of the interval (a, b) is increased. Thus, if, for convenience only, we restrict our attention to the complementary solution, Eq. 10.7g states that for a long shell the small solutions $[y(b)]$ are obtained by multiplying the matrix $[Y(b)]$, which contains some very large elements, and the matrix $[y(a)]$ which contains unit elements. For shells of increasing length, therefore, a point will be reached wherein large, almost equal, numbers will be subtracted during the matrix multiplication. All significant figures will, therefore, be lost and the solution will become meaningless.

To demonstrate this effect, the shearing force and moment at each end of clamped pressurized isotropic cylindrical shells with $a = 20$, $h = 1$, $\nu = 0.3$, and various lengths, as obtained by a computer program which is based on a predictor-corrector method, are presented in Table 10.2.

Table 10.2 Effect of Length on Accuracy

l	$\lvert Q_\varphi(0)\rvert$	$\lvert Q_\varphi(l)\rvert$	$M_\varphi(0)$	$M_\varphi(l)$	μl
5	243.70	243.76	201.67	201.80	1.43
10	367.87	368.29	556.26	558.13	2.87
12.5	360.34	360.15	610.44	613.96	3.59
15	342.88	338.40	604.29	603.77	4.31
17.5	331.10	314.64	585.01	554.59	5.02
20	325.85	295.71	571.21	458.95	5.74
25	323.86	431.75	562.29	325.64	7.18
30	323.06	1846.20	560.37	4141.20	8.62
30[a]	323.32	323.39	562.01	562.40	—

[a] In this calculation, the cylinder was replaced by three identical cylinders, each with $l = 10$.

If we bear in mind, from the symmetry of the problem, that $|Q(0)| = |Q(l)|$ and $M(0) = M(l)$, then it is obvious from Table 10.2 that the step-wise integration solution begins to break down shortly after a length of 15 is exceeded. If, in this connection, we also recall that we defined the "critical length" of the cylindrical shell by the rule-of-thumb formula $\mu L_c = \pi$, where μ is the decay parameter as defined by Eq. 5.17b, then we may note from the last column in Table 10.2 that the loss in accuracy of the stepwise integration method becomes noticeable soon after the critical length is exceeded.

The loss of accuracy can, however, be avoided, and shells whose meridians are several multiples of their critical length can be analyzed by the method of stepwise integration by breaking the shell up into a number of shell segments which will be sufficient to insure that the length of each shell segment will be less than the critical length of the original shell.[31] Thus, for example, the cylindrical shell with $l = 30$, say, would be replaced by three cylindrical shells, each with $l = 10$. The results of such a calculation are given in the last row of Table 10.2 from which the success of the multisegment method is obvious. Since the decay length has been shown in our earlier work to be dependent upon the radius and the thickness of the shell under consideration, a criterion for determining when a breakdown into several shells is required is set up, in analogy to the cylindrical shell, by requiring that

$$\mu l \leqslant 3, \tag{10.8a}$$

where

$$\mu^4 = \frac{3(1 - \nu_{\varphi\theta}\nu_{\theta\varphi})}{(R_m h)^2}, \tag{10.8b}$$

and R_m is the minimum principal radius of curvature of the shell.

If such a breakdown is indicated, let the shell be divided into M segments of the same type as the original shell for each of which $\mu l \leqslant 3$ as shown in Fig. 10.5. The subsegments are identified by S_i and the ith shell extends from s_i to s_{i+1} while the first edge of the original shell coincides with $s = s_1$ and the second edge of the shell coincides with $s = s_{M+1}$. By extension of Eqs. 10.7c, we may then write the solution over the total interval $s_1 \leqslant s \leqslant s_{M+1}$ as

$$[y(s)] = [Y_i(s)][y(s_i)] + [Z_i(s)], \tag{10.9a}$$

where s is any point in the interval, i identifies the segment in which the particular point lies and (see Eqs. 10.7d and 10.7e):

$$\begin{aligned} \frac{d}{ds}[Y_i(s)] &= [A(s)][Y_i(s)], \\ \frac{d}{ds}[Z_i(s)] &= [A(s)][Z_i(s)] + [B(s)], \end{aligned} \tag{10.9b}$$

$$[Y_i(s_i)] = [I], \qquad [Z_i(s_i)] = 0. \tag{10.9c}$$

[31] Mirabal, J. A., and Dight, D. G., loc. cit., and Kalnins, A., loc. cit. (1964). Goldberg, J. E., and Bogdanoff, J. L., loc. cit., had previously taken this reasoning one step further by replacing the shell with a large number of short conical shells (see Section 10.2*b*) and then analyzing each segment by the stepwise method.

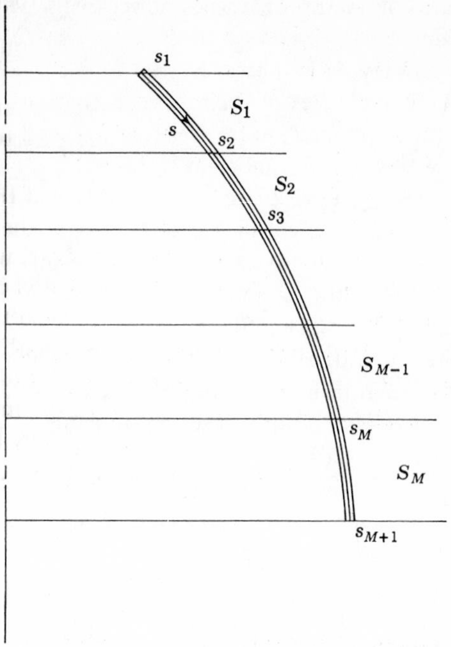

Figure 10.5

Since the eight fundamental variables must be continuous across the junctions between the subsegments we find, from Eq. 10.9a, that this will be insured if

$$[y(s_{i+1})] = [Y_i(s_{i+1})][y(s_i)] + [Z_i(s_{i+1})] \quad i = 1, 2, \ldots, M \tag{10.9d}$$

These equations can be written in the partitioned form

$$\begin{bmatrix} y_1(s_{i+1}) \\ \hline y_2(s_{i+1}) \end{bmatrix} = \left[\begin{array}{c|c} Y_{1i}(s_{i+1}) & Y_{2i}(s_{i+1}) \\ \hline Y_{3i}(s_{i+1}) & Y_{4i}(s_{i+1}) \end{array}\right] \begin{bmatrix} y_1(s_i) \\ \hline y_2(s_i) \end{bmatrix} + \begin{bmatrix} Z_{1i}(s_{i+1}) \\ \hline Z_{2i}(s_{i+1}) \end{bmatrix} \tag{10.9e}$$

so that each of Eqs. 10.9d is replaced by a pair of equations of the type

$$\begin{aligned} [Y_{1i}(s_{i+1})][y_1(s_i)] + [Y_{2i}(s_{i+1})][y_2(s_i)] - [y_1(s_{i+1})] &= -[Z_{1i}(s_{i+1})], \\ [Y_{3i}(s_{i+1})][y_1(s_i)] + [Y_{4i}(s_{i+1})][y_2(s_i)] - [y_2(s_{i+1})] &= -[Z_{2i}(s_{i+1})]. \end{aligned} \tag{10.9f}$$

Thus a system of $2M$ linear matrix equations is obtained in which the known coefficients $[Y_{ji}(s_{i+1})]$ are two-by-two square matrices, $[Z_{ji}(s_{i+1})]$ are two element column matrices, and $[y_j(s_i)]$ are unknown two element column matrices. Since $[y_1(s_1)]$ and $[y_2(s_{M+1})]$ are known from the boundary conditions, there are exactly $2M$ unknowns: $[y_1(s_i)]$ with $i = 2, 3, \ldots, M+1$ and $[y_2(s_i)]$ with $i = 1, 2, \ldots, M$. The problem is, therefore, well set.

The system 10.9f can be solved, for example, by the Gauss reduction.[32] This method leads to a triangularized set of linear equations which, for the specific case of Eq. 10.9f, takes the following form:

$$\begin{bmatrix} E_1 & -I & & & & & \\ & C_1 & -I & & & & \\ & & E_2 & -I & & & \\ & & & \ddots & & & \\ & & & & & E_M & -I \\ & & & & & & C_M \end{bmatrix} \begin{bmatrix} y_2(s_1) \\ y_1(s_2) \\ y_2(s_2) \\ \vdots \\ y_2(s_M) \\ y_1(s_{M+1}) \end{bmatrix} = \begin{bmatrix} A_1 \\ B_1 \\ A_2 \\ \vdots \\ A_M \\ B_M \end{bmatrix} \tag{10.9g}$$

where the $[E_i]$ and $[C_i]$ are two by two matrices which are defined by

$$\begin{aligned} [E_i] &= [Y_{2i}] + [Y_{1i}][C_{i-1}]^{-1}, \qquad [E_1] = [Y_{21}], \\ [C_i] &= \{[Y_{4i}] + [Y_{3i}][C_{i-1}]^{-1}\}[E_i]^{-1}, \qquad [C_1] = [Y_{41}][E_1]^{-1}, \end{aligned} \tag{10.9h}$$

for $i = 1, 2, \ldots, M$. The $[A_i]$ and $[B_i]$ are two element column matrices which are defined by

$$\begin{aligned} -[A_1] &= [Z_{11}] + [Y_{11}][y_1(s_1)], \\ -[B_1] &= [Z_{21}] + [Y_{31}][y_1(s_1)] + [Y_{41}][E_1]^{-1}[A_1]. \end{aligned} \tag{10.9i}$$

for $i = 1$,

$$\begin{aligned} -[A_i] &= [Z_{1i}] + [Y_{1i}][C_{i-1}]^{-1}[B_{i-1}], \\ -[B_i] &= [Z_{2i}] + [Y_{3i}][C_{i-1}]^{-1}[B_{i-1}] \\ &\quad + \{[Y_{4i}] + [Y_{3i}][C_{i-1}]^{-1}\}[E_i]^{-1}[A_i], \end{aligned} \tag{10.9j}$$

for $i = 2, 3, \ldots, M - 1$, and

$$\begin{aligned} -[A_M] &= [Z_{1M}] + [Y_{1M}][C_{M-1}]^{-1}[B_{M-1}], \\ [B_M] &= [y_2(s_{M+1})] - [Z_{2M}] - [Y_{3M}][C_{M-1}]^{-1}[B_{M-1}] \\ &\quad - \{[Y_{4M}] + [Y_{3M}][C_{M-1}]^{-1}\}[E_M]^{-1}[A_M], \end{aligned} \tag{10.9k}$$

for $i = M$, where $[Y_{ji}(s_{i+1})]$ and $[Z_{ji}(s_{i+1})]$ have been replaced by $[Y_{ji}]$ and $[Z_{ji}]$, respectively.

The unknown matrices of Eq. 10.9g can now be obtained in succession from the formulas

$$\begin{aligned} [y_1(s_{M+1})] &= [C_M]^{-1}[B_M], \\ [y_2(s_M)] &= [E_M]^{-1}\{[y_1(s_{M+1})] + [A_M]\}, \end{aligned} \tag{10.9l}$$

for $i = M$ and

$$\begin{aligned} [y_1(s_{M-i+1})] &= [C_{M-1}]^{-1}\{[y_2(s_{M-i+1})] + [B_{M-i}]\}, \\ [y_2(s_{M-i})] &= [E_{m-i}]^{-1}\{[y_1(s_{M-i+1})] + [A_{M-i}]\}. \end{aligned} \tag{10.9m}$$

[32] Hildebrand, loc. cit.

for $i = 1, 2, \ldots, M - 1$. This completes the formal solution of the problem.

By employing the foregoing breakdown, the loss of accuracy which is encountered when analyzing shells that are "too long" by the stepwise methods is completely avoided (see the last row in Table 10.2). Consequently, it is felt that the stepwise methods represent the simplest and most accurate approach to the numerical solution of the equations of the theory of thin elastic shells.

10.3 RESULTS OBTAINED BY COMPUTER PROGRAMS BASED UPON THE VARIOUS NUMERICAL METHODS

In all of the methods which have been described in the foregoing discussion of numerical analysis, the solution of the equations of shell theory was reduced in one way or another to the solution of a large set of simultaneous linear algebraic equations. Digital computers are eminently well suited to carrying out such procedures in a rapid manner and, for this reason, many computer programs, based on all of the methods which we have described, are available. To demonstrate the effectiveness of the computer in the solution of problems involving shells we shall, in this section, cite some typical results obtained by various computer programs which are currently in use. Available experimental data will be cited throughout the discussion in order to bring out the accuracy of the theory of thin elastic shells in general and of the computer solutions in particular.

In the interest of brevity, we shall not delve into the details of the computer programs which will be mentioned in our discussion. Such matters will be left to the references which are cited for each program.

10.3*a* Computer Solutions Based upon the Method of Finite Differences

As a first example, let us consider a segment of a toroidal shell which is loaded as shown in Fig. 10.6 by an overall θ-independent couple. An approximate analysis of this problem, based on the method of asymptotic integration that we described in Chapter 7, was carried out by Hetényi and Timms,[33] who also carried out some experimental measurements of the stresses in such a shell by means of bonded wire strain gages. The analytical and experimental results are shown in Fig. 10.6 along with results obtained by Radkowski, et al.,[34] who used a computer program based on the method

[33] Hetényi, M., and Timms, R. J., "Analysis of Axially Loaded Annular Shells with Applications to Welded Bellows," *Trans. ASME*, **82C**, 741–755 (1960).
[34] Radkowski, P. P., et al., loc. cit.

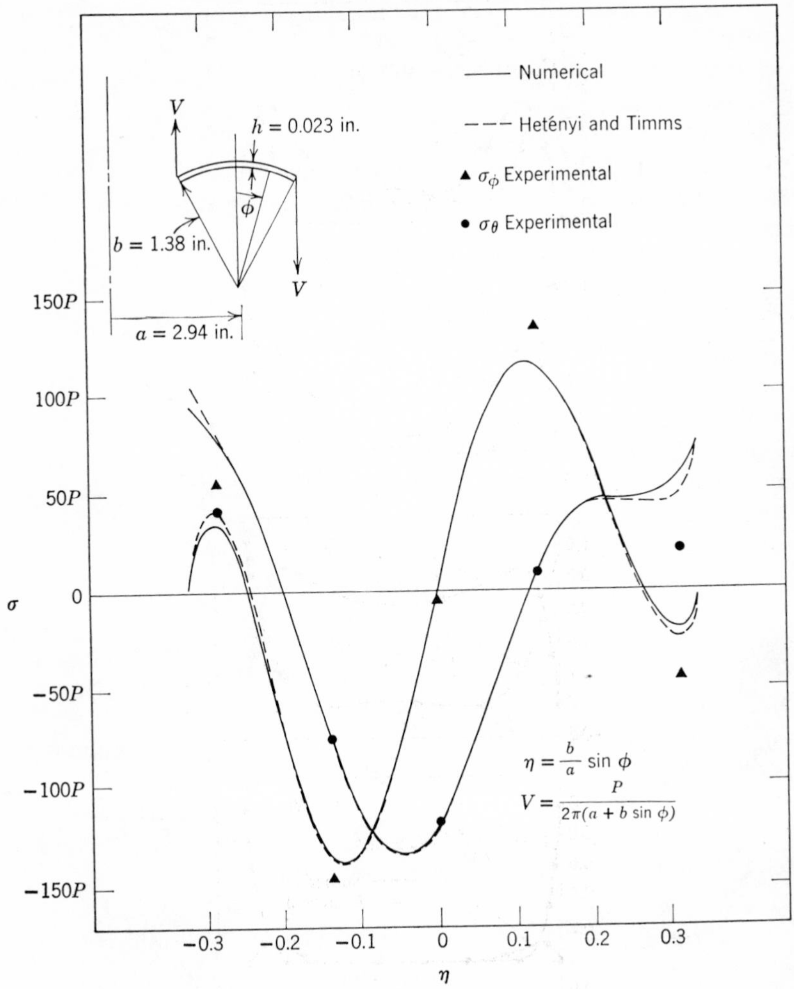

Figure 10.6 Comparison of finite difference, and asymptotic solutions for a toroidal shell segment.

of finite differences, for a toroidal segment with $a = 2.94$ in., $b = 1.38$ in., $h = 0.023$ in., and $\nu = 0.3$. The plotted data indicate that the finite difference solution and the asymptotic solution are in very close agreement over most of the extent of the shell. Also, both solutions match the experimental data quite well.

As an example of an analysis of a shell under an arbitrary loading, we next consider the complementary solution for an arbitrarily loaded isotropic circular cylindrical shell whose ends are restrained from motion and

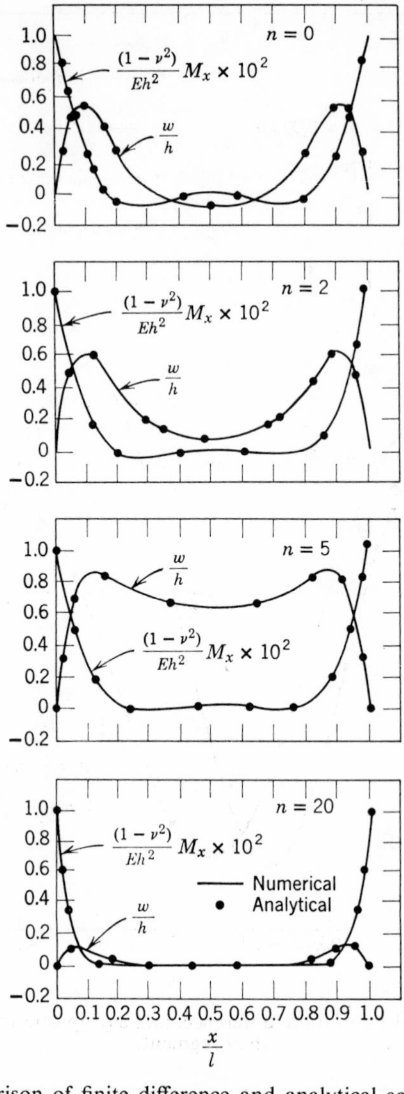

Figure 10.7 Comparison of finite difference and analytical solutions for an arbitrarily loaded circular cylindrical shell.

are subjected to prescribed axial moments; that is,

$$u_x = u_\theta = w = 0, \qquad M_x = \frac{Eh^2}{100(1 - \nu^2)} \cos n\theta, \tag{10.10}$$

at $x = 0, l$. An exact analytical solution and a computer solution based upon the finite difference method were carried out for this problem by

Budiansky and Radkowski[35] who utilized the theory of Sanders which we described in Chapter 3. Their results for a cylindrical shell with $a/h = 50$, $l/a = 1$, $\nu = 0.3$, and several values of the index n are summarized in Fig. 10.7 where the transverse displacement and axial moment distributions are plotted. It is seen that the agreement between the exact analytical solution and the finite difference solution is excellent.

To illustrate the capability of the finite difference method in the analysis of composite shells, we have prepared Table 10.3. There we have tabulated the stress indexes at the junctions of a variety of cylindrical pressure vessels with hemispherical heads as obtained by an exact analytical solution[36] and by a computer program based upon the finite difference method.[37] The stress index is defined as the stress divided by $pD/2t$, where the latter quantity represents the circumferential membrane stress in a cylindrical shell of middle surface diameter D and wall thickness t under an internal pressure p. In addition, the quantity T is the thickness of the hemispherical head. The table shows again that the results obtained by the finite difference solution agree very well with the exact analytical results.

10.3*b* Computer Solutions Based upon the Finite Element Method

As a first application of this method, let us consider the determination of edge influence coefficients for the toroidal shell segment shown in Fig. 10.8. Such a segment has been analyzed by Galletly,[38] who used the method of asymptotic integration, and by Meyer and Harmon,[39] who used

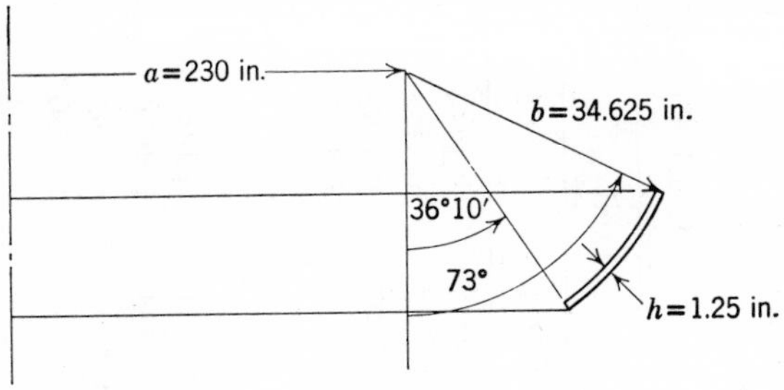

Figure 10.8

---

[35] Budiansky, B., and Radkowski, P. P., loc. cit.

[36] Watts, G. W., and Lang, H. A., "Stresses in a Pressure Vessel with a Hemispherical Head," *Trans. ASME*, **75**, 83–89 (1953). This solution has been discussed in Section 5.5*b*.

[37] Kraus, H., et al., loc. cit.

[38] Galletly, G. D., "A Comparison of Methods for Analyzing Bending Effects in Toroidal Shells," *J. Appl. Mech.*, **25**, 413–414 (1958).

[39] Meyer, R. R., and Harmon, M. B., loc. cit.

Table 10.3 Stress Indexes at Junction

			Exact Analytical Solution				Finite Difference Solution			
HEMISPHERE			Axial		Circumferential		Axial		Circumferential	
D	*T*	*t*	Outside	Inside	Outside	Inside	Outside	Inside	Outside	Inside
32	0.8	1.0	0.6767	0.5733	0.8583	0.8273	0.6737	0.5763	0.8585	0.8293
16	0.8	1.0	0.6772	0.5728	0.8582	0.8268	0.6822	0.5678	0.8569	0.8226
20	1.0	1.0	0.5007	0.4993	0.7496	0.7492	0.5048	0.4952	0.7477	0.7449
16	1.6	1.0	0.2359	0.3891	0.5619	0.6079	0.2388	0.3862	0.5587	0.6029
CYLINDER										
32	0.8	1.0	0.5331	0.4669	0.8152	0.7954	0.5318	0.4682	0.8159	0.7968
16	0.8	1.0	0.5334	0.4666	0.8150	0.7950	0.5369	0.4631	0.8133	0.7911
20	1.0	1.0	0.5007	0.4993	0.7496	0.7492	0.5053	0.4947	0.7479	0.7447
16	1.6	1.0	0.3040	0.6960	0.5824	0.7000	0.3121	0.6879	0.5807	0.6934

Table 10.4 Edge Influence Coefficients for the Shell shown in Fig. 10.8

Edge Loading	φ	$\lvert E\delta \rvert$			$\lvert E\beta \rvert$		
		Asymptotic Integration	4 cones	15 cones	Asymptotic Integration	4 cones	15 cones
Unit moment at $\varphi = 73°$	73°	990	971.49	975.80	132.5	130.6	130.8
	36° 10′	680	675.70	673.29	76.2	74.94	75.27
Unit inward horizontal	73°	11400	11156	11211	987	971.5	975.8
force at $\varphi = 73°$	36° 10′	4375	4447	4425	811	806.8	810.8
Unit moment at $\varphi = 36° 10'$	73°	776	767.8	771.8	72.6	71.33	71.64
	36° 10′	820	826.2	820.5	137.6	137.5	137.8
Unit outward horizontal	73°	4180	4232	4211	646	643.1	640.9
force at $\varphi = 36° 10'$	36° 10′	8530	8477	8396	818	826.2	820.5

a computer program based upon the finite element method. The magnitudes of the edge influence coefficients, as obtained by the two methods for the shell shown in Fig. 10.8, are summarized in Table 10.4, from which it is evident that the finite element method gives results that agree very well with the results of the method of asymptotic integration. Table 10.4 also indicates that the use of a four cone approximation in the finite element method yields results which are only slightly less accurate than the results obtained by a fifteen cone approximation (see Figs. 10.3 and 10.4).

Further examples of the accuracy of the finite element method are shown in Figs. 10.9 and 10.10 where analytical and digital computer results are given for two problems involving spherical shell segments.[40] Figure 10.9 concerns a single clamped isotropic hemispherical shell under the influence of a unit moment which is uniformly distributed around the edge of a 30 degree hole at its apex. The spacing of the conical elements as well as the geometry of the shell are defined in the upper portion of the diagram, while the theoretical and digital computer distributions of horizontal displacement and meridional bending moment are plotted in the lower portion of the diagram. The agreement between the two solutions is excellent.

A typical assembly of a hemispherical shell and a cylindrical shell as encountered in the missile industry is considered in Fig. 10.10. As indicated in the diagram, the upper chamber of the assembly is subjected to an axial thrust load while the lower chamber is pressurized. To permit a convenient analytical solution to be carried out the assembly was assumed to be isotropic; however, the finite element method is not, as we have pointed out earlier, limited to such materials. The theoretical and digital distributions of the radial displacements are also given in Fig. 10.10. Again, the agreement between the results is very good.

10.3*c* Computer Solutions Based upon Predictor-Corrector Methods

A common structure in steam power plants is the toroidal, or omega, expansion joint shown in Fig. 10.11. Approximate analytical solutions for the stresses in such joints were first obtained by Dahl,[41] who used the method of asymptotic integration as well as the principle of minimum complementary energy. In that investigation, stresses in such assemblies were also measured by means of bonded wire strain gages. The meridional bending stress distributions as obtained in the analytical and experimental investigations are plotted in Fig. 10.11 along with the results obtained by a computer program that is based upon a predictor-corrector

[40] Grafton, P. E., and Strome, D. R., loc. cit.

[41] Dahl, N. C., "Toroidal Shell Expansion Joints," *J. Appl. Mech.*, **20**, 497–503 (1953).

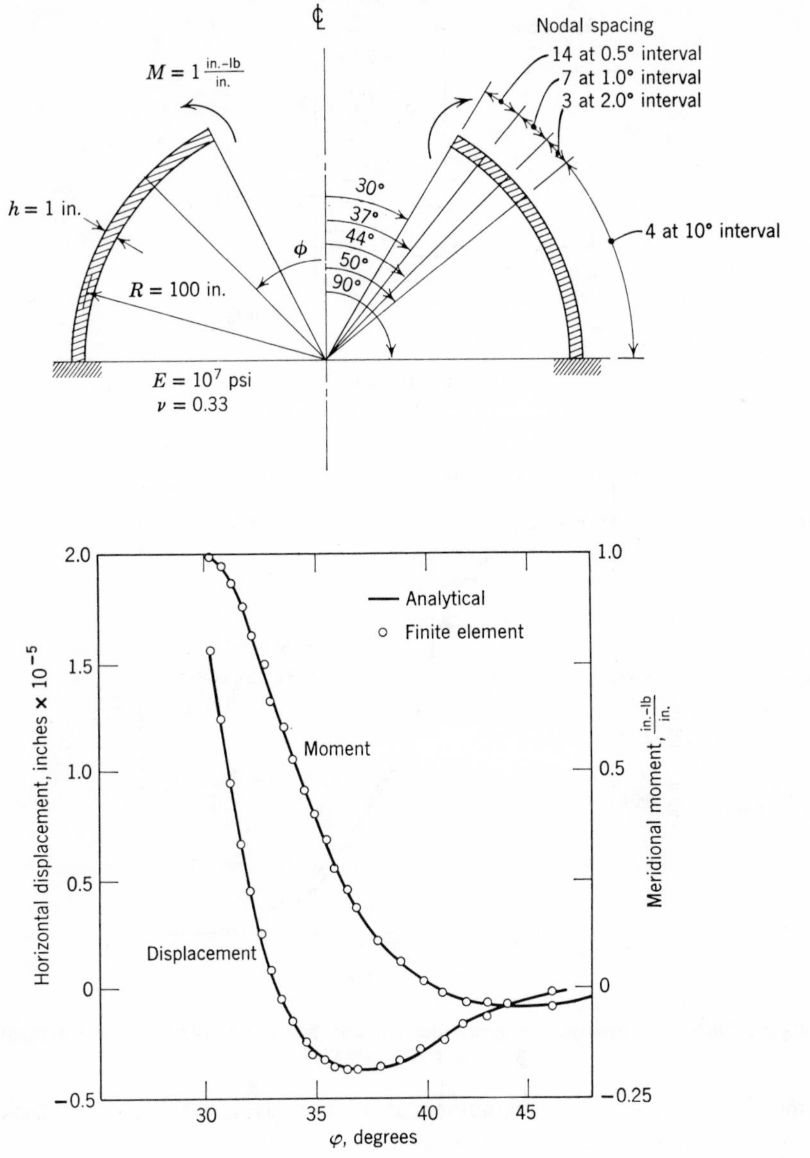

Figure 10.9 Comparison of finite element and analytical solutions for a spherical shell segment.

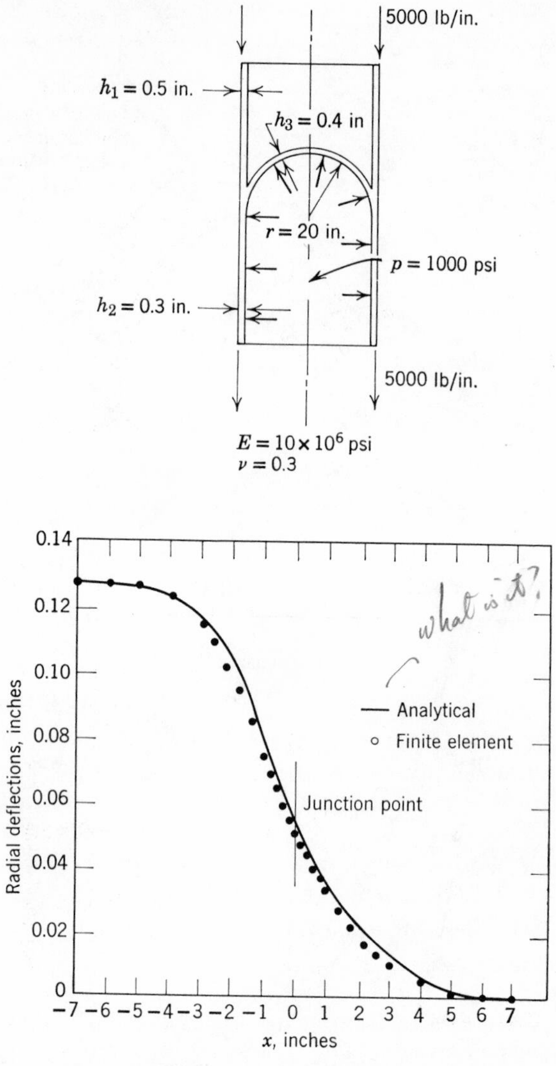

Figure 10.10 Comparison of finite element and analytical solutions for a typical aerospace shell structure.

method.[42] It is seen that the numerical solution gives, in this case, the best agreement with the experimental data.

As a final comparison of results, we reconsider the case of the clamped, isotropic, pressurized hemispherical shell for which we obtained an exact

[42] Mirabal, J. A., and Dight, J. A., loc. cit.

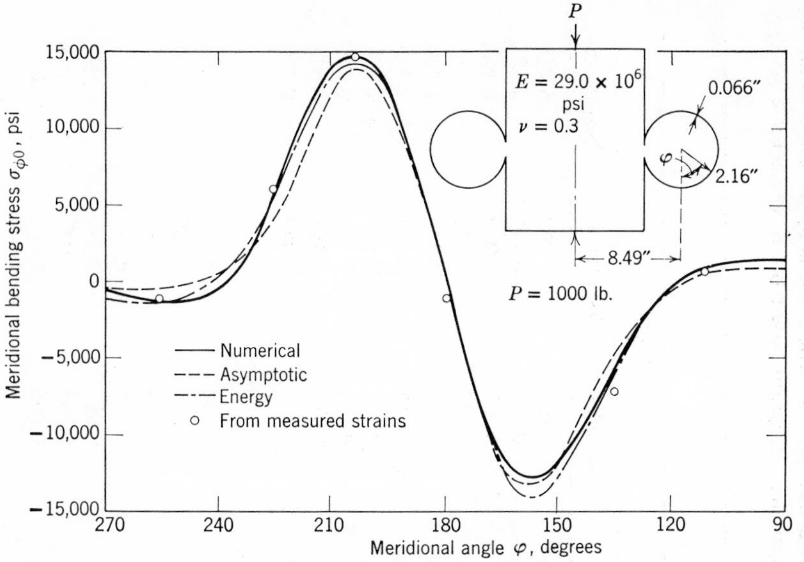

Figure 10.11 Comparison of predictor-corrector and analytical solutions for a toroidal expansion joint.

solution in Section 5.4*c* and approximate analytical solutions by Geckeler's method in Section 7.2*a* and asymptotic integration in Section 7.3*a*. We also recall that results obtained by these three solutions were compared in Table 7.1. In order to extend the previous comparison to include results from a numerical solution that has been programmed for a digital computer, we have repeated Table 7.1 here as Table 10.5 and have added columns of results which were obtained by a program based on a predictor-corrector method. The tabulated data indicate that the numerical solution gives as good an approximation of the exact results as do the approximate analytical solutions.

10.3*d* Comparison of Results Obtained for a Specific Problem by Several Computer Programs

We have given abundant examples of the accuracy of the various computer solutions in the preceding discussion. Now it is of interest to select a typical example and to compare the results obtained by various numerical solutions to an available exact analytical solution. For this purpose, let us consider the pressure vessel with a hemispherical head whose dimensions are shown in Fig. 10.12. Only one end of this assembly is of interest and, for this reason, the length of the cylindrical portion of the vessel has been chosen to be of a magnitude which is sufficient to insure that any bending

Table 10.5 Comparison of Results Obtained for Isotropic Clamped, Pressurized Hemispherical Shells by the Exact Solution, by Geckeler's Approximation, by Asymptotic Integration, and by a Computer Program based on a Predictor-Corrector Method

	$R/h = 10$							
	$2N_\theta/pR$				M_φ/ph^2			
φ (degrees)	Exact	Geckeler	Asymptotic	Numerical	Exact	Geckeler	Asymptotic	Numerical
90	0.300	0.300	0.300	0.299	− 1.066	− 1.059	− 1.059	− 1.089
85	0.371	0.369	0.373	0.364	− 0.446	− 0.437	− 0.441	− 0.456
80	0.514	0.514	0.516	0.506	− 0.061	− 0.052	− 0.059	− 0.063
75	0.669	0.672	0.670	0.661	+ 0.141	+ 0.148	+ 0.140	+ 0.145
70	0.802	0.807	0.802	0.797	+ 0.219	+ 0.221	+ 0.217	+ 0.224
65	0.903	0.908	0.901	0.900	+ 0.222	+ 0.218	+ 0.219	+ 0.226
60	0.970	0.973	0.968	0.969	+ 0.186	+ 0.178	+ 0.183	+ 0.190
55	1.009	1.010	1.007	1.010	+ 0.136	+ 0.127	+ 0.135	+ 0.140
50	1.028	1.027	1.026	1.030	+ 0.089	+ 0.079	+ 0.088	+ 0.090
45	1.033	1.030	1.031	1.037	+ 0.049	+ 0.041	+ 0.049	+ 0.050
	$R/h = 100$							
90	0.300	0.300	0.300	0.299	−10.598	−10.591	−10.591	−10.655
85	0.695	0.695	0.695	0.695	+ 1.611	+ 1.616	+ 1.609	+ 1.618
80	0.988	0.988	0.988	0.990	+ 1.591	+ 1.583	+ 1.589	+ 1.601
75	1.029	1.029	1.029	1.032	+ 0.281	+ 0.275	+ 0.281	+ 0.283
70	1.010	1.009	1.009	1.012	− 0.092	− 0.091	− 0.092	− 0.093
65	1.000	1.000	1.000	1.002	− 0.057	− 0.055	− 0.057	− 0.058
60	0.999	0.999	0.999	1.001	− 0.006	− 0.006	− 0.006	− 0.006

effects which are introduced at the lower end will not interact with the bending effects that arise at the junction between the cylindrical shell and the hemispherical head. An analytical solution for the dimensions of Fig. 10.12 has been obtained in the previously cited investigation of Watts and

$$\nu = \cdot 3$$
$$E = 30 \times 10^6 \text{ psi}$$

$L = 40$

$h = 1$

$R = 20$

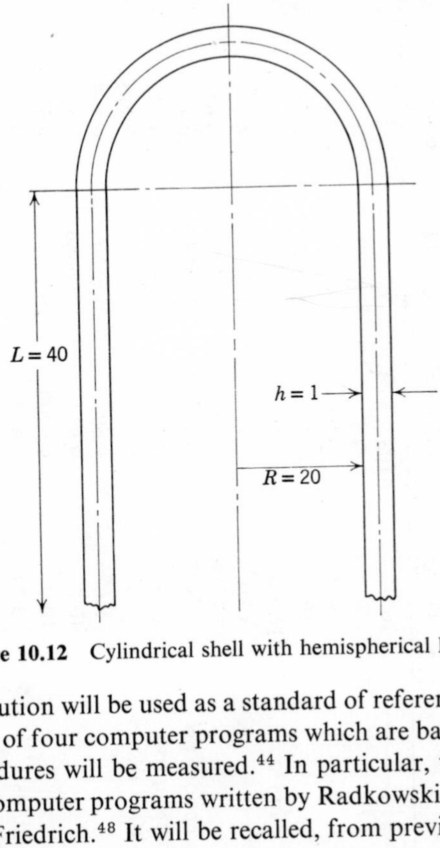

Figure 10.12 Cylindrical shell with hemispherical head.

Lang.[43] That solution will be used as a standard of reference against which the performance of four computer programs which are based upon various numerical procedures will be measured.[44] In particular, the assembly will be analyzed by computer programs written by Radkowski et al.,[45] Penny,[46] Kalnins,[47] and Friedrich.[48] It will be recalled, from previous references to these programs, that the Radkowski and the Penny programs are based upon the finite difference method, the Kalnins program is based on a predictor-corrector method, and the Friedrich program is based upon the stiffness matrix method.

[43] Watts, G. W., and Lang, H. A., loc. cit.

[44] Kraus, H., loc. cit. (1965).

[45] Radkowski, P. P., et al., loc. cit.

[46] Penny, R. K., loc. cit., also Penny, R. K., and Perryman, K. R., "VESSL I, IBM 7090 Program for Computing Stresses in Shells of Revolution," Central Electricity Generating Board Computing Department, London (1962).

[47] Kalnins, A., loc. cit.

[48] Friedrich, C. M., loc. cit.

Table 10.6 Comparison of Analytical and Digital Results for the Pressure Vessel shown in Fig. 10.12

	Finite Difference		Predictor-Corrector	Finite Element	Analytical
	Penny	Radkowski	Kalnins	Friedrich	Watts & Lang
Number of separate output points	262	103	77	80	*N/A*
Running time on IBM 7094, min.	0.78	3.5	1.15	5.8	*N/A*
Outside stress at apex, psi	9.9947	9.9939	9.9948	9.27	Not given
Inside stress at apex, psi	10.002	10.001	10.001	9.77	Not given
Normal displacement at apex, 10^{-6} in.	Not given	9.698	9.708	9.3076	Not given
Outside axial stress at junction, psi	10.014	10.026	10.007	9.35	10.006
Inside axial stress at junction, psi	9.9862	9.9735	9.9933	9.68	9.9940
Outside circumferential stress at junction, psi	14.998	15.012	14.996	14.10	14.996
Inside circumferential stress at junction, psi	14.990	14.997	14.992	14.88	14.992
Normal displacement at junction, 10^{-6} in.	7.996	8.003	7.999	7.857	Not given
Rotation at junction, 10^{-7} radian	9.626	9.597	9.599	9.30	Not given
Outside axial stress at end, psi	10.0	9.9999	9.9999	9.27	10.0
Inside axial stress at end, psi	10.0	9.9999	10.0	9.75	10.0
Outside circumferential stress at end, psi	19.999	20.0	20.0	19.07	20.0
Inside circumferential stress at end, psi	19.999	20.0	20.0	20.22	20.0
Normal displacement at end, 10^{-6} in.	11.33	11.33	11.33	11.28	Not given
Peak stress in cylinder (circumferential outside)	20.624	20.629	20.627	20.24	20.630
Location, in. from junction	6.5	6.44	6.25	9.2	6.46

The analytically and digitally computed results for the problem under consideration are summarized in Table 10.6[49] where, to keep the presentation of data down to a reasonable minimum, we have concerned ourselves only with certain key locations in the assembly.

The tabulated data indicate that, for the problem under consideration, there is excellent agreement between the results obtained by the two finite difference solutions, the predictor-corrector solution and the analytical solution. This is as one would expect because all of these solutions are based upon Love's postulates. The finite element solution of Friedrich gives results that are slightly different from the other solutions because it alone includes the effect of the transverse shear and normal stresses. According to our remarks in Section 5.6, however, the stress results obtained by such a higher-order theory are not necessarily more reliable than those obtained by a theory which is based on Love's postulates.

It is also seen from the table that problems of this type can be handled in a matter of minutes on a digital computer. The specific running times are listed for illustrative purposes only. No conclusion about the speed of any particular program should be drawn from these as they are constantly being reduced by the introduction of more efficient programs and faster computers.

As a final point of interest, we have plotted, in Fig. 10.13, the meridional distribution of stress indexes for the pressure vessel of Fig. 10.12 as obtained by the computer program that was written by Penny and Perryman.[50] The stress index is again defined as the appropriate stress divided by the quantity pR/h. Thus, $I_{\varphi 0}$, $I_{\varphi i}$, $I_{\theta 0}$, and $I_{\theta i}$ denote, respectively, the meridional stress indexes on the outer and inner surfaces and the circumferential stress indexes on the outer and inner surfaces of the shell. The curves in Fig. 10.13 indicate that the largest stresses occur in the cylindrical portion of the structure and that these are approximated fairly well by the result $I_\theta = 1$ which would have been obtained by using the membrane theory. The curves also show the localized nature of bending effects in an assembly of this type.

10.3*e* Typical Solutions that Are Made Possible by the Use of Numerical Methods

In the foregoing presentation of results, we demonstrated the accuracy of various numerical solutions of the equations of the theory of thin elastic shells. In doing this, however, we restricted our attention to simple

[49] The author is indebted to the originators of each program for making the necessary card decks and operating instructions available to him.

[50] Penny, R. K., and Perryman, K. R., loc. cit.

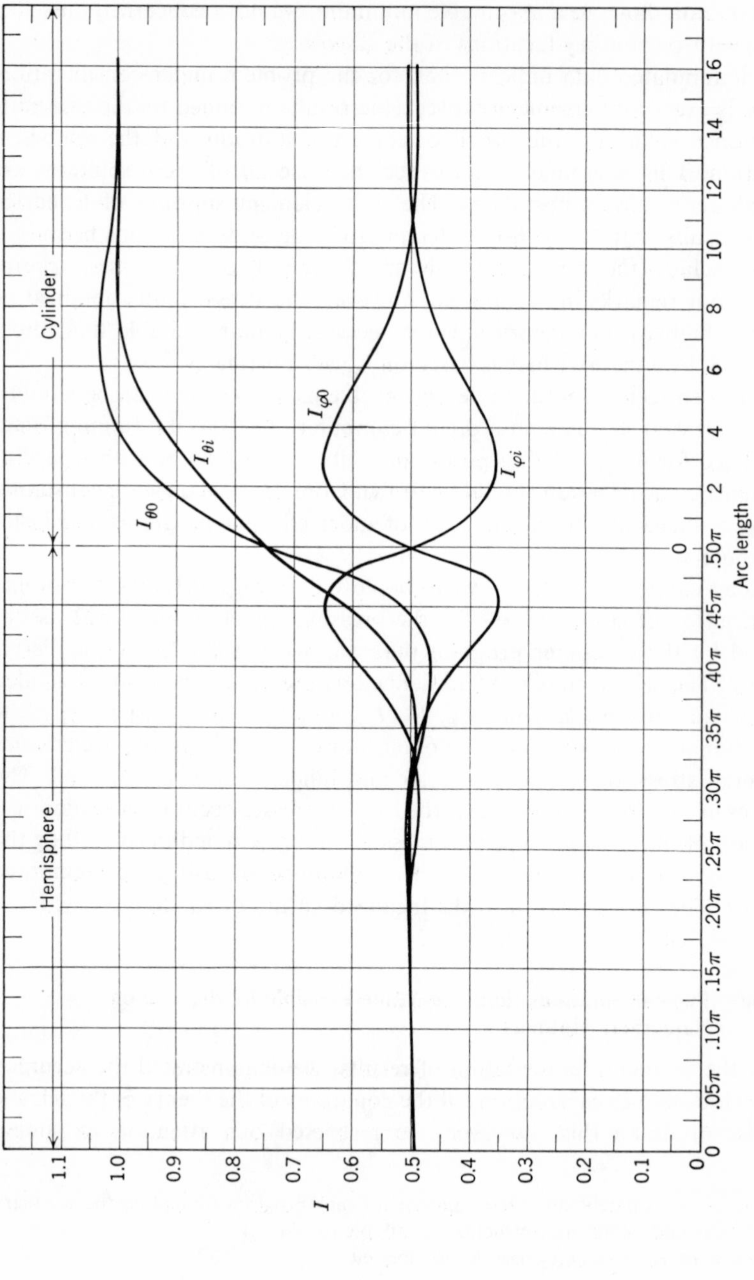

Figure 10.13 Stress index distributions in the pressure vessel shown in Fig. 10.12.

geometrical shapes for which analytical solutions could be obtained for purposes of comparison. It is now appropriate, therefore, to demonstrate the flexibility and wide applicability of the computer solutions by considering two typical industrial problems whose solutions are made possible by the availability of computer programs such as we have described here.

As the first example, we consider the analysis of a gas turbine component which is shown in Fig. 10.14. The component is essentially clamped on the bolt centerline at its left end and is subjected to an external, overall moment by a rigid shaft which enters its right end. For purposes of analysis, the

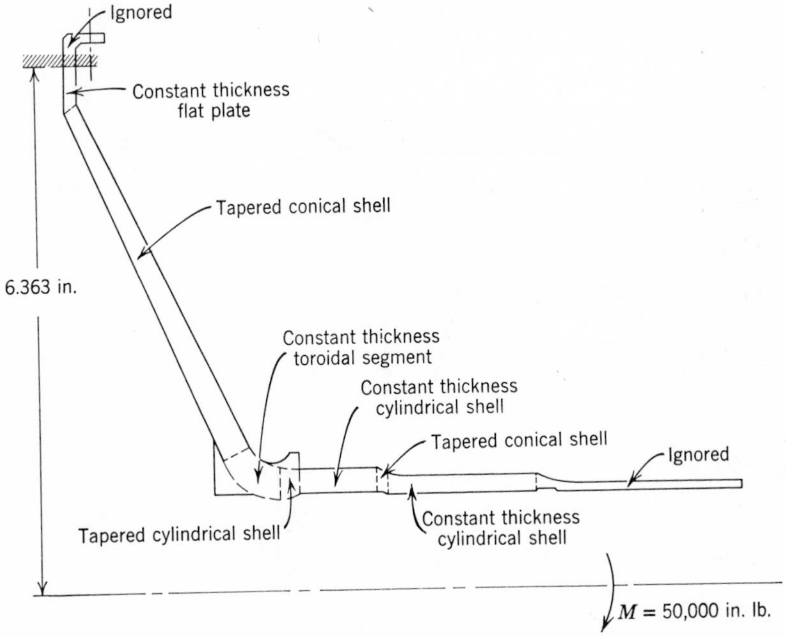

Figure 10.14 Typical gas turbine shell structure.

item is broken down into the seven shell segments which are shown with dotted lines in Fig. 10.14 and the overall end moment M is replaced by a statically equivalent axial force $N \cos \theta$. It is obvious that the determination of the stress distributions in the component by analytical means is a hopeless task. By means of a computer program, however, the problem is reduced to a routine calculation whose results are shown for the case $M = 50{,}000$ in. lb. in Figs. 10.15 and 10.16. In these plots, the stress distributions, as calculated by a computer program which is based on a predictor-corrector method, are given along with some experimental data which were obtained with bonded wire strain gages. In view of the intricate

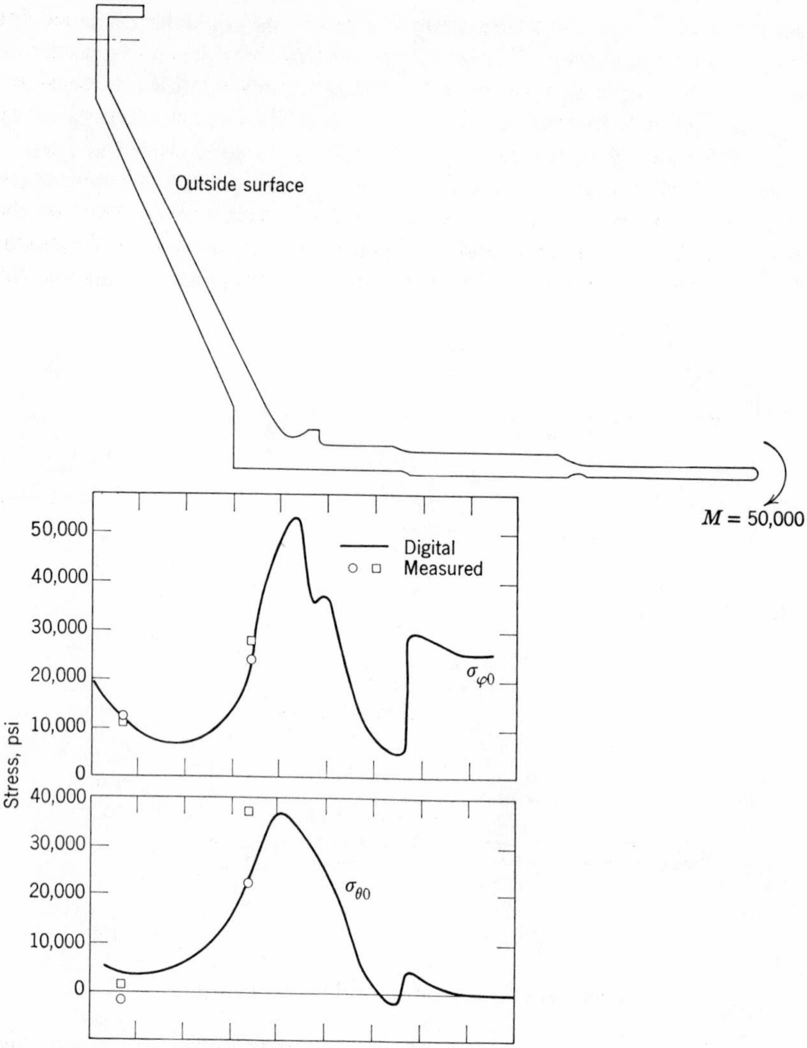

Figure 10.15 Stress distributions on outside surface of shell shown in Fig. 10.14.

nature of the component, the agreement between the digital and experimental stresses is very good.

The second example concerns the analysis of a joint which is commonly used in fiberglass construction. As shown in Fig. 10.17, the joint consists of an elongated I section with steel shims imbedded in the fiberglass rovings. In view of the fact that the materials are distributed in such a manner that the properties of the joint are orthotropic, and in view of the variation of

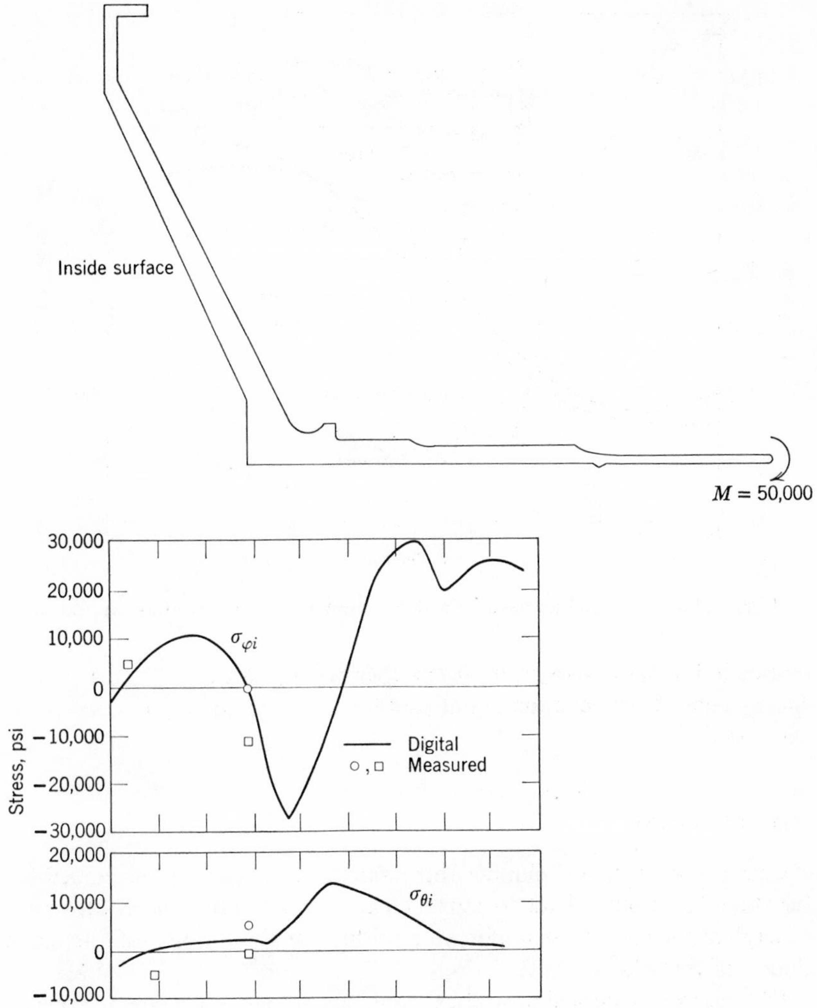

Figure 10.16 Stress distributions on inside of shell shown in Fig. 10.14.

the thickness along the joint, it is obvious that a reliable analytical solution for the stresses and deformations associated with the joint would be extremely difficult to carry out. Such an analysis can, however, be conveniently performed by a digital computer program and this has been done by an orthotropic finite element procedure.[51] The bending moment and the radial deflection distributions as obtained in such a digital calculation are

[51] Grafton, P. E., and Strome, D. R., loc. cit.

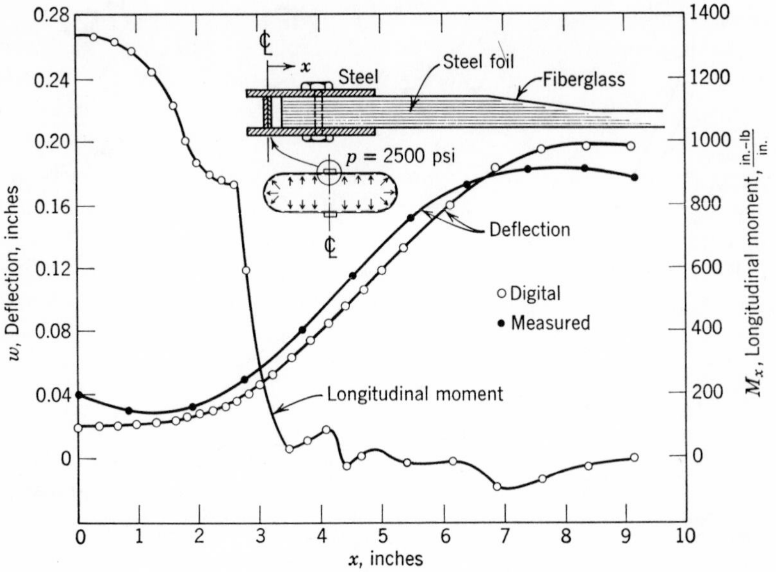

Figure 10.17 Typical aerospace shell structure: the fiberglass pressure vessel.

plotted in Fig. 10.17 along with some experimental values for the deflection. The agreement between the digital and the experimental data is seen to be very good.

10.4 CLOSURE

We have shown in this chapter that numerical analyses programmed for the digital computer lead to convenient, accurate solutions of the most general problems which might arise within the framework of the static theory of thin elastic shells.

Of the three numerical procedures that have been applied here, it appears that the stepwise integration methods, particularly the predictor-corrector methods, would be the most attractive if we should contemplate the writing of a new computer program. This conclusion is based upon the simplicity and the accuracy of the resulting formulations, and the ease with which the stepwise integration methods can be programmed for digital computation. The formulations are simple because, as we have seen, a minimum of manipulation is required to arrange the equations of the theory into the required first order equations. The methods are accurate because no derivatives of geometrical or elastic properties appear in the first order equations of the formulation and because no further numerical derivatives must be taken to obtain any of the desired results in the calculation. The latter are already the fundamental variables in the calculation and are given at each point of the interval by the numerical integration. Finally, the stepwise integration methods can be programmed more easily because they rely upon simple formulas of the type which we have presented (see Eqs. 10.4b to 10.4f).

The results which we have cited here indicate the broad range of problems whose solution has been made possible by the advent of the digital computer and the accompanying rise of the field of numerical analysis. Indeed, as far as the static analysis of shells is concerned, the availability of the digital computer has also made feasible the analysis of the more complex problems which are associated with shells undergoing nonlinear,[52] plastic,[53] and creep[54] deformation.

In addition to the numerical solutions which it has facilitated, the computer has also greatly simplified the calculation of numerical results from available analytical solutions and has made possible the rapid tabulation of any of the mathematical functions which were derived in Parts II and III of this book. Indeed, the bulk of the numerical results which were presented in the illustrative problems of Parts II and III were evaluated by means of short computer programs based on the formulas which were obtained in each of the analytical solutions.

As a final consideration, it is well to take advantage of the generality and the accuracy of the numerical solutions to reexamine the matter of particular solutions for shells subjected to static distributed loadings which we discussed in Part II. Specifically, we may recall from Chapter 7 that the solutions that would have been obtained for a given problem by the membrane theory were adopted as the particular solutions for shells under distributed loadings. This assumption takes either of two forms. In the first of these, which has already been cited in Chapter 7, we set $Q_\varphi{}^p = \beta_\varphi{}^p = 0$ and use the membrane solution for $N_\theta{}^p$ and $N_\varphi{}^p$. The particular solution for the displacement δ^p, perpendicular to the shell axis, then follows from $N_\theta{}^p$ and

---

[52] Thurston, G. A., "A Numerical Solution of the Nonlinear Equations for Axisymmetric Bending of Shallow Spherical Shells," *J. Appl. Mech.*, **28**, 557–562 (1961). Wilson, P. E., and Spier, E. E., "Numerical Analysis of Large Axisymmetric Deformations of Thin Spherical Shells," AIAA Preprint, 64-440, *AIAA Bull.*, **1**, 271 (1964). Kalnins, A., and Lestingi, J. F., "On Nonlinear Analysis of Elastic Shells of Revolution," *J. Appl. Mech.*, **34**, 59–64 (1967).

[53] Spera, D. A., "Analysis of Elastic-Plastic Shells of Revolution Containing Discontinuities," *AIAA J.*, **1**, 2583–2589 (1963) Marcal, P. V., and Turner, C. E., "Numerical Analysis of the Elastic Plastic Behavior of Axisymmetrically Loaded Shells of Revolution," *J. Mech. Eng. Sci.*, **5**, 232–237 (1963).

[54] Penny, R. K., "Axisymmetric Bending of the General Shell of Revolution During Creep," *J. Mech. Eng. Sci.*, **6**, 44–46 (1964).

$N_\varphi{}^p$ while $M_\varphi{}^p = M_\theta{}^p = 0$ from the vanishing of $\beta_\varphi{}^p$. In the second approach, we modify the foregoing procedure by using the membrane solution for $\beta_\varphi{}^p$ as well. Numerical solutions of the type which we have discussed in this chapter will now be used to show that these procedures can, in some cases, lead to considerable error.

Let us, therefore, consider[55] the open crown ellipsoidal shell and the negative curvature toroidal shell which are shown in Fig. 10.18. The stress resultant, rotation, and displacement functions for each are given by the membrane theory as the following:

Ellipsoidal shell:

$$\begin{aligned}
E\beta_\varphi{}^p &= -p\frac{k}{2}\left(\frac{a}{h}\right)\frac{(\rho^2-1)(3\rho^2+1)}{\rho^3}\cot\varphi,\\
E\delta^p &= k\left(\frac{a}{h}\right)\rho\sin\varphi(N_\varphi{}^p - \nu N_\theta{}^p),\\
N_\theta{}^p &= \frac{pka}{2\rho}(2\rho^2-1),\\
N_\varphi{}^p &= \frac{pk\rho a}{2},\\
\rho &= [1+(k^2-1)\sin^2\varphi]^{-1/2}, \qquad k = a/c.
\end{aligned} \tag{10.11}$$

Toroidal shell of negative curvature:

$$\begin{aligned}
E\beta_\varphi{}^p &= \frac{p}{2}\left(\frac{b}{h}\right)\frac{\cot\varphi}{\lambda^3\sin^3\varphi}(\lambda\sin\varphi-1)(\lambda\sin\varphi+2),\\
E\delta^p &= \left(\frac{b}{h}\right)\left(\frac{1-\lambda\sin\varphi}{\lambda}\right)(N_\theta{}^p - \nu N_\varphi{}^p).\\
N_\theta{}^p &= \frac{pb}{2\lambda^2\sin^2\varphi}(\lambda^2\sin^2\varphi-1),\\
N_\varphi{}^p &= \frac{pb}{2\lambda\sin\varphi}(\lambda\sin\varphi-1),\\
\lambda &= b/a.
\end{aligned} \tag{10.12}$$

The edge deformations and rotations in the shells of Fig. 10.18 were determined by using the foregoing membrane formulas and also by an "exact" computer solution which is based upon the Runge–Kutta method of stepwise integration that we discussed in Section 10.2*c*. The results of the computations are summarized in Table 10.8 from which it is obvious

[55] Galletly, G. D., and Radok, J. R. M., "On the Accuracy of Some Shell Solutions," *J. Appl. Mech.*, **26**, 577–583 (1959).

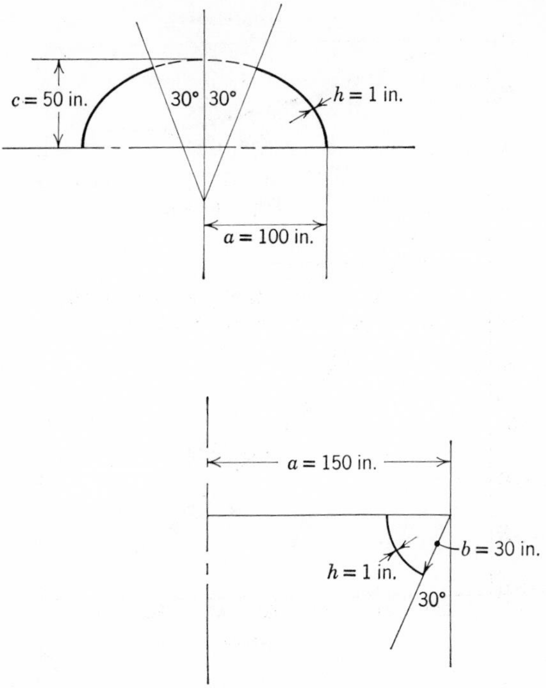

Figure 10.18

Table 10.8 Edge Rotation and Deflection due to Uniform Internal Pressure

	Membrane Solution		Numerical Solution	
	Ellipsoidal Shell			
φ (degrees)	$E\beta_\varphi{}^p/p$	$E\delta^p/ph$	$E\beta_\varphi{}^p/p$	$E\delta^p/ph$
90	0	−11,500	28.932	−12,372
30	466.45	−285.74	528.96	− 195.05
	Toroidal Shell			
−90	0	−1368	−1705.1	− 978.24
−30	−49,105	−6500.3	−7914.0	−4613.1

that the membrane solution can lead to erroneous displacements and rotations.

The stress resultants for the two shells as obtained from the numerical solution and the membrane formulas are given in Fig. 10.19. There it is

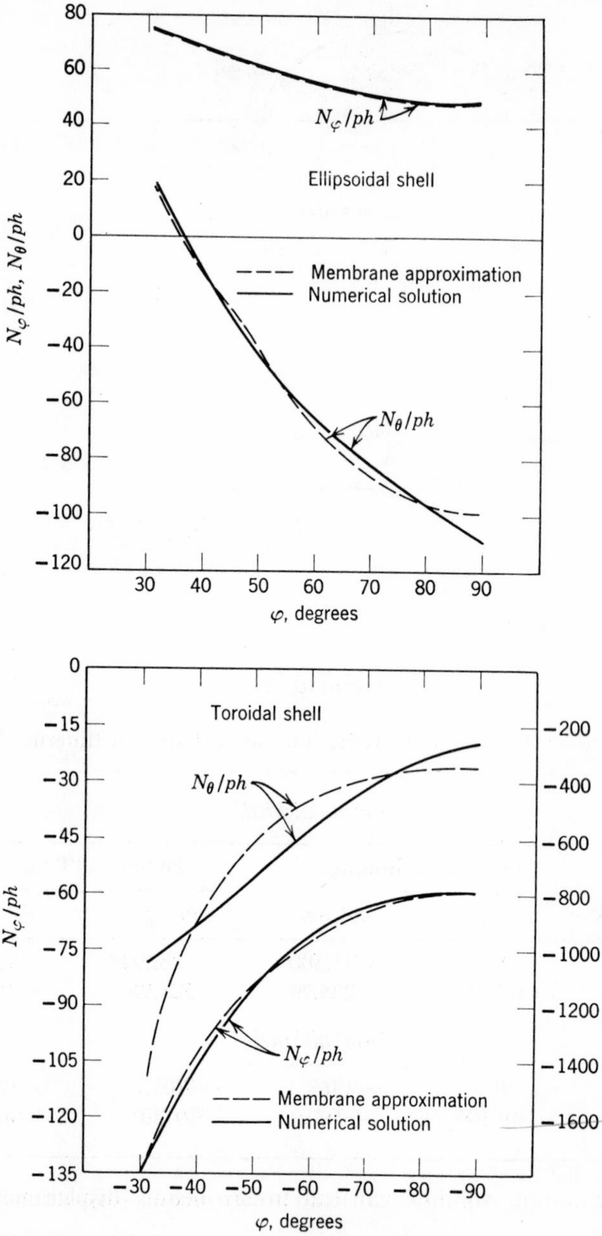

Figure 10.19 Comparison of membrane and numerical solutions for ellipsoidal and toroidal shells.

seen that, for the ellipsoidal shell, the stress resultants obtained by the two methods agree quite closely. This is also the case for N_φ in the toroidal shell. However, as far as N_θ in the toroidal shell is concerned, the result from the membrane approximation differs appreciably from the numerical solution, especially at $\varphi = -30$ degrees. As a consequence of these results, the membrane approximation to the particular solution should be used with great care in the analysis of ellipsoidal and toroidal shells, both in stress and in displacement calculations.

SUPPLEMENTARY REFERENCES

Au, T., Goodman, E. E., and Newmark, N. M., "A Numerical Procedure for the Analysis of Pressure Vessel Heads," Technical Report, Department of Civil Engineering, University of Illinois (February 15, 1951).

Klingbeil, E., "Zur Theorie der Rotationsschalen vom Standpunkt numerischer Rechnungen," *Ingr. Arch.*, **27**, 242–249 (1957).

Lohmann, W., "Beitrag zur Integration der Reissner-Meissnerschen Schalen-gleichung für Behälter unter konstantem Innerdruck," *Ingr. Arch.*, **6**, 338–346 (1935).

Münz, H., "Ein Integrationsverfahren für die Berechnung der Biegespannungen achsensymmetrischer Shalen unter achsensymmetrischer Belastung," *Ingr. Arch.*, **19**, 103–117 (1951).

Smith, G. W., "Analysis of Multiple Discontinuities in Shells of Revolution," General Dynamics/Astronautics Report 63-0044.

Wildhack, W. A., Dressler, R. F., and Lloyd, E. C., "Investigation of the Properties of Corrugated Diaphragms," *Trans. ASME*, **79**, 65–82 (1957).

Wilson, P. E., and Spier, E. E., "Numerical Analysis of Small Finite Axisymmetric Deformation of Thin Shells of Revolution," General Dynamics/Astronautics Report ERR-AN-153 (June, 1962).

Zudans, Z., "Computer Analysis of Axisymmetric Redundant Structures," The Franklin Institute, Philadelphia, Pa. (April, 1963).

EXERCISES

10.1 Break the generator of a shell into two regions A and B which are defined by $\varphi_0 \leqslant \varphi \leqslant \varphi_1$ and $\varphi_1 \leqslant \varphi \leqslant \varphi_2$, respectively. Then write the difference equivalents of Eqs. 10.1b for the entire interval $\varphi_0 \leqslant \varphi \leqslant \varphi_2$ using a mesh spacing Δ_a in region A and Δ_b in region B.

10.2 Write N_φ, N_θ, M_θ, and the deflection u_r perpendicular to the axis of the shell in finite difference form for use with the development of Section 10.2*a*.

10.3 Set up the finite element method for a case in which the displacements and the rotations are prescribed at the edges of the original shell.

10.4 Set up the finite element method for the *n*th component of the solution for a shell of revolution under an arbitrary system of loads.

11

Numerical Analysis of Shells under Dynamic Loadings

11.1 NUMERICAL FREE VIBRATION ANALYSIS OF SHELLS

Now let us consider the application of numerical techniques to the dynamic analysis of thin elastic shells. We have seen, in Chapter 8, that analytical solutions of the free-vibration problem for various shells were made possible only by restricting the development to homogeneous, isotropic single shells of uniform thickness and constant meridional radius of curvature. As in the static analysis, the free-vibration analysis of an arbitrary shell in which the foregoing assumptions on the elastic and geometric properties are relaxed can be carried out only by appealing to a numerical procedure which has been programmed for the digital computer.

On the basis of the accuracy and the simplicity of the associated system of first order differential equations, and on the basis of the ease of programming the underlying algorithms, we concluded, in Chapter 10, that the most attractive numerical methods for the analysis of shells are the stepwise integration methods. Thus, we shall concern ourselves here only with the application of this class of numerical methods to the free-vibration analysis of thin elastic shells. Since the basic features of the stepwise integration methods as they pertain to the analysis of shells were presented in Chapter 10, the present discussion will be brief. First, we shall cover the extensions which are required in the application of these methods to the analysis of freely vibrating shells. Then, we shall present numerical results obtained by computer programs which have been written for the calculation of the natural frequencies and mode shapes of thin elastic shells. These results will be compared to numerical results which were obtained with the analytical solutions of Chapter 8 and to available experimental data.

11.1*a* Application of the Stepwise Integration Methods to Free-Vibration Analysis

In Section 10.2*c*, we indicated that the stepwise integration methods are concerned with the solution of systems of first order differential equations. For free-vibration analyses, these equations can be deduced from the set 10.6d to 10.6g by setting all of the loadings and temperatures to zero and taking into account the inertia terms in the equations of equilibrium. Those equations of the set 10.6d to 10.6g that are affected by such considerations must, therefore, be replaced by

$$\begin{aligned}
\epsilon_{\varphi m}{}^{0} &= \frac{1}{A_1}\,[(N_{\varphi m} - C_{12}\epsilon_{\theta m}{}^{0} - K_{12}\kappa_{\theta m})D_{11} \\
&\qquad\qquad - (M_{\varphi m} - K_{12}\epsilon_{\theta m}{}^{0} - D_{12}\kappa_{\theta m})K_{11}], \\
\kappa_{\varphi m} &= \frac{1}{A_1}\,[(M_{\varphi m} - K_{12}\epsilon_{\theta m}{}^{0} - D_{12}\kappa_{\theta m})C_{11} \\
&\qquad\qquad - (N_{\varphi m} - C_{12}\epsilon_{\theta m}{}^{0} - K_{12}\kappa_{\theta m})K_{11}], \\
N_{\theta m} &= C_{12}\epsilon_{\varphi m}{}^{0} + C_{22}\epsilon_{\theta m}{}^{0} + K_{12}\kappa_{\varphi m} + K_{22}\kappa_{\theta m}, \\
M_{\theta m} &= D_{12}\kappa_{\varphi m} + D_{22}\kappa_{\theta m} + K_{12}\epsilon_{\varphi m}{}^{0} + K_{22}\epsilon_{\theta m}{}^{0}, \\
\frac{dN_{\varphi m}}{ds} &= -\frac{m}{r}T_m + m\left(\frac{1}{r_\varphi} + \frac{1}{r_\theta}\right)\frac{M_{\varphi\theta m}}{r} + \frac{\cos\varphi}{r}N_{\theta m} \\
&\qquad\qquad - \frac{\cos\varphi}{r}N_{\varphi m} - \frac{V_m}{r_\varphi} - \rho\omega^2 u_{\varphi m}, \\
\frac{dV_m}{ds} &= -\frac{2m\cos\varphi}{r^2}M_{\varphi\theta m} - \frac{\cos\varphi}{r}T_m + \frac{N_{\theta m}}{r_\theta} \\
&\qquad\qquad + \frac{N_{\varphi m}}{r_\varphi} + \frac{m^2}{r^2}M_{\theta m} + \rho\omega^2 w_m, \\
\frac{dT_m}{ds} &= \left(\frac{1}{r_\varphi} - \frac{1}{r_\theta}\right)\frac{\cos\varphi}{r}M_{\varphi\theta m} - \frac{2\cos\varphi}{r}T_m + \frac{m}{r}N_{\theta m} \\
&\qquad\qquad + \frac{m\sin\varphi}{r^2}M_{\theta m} - \rho\omega^2 u_{\theta m},
\end{aligned} \tag{11.1}$$

where we have assumed (see Chapter 8) that all of the variables of a given mode of free vibration are proportional to $\cos\omega t$ and the rest of Eqs. 10.6d to 10.6g are unchanged.[1]

[1] The equations of the dynamic theory of shells were first presented in the form of first order equations of the type of Eqs. 11.1 for conical shells by Goldberg and his collaborators. See, Goldberg, J. E., Bogdanoff, J. L., and Marcus, L., "On the Calculation of Axisymmetric Modes and Frequencies of Conical Shells," *J. Acoust. Soc. Am.*, **32**, 738–742 (1960), and also Goldberg, J. E., and Bogdanoff, J. L., "Static and Dynamic Analysis of Nonuniform Conical Shells under Symmetrical and Unsymmetrical Conditions," *Proc. Sixth Symp. on Ballistic Missile and Aerospace Technology*, New

The system of first order differential equations can be symbolically written (see Eq. 10.7a), in the absence of all surface loadings, as

$$\frac{d}{ds}[y(s, \omega)] = [A(s, \omega)][y(s, \omega)], \tag{11.2a}$$

where $[y(s, \omega)]$ is a column matrix which contains the eight fundamental variables of the formulation, $[A(s, \omega)]$ is an eight by eight matrix of coefficients, and ω is the, as yet undetermined, natural frequency. The solution of the foregoing system can be written formally as (see Eq. 10.7c):

$$[y(s, \omega)] = [Y(s, \omega)][C(\omega)], \tag{11.2b}$$

where $[Y(s, \omega)]$ is now an eight by eight matrix of complementary solutions which satisfy the equations

$$\frac{d}{ds}[Y(s, \omega)] = [A(s, \omega)][Y(s, \omega)], \tag{11.2c}$$

and $[C(\omega)]$ is an eight element column matrix of arbitrary constants. In the static analysis, we demonstrated that solutions which satisfy prescribed values at both end points of the generator of the shell could be found by requiring that the solutions of Eq. 11.2c satisfy the condition

$$[Y(a, \omega)] = [I], \tag{11.2d}$$

at the initial point $s = a$, where $[I]$ is the unit matrix. Evaluation of the formal solution (Eq. 11.2b) at $s = a$ then gives, as in the static case,

$$[y(a, \omega)] = [C(\omega)]. \tag{11.2e}$$

With this result the general solution 11.2b becomes

$$[y(s, \omega)] = [Y(s, \omega)][y(a, \omega)], \tag{11.2f}$$

and when evaluated at $s = b$ this expression takes the form

$$[y(b, \omega)] = [Y(b, \omega)][y(a, \omega)]. \tag{11.2g}$$

Equation 11.2g can be written in the partitioned form

$$\begin{bmatrix} y_1(b, \omega) \\ \hline y_2(b, \omega) \end{bmatrix} = \left[\begin{array}{c|c} Y_1(b, \omega) & Y_2(b, \omega) \\ \hline Y_3(b, \omega) & Y_4(b, \omega) \end{array}\right] \begin{bmatrix} y_1(a, \omega) \\ \hline y_2(a, \omega) \end{bmatrix} \tag{11.2h}$$

York: Academic Press, Volume 1, 219–238 (1961). The equations were later written, in the form of Eqs. 11.1 for arbitrary shells of revolution by Kalnins. See, Kalnins, A., "Free Vibration of Rotationally Symmetric Shells," *J. Acoust. Soc. Am.*, **36**, 1355–1365 (1964), also "On Free and Forced Vibration of Rotationally Symmetric Layered Shells," *J. Appl. Mech.*, **32**, 941–943 (1965).

where the $[Y_i(b, \omega)]$ are four by four submatrices of $[Y(b, \omega)]$. In writing Eq. 11.2h, we have also assumed that the first four elements of $[y(a, \omega)]$, denoted by $[y_1(a, \omega)]$, and the last four elements of $[y(b, \omega)]$, denoted by $[y_2(b, \omega)]$, are the prescribed variables at the end points of the generator. Since, in free-vibration analysis, the boundary conditions are homogeneous, we note that $[y_1(a, \omega)] = [y_2(b, \omega)] = 0$ and Eq. 11.2h gives

$$[Y_4(b, \omega)][y_2(a, \omega)] = 0. \tag{11.2i}$$

The trivial solution of this system of four equations in the four unknown elements of the column matrix $[y_2(a, \omega)]$ is avoided by setting the determinant of the coefficients to zero, or

$$|Y_4(b, \omega)| = 0. \tag{11.2j}$$

This represents the frequency equation of the shell under consideration and its roots ω, each corresponding to a natural frequency of free vibration, are obtained by the incrementing procedure which we described in Section 8.1. Once the natural frequencies are known, three of the elements of $[y_2(a, \omega)]$ can be found in terms of the fourth from Eq. 11.2i and the mode shapes for each natural frequency can be found from Eq. 11.2f.

The preceding analysis pertains to a shell composed of a single segment. It is susceptible to the same loss of accuracy as was encountered in the static analysis when the segment is "too long". As a consequence, the multisegment method which was described in Section 10.2*c* should also be used here whenever the criterion 10.8a is violated.[2]

If the breakdown into M segments, as described in Section 10.2*c*, is indicated, we note that the solution at any point in the assembly is given by

$$[y(s, \omega)] = [Y_i(s, \omega)][y(s_i\ \omega)], \tag{11.3a}$$

where s is any point in the interval, i identifies the segment in which the point lies and (see Eqs. 10.9b and 10.9c, 11.2c and 11.2d):

$$\begin{aligned} \frac{d}{ds}[Y_i(s, \omega)] &= [A(s, \omega)][Y_i(s, \omega)], \\ [Y_i(s_i, \omega)] &= [I]. \end{aligned} \tag{11.3b}$$

Since the fundamental variables must be continuous across the junctions of the segments, we note that

$$[y(s_{i+1}, \omega)] = [Y_i(s_{i+1}, \omega)][y(s_i, \omega)], \qquad i = 1, 2, \ldots, M. \tag{11.3c}$$

These equations can be written in the partitioned matrix form (Eqs. 11.2h)

[2] Kalnins, A., loc. cit. (1964).

and, when the matrix multiplications are carried out, we obtain the result (see Eqs. 10.9f):

$$
\begin{aligned}
&[Y_{1i}(s_{i+1}, \omega)][y_1(s_i, \omega)] + [Y_{2i}(s_{i+1}, \omega)][y_2(s_i, \omega)] \\
&\qquad\qquad - [y_1(s_{i+1}, \omega)] = 0, \\
&[Y_{3i}(s_{i+1}, \omega)][y_1(s_i, \omega)] + [Y_{4i}(s_{i+1}, \omega)][y_2(s_i, \omega)] \\
&\qquad\qquad - [y_2(s_{i+1}, \omega)] = 0,
\end{aligned}
\tag{11.3d}
$$

where the subscripts on Y and y have the same meaning as in Eq. 11.2h. Equations 11.3d represent a system of $2M$ linear homogeneous matrix equations in the $2M$ unknown matrices: $[y_1(s_i, \omega)]$, $i = 2, 3, \ldots, M + 1$, and $[y_2(s_i, \omega)]$, $i = 1, 2, \ldots, M$. Furthermore, Eqs. 11.3d are a special case, with $[Z_{ji}(s_{i+1})] = 0$, of Eqs. 10.9f. Therefore, in this instance, the Gauss reduction yields the homogeneous counterpart of Eq. 10.9g; that is,

$$
\begin{bmatrix}
E_1 & -I & & & & & \\
 & C_1 & -I & & & & \\
 & & E_2 & -I & & & \\
 & & & \ddots & \ddots & & \\
 & & & & E_M & -I \\
 & & & & & C_M
\end{bmatrix}
\begin{bmatrix}
y_2(s_1, \omega) \\
y_1(s_2, \omega) \\
y_2(s_2, \omega) \\
\vdots \\
y_2(s_M, \omega) \\
y_1(s_{M+1}, \omega)
\end{bmatrix}
= 0 \tag{11.3e}
$$

where the $[E_i]$ and $[C_i]$ are again given by Eqs. 10.9h and we have noted that $[y_1(s_1, \omega)]$ and $[y_2(s_{M+1}, \omega)]$ vanish for the free-vibration analysis. The trivial solution of the homogeneous system (Eqs. 11.3e) is avoided by setting

$$|C_M| = 0. \tag{11.3f}$$

This yields the natural frequencies of free vibration of the multisegment assembly. Once these frequencies have been determined, the $[y_1(s_i, \omega)]$ and the $[y_2(s_i, \omega)]$ can be found in terms of $[y_1(s_{M+1}, \omega)]$ from the following homogeneous counterparts of Eqs. 10.9*l* and 10.9m:

$$[y_2(s_M, \omega)] = [E_M]^{-1}[y_1(s_{M+1}, \omega)] \tag{11.3g}$$

for $i = M$, and

$$
\begin{aligned}
[y_1(s_{M-i+1}, \omega)] &= [C_{M-i}]^{-1}[y_2(s_{M-i+1}, \omega)], \\
[y_2(s_{M-i}, \omega)] &= [E_{M-i}]^{-1}[y_1(s_{M-i+1}, \omega)],
\end{aligned}
\tag{11.3h}
$$

for $i = 1, 2, \ldots, M - 1$. Any fundamental variable at any position in the shell can then be calculated with Eq. 11.3a.

11.1*b* Results Obtained by Computer Programs

In order to demonstrate the accuracy and versatility of computer programs which are based upon the foregoing numerical analyses of the free-vibration problem, it is now appropriate to present some numerical results obtained by the stepwise integration methods. To do this, we shall first compare the results obtained by the stepwise integration methods to results obtained by analytical solutions of the type which we developed in Chapter 8. This will be followed, as it was in the static case, by some representative free-vibration analyses which were made possible by the availability of computer programs.

Comparison to Previous Analytical Results. As a first example, let us consider the conical shell which is shown with its dimensions in Fig. 11.1. The shell is free at the large end and clamped at the small end in such a

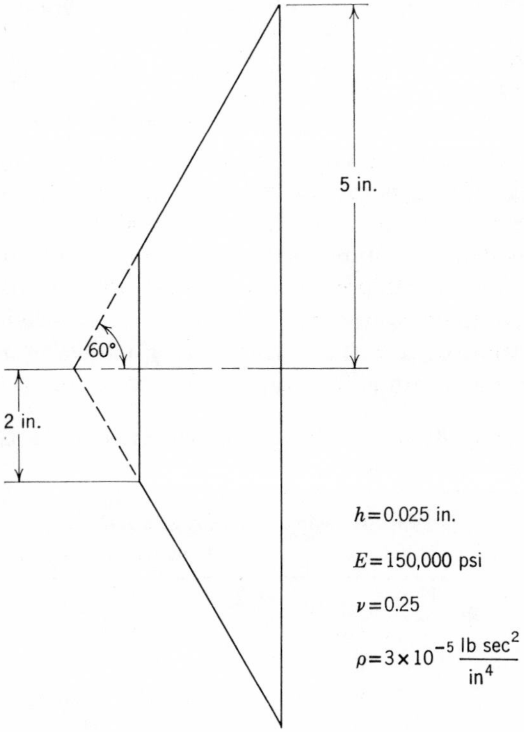

Figure 11.1

manner that it is constrained to execute vibratory motions which are independent of the coordinate θ. An analytical solution for the natural frequencies and the associated shapes of the first three modes of free vibration was first obtained by Goldberg[3] who employed the series method

[3] Goldberg, J. E., "Axisymmetric Oscillations of Conical Shells," *Proc. IXth Internat. Cong. Appl. Mech.*, Brussels, pp. 333–343 (1956).

of Frobenius.[4] These results are plotted along with similar results which were obtained by a computer program[5] based on the fourth order Runge–Kutta process (see Eq. 10.4b) in Fig. 11.2, where it is seen that the agreement between the numerically and the analytically determined mode shapes is excellent. The natural frequencies, as obtained by the two methods of solution for the mode shapes of Fig. 11.2, are given in Table 11.1.

Table 11.1 Comparison of Natural Frequencies (cps) of the Truncated Cone of Fig. 11.1

Mode	Numerical Solution	Analytical Solution
1st	1072	1071
2nd	1315	1315
3rd	1611	1610

As a second example, let us reconsider the analysis of the freely vibrating cylindrical shell which we carried out in Section 8.2. In that section, we presented (see Fig. 8.4) a comparison of natural frequencies as obtained by several analytical solutions with experimentally determined natural frequencies. Now it is appropriate to extend that comparison so that it includes natural frequencies obtained by a numerical solution which has been programmed for the digital computer. For this purpose, we have listed, in Table 11.2, natural frequencies of clamped steel cylindrical shells

Table 11.2 Comparison of Natural Frequencies (cps) of Clamped Steel Cylinders[a] (a = 3 in., h = 0.01 in., l = 12 in.)

n	Variational	Predictor-Corrector	Test
	$\frac{1}{2}$ axial wave		
3	1176	1160	1025
4	783	765	700
5	597	579	559
	$1\frac{1}{2}$ axial waves		
6	1823	1728	1650
7	1503	1435	1395
8	1338	1288	1350

[a] Here n is the circumferential wave number (see Section 8.2).

[4] Ince, E. L., *Ordinary Differential Equations*, New York: Dover Publications, pp. 396–403 (1956).

[5] Goldberg, J. E., Bogdanoff, J. L., and Marcus, L., loc. cit.

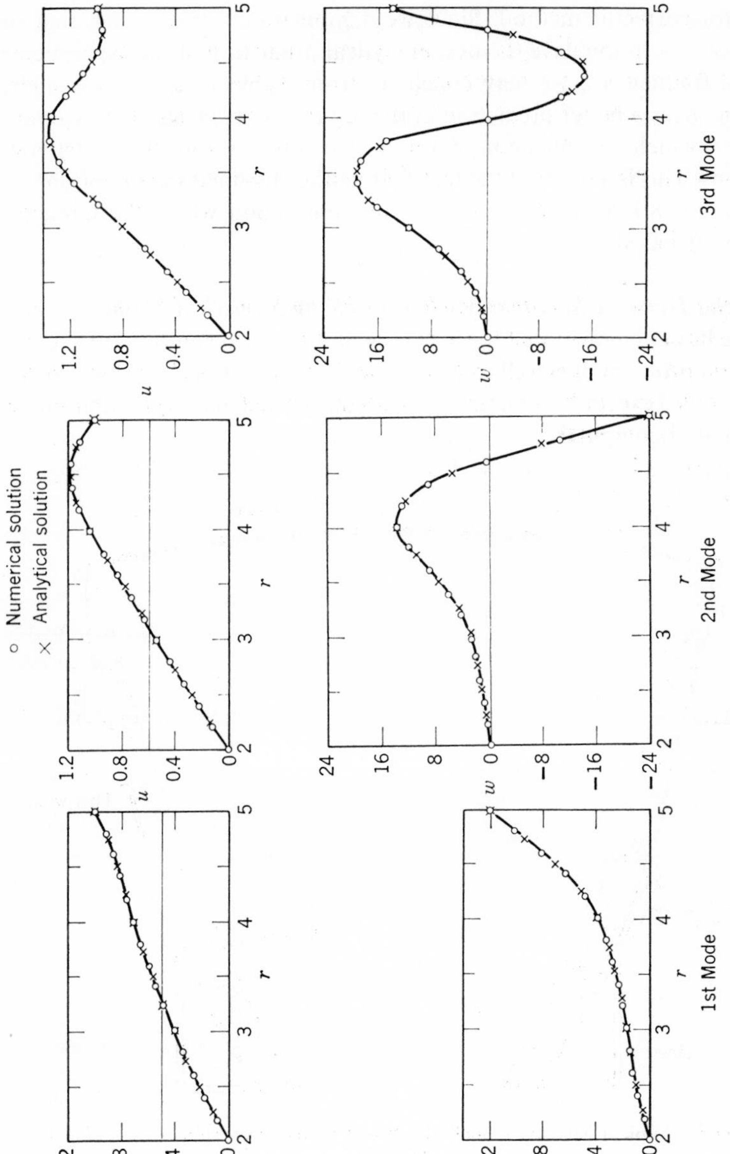

Figure 11.2 Comparison of numerical and analytical displacement distributions for the freely vibrating conical shell shown in Fig. 11.1.

as obtained by the variational solution of Section 8.2*a*, the experimental study of Koval and Cranch,[6] and a computer program based upon the predictor-corrector method. Since we demonstrated, in Fig. 8.4, that the variational solution gave the best analytical prediction of the experimental natural frequencies, we may conclude, from Table 11.2, that the digital solution gives a better prediction of the natural frequencies of the cylindrical shells which are under consideration than any of the available analytical solutions. This is a result of the fact that neither Donnell's assumptions nor assumption 8.17a are made in the equations upon which the numerical solution is based.

Special Dynamic Solutions Made Feasible by Numerical Methods. Now that we have demonstrated the accuracy of numerical solutions of the free-vibration problem, it is well to give some examples of problems which cannot be solved except by a numerical procedure which has been programmed for a digital computer.

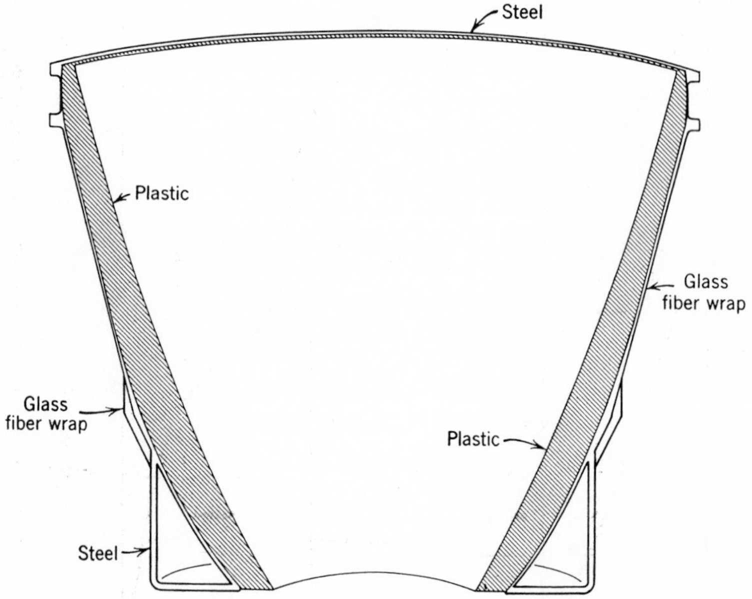

Figure 11.3 Typical aerospace shell structure: thrust vectoring nozzle of a rocket engine.

[6] Koval, L. R., and Cranch, E. T., "On the Free Vibrations of Thin Cylindrical Shells Subjected to an Initial Static Torque," *Proc. Fourth U.S. Nat'l. Cong. Appl. Mech.*, pp. 107–117 (1962).

The first of these problems concerns the vectoring nozzle of a rocket engine which is shown in Fig. 11.3. As shown in the illustration, the nozzle constructed of three types of materials which would make the analytical determination of its natural frequencies a hopeless task. However, by means of a computer program[7] based upon the fourth order Runge–Kutta process in which the nozzle is approximated by a collection of conical shells, the lowest natural frequency for the case of two circumferential waves was found to be 166 cps. Judging from the complicated nature of the nozzle, this constitutes an excellent prediction of the frequency 173 cps which was obtained in a test of the nozzle.

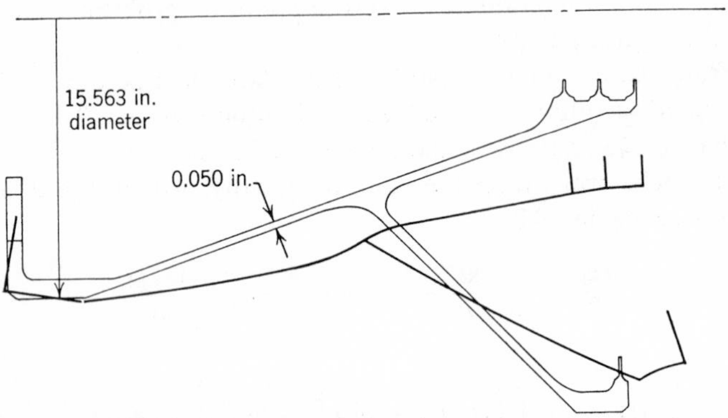

Figure 11.4 Typical gas turbine shell structure.

A second example concerns the gas turbine component shown in Fig. 11.4. When installed, the item is clamped at its left end and free at both branches of its right end. The natural frequencies of free vibration, as obtained for the component by a computer program based upon the predictor-corrector method, are compared to experimentally determined values in Table 11.3 where the agreement is shown to be good.

As a further indication of the versatility of the digital computer solution, we have superimposed on Fig. 11.4 the maximum deflected shape (exaggerated for illustrative purposes) which is assumed by the component during a free vibration with three circumferential waves.

11.2 CLOSURE

In this chapter, we have shown that free-vibration analyses of shells can be carried out with great accuracy on the digital computer. Although we have

[7] Goldberg, J. E., and Bogdanoff, J. L., loc. cit.

Table 11.3 Comparison of Natural Frequencies (cps) for the Turbine Component shown in Fig. 11.4.

n	Predictor-Corrector	Test
3	880	922
4	1010	1100
5	1410	1480
6	1710	1940

not mentioned the solution of the forced-vibration problem by numerical means, this is also possible.

For example, in this connection we may adapt the procedure of Chapter 9 to a numerical solution of the forced-vibration problem. To do this, we recall that in the analysis of the response of a shell to transient surface loads of mechanical origin the solution is governed by the differential equation (see Section 9.3):

$$\frac{d^2q_n}{dt^2} + \frac{\lambda}{\rho h}\frac{dq_n}{dt} + \left(\omega_n{}^2 + \frac{k}{\rho h}\right) q_n = \frac{G_n(t)}{\rho h}, \tag{11.4a}$$

where

$$G_n(t) = \frac{1}{N_n}\iint_S [p_1 u_{1n} + p_2 u_{2n} - p w_n] A_1 A_2 \, d\alpha_1 \, d\alpha_2, \tag{11.4b}$$

$$N_n = \iint_S [u_{1n}{}^2 + u_{2n}{}^2 + w_n{}^2] A_1 A_2 \, d\alpha_1 \, d\alpha_2.$$

If the shell is initially at rest on an underdamped foundation, say, we find from Case (a) of Section 9.3 that

$$q_n(t) = \frac{1}{\rho h \gamma_n}\int_0^t G_n(\tau)\, e^{-\lambda(t-\tau)/2\rho h} \sin \gamma_n(t - \tau)\, d\tau,$$
$$\gamma_n = \frac{k}{\rho h} + \omega_n{}^2 - \left(\frac{\lambda}{2\rho h}\right)^2. \tag{11.4c}$$

Substitution of $G_n(t)$ into the foregoing then gives (see Eqs. 9.20):

$$q_n(t) = [m_{1n}F_{1n}(t) + m_{2n}F_{2n}(t) + m_n F_n(t)]\frac{1}{\rho h \gamma_n N_n}, \tag{11.4d}$$

where

$$\begin{Bmatrix} m_{1n} \\ m_{2n} \\ m_n \end{Bmatrix} = \iint_S \begin{Bmatrix} P_1{}^*(\alpha_1, \alpha_2) u_{1n}(\alpha_1, \alpha_2) \\ P_2{}^*(\alpha_1, \alpha_2) u_{2n}(\alpha_1, \alpha_2) \\ P^*(\alpha_1, \alpha_2) w_n(\alpha_1, \alpha_2) \end{Bmatrix} A_1 A_2 \, d\alpha_1 \, d\alpha_2, \tag{11.4e}$$

$$\begin{Bmatrix} F_{1n}(t) \\ F_{2n}(t) \\ F_n(t) \end{Bmatrix} = \int_0^t \begin{Bmatrix} f_1(\tau) \\ f_2(\tau) \\ f(\tau) \end{Bmatrix} e^{-\lambda(t-\tau)} \sin \gamma_n(t - \tau)\, d\tau, \tag{11.4f}$$

and we have assumed that the time and space variations of the surface loads are separable; that is,

$$\begin{aligned} p_1(\alpha_1, \alpha_2, t) &= P_1{}^*(\alpha_1, \alpha_2) f_1(t), \\ p_2(\alpha_1, \alpha_2, t) &= P_2{}^*(\alpha_1, \alpha_2) f_2(t), \\ -p(\alpha_1, \alpha_2, t) &= P^*(\alpha_1, \alpha_2) f(t). \end{aligned} \tag{11.4g}$$

On the assumption that the free-vibration characteristics of the shell have been found with a digital computer program, we shall have available the natural frequencies of the shell and the associated displacements at every point of the mesh into which the shell has been subdivided. With the latter information, the m_{in} can be obtained by numerical integration using, for example, Simpson's Rule.[8] Then, the integrals in the definitions 11.4f of the $F_{1n}(t)$ can be carried out analytically to complete the determination of the $q_n(t)$ and Eq. 9.13 can be used to evaluate the history of the displacement at any point of the mesh into which the generator of the shell has been divided.

Other attacks upon the forced-vibration problem are also possible.[9] These involve the numerical solution of the original system of partial differential equations which governs the problem and will not be discussed here.

---

[8] See, for example, Hildebrand, F. B., *Introduction to Numerical Analysis*, New York: McGraw-Hill, p. 73 (1956).

[9] See, for example, Wolf, J. A., Jr., and Mack, E., "DASHER I: A Program for the Dynamic Analysis of Shells of Revolution," Aeroelastic and Structures Research Laboratory, Massachusetts Institute of Technology, ASRL TR 121-11, October 1965; Johnson, D. E., and Greif, R., "Dynamic Response of a Cylindrical Shell: Two Numerical Methods," *AIAA J.*, **4**, 486–494 (1966).

Author Index

Subject Index